THERE is not any exercise more pleasing or more agreeable to a truly sober and ingenious man, than this of Angling; a moderate, innocent, and salubrious and delightful exercise: It wearieth not a man overmuch, unless the waters lie remote from home: It injureth no man, so that it be in an open large water; he being esteemed a Beast rather than a Man that will oppose this exercise; neither doth it in any way debauch him that useth it: The delight also of it rouzes up the Ingenious early in the Spring mornings, that they have the benefit of the sweet and pleasant Morning-Air, which many through sluggishness enjoy not; so that Health (the greatest Treasure that Mortals enjoy) and Pleasure go hand in hand in this exercise. What can be more said of it, than that the most Ingenious most use it?

—John Worlidge, Gent., 1675

Angler's Bible

Edited by
Mark Sosin

ART DIRECTOR:
Caryn B. Seifer

ARTISTS:
Maria Barranco, Emily White

DESIGN CONSULTANTS:
Group One Creative Graphics Inc.

MAKEUP:
Eric Hieber Associates

TYPOGRAPHY:
Emil P. Popp & Son

COPY EDITOR:
Paula Ann Strus

EDITORIAL RESEARCHERS:
Miriam Korn, Diane Krantz,
Jean Markus, Robert D. Scott,
Annette G. Vernon, Sheryl Weinstein

EQUIPMENT
RESEARCH CONSULTANT:
Kenneth Lane

MANAGING EDITOR:
George M. Horn

ASSISTANT MANAGING EDITOR:
John C. Rhodes

PRODUCTION EDITOR:
Bob Dana

ASSISTANT PRODUCTION EDITOR:
Jeff Arnold

PUBLISHER:
Robert F. Scott

Distributed to the book trade by

**FOLLETT PUBLISHING COMPANY
CHICAGO, ILLINOIS.**

Stoeger Publishing Company

Copyright © 1975 by Stoeger Publishing Company

Published by Stoeger Publishing Company
55 Ruta Court
South Hackensack, New Jersey 07606

ISBN: 0-88317-017-5

Foreword

Fishing is, believe it or not, the great national sport. Far more money — and time — is spent by anglers in the active pursuit of their favorite pastime than is expended by the crowds who patronize "spectator" sports such as baseball, football, basketball or hockey. As for participatory sports — golf, tennis and the like — the number of players is dwarfed by the multitudes who go fishing for recreation each year, not to mention the increasing numbers who augment their table fare with the fish they catch.

Paradoxically, despite the astronomical numbers of fishermen, there are few books which survey the entire fishing scene: books which can be used by the novice or expert, books which record the specifications of and details about the equipment available in mind-boggling variety, books which contain genuinely useful reference material for the angler — information which cannot be obtained elsewhere.

Perhaps you are curious as to how the ANGLER'S BIBLE was born. Actually the idea began with its compainon volume, the best-selling SHOOTER'S BIBLE, which has been published for more than a half-century. Yet the ANGLER'S BIBLE is no mere imitation, but rather an offshoot. For many years, the SHOOTER'S BIBLE carried a special feature a small section headed appropriately enough, "The Angler's Bible." It was inevitable that this feature should grow into a book which could stand on its own.

Compiling, collating, cross-referencing, editing, and indexing the vast amount of information contained in the 480 pages of the ANGLER'S BIBLE was no easy task. To begin, 1,356 letters were sent to manufacturers and suppliers of fishing tackle and equipment requesting that they furnish catalog, descriptions, specifications, and photographs.

In addition a total of 178 manufacturers' representatives were contacted personally at the prestigious American Fishing Tackle Manufacturers Association meeting in Chicago last year. The thoroughness of the research is evident in the information-packed volume that resulted.

But knowing *how* is quite as important in fishing as *what to use* or *where to fish*. Accordingly, top fishing experts were asked to write and illustrate articles on their areas of specialization, and you will find the best-known and most-respected angling writers represented in our roster of authors.

Also included are a number of "angling classics" which demonstrate that although fishermen may come and go, over the years the many pleasurable experiences which befall the angler, the skills required under various circumstances, and the inner peace and satisfactions that only an angler can know — these do not change.

Some "program notes" about these classics may be in order. You will discover, for example, that Audubon's observations on nature were not limited to birds. Thoreau, author of *Walden,* cannot be described as a sportsman, yet his observations of fish and fishing attest to his keen eye as an observer of nature. A prolific author of the nineteenth century, Henry William Herbert (who wrote under the pen name of Frank Forester) is represented here, too.

No selection of angling classics would be complete without something from the beloved "Uncle Thad" Norris, whose role in American angling has been equated with that of Izaak Walton in England. Readers who may be puzzled by the geography of journalist Benedict Henry Revoil's *Salmon Lake* or by the presence of a salmon fishery in the Catskill Mountains should know that a good fisherman will never tell a story under oath. W. C. Prime was grandfather's favorite angling author, who wrote — and fished — in the classic tradition.

Charles Dudley Warner's *A Fight with a Trout* was intended to satirize the extravagances of contemporary writers on the Adirondack region. The author of *A Pickerel Yarn,* Fred Mather, was a well-known pisciculturist and supervisor of the Cold Stream Harbor hatchery, where he developed new methods of fish propagation. Sir Herbert Maxwell was the distinguished editor of *A Book of Angling,* among other works. And Professor Bliss Perry years afterward identified "R" of his *Fishing with a Worm* as L. J. Rundlett, once Superintendent of Schools in Concord, N.H. As a baseball pitcher in his Dartmouth College days, Rundlett once shut out Harvard without a single hit.

It is no exaggeration to say that there is something for everyone in the ANGLER'S BIBLE. No matter whether you are a tyro or practiced hand, whether you fish fresh or salt water, whether your fishing occupies a leisurely week or is squeezed into the tag end of a day full of cares, here is a volume that genuinely deserves a place in your library of angling books. We sincerely hope it enhances your pleasure as you practice the craft of angling.

— ROBERT F. SCOTT

Tools and Techniques

How to Choose a Casting Rod

by Lefty Kreh

Selecting the proper casting rod, whether it is spinning, fly or plug, often determines how successful you will be on the water and how much fun you'll get from your sport.

Landing a bluegill on a salt water stick or battling a husky cobia on a light fresh water rod can only bring disappointment. Some people harbor the mistaken idea that fighting a large fish on extremely light tackle is a sign of skill.

A fish fought for too long a period builds lactic acid in its system, which will later kill it — even if it is released in apparently good condition.

When you select any type of casting rod, pick one that will whip the fish in the shortest amount of time, cast a bait or lure with ease and accuracy, yet provide the greatest amount of pleasure.

Many factors go into selecting a rod. When you consider the number of hours you'll spend enjoying the tackle, it makes sense to do a thorough job of choosing a rod.

Spinning rods come in many sizes, lengths and types. The ultra-light (UL) spinning rod is a badly misunderstood tackle item. Most manufacturers fail to design UL spin sticks properly for the purpose for which they are intended.

True UL rods are tailored to be used with one-, two-, or four-pound test monofilament line. And, they should cast lures from about $\frac{1}{32}$ ounce to no more than $\frac{1}{4}$ ounce.

These rods have to be extremely forgiving. A stiff UL rod used with two-pound test line will break the line on the strike. A well-designed UL spinning rod should be soft from the tip to the butt. The action would be considered the slowest of any rod you will buy.

The rod must not only bend easily on the strike so the line doesn't break, but it must also yield when fighting the fish.

There is another reason why UL rods should be supple. If you are casting extremely light lures, you will never load the rod if that rod is stiff. Unless the rod bends into a loaded position on the back and foward casts, you lose much accuracy in presentation.

Because the rod is paired with a small, light reel, it should weigh only a few ounces. The butt can be small, and since the spinning reel spool size is tiny, there is no need for a large gathering guide at the rear.

An UL rod should average somewhere between five and six feet in length. A rod shorter than that will cast inaccurately, and a longer one causes other problems.

For general-purpose spinning in fresh water, or for light salt water work (such as bonefish, redfish, snook, ladyfish, sea trout, bluefish and school striped bass) a seven foot rod is ideal. This length is easy to carry aboard a boat, stow in a car, or work from a canoe. The length allows you to develop good leverage on the cast and will easily handle lures for the purpose at hand. For most fresh water fishing situations, you'll want a spinning rod that is designed for lures from $\frac{1}{4}$ to $\frac{5}{8}$ ounce. For salt water work you might select two rods: one that we just discussed and another to handle lures from $\frac{3}{8}$ to $\frac{3}{4}$ ounce. They should be medium action. These two spinning rods will handle most fresh water and almost all inshore salt water fishing situations.

If you fish live bait, you'll need a

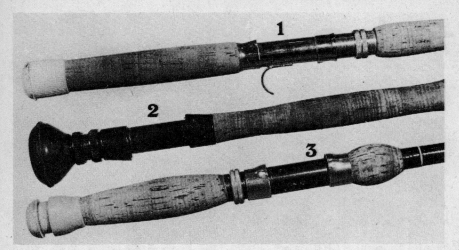

Three types of reel seats. No. 1 is chrome on brass, No. 2 is Delrin and No. 3 is anodized aluminum.

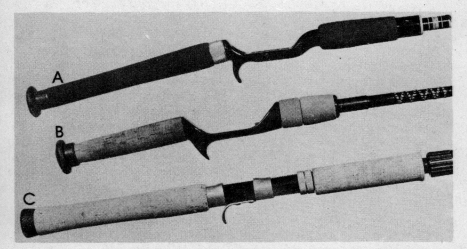

"B" shows the normal length of casting rod handle for fresh water fishing. "A" and "C" show longer length handles. The serious bass fisherman who uses extremely stiff, heavy casting rods may want to consider shifting to the longer handle, so he can cast with two hands, thus lessening the work.

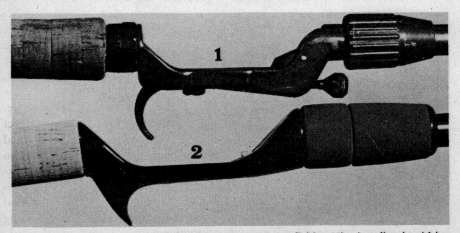

When you purchase a "worm rod" for serious bass fishing, the handle should be designed to withstand the heavy force applied against it when setting the hook.

different type of spinning rod. The problem in live-bait fishing is to be able to toss the bait to the fish without throwing it off the hook. But, you still must have a rod stiff enough to battle the fish when it strikes. This is the one place where a fast-action spinning rod offers an advantage. The light, supple tip can be loaded easily with the weight of the baitfish on the cast. Then, when the strike comes, the remainder of the rod, being rather stiff, will handle the husky fish.

You may need a heavier salt-water spinning rod if you fish off-shore for sailfish, dolphin, really big bluefish, large striped bass from a boat, and other comparable species. This rod should have a medium action and be designed to cast lures from about one-half to at least one ounce in weight.

If you plan to use surface lures where the rod is snapped quickly to make the plug pop and gurgle on the retrieve, you will need a relatively stiff rod. A fast-action spinning rod would almost be useless. As you snap the rod to move the lure, the soft tip collapses and the lure barely moves.

There are many specialty rods. The deep-jigging spinning rod is one. Anglers who fish in the tropics or along the reefline of Florida will drop heavy jigs to the bottom in from 60 to 200 feet of water, then rapidly retrieve the lures back to the boat with swift, upward pumps of the rod.

The ideal length for such a spinning rod is about eight feet. The reason for this length is that when the rod is snapped upward to lift the heavy jig, much of the upward snap is absorbed by stretch in the line. A rod shorter than eight feet will merely remove the stretch from the line, barely moving the jig. Any rod longer than eight feet is tiring to use and difficult with which to fight a fish.

Surf rods come in several sizes. If

you must cast beyond the breakers, you may need at least a 10- or 10½-footer, but if you can stand on the beach and toss your offerings a relatively short distance, you may only want a 9- or 9½-footer. Jetty fishermen find a 7½- to 8-foot rod an ideal compromise.

I suggest that you contact a good surf fisherman in your area and ask his opinion on which length surf rod to use for your region.

Two other rods are frequently used by fishermen. One of them is the plug or bait-casting rod, which almost went out of existence until modern bass fishermen rediscovered it.

When a lure is cast on a plug rod and reel, the weight of the lure must drag the line from the reel spool, forcing it to turn. This results in a rather slow lure speed during the flight to the target. The slower speed gives a longer reaction time than a similar lure thrown with spinning tackle. Because bass fishing often demands accuracy, the bass fishermen have fallen in love with this older form of gear.

Before the tournament bass fishing craze came along, the better bass fishermen used softer rods, which developed great accuracy and furnished some enjoyment for the fishermen during the fight. A medium-action rod was the universal choice.

I cut my teeth on light plug-casting tackle searching for smallmouth bass in the limestone rivers of the mid-Atlantic area. A plug rod of medium action that would toss lures from ¼ to ½ an ounce was a joy to use. Today, serious tournament bass fishermen live by the rule that you don't play with the fish in the water. As one famous bass fisherman said, "Get the bass in the boat as fast as possible, then everyone can play with him."

That thinking forced the introduction of a new type of bass rod. This stick is stiff enough to turn the boat over on a strike, and if the spinner

bait (or other lure) gets hung in a branch of a dead tree, you can yank the limb off without breaking the rod.

The modern bass tool is poker-stiff, strong enough to flay an unreasonable mule into submission, and tough enough to drive a 5/0 hook through the body of a plastic worm and halfway through the bass that takes the worm. These rods have almost no action. They barely move at the tip. Most of them are not used to cast a lure, but rather to "sling" the lure.

A comfortable pistol-grip handle has been very popular with these bass fishermen, but a few are beginning to realize that if they are going to use such brute sticks, a longer handle is much more desirable. With the longer handle, they can put the other hand at the base of the rod and double-hand the cast, developing much greater power. When hundreds of casts will be made during a day, the two-handed method relieves the casting hand of much of the strain. In the near future, I'm sure that most of the serious bass fishermen will be using two-handed casting rods for much of their fishing.

The fly rod creates more controversy than any other type of casting tackle. The delight of one fisherman is scorned by another. Most good fly rodders today agree that the basic rod should have a medium action. Fast-action rods can be used by experts who have refined their casting, but these rods have in-built problems that the average fisherman doesn't need.

The major shortcoming of a fast-action fly rod is that the tip portion does most of the moving during a cast. This short movement of the tip and the unyielding butt section cause very narrow line loops, which, unless care is taken, will result in tangled leaders and a poor presentation to the fish.

The fast-action fly rod is also

poorly designed for striking a fish. When the angler attempts to set the hook, the tip collapses, just as it does when trying to manipulate a surface lure with fast-action spinning or plug rods.

For years fly rods were classified as dry fly action or wet fly action. The wet fly action is a very slow type and most experienced fly rodders have long since abandoned the wet fly action in favor of the medium action.

For trout fishing in rivers that are rarely wider than 40 to 50 feet, such as in the east, you'll need a rod that is matched to a line from size three to seven.

The rod should never be less than seven and a half feet. There is one exception, however. If you fish the "tunnel streams" of the mountains for brook trout, where the open area above the stream is extremely tight, you may be *forced* to go to a short rod. But, short fly rods less than seven and a half feet should only be used when a longer rod will not be practical. I prefer a rod of at least eight feet for all trout fishing where there is enough room to use it. And, I would love to have one a foot longer.

There are many practical reasons for using a longer rod when trout fishing. You can hold less line on the water, eliminating line drag. You can roll cast easier, strike quicker, and manipulate the fly better. You can lead a fish more effectively during a fight, and you can dapple a lure in a particular spot that is often unreachable with a midget fly rod.

On western rivers a line from 6 through 8 in size is generally best. The longer rod theory applies here, too. Dry fly fishing on many of the heavy-water rivers in the west is extremely difficult. Much of the water swirls behind boulders, and there are so many turbulent pockets where getting a drag-free float is all but impossible with short rods.

With a long rod — one of at least eight feet — you can wade near these

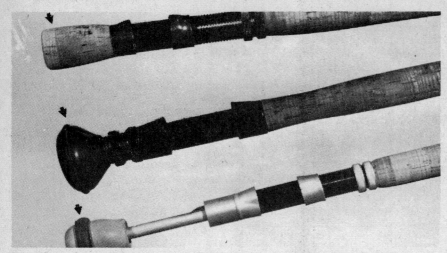

Extension butts that move the reel slightly away from the angler's belly when he fights a fish are often desirable for big fish. Here are three types that won't bruise the fisherman.

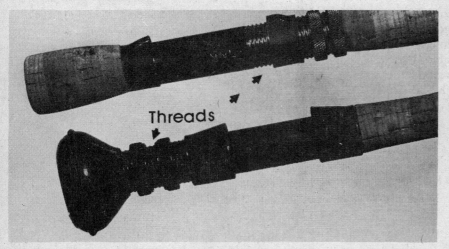

Threads

The top rod shows how a fly-rod reel seat is normally put on a rod — with the threaded portion forward. You can also position the threaded ring at the rear of the rod, giving you a built-in extension butt.

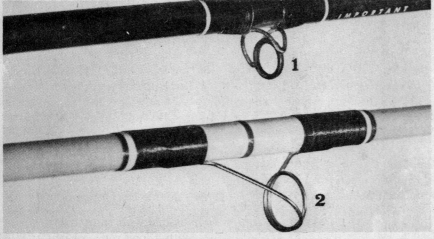

No. 1 is a bridge guide, No. 2 a flexible foot guide.

small, swirling pockets of water, drop a fly at the head of the pocket, hold the long rod very high, and keep the line and much of the leader from contacting the water. Frequently, you can get a drag-free float of several seconds, which is certainly long enough to convince any fish to take your offering. Nymph fishermen also can profit from the longer fly rod, using the added length to manipulate the lure in the choice water.

If you fish in salt water, you will need two basic fly rods for most fishing likely to be encountered around the world. A rod that handles a number nine line will do for ninety per cent of the work. Such a rod will work well for striped bass on either coast, yet will be delicate enough for most flats situations and still take the lighter offshore species.

The second rod is really a fish-fighting tool. These rods weigh from 8 to 11 ounces, are capable of lifting a heavy weight, and handle a line from size 12 or heavier. This fish-fighting rod is the one anglers use to take giant tarpon, the billfishes, large cobia, amberjack, and other husky fish that require a rod with tremendous lifting power. A well-designed fish-fighting fly rod will lift a five-pound block from the floor, with only a few inches of leader material extending beyond the rod tip, and still have some reserve power remaining in the butt section.

For bass fishing, a proper fly rod must be matched to the line size needed to cast the lures in your area. A rod that handles a size 7 or 8 line is ideal for smallmouth fishing. You will probably need an eight or nine line to toss the big poppers and streamers that old bucketmouth prefers. Bass fly rods, like all others, belong in the medium action group.

Once you have determined the length, action and lure range of the rod you are going to select, you should consider other factors. Guides are important. Their position on the

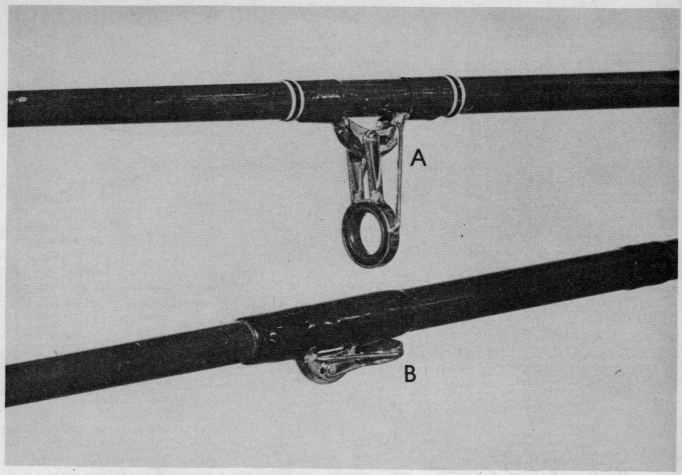

"A" shows a folding spinning butt guide in fishing position. "B" is the same type of guide, folded away.

blank can spoil a rod's action. The worst guides are the lightly chromed ones that usually come on very inexpensive rods (those listing for less than $10). Whether the rod is a spin, plug or fly stick, lightly chromed guides are going to wear quickly and will ruin a good line.

The most popular guide for all three types of rods is heavily chrome-plated. Under normal fishing conditions, these guides give good service. You can fish in fresh or salt water with such a guide and be assured that it will serve well.

Carbide is a super-hard metal (much harder than chrome) and has been used on fishing rods for many years. A fly, plug or spinning line will never wear into a carbide guide.

That sounds as though the carbide guides are the answer, but that's not so. Problems exist with carbide guides. Occasionally, but not often, you may buy a rod that has an improperly polished guide. If you do, you've bought the equivalent of a razor blade installed in a guide. One fishing trip with such a poor quality guide can ruin the line.

Another problem with carbide is that it is brittle. This wouldn't be too irritating if a guide should break on a local fishing trip. But, if you are in the Canadian wilderness and the guide breaks, you do have a cause for concern.

Carbide is not a good material to use around salt water. After one or two trips to the ocean, a crust forms

on the carbide and, when it sloughs off, you may see pits in the guide. You don't need rough spots where smooth monofilament has to slide freely.

Aluminum oxide is a major new discovery in guides. This material is not quite as hard as carboloy, but it's super-smooth, generates almost no friction, improves the casting distance, and results in less line wear.

It is the finest material I know of for spinning and plug rods. The butt or stripping guides on a fly rod should be made from this material, too. Few anglers know that when they double haul a number of times they generate a static electrical charge within the rod. Then, when they shoot the fly line, it tends to

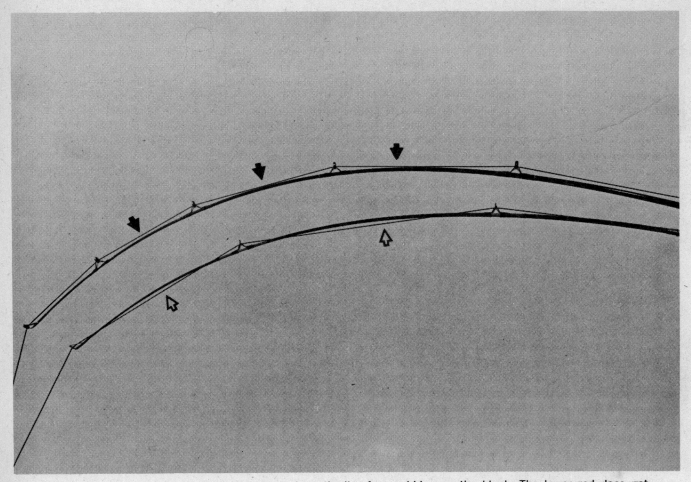

The top rod has the correct number of guides to keep the line from rubbing on the blank. The lower rod does not have enough guides. The hollow arrows indicate where the line, unsupported, has fallen well below the rod.

cling to the rod shaft. For some reason, aluminum oxide guides (which resemble the older agate guides) reduce this static charge.

One company is now marketing new aluminum oxide fly rod guides for the tip section. I haven't had enough time to thoroughly test this guide, but those I have tried have been too heavy and have spoiled the action of the fly tip section.

All of the aluminum oxide guides are made of the bridge guide style. One company makes a fold-down butt guide for spinning rods that is really clever. It makes for a nice travel arrangement and reduces the possibility of the guide being damaged when carried in a boat.

Spinning rods come with two basic types of guides: the bridge guide or the flexible-foot style, which is really a single piece of chrome-plated wire formed into a guide.

Bridge guides are fine, but they do not flex with the rod on the cast. Also, the bridge guide can be more easily damaged than a flexible-foot style. Bridge guides are heavier, too.

If you are looking for the lightest possible guide with reasonable wearing characteristics, then the flexible-foot style is the choice. However, you are limited to chrome-plated wire, whereas with the bridge guide, you may choose either aluminum oxide, carbide or chrome-plated rings.

Flexible-foot guides are not practical on plug-casting rods, and while some people use them on fly rods,

most experienced fly rodders don't care for them.

Plug-casting rods should use the bridge-guide style. Harold LeMaster, in my opinion the finest all-around plug fisherman I've met, has a theory that makes sense about the proper selection of guides for a plug rod, whether it is an eight-foot or a five-and-a-half-foot stick.

Harold, who has caught more big tarpon and smallmouths than perhaps anyone who has used a plug rod, feels that all the guides should be small, possibly no longer than 12 mm, and that they should sit low on the rod.

"A guide that sits high on the rod can easily be knocked off," Harold explains. "And, the lower the guides

Lee Cuddy battles a large cobia on a medium-action fly rod. The continuous curve shows that the rod is working well throughout its length.

sit on the rod, the greater tendency they have to stay in place."

I think he's right. Actually, there is no need, other than an aesthetic one, for each guide to diminish in size toward the tip. Harold likes the new aluminum oxide guides and has tested them extensively on giant tarpon and big snook.

On the butt section of a fly rod, I like to see a stripping guide no smaller than 10 mm on the very small trout sticks, and 12 mm on rods up to those that handle lines through size 9.

Since a rod matching a size 10, 11, or larger line will perhaps be used in salt water fishing, my feelings about guide size differs. Frequently, in salt water fly fishing, the fish, when struck, makes a very fast run, pulling up tangled line from the deck of the boat. If a tangle is not too bad and the rod guides are ample in size, a knot can slip through. But,

if the guides are as small as those used on fresh-water rods, a broken leader results. The tip guide must also be ample in size. I've seen some salt-water fly rodders aware of the tangled-line problem who made the guides large enough to let tangles slip through, but had a funnel arrangement on the tip end.

If you fly cast with your right hand, you might consider altering your fly rod for a right-handed caster. With the stripping guide in the normal position, it is situated in the middle and beneath the rod. When you make the backcast and lay the rod back waiting for the line to straighten behind you, the line between the stripping guide and your left hand is sawing across the fly rod, generating a static charge and increasing resistance to the cast.

You may want to eliminate these problems. With the rod held in the right hand and in position prior to

a cast (tip pointing at the target), you should move the guide so it tends to lean in toward the caster. Then, when the rod is brought back, the guide will be angled toward the caster and will not let the line rub on the shaft.

Reel seats are the other factor that must be considered when selecting a casting rod. Chrome-plated brass is perhaps the strongest kind of reel seat and is the universal choice for big game-fishing rods. However, these reel seats have several drawbacks, one of them being that they are more expensive. They are also heavy and, in frigid weather, colder than a loan shark's heart.

Anodized aluminum is the major choice for spinning- and fly-rod reel seats. The material is light, attractive and relatively strong. Because aluminum is soft, a little more care must be used when fishing with them; and, in cold weather the aluminum can be as chilly as the chrome seat.

Delrin, a space-age plastic, makes a superior reel seat for both fly and spinning gear. It is not cold in the winter; it is as tough as a two-dollar diner steak; and it's light and inexpensive. It also has an admirable characteristic of taking the shape of the individual reel foot as the hood is squeezed down to hold the reel in place.

Some fly rodders who chase salmon or salt water fish prefer to have a rod with an extension butt. This short addition behind the rear of the reel seat can be positioned against the angler's body during the fight. An extension butt of more than two inches is in the way on a fly rod. If it is any longer the extension will tangle the line as it is shot toward the target. Many anglers prefer a detachable extension butt, which can be placed in the rear of the rod when needed, and carried in the pocket when not in use. Be sure that any butt extension is shaped to be comfortable when pressed against the body during the fight with the fish.

Graphite, a new rod material, has entered the market. Fishermen are extremely enthusiastic. It's tremendously strong and an extremely expensive miracle material. I feel that one day this will be the material of the future, but the rods which I have tested and fished with still need to be improved.

Graphite rods do give the bass fisherman a more sensitive fishing tool. You can blindfold an angler, hand him a glass rod with a plastic worm and sinker on the line end and have him cast it out and move it along the bottom of the lake. He will feel only some of the spots where the sinker bumps the bottom. A graphite rod with the same lure attached will be so sensitive that he can feel almost every time the sinker contacts the bottom.

Graphite rods are not made of pure graphite. Most of them are a combination of fiberglass and graphite; some are a combination of some other material such as boron. Fly fishermen have raved about graphite rods. But, I am convinced — after limited use of about a half dozen such rods — that good fly casters cannot cast better or farther with them than they can with a well-designed glass rod.

However, poor casters can improve their distance and line loop with a graphite (but not improve his own casting because he is still doing the same things wrong).

The reason: graphite has to move only one-fourth as far as glass to transmit the same amount of energy. When a fly fisherman makes his forward stroke, a large, air-resistant loop is formed. The graphite rod moves over a shorter distance, forming a tighter loop that reduces resistance to the air.

The other factor that makes graphite perform better for anyone but the

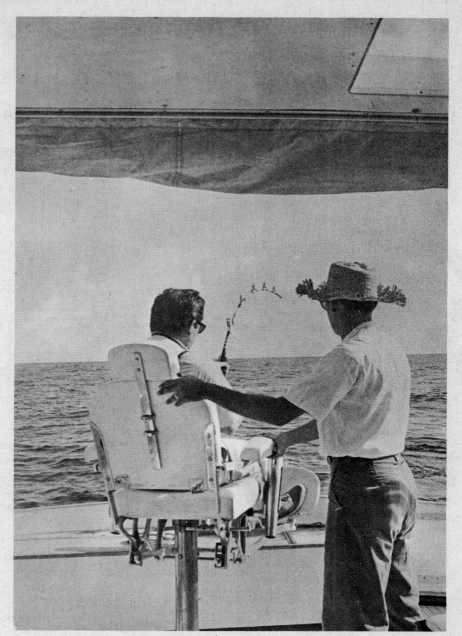

When you consider rods for fighting fish, as well as for casting, remember that length is critical. Offshore trolling rods are built almost exclusively to fight big fish, and they are almost always short.

expert caster is that when a fly-rod stroke is completed, and while the fly is heading for the target, the tip of most good glass rods oscillates up and down about 14 to 18 inches. This tip movement makes a number of standing waves in the line, which increases air resistance. Thus, the graphite, flexing only one-fourth as far as glass, reduces the standing-

wave size by three quarters. The expert caster, however, knows how to dampen that oscillation and gets no really improved effect from the graphite.

Selecting a casting rod should be done with care. After all, poor selection means many miserable fishing trips, but a good choice will provide years of fun on the water.

The Drag Is Where It's At

by Bob Stearns

If you carefully examine the tackle used by the top ranking anglers in either fresh or salt water, the one common denominator you are likely to find is a smooth drag. The angler may have taken the trouble to locate and buy only those reels that come from the manufacturer with a smooth drag. Perhaps he prefers reels that do not have good drags when they come from the factory, choosing them instead for other features (casting ease, internal strength, etc.) and electing to correct the drag deficiencies himself.

On the other hand, the one common denominator you are likely to find among the group who seem to loose their "fish of a lifetime" most consistantly is a poor drag. There's no reason you cannot stop any large-mouth bass that swims dead in its tracks with 15-pound test line if your drag works properly and you have used the correct knots — knots that don't weaken the line.

Even though some very fast fish seem to be moving at 100 mph when they take line, the truth is most of them (with the exception of the bill-fishes) really can't top 20 mph even at burst speed. Nevertheless, 20 mph is taking line from the spool at 30 feet per second. That velocity is capable of developing nearly 3500 rpm on the average small reel spool. Obviously, at that speed if the drag

doesn't function smoothly, it's all over but the crying.

The drag on your reel is simply a braking system much like the brake system that stops your automobile. It produces a certain desired level of friction, but in order to do its job properly, it must produce that friction smoothly. Jerky drag material has the same effect on your tackle that jerky brakes have on your automobile.

The drag should start smoothly, with very little extra force needed to overcome both the inertia of the spool and the starting friction of the washers (that's the tendency for the washers to stick together instead of sliding against each other). However, no matter how smoothly and perfectly the drag system works, there's always at least a tiny bit of extra effort needed to start the drag turning. For the sake of clarification as we go along, let's call this the *starting drag*.

Not all fish swim fast. Some are slow plodders, capable of covering a fair distance at moderate speed. Because of this frequent situation, a reel that has a drag capable of yielding line smoothly at relatively slow spool rpms is desirable. We can call this the *slow-speed running drag*.

At high spool rpms, as when a fast-running fish is hooked, some drag materials undergo a sudden and

substantial increase in internal resistance (friction). Unless the angler is aware of this problem and can determine whether it affects the drag in his particular reel, such a sudden increase might be more than the line can take. Let's call this situation the *high-speed running drag*. I'll explain shortly how this and the other two drag situations I mentioned earlier affect your tackle when a fish is hooked.

The amount of resistance available from any given drag system is a function of three variables: the total area of the drag washers, their coefficient of friction, and the tightness of the drag adjustment knob. A well-designed drag system must be engineered to give the best results within a relatively small space.

Usually, this is done by alternating hard and soft washers on a shaft, rather than by simply using one large washer. The hard washers are normally of metal, while the soft are some sort of compressible material. The best hard washers are aluminum or brass (sometimes chrome-plated). Stainless steel might seem attractive (and is excellent for certain lubricated soft washers such as felt or leather); however it conducts heat very poorly. Thus, it cannot dissipate heat from the surfaces of other soft washers fast enough. The result is the

Testing line drag through the water.

surfaces of those soft washers become glazed; the drag becomes erratic and jerky.

Desirable friction between the hard and soft washers is accomplished by keeping every *other* hard washer stationary on the shaft (so that it doesn't turn with the spool) by means of a slot in the center of the washer, while the remaining hard washers are "locked" (and turn with) the spool thanks to small protrusions on the edge of the washer itself. These protrusions fit into notches in the reel spool (spinning reels and sometimes fly reels) or the drag gear (revolving spool reels). The final result is that every other hard washer turns with the spool, while the others are stationary on the shaft. The soft washers simply "float" between the hard washers.

Most soft washers are made of felt, plastic (i.e., Teflon), leather, cork, or asbestos. In general, the lower the friction in each soft washer, and the larger the total area of the

drag system (i.e. more washers), the smoother the drag. Obviously, some materials are superior to others when employed as drag washers.

Several years ago I became quite curious about how a drag really works, what materials would improve its function, and what other materials shouldn't be used at all. In order to learn more, I built a "drag testing machine" patterned after one I had seen in the workshop of well-known fishing writer Lefty Kreh.

It's quite simple. Line is pulled off the reel spool by a four-inch drum driven by a high torque electric motor. The reel is mounted on a rigid stand, and drag resistance is measured by a force gauge (a refinement I added to Lefty's original design). The large motor is capable of driving the drum at speeds up to 18 mph, while the force gauge can measure drag resistance to the nearest ounce.

That drag tester has seen continuous use since I first built it. I've tested just about every possible material I

can think of, and each time something new appears I try to run it on the machine, too. Here are some of my test results:

FELT. Lubricated felt washers are one of the simplest and best materials usable in a drag system. They first appeared a few years ago in some of the medium-priced reels, and have been gaining in popularity ever since. When you buy a reel with felt washers, they usually have been lubricated by the reel manufacturer with machine oil. This is certainly acceptable, although if I run into an occasional reel that doesn't have a drag quite as smooth as I like it, I sometimes add a little Never-Seez (Never-Seez Compound Corp., Broadview, Ill. 60153), a light metallic-based grease that has superior lubricating qualities for a situation like this.

Never use a thick grease, such as wheel-bearing grease. In fact, it's a good idea to stay away from any grease except the type mentioned above. Other types of grease tend to oxidize and become thicker with age (there are some exceptions), with an adverse effect on any drag washer.

Felt as a drag material has only two minor disadvantages: it doesn't retain the lubricant quite as well as some other materials (i.e., leather), and it will eventually wear out. However, if kept lubricated, it will easily last through a season or three of very hard fishing, and it does an excellent job. Also, replacement washers are inexpensive.

LEATHER. Of all the materials I have tested, leather soaked with a heavyweight oil or a mixture of light oil and Never-Seez (the finest lubricant I have found yet) yielded the best performance on my drag machine, and fishing experience backs this up. It has a relatively low *starting* and *high-speed running drag* — only about one third more than the *slow-speed running drag*. This is excellent. Many materials more than double

Drag system from a casting reel. The components are: (1) the main drive gear, which houses the drag system; (2) a soft washer; (3) a hard washer, slotted to be fixed to the shaft; (4) a soft washer; (5) a hard washer, with protrusions to keep it fixed to the drive gear; (6) a soft washer; (7) hard washer, slotted; (8) spring washer; (9) connecting sleeve that exerts pressure on the washers when the drag adjustment star (10), is tightened. In a spinning reel, the drag washers would fit into the center of the reel spool instead of the drive gear (1), and drag adjustment would be via a knob in the center of the spool instead of the star.

from slow-speed running to starting or high-speed running drag. For example, if the slow speed running drag was set for 2 pounds, the oiled leather would show both high speed running and starting drags of 2.6 or 2.7 pounds. Some materials I tested revealed slow-speed running drag of two pounds, but starting and/or high-speed running drags of more than 4 pounds!

Leather has an advantage that is shared only by felt and by cork (to a lesser extent): as line runs off the spool at high speed, the drag tension *does not increase* in spite of the decreasing diameter of line on the spool. Most likely, the heat generated by the drag tends to thin the lubricant (reduce the viscosity) in the soft washers, thus allowing them to

slip more easily. Therefore, when using leather, felt, or cork it is very seldom necessary to loosen the drag if a hooked fish makes an exceptionally long run.

The best leather seems to be the smooth type, such as the cowhide found in the tongue of an old shoe. It shouldn't be too thick — no thicker than a dime. Avoid very soft leather (i.e. suede); it tears easily and has no place in a fishing reel.

CORK. Compressed cork is found in the drag systems of several of the more expensive reels (i.e. the Seamaster and Fin-Nor fly reels). It performs very well on my drag tester, and I have caught many very large fish with reels using it in their drag systems. It has only a slightly heavier starting and high-speed running drag

than oiled leather or felt, but is extremely durable if cared for properly.

Cork should never be lubricated with machine oil or any of the other lubricants I've mentioned earlier. When it gets a little squeaky, a few drops of a synthetic lubricant such as Neatsfoot Compound will smooth it out nicely.

TEFLON. At one time this low-friction plastic that is stable at high temperatures was hailed as the cure-all for drag troubles. While it does have many desirable characteristics as drag material, it also has some that I found unattractive.

Both the starting and the high-speed running drags are more than double the slow-speed running drag. Therefore, if you set the drag at two pounds by slowly pulling line off the reel, when you hook a fast fish you will have slightly over four pounds of drag pressure! And, as line flows off the spool and the diameter decreases, there will be a further increase in drag pressure. The result? Usually a lost fish.

However, the drag is always very smooth. In some drag systems it can be used if the user keeps in mind the characteristics of the material, and compensates for them. I still have several baitcasting reels with Teflon drag systems, and they work well. But I always fish them with a very light drag setting and use thumb pressure when extra drag is needed.

ASBESTOS. Asbestos is frequently used in reels where large drag resistance must be developed in a rather small space, such as big game trolling reels. Because asbestos has a high coefficient of friction, it also generates a lot of heat. This is an undesirable characteistic for a small reel, such as a baitcasting or spinning reel and, for that reason, asbestos is seldom used there.

Also, it is not as smooth as the other materials I've mentioned, can be somewhat erratic where the starting drag is concerned, and becomes very jerky if oiled. It must remain dry to function properly.

Only brass or aluminum washers can be used with asbestos, or the surface of the asbestos will become glazed because heat is not conducted away from the surface rapidly enough. I ran into this problem when I replaced a worn-out aluminum washer with one made of stainless steel on my only spinning reel with an asbestos drag washer. The result was horrible — the worst drag I have ever seen! A new aluminum washer like the original solved the problem, but I'd still prefer another type of drag system if the reel had enough space for it.

OTHER PLASTICS. I've run quite a few tests with other plastics, such as polyethylene, butyls, and

This 50½-lb. world record permit caught by Miamian Marshall Earnest was taken on 15-lb. test line. The drag in the reel had been modified to make it smooth.

vinyl. All of them have failed miserably: they cannot tolerate the high temperatures generated at high spool rpms. Anyway, why go to all of the trouble to unearth some exotic material when there are common everyday items that will do an outstanding job. I know a few anglers who might go that route for the snob appeal, but practical fishermen don't have time for such nonsense.

Most of the spinning and baitcasting reels on the market today have multiple-disc drag systems of the type I described earlier. Most of the larger fly reels have only one drag washer: a soft one, usually of leather or cork. Because the side plates of the reel are large in diameter, the

washer can be (and is) also large. Only one washer is really needed.

Some of the older casting and spinning reels had single-disc drag systems, and most of them worked poorly. In many cases these can be improved through the use of some of the materials already mentioned. It is best to experiment with one type, and if it doesn't work, try another. You can have a friend or one of the kids pull line off the reel to test it by running or bicycling at a good clip.

Once in a while someone comes up with a reel that has an external drag system (i.e., in the handle). I have a small casting reel (no longer manufactured) that has an external drag system, and after some effort and experimentation I finally found asbestos to be the best drag washer. Since the handles are exposed to the air, heat from the drag system is dissipated rapidly. The handles don't even get very warm.

There's more to drag then that produced by the reel itself. There's line drag through the guides, and also line drag through the water. When it comes to landing a fish, the *total* drag must be taken into account: the reel, the rod, and the water. If it all adds up to more than the breaking strength of the line, then you had better forget that fish and go look for another.

Using my drag machine, but mounting the reel on a standard rod and having another angler hold the outfit as if he were fighting a fish, I ran a series of tests to determine how much additional drag was produced by friction of the line through the guides. Below is a table of the results.

Heavy, lunging fish like this cubera snapper require a smooth drag with a low starting force. If the drag hangs even momentarily when the fish lunges, the fight is over. This drag had been modified to make it smoother.

ADDITIONAL DRAG PRODUCED BY METAL ROD GUIDES

Line Test	Line Speed	Rod Held Horizontal	Rod Held at 45 Deg.	Rod Held Vertical
8 lb.	Slow (less than 1 mph)	None	25%	40%
8 lb.	Fast (appr. 18 mph)	None	17%	31%
12 lb.	Slow	None	27%	43%
12 lb.	Fast	None	12%	27%

In other words, if the rod is pointed directly at the fish, there is no increase over the reel's drag, but if held at a 45-degree angle to the fish, there is a 25% increase with 8 lb. test and a 27% with 12 lb. test for a slow running fish. Thus, if the reel drag is set for 3 lbs. with 12 lb. test line, the drag of the line through the guides with the rod held at 45 degrees and the fish running slowly would be an additional 0.8 lbs. if you measured it at the rod tip. (27% of 3 = 0.81). If the rod were held vertical (at right angles to the fish) in the same situation, the drag at the rod tip would be 1.3 lbs. greater than the drag at

the reel. Our 3 lb. drag at the reel would now be 4.3 pounds.

The rods used for the above tests were spinning rods with a total of six guides on each rod. All of the guides were made of metal. I haven't yet had a chance to run similar tests with the new ceramic guides, but limited experience with them indicates they create significantly less friction than the metal guides.

Line drag through the water must also be taken into account. This was measured by dragging line behind my boat at various speeds, using measured lengths of line and an accurate scale. Below is a table of the results from that test.

LINE DRAG THROUGH THE WATER — Monofilament line

Line Test	Line Length (Feet)	Line Drag 10 mph	Line Drag 15 mph	Line Drag 20 mph
8 lb.	100	3 oz.	5 oz.	7 oz.
	200	6 oz.	9 oz.	12 oz.
	400	10 oz.	14 oz.	1.25 lb.
	600	12 oz.	1.25 lb.	2 lb.
15 lb.	100	6 oz.	10 oz.	14 oz.
	200	9 oz.	14 oz.	1.25 lb.
	400	12 oz.	1.25 lb.	2 lb.
	600	1 lb.	2 lb.	2.75 lb.

The above figures must be considered approximate, since there are natural variations (i.e. choppy seas, currents, etc.) which will affect the results. Under most circumstances, I'd consider them reliable within a probable error limit of 20%. Also, it is obvious that line drag is a function of three variables: the speed of the fish, the length of the line, and the diameter of the line. I haven't run the same test with dacron or other braided line, but I would expect similar results with slightly higher drag figures.

Now the drag picture is reasonably complete: the final drag on the fish as it dashes away is the sum total of the three sources of resistance — the reel, the rod guides, and the water. Because of these factors, I prefer to set my drags at approximately one fourth of the line's breaking test. If using 8 lb. test line. for instance, I would set my drag at 2 pounds *at the reel.*

If I hook a fish that runs *long* and *fast*, here's how it would add up, using a situation where I held the rod at right angles to the fish and it covered 600 feet: 2 lb. at the reel plus 31% increase in the guides equals 2.62 lbs. at the rod tip. By the time the fish has covered 600 feet at 20 mph, additional resistance of 2 lbs. will bring the final total to 4.62 lbs. — if I used drag washers that don't increase the drag as the diameter of the spool decreases. Otherwise, the total could be close to 7 lbs., and that's almost all the line can take. In fact, if the line is not brand new and unscratched, you can bet it would have parted at 7 lbs. total drag.

Now, if we run through the same exercise again with the same line and the same fish, only this time we use a drag of 3 lbs. at the reel, our final resistance to the fish would be: 3 + .93 (guides) + 2 (water) = 5.93 lbs. That's almost 6 pounds, and we're still in good shape if the line is fresh and the drag washers are the right type. Otherwise, the fish is a sure loss. That's why I prefer the "one fourth" thumb rule when fishing for fast-traveling fish. For bass, and other slower fish that dart and have fairly high sudden "burst" speeds, the situation is different.

Water resistance doesn't really enter into the picture, since those fish seldom go very far. The two critical factors here are *starting drag* and line resistance through the guides. If, for example, the drag is set for 5 lbs. with 10 lb. test line (keeping in mind that all drag "settings" are really *slow speed running drags),* and there is a 75% increase over the drag setting for the starting drag when certain materials are used for washers (such as Teflon), then the fish will be actually lunging against a resistance of 5 + 3.75 (75% of 5), or 8.75. If the rod is at right angles at the time, that 8.75 increases by approximately another 40%, or 3.5 lbs. That adds up to a grand total of 12.25 pounds of resistance against the fish, and that 10 lb. test line isn't going to take it.

For bass fishing I'd consider a drag

Jumping fish, such as this tarpon, require very smooth drag systems with low starting force. This fish will be lost if the drag hangs even slightly when it jumps.

setting of one half the breaking strength of the line as quite reasonable, and I would even be prepared to add a little judicious thumb pressure to the reel to keep the critter out of the bushes if need be. But I'd darn sure be certain that I wasn't using a reel that had a very high starting drag!

You can easily develop a feel for drag setting if you will take a few minutes and practice setting the drags with a reasonably accurate spring scale. Just tie the line to the scale, and slowly pull it off the reel, adjusting the drag as you go.

Taking good care of your reel's drag system is just as important as having the right material there in the first place. Lubricate the washers with the proper stuff regularly, and *never* put a reel away for more than a day with the drag adjustment tightened to the fishing position. Back those drags off — all the way — so the material in the soft washers can regain their compressibility. Otherwise, even the best drags will eventually deliver poor performance.

And the consequences will be another story about "the big one that got away."

A Guide to Quality Fly Selection

by Dave Whitlock

All the flyfishermen I know have one thing in common: they enjoy collecting and assembling a complete array of tackle as much as (if not more than) actually using it. Building a selection of flies is no exception. Whether they decorate hats, fly boxes, den walls, or are used to lure and catch fish, each fly must be made by hand and is the direct product of an individual's skill.

Since they cannot be mass produced like most other fishing lures, flies are subject to a lot of variations in quality. You can take any dozen flytiers, give them the same tools, materials, and pattern and have each tie one or a dozen. Every tier will inadvertently add his own individual skill to the product. However, if each has properly followed good procedure and at least duplicated the pattern as to size, shape, and material conformity, all of these flies will catch fish.

Fortunately, fish are not too conscious of tying expertise, providing the fly simulates a particular food or arouses some other emotion to provoke a strike such as the attractor patterns do. Much, however, still depends upon the fishing skill of the angler regardless of perfect or imperfect flies. Because flies are subject to many variations, the flyfishermen should know how to choose the best flies at the tackle shops, from custom or local tiers, or from mail order catalogs. Flies are often made to catch people, not fish. That's why it is important to select flies that "fish well" as opposed to those that might "sell well."

A fly that is well conceived, properly tied, and fishes correctly is still a bargain these days, because fly prices have not followed the inflationary spiral that plagues other products. Most truly expert tiers dedicate their entire lives to their work. They must sell their flies to live, but none has ever become rich. Prices asked seldom reflect the value of their work. Some have national and international reputations; others are strictly local artists. In either case, their products will reflect excellent quality, durability, fish well, and are true art forms.

Dry Fly

The dry fly is designed to float on or in the water surface and simulates some aquatic or terrestrial (landborn) insect. It may be very imitative in size, shape or color, or it may be just an attractor with a buggy shape and more contrasting or vivid colors. The most practical sizes are 12, 14, and 16. Best imitative colors are dun browns, olives, greys, cream yellows, and tan. Dry flies should be tied with water repellent materials on a very strong, high quality fine wire hook for good floatation and hooking. Hackle should be from prime gamecock neck or saddle that appears glossy, stiff, and free of web.

Key Points on Dry Fly

1. Hook should be light wire with a fine, sharp point.

2. Materials neatly applied to hook give fly a well-tied look.

3. Wings of equal length and balanced to fly size and length.

4. Hackle (glossy), even, and at 90° angle to hook shank.

5. Tail stiff and of equal length or longer than body.

6. Well-formed head, hookeye open, not crowded with thread, wings or hackle.

7. A good dryfly should be well balanced to land and float upright, whether conventional hackle type or new no-hackle style.

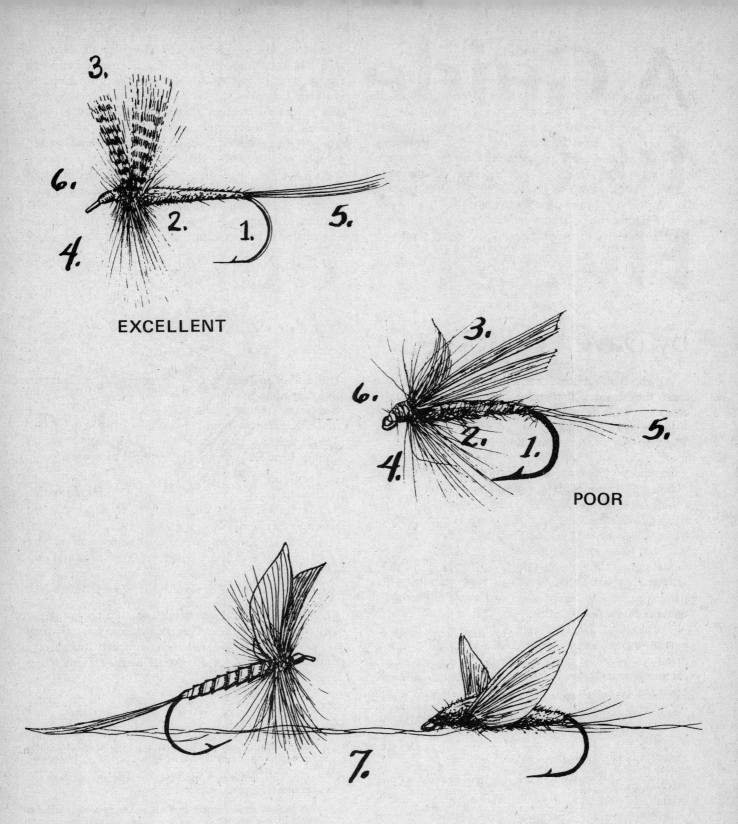

EXCELLENT

POOR

DRY FLY

Wet Flies

Wet flies are usually fished just beneath the water's surface with a natural drifting action or an erratic across or upstream action. They commonly suggest swimming or drowned insects, small fish, or crustacea. Again, natural dun colors are most effective, especially the browns, greys, olives, and black. Bright and flashy patterns are good at times as attractors or in less than clear waters. Practical hook sizes are 10 through 16. Although wet flys are tied for fishing beneath the surface, they do not have weighted bodies. Heavier wire hooks and water absorbent materials are used to reach desired depth.

it imitates or suggests live and move about. Nymphs generally imitate aquatic insects, snails, and shrimp-like crustacea. They are best when made with soft natural or synthetic materials that look and act alive in the water. Best colors are natural shades of brown, olive, grey, creams, and black. Bright and flashy colors are usually not effective. Molded bodied or hard-material bodied nymphs are seldom worth using for selective feeding species such as trout. In my opinion nymphs made of soft, water-absorbent furs and feathers are much more effective. I feel that most nymphs should be tied with medium- or fine-wire hooks and have their shanks weighted with lead or copper wires for fast-sinking capa-

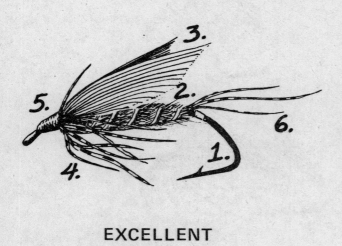
EXCELLENT

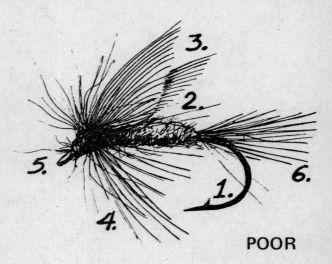
POOR

WET FLY

Key Points on Wet Fly

1. Hook should be rather heavy wire to insure positive sinking yet point must be well-tempered and sharp.
2. Materials should be soft, pliable feathers; hair; and body materials that absorb water and appear lifelike in water.
3. Wings should slant toward tail, be even, and not too bulky.
4. Hackle should be sparse, soft, and also angle toward the tail.
5. Head should be well shaped, clear of wing and hackle fibers, and not obstructing the hook eye.
6. Tail should be sparse and flexible and one-half to one length of hook shank.

Nymphs

A nymph is a type of fly that is fished at many levels below the water's surface where the aquatic creatures

bilities. Nymph hook sizes range from 8 to 16, but larger sizes and smaller sizes are practical where acquatic food of these extremes are common. Properly fished, the nymph is the most effective type of fly for trout and panfish.

Picking A Nymph

1. A nymph should be tied on a high-quality medium-weight or light wire hook with shank weighed with lead or copper.
2. There are three basic nymph lengths and shapes that will cover most aquatic creatures.
3. The basic effective nymph pattern will have a long slender body with tail and legs that are made of soft feather or hair fibers sparsely applied.
4. The head should be well formed, either large or small, but never obstructing the hook eye opening.

1. **EXCELLENT**   **FAIR**

1—X SHORT

1—X LONG

3—X LONG

2.

3.— 4.

NYMPHS

Streamers

Streamers are flies that simulate all types of small fish and minnows. They are fished from the surface to the bottom, and are usually most effective where the fish they imitate are a common food source . Various actions can be used to impart lifelike movement to the streamer. An erratic, twitching, darting motion simulates a small fish in trouble or frightened by the immediate presence of danger. Streamers range widely in size from huge 5/0 down to tiny size 14. However, those from 1½″ to 3″ in length are most practical and productive for fresh-water gamefish. White or yellow are the basic colors. Black, brown, blue, green, and gray used in combinations with white or yellow are excellent choices. The darker colors should be on the top part and lighter shades on the lower half of the streamer's wing. Bright colors and metallic materials add greatly to the streamer's attraction. There are many popular streamer patterns classified as attractors, rather than as imitators.

Although a streamer need not be weighted to fish well,

most should be. Streamer wings are commonly made of hair or feathers. Hair wings are more durable, but soft, flexible feathers absorb water and have much better action. Those made of marabou feathers have no equal for providing lifelike action in the water.

Choosing a Streamer

1. A well-tied streamer should simulate the shape of a fish with head, wings, and body on hook shank being incorporated to accomplish this form.

2. Wings too long, uneven, or bulky will cause a streamer to twist, foul during casting, and not swim properly in the water.

3. The four most practical styles of fresh water streamers are:
   Bucktail or Hairwing — the most durable streamer.
   Muddler Minnow — a combination hair and feather wing; best streamer to imitate most any swimming creature
   Marabou — feather wing; best true swimming action streamer
   Matuka — cock hackle wing gives best silhouette of minnow

1.

2.   RIGHT   WRONG

STREAMERS

BUCKTAIL

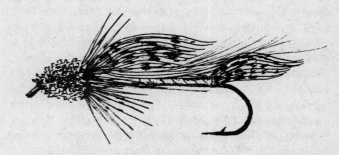

MUDDLER

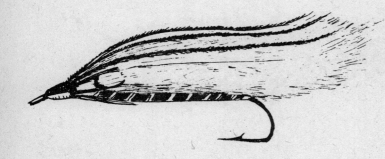

MARABOU

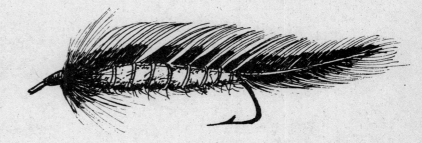

MATUKA

STREAMERS

Saltwater

Some salt-water flies are special versions of fresh-water streamers and bass bugs. They represent fish or crustacea such as crabs and shrimp, and are tied to imitate as well as to attract. Most of the early salt-water patterns were strictly simulator or attractor types, but today more are being made to imitate specific fish foods.

Besides being able to attract fish, the salt-water fly must withstand toothy fish that will damage a fly more than a hundred fresh-water fish could. Hooks for salt-water flies must be strong, rustproof, and have very sharp points. The stainless steel hook is ideal for salt-water flies. Steel that is plated with nickle, tin or cadmium will eventually rust. Sizes range from 5/0 to 8, with 1/0 being the most popular size in many fishing areas. White and yellow are usually the best colors. Metallic materials adding sparkle or flash improve the salt-water fly's effectiveness greatly. Other colors such as blue, purple, green, and red in combination with white or yellow are excellent choices.

Good salt-water flies must cast well without fouling on themselves. Wind resistance on large flies is critical, so look for salt-water flies that have ample size and silhouette, but are streamlined enough to allow long casts or to cut through stiff sea breezes.

Selecting A Salt-Water Fly

1. A good salt-water fly should be tied on a strong, rustproof hook that has a sharp point. Materials are placed to ensure hook point and gap are open.

2. Wings should be tied on the hook to prevent fouling and excessive wind resistance.

3. Good salt-water flies achieve size and silhouette without excessive material, bulk, and weight.

4. Excellent salt-water fly designs: Popping bug-minnow, multiwing streamer, blonde bucktail, and shrimp.

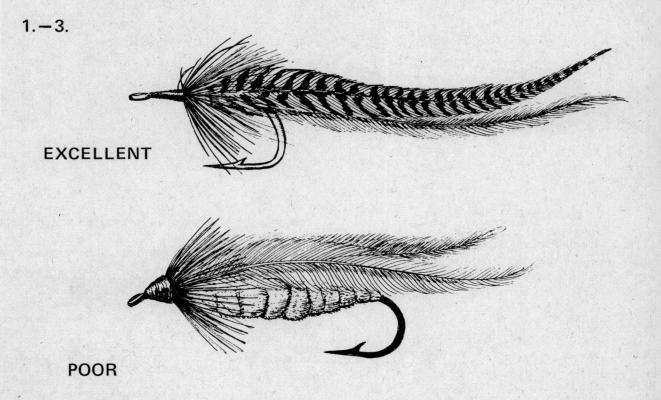

1.—3.

EXCELLENT

POOR

STREAMER—SALTWATER

POPPING MINNOW

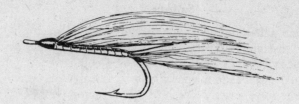

BLONDE BUCKTAIL

MULTIWING STREAMER

SHRIMP

4.

SALTWATER

Bass Bugs

The bass bug floats on the water's surface and simulates a variety of creatures that live in or fall into the water. It can be made of cork, deer hair, balsa, or light plastic to achieve floatation. Bugs are most popular for bass, panfish, and pike, but most predators will strike them readily.

Hook sizes range from 3/0 to 12. Most buggers find all these sizes effective, but sizes 1/0 and 6 are the most popular. Colors are often secondary to size and action. Black, black and yellow, red and white, yellow and green, and yellow seem most dependable. More exotic colors such as purple, chartreuse, and fluorescent oranges, yellows and greens are gaining in popularity. Most bass bugs are tied with feather tails and rubber hackle legs. These improve action, but often create wind problems and require much heavier rods and lines to cast them. I personally prefer smaller, more streamlined hard-bodied bugs, or the hair-bodied bugs because I can use lighter tackle to cast them.

If the bug has a snag guard, it will be far more versatile and much more useful in good bugging waters.

Choosing A Bass Bug

1. Types of bass bugs: Popper, darter, slider, and hairbug.
   a. Popper — Best all purpose buy. When twitched, it makes a popping noise and an erratic bubble wake.
   b. Darter — With quick, erratic pulls, this bug will pop, dart, and dive beneath the surface, returning to the top when the retrieve is stopped.
   c. Slider — This bug is fished slow or fast to make a V wake without loud noise.
   d. Hairbug — Although more expensive and harder to find, the hairbug is extremely effective when moved or simply allowed to rest on the water's surface.
2. Basic requirements for a good bug:
   a. Wide and open hook gap, not obstructed by body or tail hackle.

POPPER

DARTER

1.   **SLIDER**

HAIRBUG

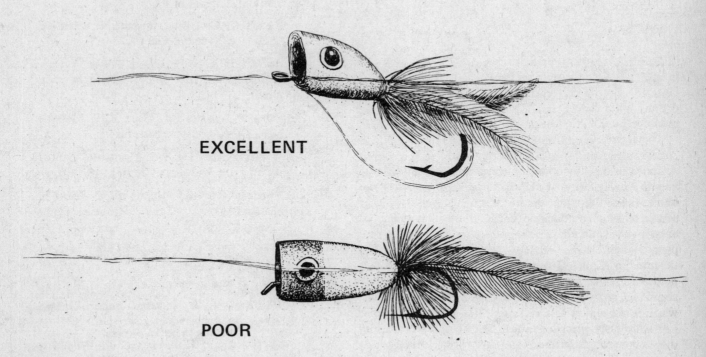

EXCELLENT

POOR

2.

BASS BUGS

b. Straight hook eye, well exposed and located on lower area of head.

c. Bug angle should have hook and tail lower than front of head.

d. Nylon loop snag guard is most trouble-free and dependable.

e. Tail feathers not excessively long or dense to interfere with bug's action or cause casting problems.

Common Qualities to Look for on any Well-tied Fly

1. HOOK. The hook should have a well-closed, even eye. A sharp, tapered point that does not bend or break under normal strain is equally important. Hook should be coated or plated to prevent rusting or abnormal corrosion. Point exposed and gap open enough to insure positive hooking in fish's mouth.

2. FLY HEAD. It should be neatly formed and thoroughly coated with varnish or cement. No loose thread should be exposed and wraps should be even and tight. The heads of flies reflect their quality and the tier's skill. Well-formed heads will not crowd nor obstruct the hook's eye but wraps should extend just over the eye-closure junction to eliminate a possible cutting edge to the leader. Head should complement general appearance and suggest functional design.

3. MATERIALS should be tied to the hook's shank evenly and tightly. If feathers or hair are loose at the base or can be pulled out easily, the fly will not last. Bug heads must be firmly glued to hook shank with strong waterproof cement and never move or twist on shank before or during use. All materials should be colorfast. Beware of dyed feathers and hair. Often, the dye bleeds after the fly is stored (unless completely dried).

Where To Buy Flies

Over the years, I've found that whenever possible, it is best to purchase flies that have been manufactured close to where I want to use them. Usually, flies tied in distant parts of the country will not have the subtle qualities required for nearby areas.

There have been a number of attempts to have North American fly patterns manufactured in Europe, South America or Asia to take advantage of lower labor costs and the availability of skilled dexterous workers. Yet few of these attempts have produced even an equivalent source of flies. American tied flies (even at higher prices) are usually an infinitely better buy. The larger American producers also have problems, but usually use qualified tiers and fishermen to oversee the daily operations. This helps to avoid the mistake the nonfishing flytier will slip into. The very best flies are made by men and women who are fishermen first.

Always examine the individual flies in any pattern display, because there will be individual differences in any group. Use the guidelines I've given for general evaluation as well as seeking advice from local flyfishing or flytying experts. Their experience often will prove to be valuable in choosing the right types of flies tied by the best tiers. If there is a flyfishing club in your area, don't hesitate to ask members for guidance. Without exception, they will help you!

If your local retailer does not stock flies, you may want to consider this list of established, reliable fly and flytackle mail order houses that supply quality flies. I may have omitted some important names, but these are the places I've had experience with. Those listed also have excellent illustrated catalogs available upon request. I am also including a list of a few custom flytiers who might help you with any special flies or information you'll need in picking the right patterns to fish a particular area.

WHERE TO BUY FLIES

Fly Shops

1. Dan Bailey's Fly Shop, Livingston, Montana 59047 (all types of flies)

2. Bud Lilly's Trout Shop, West Yellowstone, Montana 59758 (Western trout flies)

3. Pat Barnes, Barnes Fly Shop, West Yellowstone, Montana 59758 (Western trout & West Yellowstone area)

4. Leonard's, Box 393, Central Valley, N.Y. 10917 (all types of flies)

5. The Orvis Co., Inc., Manchester, Vermont 05254 (all types of flies)

6. Buz's Fly Shop, 805 West Tulare Avenue, Visalia, California 93277 (Western trout flies)

7. Fireside Angler, P.O. Box 823, Melville, N.Y. 11746 (Eastern patterns)

8. Serria Tackle, Box 373, Montrose, California 91020 (Western patterns)

9. House of Hardy, P.O. Box No. 3, Alnwick, Northumberland, England (General trout & salmon patterns)

10. Fred's Fly Shop, 117 West Main, Decatur, Texas 76234 (Southern)

11. Cal Gates Canoe Inn Resort, Grayling, Michigan 49738 (No hackle patterns & Midwestern trout flies)

12. Creative Sports Enterprises, 5831 Pacheco Blvd., Pacheco, California 94553

13. Jim Poor, Poor's Anglers All, Ltd., 5211 South Santa Fe Drive, Littleton, Colorado 80120

Custom Flytiers

1. Polly Rosborough, Box 36, Chiloquin, Oregon 97624 (Western & Midwestern patterns)

2. Darwin Atkin, 354 North York, Porterville, California 93257 (Western patterns)

3. Rene Harrop, Box 335, St. Anthony, Idaho 83445 (Western, Midwestern and Eastern patterns)

4. Bill Monaham, 6967 Silvery Lane, Dearborn Heights, Michigan 48127 (Western & Midwestern)

5. Harry Parker, 1715 South Detroit, Tulsa, Oklahoma 74120 (Midwestern & Southern)

6. Roy Patrick, 2237 Eastlake Ave., Seattle, Washington 98102 (Western)

7. Dave Whitlock, 3709 Dana Drive, Bartlesville, Oklahoma 74003 (All sections)

8. Al Troth, P.O. Box 1307, Dillon, Montana 59725 (Western)

9. Jack Allen, 1324 N.E. 3rd Ave., Ft. Lauderdale, Florida 33304 (Southern and saltwater)

10. Billy Munn, Route 1, Box 128, Bridgeport, Texas 76026 (Southern & Midwestern)

I highly recommend the persons and shops on this list. Of course, there are many more outstanding North American shops and tiers.

Proper Care Of Flies

A good fly collection is difficult to obtain and represents a considerable investment of someone's time and your money. Therefore, it's important to maintain your flies in good condition during the fishing season as well as when they are stored or idle between use. Steel, feather, hair, metallics, and even some synthetics used in flytying will deteriorate if not properly cared for.

1. Provide flyboxes and tackle-storage boxes that are roomy and ventilated. Do not overcrowd flies in these or the materials will become deformed and alter the flies' performance.

2. Store similar types together to prevent damage by one type to a more fragile type.

3. Always clean and dry a fly after use before returning it to the flybox. Wash it off in water and press dry with a soft cloth or paper towel. Whip it back and forth while still on the leader with your rod and/or place it in your vest fly patch or hat until it has air dried. If this is not possible, store it in an area separate from your other flies and dry it as soon as you return to your camp or home.

4. If you use your flies in salt water, rinse them in fresh water as soon as possible and dry them.

5. Get into the habit of removing the leader knot from the fly's eye as you cut it off the leader.

6. Should flies become ragged or out of shape during use or from improper storage, they usually can be revived by holding them in the steam jet of your kitchen tea kettle. Set each aside afterward to dry before you store them again.

7. Hair and feathers attract moths, so during storage, particularly in enclosures such as cabinets, put a few moth balls in with them.

8. Periodically, check through your files for rusting hooks, fraying of thread at head or tail, or lossening of bug heads or materials, and chipping of paint. A coat of clear, waterproof cement or varnish over these wearing or loose ends will seal them and stop further deterioration of the fly.

9. Although a fly may become frayed or worn, a little trimming, sharpening, painting, or steaming may prolong its life. Fish often prefer a used pattern rather than a freshly tied one. Most flies (like wines) improve with age.

10. Sharpen hook points and waterproof your dry flies before you go fishing. Your flies will work better, you'll save valuable fishing time, and you'll catch more fish.

11. Keep a written inventory of your fly collection so you'll always know what you have or will need to tie or buy before your next big trip.

Buying and collecting and, of course, fishing with flies is a great pastime. It is fun and interesting. When you learn how to tie at least part of your own flies, you will have acquired a year-round avocation.

Dave Whitlock's Favorite Fly Patterns

TROUT

Dry Flies:

Adams — 12, 14, 16, 18
Light Cahill — 14, 16
Royal Wulff — 10, 12

Quill Gordon — 12, 14, 16
Black Gnat — 14, 16
Multicolored Variant — 14, 16
Dun Brown Hen Spinner — 12, 14, 16, 18
Slate Tan Nohackle — 12, 14, 16, 18
Brown Bivisible — 12, 14
Henryville Caddis — 14, 16

Nymphs:

Gold-ribbed Hare's Ear — 12, 14, 16
Hendrickson Nymph — 12, 14
Golden Stone — 8, 10, 12
Brown Stone — 6, 8
Grey Nymph — 8
Montana — 6, 8
Ted Trueblood's Shrimp — 12, 14
Breadcrust — 12, 14
Tan Caddis Pupa — 14, 16
Green Caddis Larva — 12, 14
Federmouse — 4, 8
Slate Tan Emerger — 12, 14, 16, 18

Streamers:

Blacknose Dace — 6 & 10
White Marabou Muddler — 4 & 8
Muddler Minnow — 2 & 8
Black Marabou — 6 & 10
Mickey Finn — 6 & 10
Dark and Light Spruce — 6 & 10
Grey Ghost — 6 & 10
Sculpin — 2 & 8

Wet Flies:

Brown Woolyworm — 8
Black Woolyworm — 6 & 10
Black Gnat — 12-14
Lead Wing Coachman — 10, 12, 14
Quill Gordon — 12 & 14
Hornbug — 8, 10 ,12
Light Cahill — 14, 16
Royal Coachman — 10, 12

BASS

Bass Bugs:

Popper & Sliders:
Black & Yellow — 1/0 & 6
Black — 1/0 & 6
Red & White — 1/0 & 6
Yellow — 1/0 & 6

Hairbugs:

Frog — 4 & 1/0
Brown Moth — 6 & 8

Black — 2 & 6
Yellow — 2 & 6
Bee — 6
Mouse — 1/0

Streamers:

Black & White Marabou Muddlers — 1/0 & 8
Muddler Minnow — 1/0 & 6
White Bucktail — 1/0 & 6
Yellow Bucktail — 1/0 & 6
Eelworm — 1/0
Shad Minnow — 4
Perch — 2

PANFISH

Dry Flies:

Adams — 8, 10, 12
Royal Wulff — 10, 12
Black Gnat — 12
McGinity — 10
Dave or Joe's Hopper — 10
Brown Bivisible — 10

Wet Flies:

Hornberg — 10
Black Gnat — 12
Leadwing Coachman — 12
Yellow Woolyworm — 10
Black Sponge Spider — 8
Greyhackle Yellow — 12
Greyhackle Peacock — 12
Light Cahill — 12

Bugs:

Poppers — Size 8 & 10 in yellow, black, brown, bee, and red & white

Hairbugs — Size 8 & 10 in yellow, black & yellow, brown & black

SALTWATER

Popping Minnow: Size 1/0 — red and white, and yellow and red

Skipper Bug: Size 1/0 — red and white, white, yellow, and blue and white

Blonde Bucktail Streamer: Size 1/0 — white, yellow, blue and white, red and orange

Multiwing Streamer: Size 1/0 — white and red, yellow and red, red and yellow, red and orange, grizzly and yellow, and brown and grizzly

Bucktail Streamer: Sizes 4 & 1/0 — red and white, blue and white, green and white, yellow and white, and pink

Taking the Mystery Out of Monofilament

by Peter Jessurun

Nearly everyone uses nylon monofilament fishing line, but few people know anything about it. It comes in a variety of shades and is rated by its breaking strength, but, beyond that, the mystery persists. Surprisingly, most anglers take mono for granted and spool it on their reels at infrequent intervals, using it until it almost disintegrates before recognizing the need to replace it. Few fishermen probe into the properties that make this modern single-strand miracle perform so well under almost limitless conditions.

All monofilament is not the same. It's important to recognize that from the beginning. Perhaps the best analogy was offered by R. Howard Payne of DuPont some years back when he compared mono to wood. If someone offered you a wooden table, you'd want to know what kind of wood was used in its construction before you bought it. Yet, if you were offered a spool of monofilament, you would probably only ask about its breaking strength. There are almost as many variations in mono as there are types of wood in common use. It all starts with the basic formulation.

There are perhaps 100 different resins that can be used in the manufacture of monofilament and, once the selection is made, the properties of the line become limited. Monofilament is always a compromise. The trick is to achieve the best balance between such factors as line strength, limpness, abrasion resistance, knot strength, stretch, and impact strength. Some of these are inter-related; if you alter one, others are affected.

There are a handful of very serious and experienced anglers who recognize the importance of good line. They realize that it is the only link with the fish and, if the line fails, the fish is gone. Cutting corners on line is poor economy when you consider how much money it now costs for even a basic day on the water.

For some reason, the world of anglers is willing to accept monofilament line in any condition and they seldom give it a second thought. Mono deteriorates with time, but most of the problems occur as a result of abrasion. When you nick mono, you significantly weaken it. Researchers consider line to be uniform in strength. That means that if you were to shave ten percent off 10-pound test line, you would theoretically have nine pound test. However, if you nick 10-pound test, you might only have 6-pound test.

A nick creates a stress concentration in the line. When you slide your finger over mono, that minor nick might not feel like very much (but you can feel it). You can bet, however, that your line is much weaker. Nicks can occur in many ways. The most common way is when your line rubs over the back of another fish or over some obstruction on the bottom. You'll also discover, if you study the subject long enough, that tungsten carbide guides on your rod or rollers on spinning reels can also abrade a line. The best policy is to check your line constantly. If it is nicked, remove the damaged section and re-tie your hook or lure. Often, the mouth of a fish will abrade the line near the end. You might have to cut a

Tournament fisherman like Paul Chamblee pictured with a North Carolina bass know the advantages of changing lines frequently.

TOOLS AND TECHNIQUES

foot or two back after each fish, but it is worth the time and effort. One reason that the same few anglers seem to catch all the trophy fish is simply that they don't gamble and don't take changes on lines failing.

As a general rule, you should change your line at least twice as often as you are now changing it. That may sound dogmatic, but it will apply to 99 percent of fishermen. Monofilament is relatively inexpensive, and it's good insurance. Some of us are so concerned with line performance that we have even changed lines as often as twice a day. That only happens, of course, in remote regions where the target is big fish on light tackle and tackle gets torn up with regularity.

An overhand knot is particularly damaging to any line. The so-called "wind knots" that a fly fisherman gets in his leader from casting are really overhand knots and they weaken the line considerably. On the positive side, you can make good use of the overhand knot to test knot strength in mono and to determine if the line on your reel is in reasonably good condition. Assuming the breaking strength is light enough, tie an overhand knot in some mono and break it. If it's the line on your reel, compare it to new line of the same make and test. You'll know in an instant if your line has been weakened.

Some lines have poor knot strength and an overhand knot will break at 50 percent of the unknotted line strength. Any time an overhand knot breaks at 70 percent or more of the unknotted line strength, the mono boasts good quality for tying knots. Although knots are not under discussion, you should be concerned with your ability to tie knots that approach 100 percent of the unknotted line strength. When your knots are weaker than the line, you are stacking the odds against landing a trophy fish.

Tackle counters are sometimes loaded with discount or bargain lines. Usually, the reason these are less expensive is that the makers have taken production shortcuts. It might be in quality control or it could be in the choice of materials used and the process with which it was made. There are no bargains. You get what you pay for just as you do with any other product. The best advice is to place your confidence in a reputable manufacturer and use brand-name products. Alternatively, buy your tackle from an established dealer and let him help you with your decision.

Back in the dark ages of spinning, someone decided that monofilament should be ultra-limp. The fallacy that has persisted is that limp line casts better, yet repeated tests demonstrate that a medium stiff (or medium limp) line will balloon off the fixed spool of a spinning reel better than a very limp line. If total limpness were the answer, anglers would be using braided lines on spinning reels instead of monofilament. Technically speaking,

limpness can be defined as the force required to deflect the line. Mono that is too stiff, however, can cause problems, because it has a tendency to tangle.

Very limp lines do present a disadvantage. You can generally assume that the limper the line, the poorer the knot strength. Knots in monofilament begin to slip or slide just before they break. If you have an opportunity to observe under magnification a knot being broken on a testing machine, you'll detect the collapse an instant before the break. Limp mono is soft and creates a cushion or pillow effect. It is difficult to tighten a knot fully in this line; under pressure, the knot can compress, causing failure. Almost all of the top-rated light tackle fishermen prefer a medium monofilament.

Although all of us buy monofilament in terms of its breaking strength, we can sometimes be fooled. Line strength is nothing more than the break load divided by the diameter. It is a measure of tensile strength, but to fishermen, the important aspect is how strong the line is for a given diameter. The finer the diameter in relation to its strength, the better the line from a fishing point of view. With less diameter, you can get more line on a spool, it packs more evenly, casts better, offers less

Reels with full spools of line are a must for long and accurate casts plus the ability to fight husky gamesters like this bonefish.

wind resistance, and even has less friction in the water.

One would think that the ultimate line would be as strong as rope and as fine as horsehair. There are other problems. Once diameter is reduced below a certain point, impact strength is lost; the line becomes stiffer, and stretch is reduced. That's why the balance of properties is so important.

Some anglers find that one manufacturer's line is often stronger than another for a given breaking strength. The normal assumption is that the stronger line is merely better made. It doesn't always work that way. Labeling laws in the United States guide manufacturers. If the label on the spool of line says that the line breaks at twelve pounds of pressure, it cannot legally break at less. You could, however, label 30-pound test line as 12-pound test. So, 12-pound test line cannot break at 11.9 pounds, but it can break at anything over twelve pounds. That leaves the door wide open to the manufacturer's discretion.

A roller that doesn't turn on a spinning reel can abrade monofilament line, sometimes creating a year's wear in a day.

Light monofilament is the perfect choice for bass and pickerel.

The 12-pound test on your spinning reel may very well test 14.5 pounds. Line makers build in a safety margin, but the question is how much. One line may appear stronger than another of the same rated breaking strength simply because it *is* stronger.

This somewhat innocent deceit doesn't really affect the average fisherman unless he insists on entering tourna-

Tarpon on bass tackle is a possibility if you use new line and check it constantly for nicks or abrasions that might weaken it.

ments or is lucky enough to catch a fish of world-record proportions. When the testing agency puts that line on a testing machine, the actual breaking strength will be recorded. The results are sometimes disappointing to the applicant who can lose out on a record fish. There are some lines that are guaranteed to test under a certain breaking strength. Makers offer them as tournament lines, but you should be aware of another loophole.

The big question is how much under a given breaking strength the line will test. It would be great if you could buy tournament 10-pound test that actually tested at 9.8 pounds, but it doesn't work that way. At times, the variance is significant and 10-pound test might only be 8-pound test. It's legal because the label claims it will test *under* 10-pound test. The technology to make tournament lines is available, but the cost would be all out of proportion.

Monofilament line is affected by moisture. When it is fully saturated, mono contains about 9 percent water and it will lose about 12 percent of its breaking strength. This is known as wet test. There's no way to tell how much water has saturated the line at any given time. You don't have to fish a line for it to absorb water. The exchange takes place in the air as well as under water. If you live in the northern climes and store your mono in a heated basement, you'll find that the line may appear brittle and stiff. This is sometimes a sign of deterioration, but it could also be the lack of moisture in the line. Soak the line for 24 hours and then test it. The stiffness should disappear.

Experts claim that it takes 24 to 48 hours for a line to fully absorb the 9 percent water. If you catch a record fish and have to submit line or leader for testing, you may want to stack the odds in your favor legally. Most record keeping is based on wet test, but the line isn't always left in the water long enough. When you are ready to mail your line for testing, soak it at home for 24 to 48 hours. Then, put the line in a zip-lock plastic bag and put a few drops of water in the bag with the line. When it arrives, it will still be fully saturated.

Perhaps the most controversial aspect of monofilament line is stretch. Anyone who has ever tried to break mono that was tangled in the bottom or hooked in a bush knows about the stretch factor. It takes a lot of steady pulling before the line finally breaks. Braided line makers argue that dacron doesn't have very much stretch, enabling you to set the hook better and often preventing the fish from reaching the sanctuary of an obstruction before you can turn it your way. They are right, but they conveniently omit another side.

Stretch is the forgiving quality of monofilament. It poses disadvantages, but it also offers advantages. For one thing, stretch helps to slow down the problems in fighting a fish. It helps to absorb stresses and mistakes by the angler because it does yield. And, you can feel the stretch as a fish pulls away from you, signalling that you'd better give line or you'll break your quarry off. With braided lines, the breaking point is reached suddenly, rapidly, and without warning.

To be effective, stretch must be controlled. It would be difficult to picture fishing with mono if it were to go back and forth like a rubber band or a yo-yo. There has to be a certain amount of stretch, but it must be limited. As a general rule, the stiffer the line, the less stretch it has; the limper the line, the more stretch. You can remember this by thinking in terms of wire and rubber bands. It's obvious which one has more stretch, and the same with monofilament line.

When you lift the rod to set the hook or pump a fish, you must first pull the stretch out of the line before anything moves on the other end. This, of course, varies with the distance or amount of line that is out. That's also the reason why big-game fishermen using lines with breaking strengths over 50 pounds prefer a braided line. They simply cannot pump a fish with monofilament because most of the time they are fighting the line and its stretch instead of the fish.

It is technically possible to reduce the amount of stretch in monofilament significantly. When you do, however, you disturb the balance of properties and affect the impact strength of the line. That is not the same as breaking strength. Breaking strength is a static test determined by a steady pull. Impact strength is the ability of a line to withstand a sudden shock or load. In many fishing situations, impact strength is much more important than breaking strength because a surge by the fish loads the line and isn't measured by breaking strength.

Shock resistance or impact strength is determined by the length of line over which the load can be distributed and the rate of loading. The best example I can think of occurs dozens of times every day in any busy bakery. Watch the girls behind the counter tie cake boxes with string and then break the string in their hands. They allow a U to form in the string and then snap their hands apart. It would be much more difficult to break the string with a steady pull. Try it. As they snap their hands apart, they load the string very rapidly and there isn't much area to dissipate the shock. The string breaks. That's why so many fishing lines break when a fish is close to the boat, sees the net or gaff, and makes a sudden lunge away. You don't have much line out to absorb the shock and the wild dash of the fish loads the line very quickly.

Abrasion resistance is a quality built into a line and, although most anglers believe that hard-type mono has more abrasion resistance, it is not influenced by the hardness or softness of the line. Nylon monofilament is a tough material and can withstand a certain amount of abrasion. Some lines will do better than others, and they are the ones that should be preferred, providing,

Big fish create tremendous stress on light gear. The angler pushes the rod at the fish to relieve the pressure of the sudden surge.

The stretch in monofilament is a forgiving property. You can put a great deal of pressure on the line and actually feel the stretch coming out of it.

of course, that they meet the other requirements of good mono.

Filament specialists claim that—all things being equal—soft mono is less likely to abrade than hard mono, again making a comparison with a rubber band. The softer material will move away from a hard object such as a rock or tree. It's like trying to cut a rubber band with a knife. As the knife touches the rubber, it moves away from the knife. Try the same thing with a harder material, and the knife will sever it instantly.

Loading monofilament line on a conventional reel or a bait caster seldom presents any problems. If you are using interconnected spools, tape them together, insert a pencil through the hole in the middle, and crank the line on the reels. A bulk spool merely needs an axle to revolve on; a pencil, round file, or any similar object will do. Trouble develops, however, with spinning reels, and the culprit is line twist.

You cannot eliminate twist completely no matter what you do. The best solution if you buy your line from a dealer is to have him spool it for you on his line-winding machine. It's easy enough, however, to spool your own. There are some plastic line-winding devices available that hold up to a quarter-pound spool of line and they clamp right on your reel. If you can find one, it will be worth the investment of a couple of dollars. Some specialists advocate turning the spool of new line sideways. It will come off in one direction from one side of the spool and from the opposite direction if you turn the spool over. The trick is to get the line coming off the spool in the same direction that it goes on your reel.

Experts point out a fallacy in this method. They claim that the diameter of the reel spool differs from the diameter of the bulk line spool. That means a certain amount of twist will occur. These specialists claim you can do just as well putting a pencil through the spool and letting the twist go on the reel. It comes off with each cast and goes back on with every retrieve.

Whenever you fill a reel spool, you should have tension on the line so that it packs solidly and evenly. Spools should be completely full. On a conventional reel, be sure to leave enough room under the pillars so the line doesn't pile up and jam the reel. That can be bothersome when a fish is on the other end. With spinning, the spool should be filled to within one-eighth inch of the lip. It is discouraging to see anglers trying to cast spinning outfits with two-thirds or half a spool of line on the reel. The friction created as the line tries to climb over the lip of the spool severely limits the distance and even the accuracy.

When you squeeze a sponge and then release the pressure, the sponge will return to its original shape. This is called memory, and it is a property common to monofilament. Mono is constantly trying to return to its original shape or position whenever a force is applied. The pressure exerted by monofilament in its attempt to return to its normal shape can be unbelieveably strong. In fact, it is often enough to spread the spool of the reel. Here's how it happens. You fight a fish and, as you pump your quarry toward you, the line is packed on the reel under pressure. Most of the stretch has been taken out by the force of the fish on the other end. The mono is trying to

The barracuda is a speedster that streaks across the shallows when hooked. Fine-diameter monofilament is important to reduce line drag.

For big fish with heavy tackle, braided line is a better choice than monofilament. Otherwise, you spend more time fighting line stretch than the fish.

return to its original shape and sometimes it does so at the expense of the reel spool. Whenever you fight a good fish, be sure to strip off about 100 yards of line and reel it back. That will permit the line to absorb the stretch and return to its original position.

There is nothing more frustrating than monofilament line that has twisted. Instead of ballooning off the spool, countless twists ooze off when you try to cast, fouling in the rod guides and causing untold problems. Twist usually occurs in two ways: you either use a lure that spins without a swivel or you crank the reel without regaining line. The first is easier to correct. Whenever you use a lure that revolves in the water or are fishing with bait that could spin when you reel it in, you should have a swivel on the line. Don't sacrifice quality in a swivel. A good one will keep the line from twisting, because the swivel itself rotates, eliminating the twist from building in the line.

The second plagues beginners and there are times when even veteran anglers fall victim to it. Every time the roller on your bail makes a revolution around the spool and the line doesn't move, you have added one twist to the line. This can compound. It generally happens when you are fighting a good fish and start cranking on the reel. Unless you pump the fish toward you and regain line on every crank of the reel handle, the line will twist. It takes experience to overcome the tendency to merely wind when you hook a fish.

Removing twist is not always easy. If you are in a moving boat, cut off all terminal tackle including any swivels and let the line trail out behind the boat. Keep the boat moving for a period of time and, hopefully, the line will untwist. Then, crank it back on the reel. If you cannot remove the twist, you have no alternative but to throw the line away and be more careful with the new line. Twist can greatly weaken a line, and it is senseless to fish with mono that is twisted.

Since monofilament is the only thing between you and the fish you want to land, it is important to select the line carefully and replace it when it gets worn. It's less expensive and easier to buy bulk spools, carry them with you, and change the line when necessary. If you devote the same effort to selecting fishing line as you do a rod or reel, you'll quickly take the mystery out of monofilament.

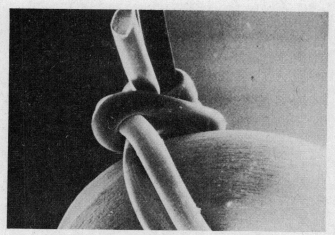

The doubled loop in this palomar knot cushions the tension and protects against breakage.

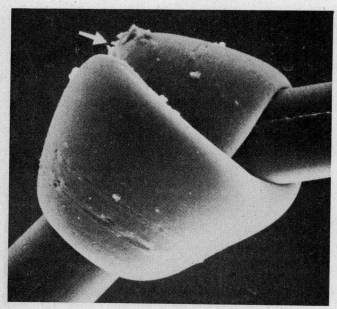

Viewed through a scanning electron microscope at the DuPont lab, an overhand knot begins to break under pressure (arrow). One strand of line is actually cutting the other in this knot.

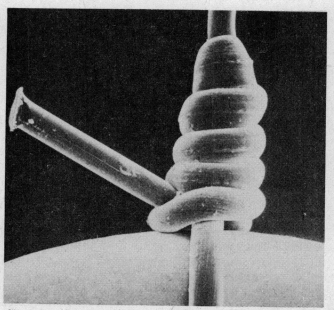

At a magnification of 60x, you can see why a clinch knot offers good strength. The turns cushion the line and prevent cutting.

Bass and Light

by Bob Underwood

Not one of a half-dozen patients seated in the waiting room looked up when I walked in. A few were reading, one was obviously lost in thought, and the rest were talking quietly. The receptionist smiled as I approached. "May I help you?" she asked.

"Uh, yes . . . I believe you can," I answered hesitantly. "I'd like to make an appointment."

"Yes, sir! Your name?" "Is it for glasses?," she asked. I looked around the waiting room, stepped a bit closer to the desk, and leaned over it. "Well, ah . . . I don't have a problem with my own eyes. You see, I have this bass . . ."

"Did you say bass? You mean a fish bass?" She looked apprehensive.

"Yes! That's it! I want the doctor to examine the eyes of a bass I have . . ."

"You want the doctor to look at the eyes of a fish?" She was unbelieving. I assured the woman that was exactly what I wanted. I could feel the eyes of everyone in the room on me. I felt myself flush.

"Please wait, sir," she said as she stood up. "I think Dr. Thomas would like to hear this!" She walked into another room. I looked nonchalantly around. Those in the room carefully avoided my eyes. A woman held up an open book while a rapid conversation took place behind the cover. A voice behind me said, "I'm Dr. Thomas. What's all this about a fish?"

Instantly, all eyes were on me again. "I'd like you to examine the eyes of a bass for me," I blurted out. I told him I was several hundred hours into an underwater study of the bass, and my findings thus far contradicted all I had ever heard or read about light and the eyes of this fish. I explained that I had a theory, but before I could proceed with my own experiments I needed a sound, solid basis on which to work. I told him I hoped that with his knowledge and instruments, he could furnish the basis.

He was smiling and shaking his head. "Do you have this fish with you?" I replied that I didn't but, if I could just have an appointment, I'd bring it in. I explained my theory and the reasons for it. Turning to the receptionist, he said, "Make an appointment for a Mr. Bass." He chuckled. "I wouldn't miss this for the world!"

My first surprise in the underwater world of the bass lay in finding schools and individual fish in places where they weren't supposed to be. (There's a long-held theory that light bothers the eyes of bass, making them avoid it.) I was finding as many bass holding in areas of bright light as in areas of shade, cover, and the darkness of depth. And by "holding" area, I mean a zone (as opposed to that of the "prowling" bass) in which bass remain concentrated during those hours when they are not actively searching for food. Prowling areas are those through which fish must enter or pass in the course of their feeding activity.

I asked Dr. Thomas to use his instruments and knowledge to answer one question for me. Is the eye of the bass able to control the amount of light entering that eye? Three hours of extensive testing, with the examined bass both in and out of the water, shows conclusively that it does!

To these findings, which I'll discuss in a moment, I can add the results and conclusions of my own underwater observation and testing. Many additional hours of tests and observation were performed with the use of a test tank to probe further into the relationship between the eye of the bass and light. Sight is immensely important in all actions of this fish involving feeding, color perception, and the taking of lures and live bait.

Light does affect the bass's eye. The absence or presence of light will often determine the holding areas of the bass. Not because of the long-held belief that light bothers or hurts the eyes, but because the absence of light is a safety factor to which they have been conditioned. As fry, they either learn the value of darkness and cover, or perish — victims of an unbelievable number of predators, including their own kind. If, however, other means of avoiding or escaping danger are immediately available to them (cover, depth) they will, without hesitation, hold in areas of bright light.

In all my underwater observation it was quite obvious that the size of the bass had much to do with its acceptance or avoidance of light. The smaller the fish, the more dependent it was on cover; the larger the fish, the less dependent. Bass seem to know that the smaller they are, the more apt they are to be attacked by predators. The larger bass lose this to some degree, showing little fear of being caught in the open. In fact, the only time these larger bass showed a preference for cover was when they were actively engaged in hunting for food; this, because of their method of attack from ambush.

Measurements of the focal distance of the bass's eye reveal an increase in lens curvature which will let in five times more light than the human eye. If humans could let in this increased amount of light, they would have almost perfect night vision with the exception of color perception in the absence of light. But we have no color perception after dark, anyway. And this is what happens to the bass when it is in the darkness of the depths or the shallow-water darkness of night. Although able to see an object as an object, it is unable to distinguish colors.

Its feeding methods at night are exactly the same as in the daytime hours, relying on movement of prey to send out pressure waves to be pcked up through its lateral line system and announcing that something is there. Location of prey is determined by these wave pressures, but once located, the eyes of the bass take over and the shape, size and actions of the prey convey a message to the brain which results in the decision to take or not to take.

The bass's vision is close range; it is nearsighted. Should the object be moving quickly, it may not even see it clearly. Thus the action of the prey is important for it must stimulate a reaction that results in a positive decision. If moving slowly or not at all, then the prey's size, shape and prevous action is important.

Every bass fisherman who has ever fished a plastic worm during day or night has experienced the following: the worm is cast out and allowed to settle to the bottom, usually in some type of cover. The fisherman pauses, perhaps to light a cigarette or pour a cup of coffee, leaving the lure resting on the bottom for a length of time. Suddenly, he is brought to attention by the feel or sight of his line moving away in the water. A bass has picked up the worm. It wasn't moving. How did the bass pick it out from all the limbs, weeds, or debris surrounding it? By sight.

When the plastic worm struck the surface of the water and began its fluttering journey to the bottom, movement through this medium sent out pressure waves which were picked up through the lateral line system of a nearby bass. Alerted by this sense that something had fallen or entered the water, the bass then moved to the approximate location of the object. This object, however, having reached bottom, had ceased to move, thus causing the pressure waves to stop. Should this occur in daylight hours, color would be an important factor in location, because bass can see and distinguish colors.

At night, however, color perception is lost and thus is no longer a factor. But night vision enables the bass to see the size and shape of an object and distinguish it from other objects. The shape and size are right. It is not a limb, weed, or bit of debris. So the bass picks it up. Now "feel" influences the final decision to swallow or not to swallow. The object is soft and pliable. It's good. The bass swallows it and moves off.

The bass is not, at this time, depending on a sense of

Overcast days are excellent for fishing not because of light bothering the bass's eye, but because the light "danger factor" is lessened.

smell. We have no lures that duplicate the smell of anything the bass preys on. I eliminated this aspect by taking a number of unscented plastic worms, placing them on the bottom for three days in the area I planned to fish. I reasoned that in this length of time these worms would take on the smell of the water surrounding them, eliminating any other smells. Then I fished these worms alongside other untreated plastic worms. I did not handle the worms other than to place them, while still underwater, into glass jars filled with that same water. Plastic gloves were subjected to the same treatment and these were placed over the hands before touching the treated worms. Worms subjected to this treatment were fished during daylight hours and after dark. Bass showed no preference between the treated and the untreated worms.

Using the test tank, I subjected various foods to the same treatment. At the same time, I subjected various non-food objects to the same soaking. So that movement would not be a question, I immobilized the food variety by several methods, including death. Bass didn't take many dead objects, because these fish prefer to kill their own food. Yet when hunger took over, they did feed. Without variation, in light and dark, the food objects were seized by the bass. Thus, there is no other possible conclusion than that the eyes were responsible for the detection.

The bass in this test tank were now subjected to experiment designed to demonstrate the importance of the eyes in location of food. Here I subjected the fish to both moveable and immovable prey. For this experiment, I hooded the eyes of the bass, using latex material dense enough to exclude all light. When these hoods were in place, the bass were able to locate and distinguish immovable food only after numerous attempts and with difficulty; always touching the food gingerly with their lips before executing the feeding action of inhaling the food.

Moveable food (minnows, crayfish, etc.,) would eventually be taken but, again, only after numerous attempts and with difficulty. It was equally obvious that were these moveable objects not restricted to the confines of the tank, the bass would not have been able to capture a large percentage of them, due to the fact that most of the minnows and baitfish were able to execute faster and more intricate maneuvers than the larger predators.

One other item of importance: the location of bass between the surface and bottom in varying degrees of light. During the daytime hours, these fish will be in locations varying from just below the surface to anywhere off the bottom. But, as light decreases, such as the afternoon fading into evening, the bass will gradually move lower and lower until, in the almost complete absence of light, it will be just off the bottom. Apparently, what it is doing is positioning itself below his prey, outlining the object against available light. In deep water, the bass may not be near the bottom, but will occupy a similar position to facilitate this happening. Again, it is only logical to assume that this positioning allows maximum use of the eyes in determining what is edible and what is not.

The human eye is rather flat compared to the bulging eyeball of the bass where the lens extends beyond the iris. Light control in the human eye is accomplished by the opening and closing of the iris: wide and round in dim light, a mere pinpoint in extreme brightness. Because the iris in the eye of the bass does not react in this manner, bassmen have assumed there is no apparatus for light control.

The bass has three methods of light control within the actions of his eyes. Working together, these three methods give it all it needs to function within its water world and control light to the extent of its needs.

The first fact that Dr. Thomas discovered in our testing sessions was that the bass being examined did not exhibit an avoidance reaction to light. Indeed, at times it appeared that the bass was attempting to focus directly on the light source. Never did it show signs of discomfort.

From previous studies, I knew that the focusing action of the bass's eye is accomplished by forward and backward movements of the lens, controlled by a muscle called the "retractor lentis." Dr. Thomas observed and pointed out that the opening between the iris and lens (the pupil) was quite small when the backward movement was at a maximum. But as the forward movement began and the lens began to protrude beyond the pupil area, this opening began to elongate, reaching a maximum at the forward limit of the lens movement. At this point, there is a definite increase in opening of the pupil area as well as a definite increase in area of protrusion of the lens.

Let's look at the opening in the pupil area. This movement can be compared to that of a door. At the maximum backward movement of the eye, this opening is quite small, thus the amount of light entering is proportionately small. Now, as the forward movement begins, the opening begins to widen, allowing more light to enter, and reaches its maximum when the lens is fully protruded in a forward position.

We can liken the protruding lens movement to a ball pushed through or retracted into a narrow opening in a wall. On the outside of this wall a flashlight is placed in such a manner that its light is parallel to the wall, and turned on. Now we retract the ball so that only a minute portion of its curvature is visible beyond this wall; notice that only a small portion of light strikes this curvature.

A plastic worm fished "dead" can still be seen as an object even though it is lying still among limbs, brush, etc.

Author maintains that a bass can see after dark thanks to the light-gathering capacity of its eyes. Lure was a black plastic worm.

Now, we begin to push the ball outward. The more curvature visible, the more light striking it.

That is how light rays work on the eye of the bass with the forward and backward motion of the lens. With the lens in the maximum retracted position, only a small fraction of the light rays passing from the side strike the lens. The rest pass by. As the lens moves outward, increasing the visible curvature, more and more light rays strike with less and less able to pass by. A light ray striking the lens is refracted in. The more light rays hitting the object, the more that are refracted in. So the protuberance or retraction of the lens, while basically a focusing movement, is another definite method of gathering, (or shutting off) light. Some may maintain that because the eye of the bass is filled with a liquid approximating the density of water, this light refraction is not great. But the lens itself has a very high index of refraction and this must be considered as a means of light control.

The third method of light control involves a pigment in the bass's eye, called melanin.. Its purpose is, quite simply, light control, and it works in this manner: bass have rods and cones in their eyes just as we do. Rods give the ability to distinguish the greys and shades of greys;

cones give the ability to distinguish the colors. In bright light, this melanin pigment shades the sensitive rods, cutting off or restricting the amount of light reaching them. At the same time, the contractile elements in the base of the rods move the sensitive cell tips in such a way that the rods are retracted away from the lens. In dim light and darkness, these contractile elements move the rods toward the lens, an action designed to gather light. At the same time, the melanin pigment moves to allow the photosensitive cells to become fully exposed to whatever light is available.

Cones move toward the lens in bright light and away from the lens in dim light. The melanin pigment is concentrated toward the rear of the cones in bright light and moves toward the front of the cones in dim light. Thus, in darkness or dim light, color perception is lost, but the ability to see objects is maintained. Therefore, we have the third fact — that bass can and do control the amount of light entering their eyes.

There are indeed definite factors that control the location where a concentration of bass is likely to be found in a given body of water. You can now mark off one that you might have thought made a difference. Light. It does not bother the eyes of the bass.

Finding the Pattern in Fishing

by David Elliott Lee

The life style of fish, like all other animals, is tailored to their environment. Survival is predicated upon an adequate food supply, protection from natural enemies, and physical comfort within the tolerance limit of the species. The modern-day bass fisherman introduced the word "pattern" to describe the behavior of his quarry at any given moment in a body of water. Not all bass are doing the same thing at the same time, and there may be several patterns in effect simultaneously.

It soon became obvious to the new breed of bass enthusiast that the more difficult aspect of his sport was locating the fish. Catching them became secondary and could be accomplished once the bass were found. Pattern developed into a broad concept that covered every eventuality from water depth, temperature, time of the day and year, to the lure used and the speed of the retrieve. Bassmen reasoned that if they could uncover the pattern or one of several patterns, they would have a successful day.

The same principles apply to all types of fishing, and anglers of every persuasion spend more time attempting to unravel the mystery of where the fish might be than actually baiting their quarry. Until "pattern" entered the vocabulary, there was no single word in the language to describe the technique of searching for fish. Even today, "pattern" is limited in its usage and you will seldom hear a fisherman (other than a bass angler) say that he has to establish a pattern.

If you plan to catch northern pike, you know from experience that the fish will either be along rocky dropoffs or in the weedbeds. Sometimes they are well back in the weeds, and on other occasions they are ready to strike a lure that moves in front of the bed. In the spring, they may be in some of the rivers that empty into the lake or near the inlets. You may not have had a word for it, but when you looked for those pike, you were actually finding the pattern. Once you caught a fish or two, you found similar terrain and worked it the same way that had proven successful.

The famed peacock bass of the Amazon Basin is a savage striker and a much tougher fighter than our own largemouth. Everything you've heard about this golden, multi-hued gladiator is probably true and, when conditions are right, it's not difficult to hook more than 50 fish a day. I fully expected to do just that when I journeyed to the jungles of Colombia and fished the lakes at El Dorado. Working shoreline cover (which is the accepted technique), we only managed to raise a few fish the first day.

Because I was in a new area, I had relied on the guides and didn't bother to second-guess them. The next morning as we paddled along an obstruction-filled shoreline, there was a commotion down the lake in the shallows. Squawking egrets and herons rose above the water and out of trees, scolding a school of bass below. Then, I realized what was happening.

The river had been rising steadily as a result of rains up-country. As the water level rose along the perimeter of the jungle, small baitfish moved into the newly flooded areas to feast on the abundance of insects that washed into the lake. Schools of peacock bass prowled the shallows, crashing pods of minnows that were feeding on the insects. The pattern was so simple and so evident that it made me feel foolish not to have thought of it sooner. We changed our tactics and concentrated on the newly flooded areas. That's where the bass were; the fishing was great.

Patterns are equally important in salt water. White

marlin fishermen along the Middle Atlantic coast know that if fish are located on the 20-fathom curve off Virginia, they will probably be at the 20-fathom curve off New Jersey. No one, to my knowledge, knows why, yet it happens often enough to make it fact. We can only assume that water conditions and the food supply suit the needs of the fish at that depth.

Most anglers who visit the shallow, tropical flats for the first time are amazed at the apparently mystical powers of local guides. These skippers can position a boat or start poling a flat, look at their wristwatches, and announce to astonished clients when and where they will see fish. It's mind boggling when it happens just as predicted.

There's no great mystery to the whole procedure. The guide knows from experience that fish will take a certain route on a particular stage of the tide, and he is there to intercept them. You might say that he knows the pattern that the fish will follow. Every member of that species might not be doing the same thing at that instant, but enough tarpon, bonefish, or permit are in tune to make it interesting.

Regardless of the type of fishing he prefers, the competent angler is observant and alert. That's really the key to finding a pattern. Too often, a fisherman just doesn't see the obvious. Overlooking water conditions at El Dorado for peacock bass is a perfect example. If it hadn't been for those birds angrily complaining about the fact their serenity had been disturbed, I would probably have concluded that the travel folders exaggerated the whole fishery.

Top bass fishermen have exceptional memories and have honed their senses to analyze everything taking place. They can recall in minute detail the circumstances surrounding the catching of any fish. Ask them and they can tell you water depth, temperature, type of cover, speed of retrieve, what the lure was doing, and a dozen other bits of information that would escape most of us.

Patterns can be subdivided into type of terrain and depth of the water. Type of terrain is primarily a matter of observation. If you're fishing a shoreline for bass and happen to get a strike on the edge of some lily pads, file the data away temporarily. If the same thing happens at the edge of the next set of pads, you might be on the way to finding a pattern. Instead of continuing

Bass moved out to the edge of the timber late in the day and only wanted a lure if it paralleled a fallen tree.

Fishing the correct depth is the most important factor in catching bass.

down the shoreline, crank up and run for the next bunch of lily pads. You'll know soon enough if your thinking is correct.

Being alert to types of bottom is equally important. Looking at the bank of a lake, you notice that it changes from mud to gravel at a spot where you caught a fish. Assume immediately that the fish wasn't there by chance alone. Stay alert to other changes in bottom structure. The fish may be at those places where the mud meets gravel or they could be on the border whenever the bottom changes.

Fish seldom do things on a random basis. We might not understand why bass are back in the timber or in front of fallen trees or suspended at mid-depth or in a creek channel, but they are there for a reason. If the conditions are correct for one fish, they should be right for other members of the same species. Any fish that deviates considerably from its basic life style, does so for only a very short period of time and for a compelling reason.

This wintertime bass from North Carolina's Lake Gaston was in 25 feet of water.

A veteran bass fisherman knows that water depth is the most important factor in locating fish. In fact, depth is vital in practically every type of fishing. If anyone shows you a stringer of fish, your first question should be about depth. Don't worry over what lure he might have used or where he fished. That's relatively unimportant compared to the depth at which the fish were taken. As you launch your boat, don't hesitate to question the marina operator or anyone on the dock about the depth of the bass. Armed with that critical piece of data, you can catch fish.

When you know the depth, you'll also have an idea of the temperature zone that the bass prefer at the moment. It's easy enough to check that by dropping the thermistor of your temperature gauge over the side and reading the dial. Take a topo map of the lake or, if you don't have one, use your depth sounder to locate fishy type places of the same depth at which the bass were reported taken. Try several different spots and, if you don't score, you will have to assume the information was incorrect and determine your own depth.

The fastest way to find the correct depth on your own is to locate a long sloping point that eases off into deep water. A tapering point is much better than one that drops off suddenly. If you can discover one with a creek channel nearby, you're ahead of the game.

Ease your boat near the shore and start to fish the point. Make a series of fan casts, covering both sides of the peninsula and also the middle. Then, move about a half cast deeper and do the same thing again. When you hook a fish, mark the depth and you now have a clue to the pattern. Other structure in water of the same depth should produce more fish for you. It's important, however, to work a sloping point carefully. If you don't score on one, try another. You can also fish from deep to shallow, but it is much more difficult to keep a lure near the bottom. There are times, however, when fish want the lure coming from shallow to deep instead of creeping shoreward from the depths.

Another technique is to parallel a sloping or stepped bank and cast into shore at a 45-degree angle. Walk the lure down the steps until you find the fish and the proper depth. There are some other guidelines that can be useful: fish will be shallower in a dark-colored or muddy lake than they will be in a clear lake. If the water is off-color, the fish could be within 15 feet of the surface, but in a deep, clear lake where you can see a lure 10 feet down, the fish might be feeding as deep as 30 feet.

There are times when oxygen can be a vital factor. This is particularly significant during late summer on some lakes when decomposing plant life uses up the oxygen below a certain depth. The word "oxycline" has entered the bass fisherman's vocabulary to denote a level of rapid change in oxygen content. In some lakes, there will be no oxygen below a certain depth and you're only wasting your time if you fish too deep. The primary method of determining this is with one of the new oxygen meters on the market, but, if you don't have one, look for other signs. If you see shad, minnows, and gar dimpling the surface in one part of a lake and not in another, you might suspect that lack of oxygen is a problem. All fish need this vital ingredient to survive.

You can save a lot of time if you have topographical maps or navigational charts of a lake or river to provide you with accurate depth information, but not all topo maps have depth information on them. With the right map, you can easily pinpoint areas of similar depth, but without this valuable aid, you'll have to search at random. If you know someone who has the necessary maps, take the numbers and order your own set. There's also another way. The Map Information Office (Reston, Virginia 22092) is a government agency charged with the responsibility of supplying information on the availability of maps. Drop them a note telling them the lake you intend to fish and they will reply promptly, listing the maps available. Be sure to make it clear that you want maps with depth information. Don't send any money. They'll tell you where to order the maps.

If you take your bass fishing seriously, you may want to order two sets. Take felt tip markers in different colors and connect areas of identical depth. Start with normal pool elevation and trace the shoreline. The best maps have the closest depth interval. A map with five-foot intervals is much better for your purposes than those with 20-foot intervals. After you have finished coloring your map, the lake will take on new meaning for you and you'll suddenly get a feeling for that body of water.

Most lures fall at the rate of a foot a second. There are variations, of course, but this is a general guideline and an important one. Your depth sounder will tell you how deep the water is below your hull, but you have no way of accurately telling water depth at the spot where your lure is falling.

The answer is the countdown method in which you tick off the seconds mentally until the lure touches bottom. It's as easy as developing a rhythm of "1,000 and 1," "1,000 and 2," "1,000 and 3," etc. Practice with a clock in front of you until you become fairly adept at counting off the seconds. Then, when you make a cast, you'll know where your lure is and how deep the water is under it. If you're fan casting a point, it's easy to miss the structure and have your lure land over the dropoff. The countdown method will tell you immediately that

An oxygen meter (left) and a thermometer are two of the most valuable tools for finding pattern.

something is wrong. And, if fish are suspended, you can determine the depth by counting.

Water depth can be critical in many other types of fishing. Most lakes have a transitional zone marked by a thermocline in which, by definition, the temperature changes half a degree for every foot of depth. You can determine this easily by dropping a thermometer over the side and reading the dial. Fish will almost always be in the thermocline or just above it.

In trolling for lake trout, Pacific salmon, and similar species including big brown trout in impoundments and reservoirs, you must locate the thermocline and then troll at or slightly above this level. It's easy to do. Move out over deep water and use your thermometer to determine the thermocline depth. Then, start shoreward until you find this depth. Follow the contour of the bottom at or near thermocline depth and you'll be fishing in an usually productive zone. You'll have to experiment with trolling speed, weights, and length of line to ensure that your lure or bait is at the proper depth.

There's another way to determine the depth pattern that can be effective. Start with your thermometer and the knowledge that bass are most comfortable between 68 and 75 degrees. That doesn't always mean that they will be in water of that temperature, but it is a clue. Locate the depth at which this comfort zone occurs by reading the thermometer. Let's say it occurs at 15 feet in a particular lake.

The next step is to study your topo maps carefully, and locate areas that are 15 feet deep with the type of structure that would probably hold bass. Remember that this is an approximation and if a spot at 16 feet looks particularly promising, try it. Work various places at the preferred depth until you catch a fish and prove your theory. If you can't take a bass, check the temperature again or concentrate your efforts on sloping points.

If you fish a lake often, you have the advantage of knowing in advance the type of pattern the bass may be following. It may not always be true, but you do have a starting point. There is also another advantage. When you locate one type of productive terrain or the right depth, you instantly know other places on the lake that will meet these requirements.

High-powered, speedy bass boats have many things going for them and they can shorten running time between areas. However, anglers who own these performance craft sometimes fall into the trap of covering too much territory. They reason that the boat is fast and they can hop from spot to spot quickly, but the miles take their toll. A better approach is to select one part of a lake and concentrate your efforts right there. It's amazing how many good spots there are in just one arm of a lake and, once you determine the pattern, there should

be similar places nearby. You can bet that the bass aren't concentrated on a few points in all that water. If you think through the problem, you should be able to limit out in a relatively small area.

Seasonal patterns are another consideration. During the winter, the fish are often deeper than they are in the spring and fall. A few warm days, however, can cause them to suspend in the treetops of submerged timber or perhaps move shallower. In the summer, the fish can also be deep, although oxygen will be the limiting factor. If they do work into shallower water, it is often at times of limited visibility and when water temperatures in the shallows moderate. That means that you could find them there at daybreak, dusk, and at night.

Bass are shallower in the spring and fall. When the water temperature in the lake rises to the high 50's or the low 60's, the bass will move in on the spawning beds. How shallow they go depends on the clarity of the water and the amount of cover available to them. Experienced

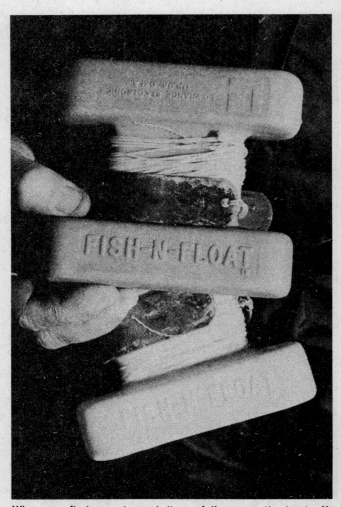

When you find a spot, mark it carefully, move the boat off, and then cast.

anglers constantly check water temperature at this time of year and look for the fish on the beds.

In many lakes, early spring fish will be found in the back ends of creek coves where the water temperature is slightly warmer and where there is a better chance to find food. Fishing the stickups in the back of these coves can be very productive.

Fall is another transitional period, and bass often move into shallower water for a last feeding spree. Latitude and water temperature play a role, but it is a seasonal pattern and you should be aware of it. They will eventually move out into deeper water for the winter.

It's one thing to circle a spot on a contour map and quite another to find it out on the lake. With a little practice, however, you can learn to orient the data on the map to the actual surroundings. Pick out the most obvious features and identify them first so that you are certain you are in the right general area. Then, you can look for the specific places. Your depth sounder will be an invaluable tool and, if the water depths on the chart are accurate, you can often use the depth sounder to help you find the exact place that you are seeking.

Marker buoys should be kept handy and ready to be dropped instantly. If you think you've found what you are looking for, flip a buoy over the side and continue to check your bearings. You can always recover the buoy if you are wrong. At the same time, you should understand the principles of triangulation. If the map or chart has a compass rose, you can get approximate bearings of the spot from known landmarks or by using points of land as a reference. When you do find the spot, look for objects on shore that you can use for bearings. If possible, line up a couple of objects to form a range line. Then, establish another range as close to right angles to the first as possible.

You have now triangulated your position and if you take the time to jot the readings in your notebook, you can find the exact spot every time. In selecting objects for a range, make certain that they will look the same or close enough to identify during all seasons of the year. A big tree crowned in greenery during the summer could be tough to pick out in the colder months when the leaves are gone and only the bare branches remain.

Establishing a pattern is an important ingredient in any type of fishing. The casual angler often ignores the need for trying to determine where fish are most apt to be. His approach is a random one in which he continuously casts a lure without ever trying to figure out why he does it or where he is fishing. Most of these fishermen have a tremendous desire to catch fish, yet they are more concerned with gleaning privileged information from others than in trying to work the pattern out for themselves.

It's easy to list rules and formulae, but the magical ingredient is the ability to observe. Surprisingly, a number of anglers never hear a surface commotion or don't notice that the lily pads on a calm day are moving back and forth in one small area. Memory is not always our most reliable faculty. Take the time to keep a log. The more you write down in a notebook, the better your chances of catching fish in the future.

Don't cut corners when you keep a log. Record weather conditions, where you fished, what happened and, cover your failures as well as your successes. At first, a log will seem wasted because you can remember what happened a couple of trips back. But, in time, you won't remember and, when the going gets rough or you face a particular situation, you can open the log and glean valuable information.

Unless you are looking for a pattern, you will never find it.

Marker buoys should be kept handy near the helmsman's seat and ready for instant use.

Understanding Flylines and Leaders

by Dave Engerbretson

"I'd like to buy a fly line, please."

"Yes, sir. What weight would you like?"

"Well, uh . . . ."

"Will that be a double taper or a weight forward?"

"Well, I don't really . . . ."

"Did you want a floating or a sinking line, or maybe a sinking tip or a wet head?"

"Uh, you see, I . . . ."

"Now, we have slow, medium, or fast sinking in both full lines or shooting heads. And, of course, we have a variety of colors. What would you like, sir?"

To a beginning fly fisherman, the awesome variety of fly lines truly boggles the mind. It's almost enough to make the faint hearted forget the sport altogether. Fortunately, the situation isn't nearly as hopeless as it appears at first.

In order to understand fly lines completely, one must first be aware of a few basic principles. First, any fishing rod is essentially a spring. It must be bent to store up energy which is then transferred to the lure during the cast. Just as various springs require different forces to stretch them, fishing rods require different weights to cause them to bend.

In spinning and bait casting, the necessary weight is concentrated in the lure. However, in fly fishing the fly is practically weightless, so the casting weight must be concentrated in the line. One problem in purchasing a fly line, then, is to match the weight of the line to the stiffness of the rod with which it will be used.

In fact, probably the most critical factor in governing flycasting success is "balanced tackle." That is, the line must match the requirements of the rod. No caster can perform his best with a mismatched outfit, and many novices have been completely discouraged by their inability to learn to cast well simply because their line did not match the stiffness of their rod.

Thankfully, the task of matching a rod with the proper line is usually quite simple, since most manufacturers now stamp their rods with the suggested line size. Until experience is gained, the novice would do well to stick with the manufacturer's recommendation. Incidentally, Scientific Anglers, Inc. (P.O. Box 2001, Midland, Michigan 48640) offers a free chart which lists the line requirements of almost all rods currently being manufactured. They will also assist with selecting a line for an outdated rod.

Until the 1940's, all fly lines were made of silk. Therefore, lines of equal diameter weighed approximately the same, and were marked with letters from I to A to indicate their diameters. However, with the appearance of new synthetics such as nylon, dacron, and various plastics, manufacturers began to use different combinations of materials. Lines of equal diameter no longer weighed the same.

Since it is the *weight* of the line that is critical and not its *diameter*, the American Fishing Tackle Manufacturers Association (AFTMA) developed a new system of standardization in which fly lines are labeled according to the weight in grains of the first thirty feet of line exclusive of the short level tip on a tapered line. In this system, numbers from 1 to 12 are assigned to lines with weights of from 60 to 380 grains.

Fly Line Standards (American Fishing Tackle Manufacturers Association)

Number	Weight*	Number	Weight*
1	60	7	185
2	80	8	210
3	100	9	240
4	120	10	280
5	140	11	330
6	160	12	380

*Weight in grains of the first 30 feet of line, exclusive of any tip, as measured from the front of the taper. Each weight may vary slightly for manufacturing tolerences.

Every fly line is now labeled with an AFTMA code based upon its weight. If your rod calls for a line of weight #6, you can be assured that any manufacturer's line of that size will fit. The diameters of various #6 lines may be different, but their weights will be similar.

Weight, however, is only part of the fly line story. Lines are also made in several shapes, and with different floating or sinking capabilities. The complete AFTMA code, which comprises combinations of letters on either side of the weight number, also gives information concerning these characteristics.

Lines which are of uniform diameter throughout their entire length are called *level* lines, and are designated by the letter "L" in front of the weight number. For example, L-7. The *double tapered* (DT) line has a "belly" of uniform diameter, but tapers to a fine point at each end, while a *weight forward* (WF) line has a short front taper, a short, heavy belly, and then tapers to a long length of light "running line." Certain manufacturers refer to their weight forward tapers as "Rocket Tapers" or "Torpedo Tapers."

Weight forward lines can also be purchased with even shorter front tapers and heavier bellies for use in casting heavy, air-resistant bass bugs or saltwater flies. These are referred to as *bass bug tapers* (BBT), *saltwater tapers* (SWT), or *saltwater weight forward tapers* (SWF).

A special distance casting line called a *shooting head* (SH) consists of only the first thirty feet of a weight forward line, and must be attached to a light monofilament running line.

By now, the code on the fly line box should begin to make some sense. A line marked DT-6, for example, will be a double tapered line of 160 grains; a WF-8 will be a weight forward design with a weight

The beginning fly fisherman is often mystified by the wide variety of fly lines which confront him.

of 210 grains, and so on. Of course, it is not necessary to memorize the grain weights of each line. You need only know that the larger the number the heavier the line, and the particular number your rod requires.

Information concerning the floating characteristics of a line is contained in the letters following the weight number. The letter "F" indicates a floating line, the letter "S" a sinking line, and the letter "I" an intermediate line which will sink slowly unless greased to float. Still other lines are designed so that either the first ten feet or the first thirty feet will sink while the remainder floats. These lines are referred to as "wet-tips" and "wet-heads," respectively, and are indicated by the code letters F/S.

One more variable with sinking lines is the sinking *rate*. Some lines sink slowly, some moderately, and some very rapidly. This feature gives the angler a degree of control over his fishing depth in all types of water. The information about the sinking rate is not a part of the AFTMA

code, but will be indicated on the label somewhere near the code.

The complete line code, then, consists of one or two letters preceding the line weight number to indicate its shape, and one or two letters following the line weight number to indicate its floating characteristics. For example, WF-8-F, DT-6-F/S, or WF-7-S.

If you now own a fly rod, the choice of line weight will have been made for you. Buy a line of the weight indicated on the butt section of the rod. If the rod has no line size recommended, a knowledgeable friend or tackle dealer should be able to make a suggestion. Some dealers have a chart on which the rod can be mounted and a weight hung from its tip. The degree of tip deflection will be a reasonably good indication of the line weight required to balance the rod's action. Incidentally, the length of the rod alone is not sufficient information to allow the accurate selection of a line. Some short rods require light lines while others need heavy lines, and the same is true of long rods.

If you are planning to purchase both a rod and a line, the problem requires a little more consideration. In most cases, it will be a good idea to select the line size which will be appropriate for your fishing *before* buying the rod. Don't purchase the rod first and then be in the rather awkward position of trying to decide how it can be used, or finding that you have the wrong rod for your type of fishing.

The proper line for *your* particular fishing will be determined by a number of factors such as the species of fish, size of the flies, type of water, average casting distances, and wind conditions you expect to encounter.

In general, trout fishing in smaller streams with relatively small flies can be handled adequately with a rod that carries a #5 or #6 line. Trout fishermen using large flies on bigger rivers often prefer a #7 or even a #8 outfit. The #8 outfit would also be a good choice for fishing under windy conditions, or for use with bass bugs or big streamers for pike and other larger gamefish. A fisherman who specializes in panfish might prefer a #7 line, while the steelheader and salmon fisherman may use a #9 or #10. The #11 and #12 outfits are rather specialized for long casts with very large flies under windy conditions. The light #3 and #4 outfits are used with the smallest flies in the most delicate situations.

There is no single best all-around line. If I were to own a single fly rod, my choice would be either a weight #7 or #8 depending upon the type of fishing I expected to do the majority of the time. Of course, if I were going to specialize in Eastern type trout fishing, the #5 or #6 would be my choice. The Eastern fly fisherman who wants to fish for trout, panfish, bass, and maybe pickerel or pike would do very well with a #7 line. If he wanted to fish for bass and

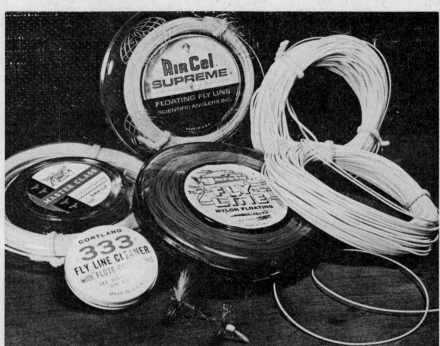

Probably the most important factor in fly casting is having "balanced tackle". That is, the weight of the line must match the action of the rod. Many casting problems which confront the novice fly fisherman can often be solved simply by changing the weight and style of the fly line being used.

pike primarily, and occasionally some trout, the #8 might be a better choice. For the one-rod Western fisherman, it's hard to beat a #8 outfit; it can do almost everything.

One of my pet rods is an eight-foot split cane beauty which is equally at home with either a #7 or #8 line. If you can find a rod which will comfortably handle this line range, you've got it made.

Is the taper of the line important? You bet it is! The shape of the line plays an important role in the presentation of the fly and the control and distance of the cast.

To make a delicate presentation of the fly, the casting energy must be progressively dissipated as it flows down the line and leader. When it reaches the end of the line, there should be just enough power left to turn over the leader and the fly. This is accomplished by tapering the line. Each successively thinner portion of the line passes on a little less energy than it received, and this is what dissipates the energy. With a level line, energy dissipation does not occur, and it is all but impossible to make a gentle presentation of the fly. In addition, since the entire level line is rather heavy, long casts will require more energy just to pull out the weight of the line. While the level line is the least expensive, it has little else to recommend it. Unless economy is an overriding factor, I would suggest avoiding the level line for most types of fishing.

For many years, fishermen have felt that the double tapered line would make a more delicate presentation of the fly than a weight forward type. However, a closer look at the taper dimensions of these lines shows that there is no reason why this should be true. As the illustration indicates, the dimensions for the first thirty feet of either a double taper or a weight forward taper are identical. Assuming a ten-foot leader, this means that either line will perform the same with casts of up to forty feet. With casts in excess of that distance, the weight forward line will have a definite advantage, since the "head" will only have to pull out the relatively light running line. Casting distance will be reduced with the double tapered line because the entire belly has the same heavy diameter. The best fishermen strive to keep their casts as short as possible, but when distance is called for, why not have a line that will work to your advantage? A properly designed weight forward taper will cast every bit as delicately as a double taper, and I now use this style almost exclusively.

There are, however, two disadvantages to a weight forward line. When one end of a double taper becomes worn, the line can be reversed on the reel, and the unused end becomes the new tip. This cannot be done with the weight forward design. Secondly, the double taper will roll cast farther than the weight forward. If the situation calls for a lot of long roll casting, the double taper is the better choice.

Generally speaking, fly fishermen find the floating line to be the most versatile, and this type should probably be your first choice. When there is need for a sinking line, one of the sinking tip models would be a good choice. These can be obtained with tips that sink at a variety of rates and allow you to fish comfortably at depths of six or eight feet if necessary. A tip which sinks at a moderate rate is probably the most useful. Except for lake fishing where a full sinking line may be required, a sinking tip line is much easier to control on the water. I rarely use a full sinking line if it can be avoided.

Although the color of the fly line seems to make no difference to the fish, it is quite important to the fisherman. In most cases, I suggest getting the brightest line you can find. White is good, but blaze orange and red are even better, because they can be seen even under very poor lighting conditions. When the light is failing and the fishing is getting tough, why handicap yourself with a line that is difficult to see?

Today's fly lines will give many seasons of use with a minimum of care. However, they are not indestructible, and a few simple precautions will greatly contribute to their durability. Cleanliness, especially with floating lines, is especially important. After a floating line has been in use for some time, it will accumulate a coating of algae and dirt which absorb water and cause the line to sink. A periodic cleaning with soap and water or one of the commercial line cleaners will keep the line in perfect floating condition. Line greasing preparations containing petroleum derivatives should be avoided. They will cause the line to dry out and crack. Over a period of time, the cracks can even cause the line covering to peel from the core.

Excessive heat can cause the same problem, and care should be taken not to leave the reel on the dashboard or in the rear window of your car where temperatures can easily exceed

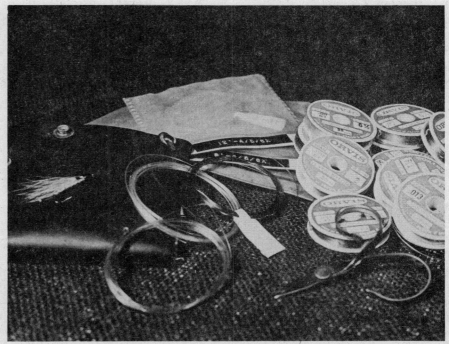

Commercially available leader tying kits allow the angler to design and construct his own leaders very economically.

150°F. on a hot day.

After applying insect repellent to your face, wash your hands carefully so the solution will not be transferred to the line and harm its finish.

It goes almost without saying that fly lines should be kept from under foot when walking or in a boat, but this seems to be the way most of mine meet an untimely end.

No discussion of fly lines would be complete without consideration of the final link in the system: the leader. The leader serves several important functions. It provides an almost invisible connection to the fly, allows continued energy dissipation from the line to permit a delicate and controlled presentation of the fly, and it allows the fly to float or drift as though it were free of any connection at all. These functions can best be performed by a leader which, like the line, is tapered.

Two types of tapered leaders are available: knotless styles and compound tapers (made by joining successively finer diameters of level nylon with blood knots). Many experienced fly fishermen prefer the compound type and, "roll their own" to develop the exact taper required for a given situation — at a fraction of the cost of ready made leaders.

While there are differing opinions as to the ideal taper for a leader, the "60/20/20 Rule" has gained the most widespread acceptance. This rule says that 60% of the total leader length should be made up of heavy nylon. The next 20% should be composed of a series of very short sections which rapidly decrease in diameter, and the final 20% makes up the fine tippet.

Leader material should not be purchased for breaking strength alone.

FRESHWATER LEADER SPECIFICATIONS
(Courtesy of the Orvis Co.)
7½-Foot Leaders

OX	1X	2X	3X	4X
24"—.019"	24"—.019"	24"—.019"	24"—.019"	24"—.019"
16"—.017"	16"—.017"	16"—.017"	16"—.017"	16"—.017"
14"—.015"	14"—.015"	14"—.015"	14"—.015"	14"—.015"
9"—.013"	9"—.013"	9"—.013"	6"—.013"	6"—.013"
9"—.012"	9"—.011"	9"—.011"	6"—.011"	6"—.011"
18"—.011"	18"—.010"	18"—.009"	6"—.009"	6"—.009"
			18"—.008"	18"—.007"

9-Foot Leaders

OX	1X	2X	3X	4X	5X*
36"—.021"	36"—.021"	36"—.021"	36"—.021"	36"—.021"	28"—.021"
16"—.019"	16"—.019"	16"—.019"	16"—.019"	16"—.019"	14"—.019"
12"—.017"	12"—.017"	12"—.017"	12"—.017"	12"—.017"	12"—.017"
8"—.015"	8"—.015"	8"—.015"	6"—.015"	6"—.015"	10"—.015"
8"—.013"	8"—.013"	8"—.013"	6"—.013"	6"—.013"	6"—.013"
8"—.012"	8"—.012"	8"—.011"	6"—.011"	6"—.011"	6"—.011"
20"—.011"	20"—.010"	20"—.009"	6"—.009"	6"—.009"	6"—.009"
			20"—.008"	20"—.007"	6"—.007"
					20"—.006"

12-Foot Leaders

4X	5X	6X	7X*
36"—.021"	36"—.021"	36"—.021"	28"—.021"
24"—.019"	24"—.019"	24"—.019"	18"—.019"
16"—.017"	16"—.017"	16"—.017"	16"—.017"
12"—.015"	12"—.015"	12"—.015"	14"—.015"
7"—.013"	7"—.013"	7"—.013"	12"—.013"
7"—.011"	7"—.011"	7"—.011"	7"—.011"
7"—.009"	7"—.009"	7"—.009"	7"—.009"
7"—.008"	7"—.008"	7"—.007"	7"—.007"
28"—.007"	28"—.006"	28"—.005"	7"—.005"
			28"—.004"

*The 9'-5X and the 12'-7X are the author's tapers.

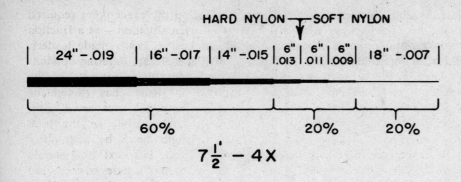

HARD NYLON — SOFT NYLON

| 24"-.019 | 16"-.017 | 14"-.015 | 6" .013 | 6" .011 | 6" .009 | 18"-.007 |

60%   20%   20%

$7\frac{1}{2}' - 4X$

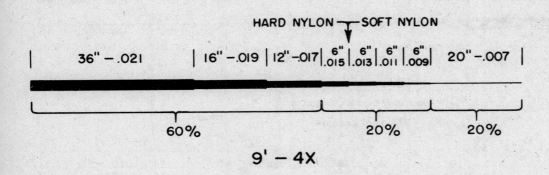

HARD NYLON — SOFT NYLON

| 36"-.021 | 16"-.019 | 12"-.017 | 6" .015 | 6" .013 | 6" .011 | 6" .009 | 20"-.007 |

60%   20%   20%

9' — 4X

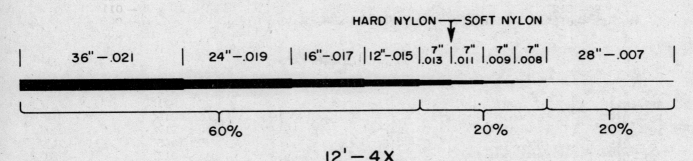

HARD NYLON — SOFT NYLON

| 36"-.021 | 24"-.019 | 16"-.017 | 12"-.015 | 7" .013 | 7" .011 | 7" .009 | 7" .008 | 28"-.007 |

60%   20%   20%

12' — 4X

SAMPLE FLY LEADERS

Energy is transmitted by the diameter of the material; not by its breaking strength. Unfortunately, materials produced by different manufacturers may have equal breaking strengths, but will often have vastly different diameters. If breaking strength alone is used when joining leader sections, pieces of finer diameter nylon may be joined to heavier pieces, and the leader will fail to perform properly.

The best solution is to purchase only leader material labeled with the diameter in thousandths of an inch in addition to the breaking strength. If this isn't feasible, you must either stick to nylon made by a single manufacturer or measure it yourself with a micrometer.

In order to receive and transmit energy from the line properly, the butt section of the leader should be approximately two-thirds the diameter of the line tip. For most lines, this works out to a butt diameter of between .019" and .021". To maintain knot strength, each successive step in the leader should vary from the last by no more than .002".

Formulas for a number of excellent leaders are given in the table titled *Freshwater Leader Specifications*.

It is also important to realize that not all leader material is alike: some is hard and some soft. To make a leader which will perform all of the functions required of it, both types of nylon should be utilized. Generally, hard nylon is used through the heavy portion of the leader, and softer material from about halfway through the tapered sections to the tippet. The stiff material in the butt

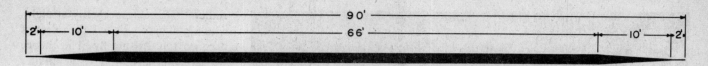

DOUBLE TAPER (DT)

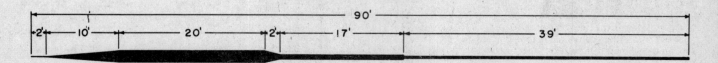

WEIGHT FORWARD (WF)

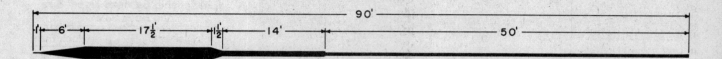

BASS BUG TAPER (BBT) or SALT WATER TAPER (SWT)

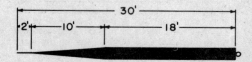

SHOOTING HEAD (SH)

FLY LINE TAPERS

sections helps the leader to "turn over," while the soft tip sections allow the fly to float more naturally. In addition, soft nylon usually has a greater breaking strength for its diameter which may be important in fine tippets.

Often a point of confusion for the novice is to hear more experienced fishermen discuss leaders in terms of X's: for example, 3X, 5X, and so on. This is a carryover from the days of gut leaders. The X's refer to

the diameter of the tippet material, *not* its breaking strength. The use of X's is simply a convenient way to avoid speaking in terms of thousandths of an inch.

The easiest method for understanding the "X terminology" is to remember the Rule of 11. Material that is .011″ in diameter is designated as 0X. For each decrease of .001″ in diameter, the X number increases by one. Thus, subtracting the X number from .011″ yields the

diameter of the material. For example, 2X is .009″, 4X is .007″, and so on.

The length of your leader depends upon many factors. In most dry-fly trout fishing or clear water nymphing, a nine-foot leader is about right. Bass and panfish leaders are generally no more than seven and a half feet in length. If it should be necessary to sink the fly to the bottom, it may be desirable to shorten the leader to as little as four feet. This

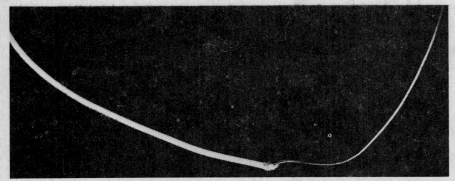

Leader material that is too soft or too fine in diameter will cause a "hinge effect," and will not allow the efficient transfer of casting energy from the line to the leader. The leader will be difficult to "turn over" on the cast, and the fly will not be presented properly.

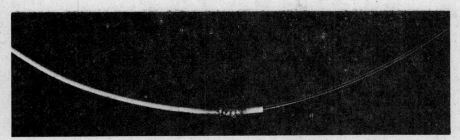

In order to efficiently transfer the energy of the cast from the line to the leader, the butt of the leader should be approximately ⅔ the diameter of the line tip (about .019"-.021"), and should be of the stiff type nylon. Most anglers make the line/leader connection with a smooth and secure needle knot coated with Pliobond cement. Leaders are then changed at the first construction knot rather than at the line connection.

Fastening the leader to the line with a simple jam knot may be quick and easy, but the knot does not permit the smooth flow of energy from the line to the leader, and it is liable to hang up on the rod guides due to its bulkiness.

rather than being perfectly straight. This significantly delays the onset of drag on the drifting fly. The theory works especially well with smaller flies, and I would suggest that the more experienced fisherman might find the latter quite useful in certain situations.

It is also important to match the tippet diameter to the size of the fly. If the tippet is too fine, the fly will fail to turn over and will land in a pile of nylon which will discourage all but the hungriest fish. The situation can be rectified in part by shortening the tippet when a larger fly is to be used, but the best result is achieved by cutting the leader back and attaching a tippet of the proper diameter.

Relationship Between Tippet Size and Hook Size*

Tippet Diameter	Hook Size
.011" (0X)	1/0- 4
.010" (1X)	4- 8
.009" (2X)	6-10
.008" (3X)	10-14
.007" (4X)	12-16
.006" (5X)	14-22
.005" (6X)	16-24
.004" (7X)	18-28
.003" (8X)	18-28

*Note: The above recommendations are for normal flies; those tied extra full or on heavy wire hooks should be used with the next heavier size tippet. Flies at the large end of the hook size range would generally cast better on the next size heavier tippet, while those at the smaller end of the hook size range would often be better suited to the next size smaller tippet.

The relationship between the fly rod, line and leader is very intimate, and it is critical to successful casting and fishing that each of these components matches the other two. Initially, the situation may appear hopelessly complex to the novice, yet it is really quite straightforward when approached in a thoughtful manner. Spend the small amount of time required to gain a mastery of these few fundamentals and you will ensure a lifetime of casting and fishing pleasure.

avoids a situation where the line is deep, but, due to a long leader, the fly drifts well off the bottom.

On the other hand, if very small flies are being cast over wary fish in exceptionally clear water, leaders of twelve to fourteen feet are not uncommon. Regardless of length, however, the 60/20/20 rule is generally followed. A well-designed twelve-foot leader will turn over as easily as one of seven feet, and there is no reason for the novice to avoid such leaders when the situation requires them.

A small group of innovative fly fishermen exists who seem to break the rules of leader design with very good results. These men design their leaders with butts of not more than .017" or even .015". However, they then basically follow the 60/20/20 rule and use both hard and soft nylon. While such leaders do require more casting "punch," they fall to the water in a series of snake-like wiggles

Getting Started in Fishing

by Jack Fallon

At last, Al Parolisi was the Compleat Surf Angler. Rod, reel, line; a box full of terminal tackle, lures, and accessories; even a set of waders so he could stride into the foam and add a few more feet to his casts. This was the outfit for which Al had been saving for more than a year.

Okay, he acknowledged, so it wasn't the best in the world, but like the salesman had said, "Unless you're a millionaire, you've got to be willing to make a few compromises." He'd seemed honest enough, and he sounded as though he knew surf fishing.

But he didn't. The metal ferrules on Al's rod fit so poorly that they kept popping apart when he cast. After two hours of operation, his reel's bail spring broke. After six, its gears were worn. His line, frayed from rubbing against rusting guides, broke on the first really good fish he hooked, and after only a couple of hours among barnacled boulders, his plastic waders provided about as much protection as a pair of panty hose.

Al has given up surf fishing.

"Too expensive," he says.

Ironically, in the same store for only a few dollars more he could have bought an outfit that would have fulfilled all his dreams.

This was going to be a trip to remember for Norm Parsons and eight-year-old Norman, Jr. For years now Norm's busy schedule had been broadening a breach between him and his son. A day of striper fishing, he figured, that's what they needed. Norm had chartered the best skipper, selected the best date, and now they were approaching the turbulent tide rips around Cutty-hunk Island, the best striped bass waters in the world. Excitement, thrills, adventure — what better way to achieve closeness between father and son.

After three uneventful hours of trolling, the boy's enthusiasm had been jostled into a queasy boredom. When, after another hour, he finally hooked his first fish, his father's well-intentioned but intimidating, "Okay now, hold on, pump and reel, pump and reel, *don't lose him,*" filled him with fear of failure. When the fish broke free because the boy let his awkward wire line jam his unfamiliar reel, he broke down and cried.

Norm Senior is still trying to figure out what he did wrong. Norm Junior could tell him, if his dad weren't too proud to ask.

Dave Warren had it made: successful business, grown children, good health. Now he was ready to take on those trout he had been dreaming about all these years.

"The works," he told the salesman. "Give me one of those fly rods, a reel, a line — everything."

"Fine, sir. And will you be fishing dry or wet?"

"Huh?"

"Dry flies or wet flies, sir? The dry fly floats on top of the water like a live insect and needs a floating line to deliver it properly. The wet, which requires a sinking line, simulates a submerged insect and, in the case of nymphs, an unhatched insect. The streamer, of course, stimulates a small baitfish and is also a wet fly."

"Uh, of course. Well, better make it a floating line. Only way to see what's going on, right?"

"Right, sir. Or, as they say, 'Right on.' Heh, heh. Now, will you want your line level, double-tapered, or weight-forward? Myself, I use a DT5F, or, as it was designated in the former code, HDH. . . ."

These days Dave Warren spends a lot of time puttering around in his garden and wondering whatever became

Get involved in fishing and Opening Day automatically becomes another holiday.

of the plain old fishing they used to do when he was a kid.

Bill Mitchell thought it would be great fun to invite his fiancée, Joyce Upton, along on a night of plugging a pond for largemouth bass.

"Might as well learn right in the beginning why this bass fishing means so much to me," he told her.

Joyce was delighted. "Sharing," she thought, "that's the rock on which enduring marriages are built. Besides, it should be fun."

And it should have been: bright breezeless summer night with trampolining bass shattering the darkness all around their pram. But Bill had forgotten the bug spray,

and every insect in the world seemed to be bombarding Joyce: in her hair, in her ears, in her eyes, up her nose, sleeves, pantlegs. She slapped, she squirmed, she stomped, and in the process put down every fish in the pond.

"Here," growled Bill, handing her one of his cigars, "it won't taste good, but it works."

It did, but it burned her eyes and turned her stomach. Eventually she threw up all over Bill's boat.

For four days Joyce's face resembled a warty squash. She wouldn't go out of the house; she wouldn't let Bill come in. After that, things never were quite the same between them.

Pay-as-you-go ponds are great places to practice as well as to get a head start on the season.

The names are fictitious, but the scenarios are fact. Even with 62 million Americans already fishing for sport, there are many more who would like to but don't. Some try it, have a miserable time, and conclude reluctantly that they must lack the requisite muscle, mentality, or masochism to make a go of it. Others, bewildered by the esoterica of line strengths, retrieve ratios, hook sizes, and flyline codes, don't even bother trying.

The main cause of failure for first-time fishermen is expecting the wrong thing. One man sees a mammoth marlin caught on TV and concludes that this is for him. Anything less is a letdown. The hours spent stalking such a trophy, the years devoted to learning what to do after it has been hooked don't even enter his mind.

Another recalls the carefree Huckleberry Finn fun he used to have plucking sunfish from a hometown pond. Just the thing for his frazzled nerves, he figures, ignoring the fact that he no longer is the same wondering wide-eyed youngster. When his boyhood joys keep getting stopped short by thoughts of unpaid bills and uncut lawns, he concludes that fishing just ain't what it used to be.

Ironic. Fishing has something wonderful for almost everyone — man, woman, and child. Between the extremes of epic blue-water encounters and right-down-the-road bobber-watching is a vast variety of experience. It ranges from excitement to tranquility, from socializing to solitude, from arm-aching exercise to just drifting and dreaming. Fishing is the complete recreation and, in the true sense of the term, a re-creation of body, mind, and spirit. The payoff is well worth a few minutes of your time to consider what you are hoping to find in fishing and what, in terms of effort, expense, and attention, you are willing to pay for it.

Answers can't be conclusive, of course. The only way to find out for sure if you will enjoy a given method, species, time, terrain, or location is to experience it. Books can convey the thrill of the chase and the exaltation of the catch, but heat, cold, bugs, fatigue, and inundated waders are part of the picture, too. For these, words simply aren't enough. No writer has yet captured the clammy, crotch-clutching, butt-burning discomfort of driving home in soggy underwear.

Nevertheless, an honest assessment of what you are seeking, and your ability and willingness to achieve it, can lower the odds against disappointment. Is big game fishing your bag? Fine, but can you afford the hundred-and-more-dollars-a-day charter fees? Does taking trout on dry flies fascinate you? Great, but are you willing to learn the lore and the language and to put in a long

Flounder from a bridge is an easy and exciting way to launch a fishing career.

apprenticeship of practice, practice, practice? Striped bass from the surf? Sure, providing you have the strength and the stamina. Snook, bluefish, landlocked salmon? Superb species, but how far will you have to travel to reach them?

All of these goals are available, all are achievable, but like most lofty aspirations, all are best reached a step at a time. The first step should be to try your wings in a simple situation with manageable equipment.

Today's tyro commences his angling career with better weapons than the best available little more than a generation ago, when fiberglass rods, spinning reels, and extruded nylon line had barely made their debuts. Furthermore, thanks to technical advances, volume production, and mass merchandising, the price is right. Fifty dollars can buy an excellent outfit — rod, reel, line, lures, plus a few accessories such as hooks, sinkers, and swivels. Half that amount can buy a good one.

These prices apply to bait casting and fly fishing as well as to spinning, but my advice to the novice is to start with spinning. In bait casting, the velocity of the reel's rotating spool requires a super-sensitive thumb to control it. Until you have cultivated yours, you will be plagued by backlash-induced tangles. Fly fishing is a specialized techniques; for the inexperienced severely limited in where and when it can be used. Its requirement for casting line rather than lure necessitates special equipment and practiced delivery. With spinning,

Sunfish in close-to-home ponds provide sport and an opportunity to practice.

you will catch on quickly and enjoy trouble-free tryouts in the widest assortment of circumstances.

Another recommendation: don't expect, or even attempt, to find an initial outfit with which you will live happily ever after. First time around, understandably you have no basis for making such a selection. Your starting outfit should be chosen with an eye to experimentation, to enable you to try as many different types of fish and methods and waters as possible without being either over- or underarmed.

In some ways this requires an even more discerning eye than you will need in later years, after you have decided to concentrate on a favorite form of fishing. Without the guidance of an experienced fisherman-friend, you might well wind up buying nothing more than a $25-$50 contribution to next year's garage sale. Whenever possible, therefore, seek reliable advice about where to shop, what to look (and look out) for, how much to pay. Then make the rounds of recommended stores. After you have narrowed your choices down to two or three selections, see if you can persuade your friend to come along and give his blessing to your eventual purchase.

The three main outlets for fishing tackle are mail-order houses, discount stores, and tackle shops. Many mail-order catalogs offer ultra-high-grade merchandise with commensurately high prices; others specialize in pig-in-a-poke bargains. Avoid them both. With the former you'll be paying too much for training tackle; with the latter you might not be paying enough. Later on you can shop by mail when you see exactly what you want at a price

No time to fish? Try nights. Competition is at a minimum, and fish like these rainbow trout are waiting to take you on.

you know is reasonable. Like me, you might even develop a weakness for an occasional investment in one of those mystery grab bag assortments. For your first outfit, though, never buy blind.

Discount houses generally offer lower prices than tackle shops, but their fishing counters too often are manned by employees who don't know a lure from a lyre. My apologies to those who do, but I'm afraid I've had my questions answered once too often with, "Sawree, but this isn't my usual department."

The few extra dollars you pay in a store that specializes in fishing, or at least in outdoor sports, can be more than repaid with words of sound advice. How gratefully I remember the shopowner on California's Russian River from whom I bought my first surf rod. After a trans-continental business trip, I had driven there from San Francisco for a once-in-a-lifetime joust with the fabled searun rainbow trout, the steelhead. On the cross-country plane, I had refused to relinquish my rod to the stewardess. In my hotel room, I had slept with it on a chair alongside my bed, yet despite my coddling, I pinched it while closing my car door prior to rigging up at the mouth of Austin Stream. First cast, it folded like a strand of wet spaghetti.

This shopowner had me at his mercy, yet he couldn't have been more accommodating. After devoting nearly an hour to finding out what kind of fishing I would be concentrating on back East — species, size, waters, terrain — he sold me, for even less than the $20 I told him I could afford, a 7½-footer that proved to be an ideal compromise between steelhead and stripers.

Characteristics to check in a rod are length, weight, strength, resilience, integrity, hardware, wrapping, and "feel." Customary lengths range from the five-foot wands employed along brush-bordered trout brooks to the 13-foot surf rods designed for heaving heavy payloads from an ocean beach. A rod's length, of course, should be matched to its user's height. For most adults, a 6½- to 7½-footer offers the broadest range of employment.

Lightness and strength are blended beautifully in the tubular fiberglass from which most of today's spinning rods are made. Rods of solid glass are usually less expensive and leave something to be desired. Tubular fiberglass is a better choice for all-around employment. I have been wary of solid rods ever since a friend fractured his like a dried branch while playing a pair of modest-size flounders.

Resilience is that quality which determines how quickly a bent rod resumes its original shape. You will want whip enough in your rod to deliver a light lure, to telegraph a tender nibble, and to enable you to make the most of a small fish's fighting qualities, yet you also will want stiffness enough to help in braking a big fish. Keep experimenting until you think you've hit the right combination.

A rod has integrity when it works as a single unit, even thought it's made up of several sections. The secret is snug and secure ferrules, those male-female fittings where sections join. Metal ferrules are troublesome: too loose, they rattle; too tight, they can't be pulled apart. In time, they tend to get dented and work loose. Glass-to-glass ferrules add a few dollars to your rod's price, but the money will be well spent.

Integrity, by the way, also is influenced by how your rod's shaft is joined to its handle. Does it look solid, secure, well designed, carefully constructed? Is glue daubed sloppily around the joint's edges?

Hardware consists of line guides plus the metal rings for holding your reel in place. Avoid reel-securing rings of the slip-on type; they also slip off. And be sure that your rod has two of the screw-on types. A second is needed to keep the first from backing off.

Guides normally are held in place with tightly wrapped thread covered with varnish. You may not be able to confirm a good wrap job by visual inspection, but you can assure yourself that guides are secure by flexing and twisting a few.

First thing to check on your line guides is alignment. Sounds elementary, I know, but once I almost bought a rod that had half of its guides on the wrong side. Be sure the guides are made of corrosion-resistant metal, especially if you plan to fish in salt water. Rubbing against rust frays lines.

Some guides are lined with ceramic to reduce friction. In my opinion, the few extra feet that these liners might add to your casting are not worth the worry over one falling out when you need it most. This happened to me once when, after several hours of unproductive prowling and plugging, I finally got into a school of hungry striped bass and promptly severed my line on the guide's sharp inside edge.

Fun and food through winter ice. Total investment: about 50 cents' worth of equipment.

Your tip top guide, at the outside end of your rod, deserves special attention because your line rubs hard against it during every cast, every retrieve, with every played fish. Unless your tip top is made of extra hard metal such as carborundum alloy, your line will wear grooves in its edges.

A rod can score high in statistics, yet flunk the most important test of all: how does it "feel?" This is a personal thing, a matter of compatibility. Its roots are deep and untraceable. You don't try to define it or describe its presence or explain its absence. You just know. The shape of your rod's handle and the way your rod matches your reel are part of it, but so are things such as muscle development and color preference. Watch a child try rod after rod until a "This is it" smile lights up his face. Then you'll know what I mean.

Spinning reels are either closed-face or open-face. In the former, a hood with the general configuration of a cone covers the reel's face, and line feeds through a hole at the cone's apex. A button releases line for casting, and an adjustable drag enables a running fish to pull out line against pressure.

In the open-face reel, a wire loop (called a bail) is pushed to one side prior to casting so line can leave the spool without interference. With the first crank of the reel handle, the bail automatically snaps back into place, controlling line placement on the spool. This reel also has an adjustable drag.

For years I thought closed-face reels were just children's toys, suitable for little league fish such as sunnies and suckers, but not up to handling anything with real muscle. Then I fished Maine's Moose River with Nate

Crappies on a fly rod offer fun galore while sharpening your technique for trout and salmon.

Brown, a fan of closed-face reels. Nate watched indulgently while I tried vainly to coax a salmon from the rumbling turbulence below Brassua Dam. Then he ambled casually around the bend, returning ten minutes later to drop four pounds of shimmering silver at my feet and ask, "This what you're looking for?" Still, I never have felt comfortable with closed-face reels. I always have the feeling that there might be something going on under that hood — sand collecting, salt accumulating, a tangle developing — that I should know about.

What test line should you use? For fresh water, 6-8; for salt water, 10-12. A line's test, remember, does not designate the maximum weight of the fish it can handle. A running fish puts only a modest strain on a line that's leaving its spool against a softly set drag. Hold your rod high, take your time, stay loose, and you can tame enormous fish on light line. How enormous? The International Game Fish Association's records for its recently established 6-pound-line class include a 33-pound striped bass, a 71½-pound tarpon, a 91½-pound mako shark, and a 205-pound striped marlin.

When buying line, beware of those "mile and a quarter for a buck and a quarter" bargains. Buy the best blend of lightness, limpness, and strength that your budget will allow, and be sure to wind it into your reel in the same direction it comes off the packaged spool. Otherwise, you'll be winding on troublesome twists. Better still, buy your line from a vendor who will wind it on for you by machine. Not only will you be assured of evenly laid twist-free line under uniform tension, but you'll economize by buying only as much as you need.

If you fish with bait, you should know a little bit about hooks. For now, never mind the fine points about penetration angles, sizing codes, or the difference between a Siwash and an O'Shaughnessy. These are important and fascinating aspects of the craft of fishing, but in the beginning, mechanics are enough.

First, if salt water will be your beat, be sure your hook, like the hardware on your rod and the parts of your reel, is made of corrosion-resistant metal such as stainless steel, or at least has a corrosion-resistant plating. Then match your hook to the mouth and strength of the fish you'll be seeking. A codfish hook, for example, won't even fit in a flounder's miniscule mouth, but a bulldogging cod will straighten the fine wire of a flounder hook. You'll need long shanks on your hooks for protection against the sharp, line-severing teeth of pike and bluefish as well as for freeing barbs from the gullets of gulpers such as flounder and brook trout. Finally, make sure the points are sharp. Even fresh-from-the-package hooks sometimes need sharpening. A fine file or sharpening stone should be in every tackle box.

As for lures, there are . . .

Lures that sink and lures that float,
Lures for shore and lures for boat,
Lures of metal, wood, or plastic,
Lures that leap as if they're spastic,
Lures that wiggle, spin, or wobble
Like a little fish in trouble,
Lures with twists and bends and bevels,
Lures that swim at sundry levels,
Lures that "pop" or "blup" or splash,
Lures that dawdle, lures that dash,
Lures in reds and greens and blues,
Lures in all the rainbow's hues,
Lures that look like worms — delicious! —
Lures that counterfeit small fishes,
Lures that swim in softest silence,
Lures that ape the vilest violence,
Lures that slink and lures that lay there,
Lures that lack, but wink and "Hey, there,"
Lures that during darkness stay alight,
Thanks to bulb and trusty Rayolite.
With lures produced in such profusion,
It's little wonder there's confusion.

If there's any area in which the novice angler needs guidance, it's in buying lures. Not from some stranger behind a counter who might be licking his chops at the chance of unloading his collection of clunkers. Tell that fisherman-friend of yours where you'd like to fish and what you'd like to fish for, and he'll suggest a few old standbys that have worked well for him. Once you're committed to fishing, you'll quickly acquire the knowledge that will enable you to expand your fishing arsenal intelligently.

Beyond the basics of rod, reel, line, hooks, and lures, there are few items you'll really need for Phase I fishing. No point in spending $20 for a vest or $30 for a set of chest waders when a couple of disappointing excursions might convince you that your money would have been better invested in a new set of hedge clippers. Check with your fisherman-friend again. You won't be imposing. One of the joys for real fishermen is sharing, and this includes the fruits of one's labors as well as on-the-spot excitement. In a few years, you'll be able to pass the favor on to another tyro.

One accessory that's an absolute necessity for a youngster is a tackle box. No buccaneer ever enjoyed a chest full of doubloons more than a boy does his box full of tackle, especially if it's just like his dad's. Yet, while it's a great idea to surprise your youngster with a new tackle box, never do so with a new outfit. Sure, you'll feel good when his face lights up like a summer sunrise, but the clouds will move in as soon as he starts finding more suitable items that he could have discovered himself if you had let him do his own shopping.

The codfish, a head boat favorite, is caught by novices as well as veterans.

Suggesting where and how a man should go about cutting his fishing teeth is a little like recommending that he consult a marriage manual before his first date. In both cases, much of the fun is in improvising, experimenting, discovering, and occasionally even making a fool of yourself. Besides, what worked for me won't necessarily work for you. That great American institution, the head boat, ignited my fishing fuse, but you might find head boats too crowded. A sewage outlet where some of Massachusetts' biggest suckers resided was one of my most exciting boyhood discoveries, but few adults would find it appealing.

If you're an adult who wants to find out about fishing, my advice is to hurry up and get out there. You've wasted too much time already. Chances are, that fisherman-friend who's been helping you with your purchases will have invited you along already. If not, ask him. If he can't make it, perhaps he can aim you in the right direction.

If you're an adult who already knows about fishing and wants to share his joys with a youngster, you're really in luck. Life is about to open doors to delights that will top any you've ever experienced together. To guide you along the way, here are ten suggestions from a fisherman-father who has traveled the yellow brick road with three sensational sons and three spectacular daughters.

1. Let them do their own fishing.
2. Make sure they have action.
3. Keep them comfortable.
4. Don't force them.
5. Start them in gentle waters with simple methods.
6. Equip them properly.
7. *Make* time, *take* time.
8. Learn as well as teach.
9. Include your daughters.
10. Enjoy them while you can.

The Care and Feeding of Fishing Tackle

by C. Boyd Pfeiffer

I ran the line off the reel, through the guides of the rod and tied on a lure. When I tried to make the first cast on that bass lake, the reel handle would not — and I mean *would not* — turn. Fortunately, I had a spare rod and reel, but previous negligence after a trip to the Bahamas cost me the use of my favorite outfit that day. Later at home, I found the main ball-bearing race completely frozen. It had to be replaced before the reel could be used.

Tales like this are all too common, but they don't have to happen. Normally, I am careful about my equipment, and this one lapse only caused me to redouble my efforts since then.

Caring for tackle is easy, economical (when you consider the cost of replacement tackle), and can prevent a fishing trip from becoming a disaster when the equipment fails in a tight situation.

Most new rods, reels, and lines do not require any immediate care before use, but I make sure that I save and file any instructions that come with tackle. That way they will be available for future checking when maintenance is required. Most reel brochures also contain parts lists and prices for repairs, along with a parts and service department mailing address.

Once I start using new rods, reels, lines, or lures, I give them regular maintenance. And "regular maintenance" means just that — at the end of each fishing day, with a more thorough examination at the end of a longer fishing trip and a complete checkup at the end of each fishing season. Equally important is proper care while fishing, to prevent needless repairs after trips or breakdowns while on trips.

RODS — Fiberglass fishing rods of today are relatively maintenance free, but still require care. More rods are broken in car and home doors than over the fishing grounds.

Proper care of a rod means keeping it in its case on trips, except when it is ready to be used or to go into the rod racks of a boat. Many rods come with cases; for those that do not, rod cases are available for purchase. Cases can be made easily from plastic, heavy cardboard, or aluminum tubing. Place each rod in a separate rod bag to protect it from damage in a hard case, particluarly when more than one rod is fitted in a large case, as for air travel.

When using, do not knock a fiberglass rod against anything. This can result in a slight fracture of the glass blank, which will then fail — later in the day, a month later, or several years later. Since fractures are usually impossible to detect, the only solution is to protect the rod from such blows while fishing.

After a day of fishing, check the rod over carefully. If you have been fishing in scummy water or in salt water or if the rod has picked up algae or dirt, wash it off. I usually take the rods into the shower with me at the end of the day and scrub them down with a washcloth, paying particular attention to the guides and reel seat.

After drying the rod, check it over from tip to butt.

Proper storage is essential for protecting tackle in the home between trips. The author's rods are hung horizontally, using nylon loops for the handles and large cup hooks for the rod blank.

After each rough trip, lay out any plugs used and wash them down with a garden hose. Such quick action will prolong hook and hardware life.

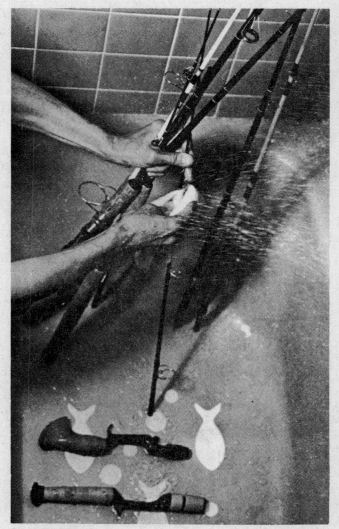

Fresh water scum and salt water deposits can be easily removed from rods by washing them in the shower. A wash cloth is helpful for scrubbing guides and metal reel seats.

Make sure that guides are not grooved, bent or broken, any one of which will require replacement before the next trip.

If you still find dirt around the guide frames, scrub them again with a small brush. An old toothbrush, mascara brush, gun-cleaning brush or typewriter brush will do.

Check the ferrules, and use a pipe cleaner or gun-cleaning brush to remove any dirt that might have accumulated. This is just as important with glass-to-glass ferrules as with the standard metal ones. A bit of sand or grit can score the glass and weaken it when the rod is

Reels subject to hard use or to salt water are best washed in a sink of warm water immediately after returning from each daily trip. They can be soaked for a short time, then scrubbed down, allowed to dry, and sprayed with a demoisturizer.

Reels should be regularly sprayed with a demoisturizing agent after each trip to keep them corrosion free. Agents like LPS #1, CRC, P-38 and WD-40 are all good.

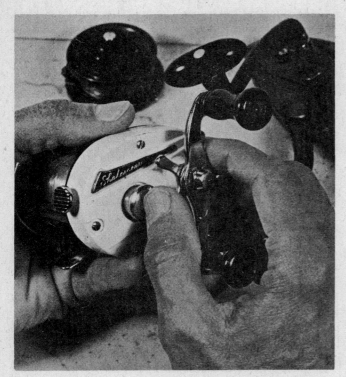

Reel drags can become deformed and inoperative if they are left "on" or tightened down for long periods of time. Take time after each trip to check each reel and to loosen the drag.

ferruled the next time. The threads of locking reel seats can be cleaned the same way using lighter fluid on a brush or pipe cleaner to remove any dirt.

This same general checking should be carried out after each prolonged fishing trip, taking even more care to check guides, windings, ferrules, and reel seats. Line will eventually groove all but ceramic guides, so check them with a fine-mesh woman's stocking. Run the stocking through the guide, and if it catches, replace the guide. Check at this time also for loose windings, and replace any that are nicked or cut. If there is no time for this, wrap them with tape, and reserve an evening at the end of the season for proper repairs.

After each long fishing trip, also check for loose ferrules. These occur in either of two ways. The two parts of the ferrules can become loose, or one part of a metal ferrule can become loose on the rod blank. Replace them or have them replaced or repaired by a competent repair center.

At the end of each season, go over the rod thoroughly again, checking all parts and fittings. Any that are loose, worn or broken that have not been taken care of during the season should be repaired now. If you are not familiar with how to replace or repair various parts, check with someone who can do this, or send the rod out to a qualified tackle repair service.

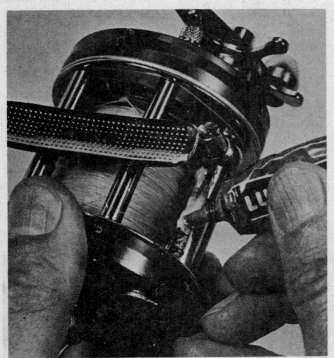

Casting reels require a great deal of grease on the level wind gears and pawls. After each trip, be sure to check and grease these parts if necessary. Other parts of reels should be checked, greased and oiled, following the manufacturers' instructions.

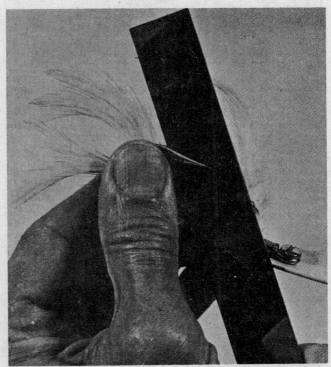

Hooks will become dull as a result of bouncing around in tackle boxes, the corrosion of water, hooking fish, and striking rocks, stumps and other obstructions. Be sure to check them regularly and to sharpen them when necessary.

TOOLS AND TECHNIQUES

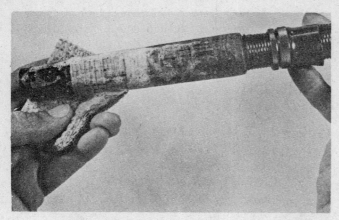

After several fishing trips, the cork grip of rods will become dirty. Rod grips can be restored to their original appearance by washing in soapy water and scrubbing with a soft nylon pot scrubber. Abrasive cleansers also work well.

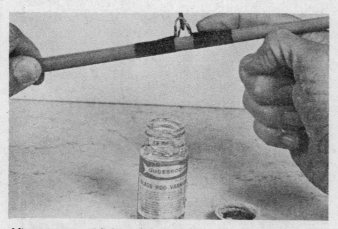

After a season of fishing, heavily used rods will have lost some of the protective finish, or varnish, on guide wrappings. To keep rods looking new and to prevent windings from becoming cut or worn, give each rod a few coats of varnish. Apply the varnish on with your finger, as shown, to prevent bubbles from forming in the cured finish.

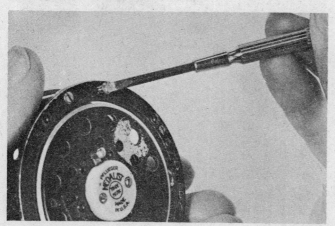

After each season, check for loose screws on reels and other tackle. Tighten if necessary. Here, a screw is being tightened on a fly reel.

REELS — The gears and moving parts of fishing reels pose more problems and are subject to more breakdowns than any other piece of tackle. Largely this can be prevented by a regular regimen of care, and by proper use in the field.

As with rods, carry reels in cases or in a tackle box until they are to be used. Do not lay them down in the sand or dirt where they can pick up grit that will ruin them.

After each fishing day, check the reels over carefully. If they have been used in salt water or dirty freshwater, place them in a basin (I use the kitchen sink) of warm water, and scrub them off with a washcloth to remove any dirt or salt deposits. Do not place them under the faucet or wash them with a garden hose because this will tend to force any dirt into the reel casing. Use small brushes to remove any stubborn dirt, particularly checking the roller in spinning reels and the level-wind mechanism in casting reels.

Remove the reels, allow them to dry and spray them with one of the moisture-removing sprays such as LPS #1, WD-40, CRC, or P-38. Loosen the drag on all spools; a tight drag left on will deform the drag washers and possibly ruin them for future use. In any case, it will shorten the life of the drag.

Follow the manufacturer's instructions about oiling and greasing the reel. Most spinning reels should get a light oiling at the roller, reciprocating shaft, rotating cup, handle shaft, handle, and the two bearings at either end of the bail.

Casting reels should get a light oiling at the handle shaft, handles, star drag, groove for the tip of the level wind guide, and at oil ports at the end of the spool axle. Grease the level wind mechanism on the underside of the reel with a lubricant specified by the manufacturer.

Give heavier salt water reels the same treatment, with particular attention to the oil ports that most of them have for this purpose.

Give fly reels a light oiling on the shaft and handle knob as well as the drag lever or knob. Take care not to get oil on the drag itself, unless it is called for in the instruction booklet. And keep oil off the line, for an oily line will pick up dirt.

After each long fishing trip, follow the above advice, but also give more attention to the reel screws, any loose parts or any stiffness. Often the vibration of cars, boats or planes can back out screws. Check regularly, so that these are always tight.

At the end of the season, set aside a day to go over all your reels, checking and dismantling them *one at a time*. Use an egg carton, biscuit tin, ice-cube tray or similar box with compartments to keep the reel parts separated in the order in which they are removed. A complete dismantling is not necessary. For spinning reels, remove the side plate (held by several screws) and check the grease inside. If it looks clean and the parts are not worn, replace the side plate. Check the bail, paying special attention to the roller, since this is where line becomes frayed if the roller is grooved or not rolling properly.

Run the line under the roller and pull it off the spool against a light drag to be sure that the roller is moving as the line goes out.

To check casting reels, remove the side plate or plates, check the gears, and grease as above. Check the pawl in the level wind mechanism at the bottom of the reel by removing the screw that holds it in place. If it is worn, replace it. Salt water reels lack the level wind mechanism, but otherwise should be similarly checked.

Fly reels can be easily dismantled. Since these are "open" reels, they are subject to accumulations of dirt and should be thoroughly checked and cleaned, if necessary.

If any of the reels show dirty grease, a lack of grease, or have a lot of grit on the gears or inside the gear housings, clean them thoroughly while they are apart. Use a small pan of solvent, such as kerosene, lighter fluid, mineral spirits or gasoline. If using kerosene or gasoline, work outside *only* and, for the others, work in a well-ventilated area.

Soak each reel part, with the exception of plastic parts. Sometimes solvents can react with plastics to soften them or cause a chemical reaction on the surface. For this reason, do not place the line-filled spools in the solvents. Except for these, clean the parts with small brushes and pipe cleaners. After they are clean, dry them, replace in the order in which they were removed, and grease each part as called for in the reel instruction booklet.

LINES — When you consider that fishing line is the cheapest part of any tackle and that it is the only thing between a fish and our rod, it is false economy to keep line longer than one or two seasons. Under heavy use, it should be replaced even more often.

At the end of the season it is best to dismantle each reel for cleaning, oiling, greasing, and any repairs. An egg carton (as shown), a biscuit tin, an ice cube tray, or a similar container will segregate the parts as you remove them. This will make it easy to reassemble the reel.

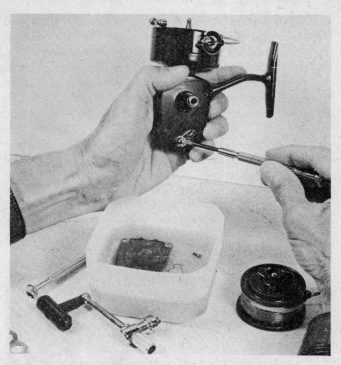

When cleaning a reel at the end of the season, solvents such as gasoline and kerosene are ideal for removing old grease and oils. Take care not to place plastic parts in any solvent, because the solvent will cause a chemical reaction, and will ruin the plastic part. Note that the plastic handle on this reel has not been placed in the solvent, and will be cleaned separately.

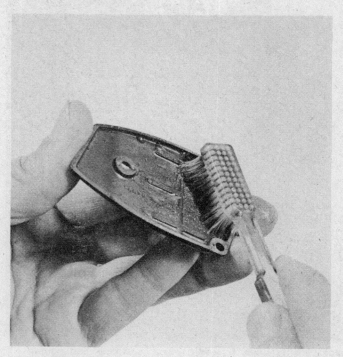

Old toothbrushes, gun cleaning brushes, and typewriter brushes are ideal for cleaning reel parts.

The best care of line is to check rod guides for nicks, and rollers for smoothness and that the line runs freely, as described earlier. A nicked or grooved guide or roller in a spinning reel can give a line the equivalent of a season of wear in less than a day.

Another problem is the twisting of line while fishing or as a result of improper spooling of new line on a reel. For spooling, casting, fly, and salt water conventional reels, the new spool of line should be placed on a pencil, with the line coming off the spool in the same direction as the reel spool is turning.

For spinning reels, the best method is to get one of the new line-winder devices that are currently advertised. An alternative is to place the new line spool so that the line comes off the end of the spool. Make sure that the line comes off the spool in the same direction that the line is laid down on the reel spool. If the line starts to twist, reverse the spool. Keep the new line under some tension as it goes on.

All lines (particularly mono) should be kept out of the sun when not in use, and kept away from oil or grease. Oil or grease itself will not harm the line, but oily line will pick up dirt, causing damage to line, rod guides, and roller bearing.

Line that has been used in salt water should be washed after use, and the easiest way to do this is to wash the line carefully on the reel as the reel is being washed in warm water.

Often line life can be extended by removing a few feet of line at the end of each day's fishing, or several times a day if fishing on the bottom or around obstructions. Line becomes worn from rubbing against sand, rocks, pilings, and other obstructions.

Lead core or wire line must be carefully handled since the slightest kink will cause the line to break — usually on the next strike of a fish. Roller tips should be used on any rods used with wire line to minimize bending and kinking.

Fly lines have some real enemies in chlorinated solvents. These chemicals extract the line plasticizers which keep fly lines supple and prevent cracks from developing in the line surface. Gasoline, insect repellents, and suntan lotions are principal offenders. Always wash or at least wipe your hands after handling such products and before handling fly lines.

Fly lines should be cleaned regularly at the end of each fishing day, particularly after fishing in scummy water. When the fly line picks up scum or algae, the scum in turn picks up dirt, causing wear on the line and guides, making the line sink. Clean the line with the manufacturer's line cleaner.

LURES — After a day of fishing, any lures used should be checked for bent or dull hooks, chipped paint, loose eyes and hardware. Sharpen hooks or replace them by cutting them off, adding new ones with sturdy split rings.

If the lures were used in salt water, wash them off. This is easier than it sounds. I place all my lures on a patio table, turn the garden hose on them, and allow them to dry in the sun. Just make sure that small children and pets can't get at them before they go back into the tackle box.

At the end of the season, remove the hardware from worn plugs, give them a new paint job, polish spinners and spoons with a good metal polish, repaint any worn bucktails or jigs, and pop them into the fly-tying vise for a new tail, if necessary.

Soft plastic lures (lizards, worms, etc.) require little care, but should be separated from other lures in the tackle box and should only be placed in tackle boxes that are advertised as "worm proof." Other tackle boxes, and contact with plastic lures, may cause the two types of plastic to react. The plastics soften, paints become sticky, and the worms erode the plastic trays. Fortunately, most boxes sold today are worm proof. If there is any doubt about the type of box you have, keep the worms in containers specifically for them, or store them in a plastic food bag.

Most tackle maintenance is nothing more than common sense, care in the field, and a routine of regular checking maintenance. On all prolonged fishing trips, I carry a small ulchek box which serves in the field as an emergency first aid kit for tackle.

Periodic maintenance on a daily and seasonal basis, can make tackle breakdowns almost as obsolete as Izaak Walton's horsehair lines.

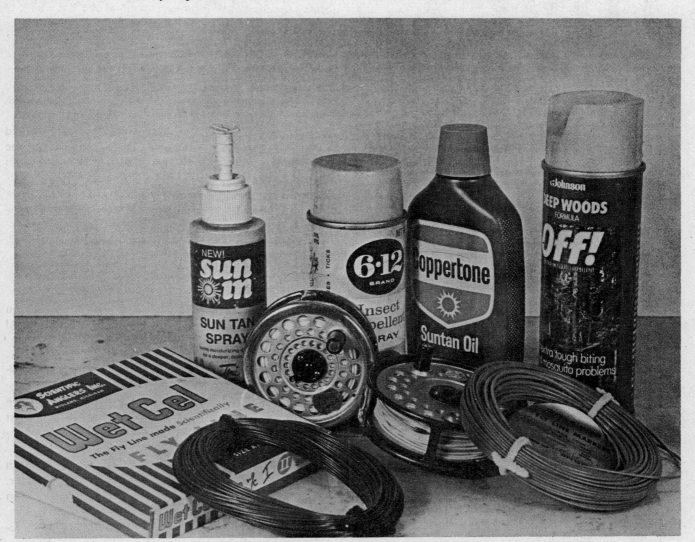

Products with chlorinated solvents are very destructive to expensive fly lines. Gasoline, insect repellent, and suntan lotions have the same effect. The products shown here *should not be allowed to come in contact with fly lines*. When handling gasoline, suntan lotions or insect repellent, wipe hands thoroughly before fly fishing again.

Basics of Trout Fishing

by Charles F. Waterman

Trout fishing is surrounded by a sea of literature, which often makes it sound very complex, but it doesn't have to be. Some of the world's most experienced anglers fish only for trout, yet bent pins have also caught their share.

There are those who seek the most difficult fish and will travel great distances for the extra challenge of sophisticated trout, while others spy on hatchery trucks in the hope of greeting pellet-fattened simpletons as soon as they strike the water. Most trout fishing is somewhere in between.

Fishing difficulty is partly a matter of water and partly a matter of fish species. The brook trout is supposed to be a chump, while the brown trout is credited with the most intelligence of all, but when in the same waters, they may behave much alike. The brookie needs cold and very pure water. The rainbow can survive in warmer water than any other trout, but the brown, introduced about 100 years ago from Europe, is regarded as more resourceful.

The cutthroat, a Westerner, is easy to catch (sometimes), but put him in a placid stream where he's fished over daily and he can get tough. All American trout except the mackinaw, or lake trout, have races that go to sea. The steelhead—a true rainbow—is best known, and steelhead fishing is highly specialized.

We'll talk mainly of stream fishing. That's no discredit to the lakes but lake fishing for trout can be much like lake fishing for other species. Stream fishing for trout is quite distinctive.

If you don't use bait, I'd say that the easiest way to catch a stream trout is with spinning tackle and small spoons. When spinning gear became popular 30 years ago it was said they'd have to outlaw it, because it would clean out the streams. That wasn't and isn't true, but spinning gear can convert a neophyte into a trout fisherman in a matter of minutes.

How does it compare to fly fishing? Well, it beats flies on some big waters but the most productive year-in-year-out anglers I know use flies. The fact that fly fishermen are likely to be more serious about their sport has a lot to do with it.

You can catch trout in big rivers simply by throwing and cranking with heavy tackle but I think there's more spinning skill required on small creeks. Get a very light rod, use 4-pound line or lighter and throw a shiny little lure of a sixteenth ounce or less. The casts are short and you'll learn to place them so the lure swings down and across current on the retrieve. It is the down, around, and across route that takes trout and it's generally best to have the lure near the bottom. Most good spinfishermen retrieve pretty slowly if they have enough current to keep the dingus working. They scrape the bottom a lot and they lose their share of lures through hangups.

Dainty open-faced spinning reels are fine for this, although some good fishermen use closed reels. On small streams you won't need much line capacity but you do need a sensitive drag with your light line. We'll read a little water later on.

Fly rods are shorter and lighter these days because the materials are better. Most beginning trout anglers start with glass rods although a friend of mine decided his wife should begin with a $300 Leonard split bamboo. He figured if she didn't take to fly fishing he could always keep the rod himself.

It's pretty hard to buy a really bad fly rod of any material these days. Match it with the proper line and it'll work. The manufacturers sharpened up a few years back and standardized their line weights and rod actions. A six line goes with a six rod and it'll match pretty well, whether or not you like the individual rod action. Beginners should avoid short-rod cults as well as those for extra long rods, extra stiff rods and extra soft rods.

Some of the best trout water may be found at your back door. This meadow stream has both browns and rainbows.

Later they can join one of these sects or start their own. To begin with, a rod of 7½ to 8½ feet taking a double-tapered number six or number seven line gets a beginner off to a conservative start. A simple single-action reel is a good beginning; he can go to an automatic later if he wants to. It's better to economize on the reel than on the rod or line. He can buy ready-made tapered leaders and make up his own later. There are all sorts of lines, but the double-tapered floater will do for a lot of fishing and many fine anglers have never used anything else.

If you're not a collector, go easy on fly purchases unless you know the favorites for the places you're going to fish. A fly fisherman who travels a lot for a few years would rather not know how much he has invested in flies he'll never use. I have seen a single fisherman carrying a thousand bucks' worth of flies in his car yet I doubt he used thirty dollars' worth during a busy season. But, if pretty flies turn you on, have fun. Maybe you'll eventually want to tie your own and, as in the rest of fly fishing, there's nothing supernatural involved.

Releasing a cutthroat trout in a western creek filled with underwater vegetation.

You'll need a vest, and for most stream fishing you'll need waders, generally with felt soles or metal studs. Waders will be a problem you'll probably never solve. They puncture, they tear, and they seep, but perhaps you'll be lucky. Test them before you walk into deep, cold water far from home. Put the things on and sit down in a bathtub full of water. You'll look funny but you'll feel smart—and possibly damp.

A good trout fisherman who can judge water and cast will catch trout anywhere, for trout are trout—but new waters will take a little study. Don't be afraid of anybody's creek. Study it and catch fish.

Streamers and spinning lures generally imitate baitfish and they're fished about the same. You can break the other flies into three classes:

Dry flies represent insects floating on top of the water. Generally they are floated with the current. A "dragging" dry fly moves unnaturally because the current pulls on the line or leader.

Light casting tackle and small spinners are an effective combination for trout.

Closed-face spinning reels are good for big trout on small streams. This brown weighs more than three pounds.

Wet flies represent drowned insects and are fished in many ways. They can be drifted naturally or they can be retrieved slowly.

Nymphs represent water-bred insects that have not yet hatched into flies. In moving water they are often cast upstream and allowed to drift naturally, sometimes near the surface and sometimes near the bottom. But the uses of nymphs and wet flies overlap and only a trout knows what he thinks a wet fly is.

For almost 200 years, trout fishermen have argued whether flies should be nearly exact imitations of real insects or simply give an impression of something good to eat. Both kinds work, although often at different times.

"Matching the hatch" is simply using a fly that closely resembles observed natural flies in size, form, and color. Sometimes matching the size is enough. Again, to the disgust of highly scientific fishermen, a somewhat larger fly will be selected from a bunch of naturals by a trout who thinks a "stranger" looks better than the regular menu. Try it but don't count on it.

Some water is easy to read, especially in smaller streams, because there are only small sections where a trout could live if he wanted to. There are some rules about the water a trout will hold in and where he'll strike.

Fish in fast current are easier to fool because they have little time to study what they're going after and because they can't see it too well in broken water. A fish in fast water is likely to be feeding, because if he were loafing, he'd be where he didn't have to swim so hard. There may be an exception when trout need more oxygen and find it in the fast stretches.

The ideal place for a feeding trout is at the edge of water that carries food, but in a position where he doesn't have to work hard except when he noses forward to

Rapid, shallow streams place a premium on careful casting. This fisherman has hooked a rock-hunting fish that is swinging downstream.

feed. When found in the same stream a rainbow is likely to prefer faster water than the brown trout.

A trout wants concealment for his own safety but feeding competition can push him into water he wouldn't ordinarily occupy. Naturally, the larger fish have first choice of lies and those are likely to be more difficult places to reach with a fly or lure. Bigger fish tend to prefer somewhat deeper water. Undercut banks can be very difficult places to fish, especially for fly casters seeking a natural drift.

Good holding spots can exist in surprisingly fast stretches. It is easy to see the good places near a boulder that protrudes above the surface. Below the obstruction will be a patch of nearly dead and often shallow water where fish may lie, but if they are feeding they are likely to be near the current edges where the divided flow comes down on either side of the rock. A lure or fly that comes down beside the boulder takes the route of a natural bait and is likely to be taken first as it passes the "dead" area. The fish watches that current, even though it may be lying in the quiet part directly below the obstruction.

Above a boulder is a cushion of water that is somewhat backed up by the rock and the cushion is ignored by many beginners. It appears faster than it is.

Similar feeding spots exist around submerged boulders and when you work deep, swift water you should look for indications of underwater lumps. They are marked by boils and bulges, and you can visualize what's going on down where the fish live. Even when the surface slopes visibly, there can be spots near the bottom where a fish can hold with his fins working gently. Most trout spend most of their time near the bottom.

Many trout, especially in small streams, feed a great deal on terrestrials: insects that live on land and fall in by accident. A grasshopper is an obvious example and easily seen. When grasshoppers are plentiful in grass or weeds near water deep enough to hold fish, an imitation hopper can be deadly, especially on windy days. An opportunist friend of mine found himself treated coolly by some master anglers on a very difficult stream. The classic experts were trying to match some tiny mayflies the educated fish were taking avidly—and not having much luck. My friend saw there were plenty of grasshoppers around so he put on a big imitation, slapped it down near shore, and found the fish would rather have a Number 10 'hopper than a Number 20 mayfly. Another angler gently explained that this wasn't quite following the rules. Maybe not, but he put the fish back anyway.

I have a rule that a good fisherman should fish with his boots as much as his rod. Go to a well-fished stream and you'll note that almost everyone fishes every pool from the same spot. If you don't see the fishermen, you'll see the tracks where they have stood or walked in. Generally, it's the obvious place for covering the water. Chances are they aren't showing their attractions to at least part of the fish. Study the water and don't be afraid to walk, wade or sneak to an unusual casting spot. At least you can show your fly or lure from a different angle and it works more times than you'd think.

I sometimes suffer from what I call the hotspot fixation. I walk up to a pool, see where the fish *should* be and then jockey into position for it, ignoring the rest of the water. Chester Marion, one of the world's great trout fishermen, once took me to a beautiful western creek where fish were rising to natural flies in what was obviously a perfect spot. I waded out and went to work. Chester said he'd just watch. It was one of my better days but, although I cast with a flourish and was pretty proud of my presentation, I couldn't raise a fish. Then I heard splashing back toward Chester.

"That one had moved in behind you," he remarked, his rod bent sharply.

I went back to my casting with my ears a little warm. Then more splashing back there.

"Look at that," Chester said wonderingly. "I hooked that one right below you."

Many of us stand where we should be fishing.

A trout "pool" is almost any fishable section, generally a bit slower than water upstream or downstream. American trout fishermen divide pools into three parts. The "head" of the pool is generally where fast water runs into a deeper and slower stretch. The "tail" of a pool is where the water prepares to speed up again. Generally the tail of the pool is wide and shallow. The center part of the pool is sometimes called the "waist" but that's not a very common term.

The pool's head is the most logical place for a trout to lie. The fast water generally comes from a rocky section, likely to be a good place for insect hatches. There will probably be an eddy and certainly there will be comparatively quiet water adjacent to swift current. Generally, the head of the pool is the best spot, and nearly all fishermen give it a whirl. Since dry-fly fishermen and many nymph fishermen work upstream, they have a tendency to hurry in the lower parts of the pool. Especially in smaller streams, it's possible to scare most of the fish out of their scales by sloshing through the shallow tail area. It's a chain reaction that begins with fingerlings in the extreme shallows and can carry over to big fish at the head.

There are times when the tail of a pool is the best place to fish, usually in late evening or early morning when worthwhile trout are willing to expose themselves in shallow water. Some of the best spawning areas are located in the shallow pool tails where gravel is likely to be suitable. "Shallow" means anything from six

inches in a small Maine brook to two feet in a heavy river.

Now we have to do a little stream classification. The creeks and rivers that are fed by surface rainfall or melting snow can be called "free stone" streams. Their level rises and falls with the precipitation or the snow runoff. They can be muddy or very clear and the amount of water varies continually. Insect hatches are frequently irregular because of the unpredictable water conditions.

The other general type of stream is fed by underwater springs or by a system of seepage that keeps the water level fairly constant. These can be "limestone streams," "chalk streams" (as in England), or "spring creeks," as they are generally called in the West. Here the water levels, temperatures, and consistent water clarity cause insect hatches to be more predictable. Such streams have large trout populations, but the fishing is rather delicate and tough for a beginner.

Generally speaking, eastern trout fishing is in smaller, slower streams and with smaller flies, but that's no fast rule and some of the very small creeks of the West can be sophisticated. Again, you'll usually find that trout of the high mountain country as reached by pack trips are

Spinfishermen wade wet and catch big trout in big water.

easy to catch once you find them, whether they're rainbows, brookies, cutthroats, or the prized golden. But that's another generality. George Anderson of Livingston, Montana, a western trout fisherman of wide experience, speaks of Colorado pack trips during which he and his friends walked away from fishing that was too easy and crawled around on hands and knees to work on tough goldens. That's a common situation with experienced anglers.

Here are some generalities about water conditions and fishing methods. In high, muddy streams bait can be the only thing that will take fish. If the water ranges from murky to just a little off, streamers, wet flies and hardware should be productive. Dry flies and nymphs are at their best in clear water, and the best mayfly hatches generally come in spring and early summer.

"Big waters, big streamers" is a pretty logical rule and some of the largest fly-caught fish come from big western rivers in the fall. Generally these whoppers are brown trout getting ready to spawn. The rainbows spawn in the spring. That doesn't mean rainbows won't take big streamers in the fall, simply that they aren't quite as ready as the browns.

Steelhead fishing is slightly different from other trout hunting and sometimes classified separately. Steelhead are sea-going rainbows which return to fresh water to spawn. Most steelhead are caught near the bottom with lures and with deep-drifted flies on sinking lines. Some of the most effective lures and flies are frank imitations of salmon eggs and, where eggs are legal, they are probably the most effective of all, but they require special skills. However, in clear waters, steelhead sometimes

Long outboard river boat is help to fishermen working large rivers for steelhead. Most of the fishing is done by wading but the boat furnishes transportation from drift to drift.

"Float fishermen" beach their boat to cast from shore. A boat, even on the smaller streams, sometimes get anglers to waters they couldn't reach otherwise.

take dry flies. There are consistent dry-fly waters for steelhead but you're going against the current if you try to make dry-fly water of a river that's traditionally a deep-lure place. If the steelies there were good dry-fly takers, the chances are it would be well known.

Most trout lakes are fairly deep, and most lake fishing for trout requires lures or flies that go down. There are exceptions when trout gather at the mouths of streams that feed into the lakes and behave much the same as stream fish. High mountain lakes are frequently the easiest of all trout fishing but sometimes they are impossible. It's a matter of temperatures in most cases and just after the ice leaves is likely to be the best time of the year. At that time, even lake trout may be on top.

And now a concluding classification of trout waters on a completely different basis. There is the put-and-take trout stream in which trout reproduce little if at all and hatchery fish are planted in catchable size to be caught soon or never. These are generally the easiest fish to take. There is the stream containing completely wild trout that sustain their own population without help from any new introductions. Then there are the streams that have a wild population which is supplemented by occasional plantings which may or may not reproduce. The hatchery fish are usually easier to catch, but there is growing disfavor for this system since planted trout are believed to reduce the self-sufficient wild ones.

It's an endless subject and it's fun.

The Science of Trolling

by Frank T. Moss

There's a lot more to successful game fish trolling than just dragging some lures through the water behind the boat, hoping for the best. Trolling is one of the oldest recorded methods of fishing. Historical research shows that more than 2000 years ago, the ancient Polynesians caught a good portion of their food by trolling bone and shell lures behind their great twin-hulled sailing canoes during their early migrations over the vast Pacific.

Modern anglers are rediscovering many of the ancient trolling secrets known by the South Sea Islanders and handed down by word of mouth from generation to generation. One of the most important secrets is this: any boat moving through the water creates sound and pressure waves that stimulate many species of fish. Another is that particular species of fish are definitely attracted to lures and other objects trolled in the boat's wake. These fish also have distinct preferences about lure speed, action, shape, color, and distance from the stern.

Far from being a haphazard undertaking, trolling with modern boats and tackle has been refined to a fairly exact science. The fisherman who understands these methods can go anywhere in the world on salt water or fresh, and catch fish. Let's see what really makes trolling tick. A logical way to start is by breaking trolling down into its four basic techniques. These are:

1. Direct surface trolling without auxiliary equipment.
2. Surface trolling with outriggers.
3. Deep trolling with wire line.
4. Deep trolling with downriggers, which are actually underwater outriggers.

Direct surface trolling

This is the most widely practiced technique, and it is very effective for locating fish that otherwise cannot be spotted by surface observation. It requires a minimum of equipment and the angler often has the pleasure of seeing the fish take his bait or lure on the surface. To be successful, you must find the proper combination of lure type and action, line length (distance of the lure behind the boat), boat speed, and lure placement pattern.

Trolling for school tuna is a classic example. Every boat seems to have one best tuna trolling speed, which may be anywhere between four and nine knots. You will have to discover your own boat's best tuna trolling speed by experimentation, but five to seven knots is a pretty safe speed range for most boats. The most effective choice of lures depends on the species you're after and local preferences of the fish. The various tuna species appear to respond to Japanese and similar feather or nylon lures in the following order of color preference.

Bluefin tuna: Red-and-white, white, yellow, green-and-yellow, black-and-white, blue-and-white, black-and-red.

Yellowfin tuna: Yellow, green-and-yellow, white, red-and-white, black-and-white, blue, black-and-red.

Albacore: White-and-red, white, yellow, green-and-yellow, chrome (metal jigs), blue.

Bonito: Yellow, white-and-yellow, green-and-yellow, white-and-red, black-and-white, black-and-yellow.

In trolling for the smaller offshore game fishes, the length of your trolling lines and the pattern of your lures are interrelated. When I was running an offshore charter boat at Montauk, N.Y., some years ago, we used an exploratory trolling pattern of six tuna lines arranged in the following manner: two lures were trolled at 20-25 feet behind the boat, two at 45-50 feet, and two at 75-80 feet. This staggered lure pattern helped us find the lure distance that worked best for any given day.

When a tuna struck one of the lures, we kept the boat moving at trolling speed for a short time, hoping that more would strike. Sometimes they would and sometimes they wouldn't. Later, when we got under way to troll again over the productive area, we would adjust all the lines to place the lures at the trolling distance of the lure or lures that produced the first strike.

If we continued to troll with the exploratory pattern of short, medium, and long lines, we usually would get one or two hits the next time we passed over the fish. But if we had all the lures adjusted to the same length, we often filled the lines with fish, rapidly increasing the score for the day.

The massed group of lures speeding through the boiling wake of the boat seemed to produce a competitive mood in the school tuna. We also found that by shortening the lines we could often bring the effective trolling distance to only 15 or 20 feet from the stern. This, of course, made for fast, exciting fishing.

Table 1 gives recommended tackle, line length, and trolling speed for ten popular species of small to medium salt water game fish usually taken by direct surface trolling. The "Line Test" column indicates the line class of the recommended tackle.

Two bucket seats in the stern of this small boat improve angler comfort for inshore trolling.

Table 1

SURFACE TROLLING
(Small to medium game fish, salt water)

Species	Lure	Line Test	Line Length	Speed
School bluefin	Feather	50	15-50'	4-7 kn.
" yellowfin	Feather	50	40-60'	7-9 kn.
Blackfin tuna	Feather	20-30	60-80'	4-8 kn.
Albacore	Feather	30-50	30-70'	8-9 kn.
Bonito	Feather	20	40-80'	6-9 kn.
Striped bass	Nylon jig	20-30	40-70'	4-5 kn.
Bluefish	Nylon jig	20-30	30-50'	3-4 kn.
Pollock	Feather	30	40-50'	3-4 kn.
Dolphin	Feather	30	30-50'	3-6 kn.
Wahoo	Spoon	50	30-80'	3-5 kn.

Don't try to troll too many lines at one time. It's better to pull two, three, or four lines that fish well instead of five or six that are constantly tangling. Install rod holders in the boat's cockpit so they hold the rods in a good trolling pattern. You can fish tackle up to 30-pound line class with just a good belt socket, but for tackle in the 50-pound class and heavier, you'll need fishing chairs.

An important point to remember is that some lures work well over a wide range of trolling speeds while others work equally well only when trolled slowly, medium, or fast. Learn to avoid mixing fast lures with slow lures, thereby fishing some of your baits at the wrong speed. Here is a fairly generalized breakdown of trolling speeds and the lure types that work best.

Slow speed (1-3 knots): Plastic eel, bass-rigged black natural eel, plastic worms, small spoons, trolling flies, diving plugs, swimming plugs, small surface plugs.

Medium speed (3-6 knots): Nylon fiber eel, nylon jig,

Four anglers troll in comfort from a 17' center console out-board fisherman.

plastic outrigger bait fish, natural outrigger bait fish, large surface plugs, negative-buoyancy diving plugs, large spoons, metal casting jigs.

High speed (6-9 knots): Konahead and Knucklehead lures, cedar and bone tuna jigs, nylon jigs, rigged "swimming" natural mullet.

All-speed lures: Most Japanese feather lures, some nylon-skirted lures, small natural black eel, "Drone" spoon, chrome-plated diamond jig.

Surface trolling with outriggers

Until recently, fishing for game fish with outriggers was considered pretty much of a big boat technique. The advent of small, fast, open or semi-open fishing boats in the popular 19- to 26-foot class, however, has opened outrigger fishing to a vast armada of fishermen, especially those who enjoy using light tackle. Outriggers are employed to give life and separation to surface trolling lines, particularly when natural or artificial fish baits are used. They are especially effective on all billfish, some of the larger tunas, dolphin, game sharks, and any other fish that like fast, surface-running prey.

The long metal and fiberglass outriggers used on many large tournament sport-fishing boats cost thousands of dollars, but owners of open boats can equip their vessels with equally effective smaller outriggers at a fraction of the cost of the larger ones. Large or small, outriggers should be installed so they "wing out" at an angle of about 45° in the fishing position, with the outrigger tips raked aft so the release clips are about abreast of the boat's stern. In operation, an outrigger works this way:

First, a prepared bait (mullet, balao, eel, or other

A fishing chair, stern tiller, and handy motor controls make single-handed trolling possible in this 26' Cuttyhunk bass boat.

A socket belt and light shoulder harness helps anglerette Ellie Heckert fight a Cozumel sailfish on 20 lb. class tackle.

small fish) is attached to the fishing line by means of its wire or nylon leader, and the bait is then drifted behind the slowly moving boat to a proper distance. This may be anywhere from 40 to 90 feet. The fishing line from the rod tip is then seated in the release clip attached to the outrigger outhaul halyard. The reel is given free-spool while the line is hauled out to the outrigger tip. The rod is then adjusted to light striking drag and the "click" is engaged.

When a fish strikes at the skipping bait, the sudden increase in tension rips the fishing line from the adjustable release clip, letting the fisherman fight the hooked fish with no further assistance or hindrance from the outrigger. *Table 2* shows typical bait selections, classes of tackle, line length, and trolling speeds for surface outrigger trolling for ten popular big game species.

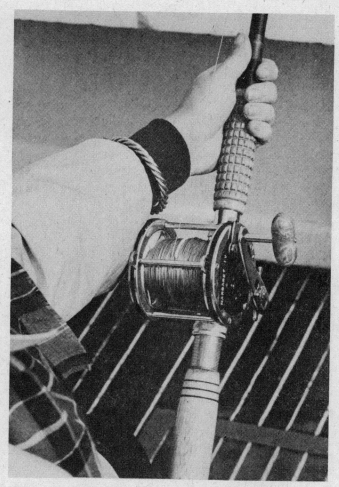

Typical wire line deep trolling outfit includes a 3/0 star drag reel partially filled with 50 lb. class soft line backing and a measured shot of .024" (45 lb. test) soft drawn solid Monel wire. Rod is equipped with roller guides.

Table 2
SURFACE TROLLING
(Big game, salt water)

Species	Bait	Line Test	Line Length	Speed
Sailfish	Balao	20	30-60'	3-5 kn.
White marlin	Balao	30	25-75'	3-4 kn.
Blue marlin	Mullet	80	40-80'	3-5 kn.
Striped marlin	Halfbeak	50	30-50'	3-5 kn.
Black marlin	Bonito	130	40-80'	3-6 kn.
Swordfish	Squid	80	60-90'	2-4 kn.
Big yellowfin	Mullet	80	30-70'	5-8 kn.
Giant bluefin	Herring	130	40-70'	3-5 kn.
Blue shark	Squid	50	30-70'	3-5 kn.
Mako shark	Mackerel	80	30-70'	4-6 kn.

Can outriggers and their baits be combined with direct surface "flat line" lures for trolling? They certainly can, and a combination of, say, 2-4 tuna flat lines fished directly from the stern and two light baits fished from the outriggers is very widely used. In this case the outrigger baits should be balao, mullet, small squids, natural eels, or any similar baits that work well in the medium speed (3-6 knot) range. What precautions should be followed when fishing outriggers?

1. Make sure a specific angler is assigned to each outrigger line while they are being fished.

2. Adjust boat speed and line length to obtain the best surface skipping action from skipping baits.

3. Have plenty of rigged baits handy in the cockpit ice chest. Never let yourself be caught in hot fishing action with no extra baits rigged.

4. Change baits as soon as they show signs of becoming washed-out and waterworn.

5. Pre-set your reel drags for a striking drag (point of tension at which the drag just starts to slip) of not more than a quarter of the line's breaking strain. Don't guess at this setting. Use a small spring balance to find the proper drag setting.

6. If you plan to fish competitively, drill your anglers in advance on good outrigger fishing procedures so you won't get into "Chinese fire drill" situations during fast action in a tournament.

Deep trolling with wire line

Because wire handlines were and still are used for deep trolling in some types of commercial fishing, the International Game Fish Association has never recognized rod and reel catches of game fish for record status in which wire line has been used. Nevertheless, wire line for deep trolling is extremely effective and widely employed by sporting anglers in many areas.

One major benefit of wire line over heavy trolling sinkers attached to soft fishing line is the fact that you don't have a single big lump of weight between you and

Downrigger carries fishing line and trolling lure to depths in excess of 100 feet.

the fishing lure. The wire acts as a linear sinker and two or three ounces of wire will achieve the same depth at the same trolling speed that you'd get from a sinker weighing a half pound or more.

Three basic types of trolling wire are now used: lead-core wire that has a braided nylon or Dacron coating; braided or twisted multi-strand bare Monel wire; or solid soft-drawn Monel wire. The latter is most popular on salt water, and has a length/depth sinking ratio, when fished with a standard 1-ounce trolling lure, of about 8-1. This means that 100 feet of wire line in the water should troll the lure at a depth of about 12½ feet at a standard trolling speed of about 3 knots.

Some anglers fill the reel spool entirely with wire line, but others consider this wasteful and unnecessary. A typical trolling outfit for striped bass, bluefish, most salmon, and the like would be made up as follows:

Rod: Any good fiberglass trolling rod designed to work with the selected breaking-strain class of line. It must have a roller tip-top and either roller or Carboloy guides, a standard trolling butt, and ring-locking reel seat.

Reel: Any reliable, smooth-working salt-water star drag model with a fairly wide spool, in size 2½/0 to 4/0, with gear ratio of 3-1 or 4-1. Fill the reel two-thirds full of monofilament or Dacron backing line according to the following formula, which also gives the matching wire diameter and breaking strain.

Wire diameter	Approx. wire test	Backing line test
.015″	15 lb.	20 lb.
.018″	25 lb.	40 lb.
.021″	35 lb.	40 lb.
.024″	45 lb.	50 lb.
.027″	55 lb.	60 lb.
.030″	70 lb.	80 lb.

Pre-measure the shot of wire you splice onto the backing line to suit the depths of water you expect to fish.

Depth to 15 feet, 100 feet of wire line.
Depth to 30 feet, 200 feet of wire line.
Depth to 45 feet, 300 feet of wire line.

Splice the wire to the backing line by first making a small loop in the end of the backing. Then, tie the wire into the loop with a Becket Bend. Finish off the tag end of wire with close finishing turns around the standing part of the wire. Wrap the splice with dental floss.

Experienced wire line trollers make up several units of deep trolling tackle, all with identical shots of wire on the reels. They almost always troll lines of the same length and lures of appropriate speed-action for the fish in question. Deep trolling speeds are usually fairly slow, 1-4 knots, but many beginners tend to troll too slowly, hanging their lures up in the bottom.

An electronic sounding machine is an absolute must

Six popular salt water medium-speed trolling lures.

(top column) No-Alibi lead head striper lure.
Kramer parrot-head striper lure.
Slim-Jim sand-eel lure.

(bottom column) Smiling Bill nylon jig.
Upperman bucktail lure.
Florida bottom-scratcher jig.

for any kind of deep trolling. Here, the small, inexpensive flashing sounders are ideal for small boat installations. A recorder has the advantage of making a permanent record of the soundings the boat achieves. Perhaps the best sounder for inshore and offshore trolling is one of the combination flasher-recorders now available with depth ranges to about 600 feet. Costs range from $450-$600. Portable flashers suitable for use in small boats cost as little as $90.

Deep trolling with downriggers

The downrigger, or underwater outrigger, is not a new invention. I used a version of the downrigger when I first started fishing at Montauk, back in 1938. But modern downriggers, sparked by the relatively new

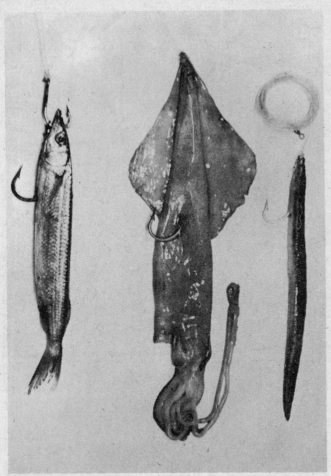

Three typical outrigger trolling baits (right to left): Rigged eel, whole squid, balao.

salmon fishing in the Great Lakes, are a far cry from the crude lead and sashweight sinkers we used in the days before World War II.

The downrigger works by using a heavy weight and a line-release clip to carry a monofilament or Dacron line to any depth within the range of the downrigger's weight support wire. When a fish strikes at the deep-trolled lure, the sudden increase in tension pulls the line clear of the weight's release clip, enabling the angler to fight the fish unencumbered by weights on the fishing line. Downriggers are "legal" trolling equipment by recently adopted I.G.F.A. tackle rules, provided wire line is not also employed on the rod and reel itself.

Modern downriggers have large metal spools with a circumference of a known value (usually two feet). This facilitates knowing exactly how deep the weights are fishing. Some have electric drives, and at least one model is equipped with a remote temperature-sensing device that helps the skipper locate the thermocline, or boundary layer between warm surface water and the deeper cold water.

In the Great Lakes and some ocean fishing areas, bait and game fish are known to congregate along the thermocline level. Remote-reading temperatures probes are used to find the depth of this level. Then, the downriggers or wire trolling lines are adjusted to troll their lures at this desirable depth. *Table 3* combines a recommended type of lure with either wire or downrigger fishing method, effective depth range, and effective trolling speed for ten popular species of salt and fresh water game fish that respond well to deep trolling.

Table 3
DEEP TROLLING
(salt and fresh water)

Species	Lure	Type of rig	Depth	Speed
Sea salmon	Spoon	Downrigger	30-100'	1-3 kn.
Striped bass	Nylon jig	.024" wire	10-40'	3-4 kn.
Bluefish	Nylon jig	.021" wire	10-40'	3-4 kn.
Pollock	Feather	.024" wire	10-40'	2-4 kn.
Grouper	Feather	.027" wire	10-40'	2-3 kn.
Kingfish	Spoon	Downrigger	20-80'	3-5 kn.
Mackerel	Tin jig	.015" wire	10-30'	2-4 kn.
Lake trout	Spoon	Downrigger	Thermocline	1-3 kn.
Coho salmon	Spoon	Downrigger	Thermocline	1-3 kn.
Chinook salmon	Spoon	Downrigger	Thermocline	1-3 kn.

Rules for successful trolling

Whether you troll deep or on the surface, on salt water or fresh, following this set of simple rules will increase your success and make it easier to get along with other trolling fishermen.

1. Troll at the proper speed for the fish and the lures you are using. Overspeeding and underspeeding merely reduce your scoring average.

2. Plan your maneuvers ahead to take advantage of tidal currents and wave patterns.

3. Fish the shortest lines that will catch fish. This reduces the amount of time it takes to bring fish in, and reduces the possibility of other boats running over excessively long lines.

4. Make your turns wide and even. Slow, sharp turns tend to cause line tangles and will hang up deep trolling tackle on the bottom.

5. Avoid crossing another boat's lines, and don't force another boat to stop or turn sharply to avoid your lines.

6. Troll during the run of the tide, either ebb or flood, when fishing activity is fastest. Most ocean fish take a rest during high or low slack water.

7. Keep your lures and hooks clean. After a storm, when fish are often active, the water is usually dirty with seaweed and debris that will foul on your hooks. Dirty hooks never catch fish.

8. Avoid running fast near other boats that are trolling. Most fish are tolerant of low-volume boat noise, but a fast boat racing through a trolling area will put the fish down.

9. Keep a record of your fishing activities so in the future you can plan to take advantage of good tidal and weather conditions as they become apparent.

10. When other trollers catch fish and you don't, avoid sitting there just grinding your teeth, getting more and more frustrated. There's always a reason. Don't try to "think like a fish." Fish can't think. They can't sit back and analyze what we do to them the way we can figure out what they're doing to avoid capture.

Think like a human. Go through a logical process of elimination to find out what you are doing wrong. It may be boat speed, or it may be line length, lure depth, or lure type, color, or action. The smart fisherman is the one who can think his way out of a tough fishing situation, and this is something you have to learn for yourself. But when you have this skill, you can go anywhere in the world and catch your share of fish.

An effective three-rod rod holder arrangement on a modern light fighting chair.

BASIC FLY TYING

by Kenneth E. Bay

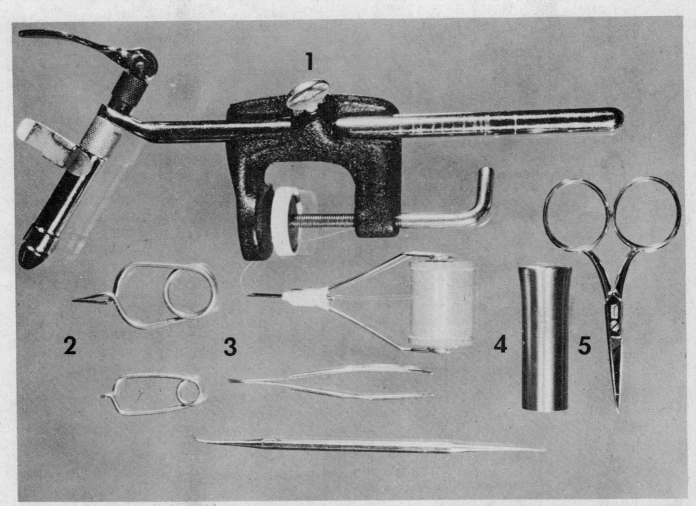

1. Fly tying vise with removable material clip. 2. Two sizes of hackle pliers. 3. All metal bodkin, tweezers and bobbin with thread. 4. Cylindrical metal tube (lipstick case) used to even tips of hairs such as bucktail. 5. Scissors. Note fine points and large finger holes.

If you can tie a shoelace, you can tie a fly. I say this based on several years' observations of novice fly tiers, including eight-year olds, mature adults, and people whose fingers were swollen from working in the cold. They have all become good fly tiers, limited in the proficiency only by the time they could invest in practicing this craft.

You can tie flies — whoever you are or whatever your lifetime endeavors — but, like piano playing or golf, it will require some practice. Specialized tools are needed and, un-less there is a fly-tying supply house near your home, you'll have to order your suppies by mail from one of the catalog houses.

Start with the following tools:
- Lamp
- Fly Tying Vise
- Scissors
- Hackle Pliers
- Bobbin
- Bodkin or dubbing needle

Lamp: The high-intensity lamp is the best light source you can find. It is available at one of your neighbor-hood stores. If you still have an old-fashioned gooseneck lamp around the house, it can be used if fitted with a 100-watt bulb. The high-intensity light is a lamp that was designed with the fly tier in mind, because a strong, direct light source on your work is important.

Tying Vise: The cam-lever type vise is the most popular in use today and will be featured prominently in the tool section of most catalogs. You'll recognize it by its hardened jaws, a clamp on the base for attaching to the table, and by the lever itself. It is easily broken down for portability.

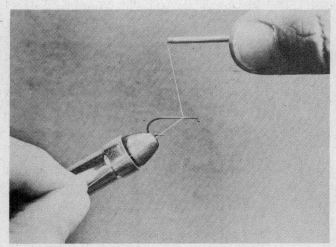

Apply thread to hook using the jam knot: a procedure de-signed to wrap thread over itself, fastening it to the hook. After snipping off the stub, wrap thread on hook shank down to the bend to form a base on which to build the fly.

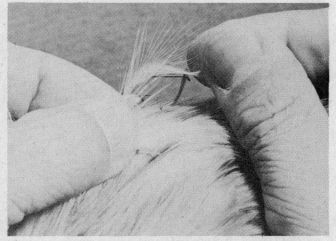

Remove 8-12 fibers from a large hackle feather and roll into a tight bunch with your fingers.

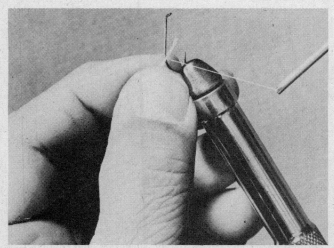

Hold the hackle at a 45-degree angle just over the bend of the hook and make one turn of thread over the fibers.

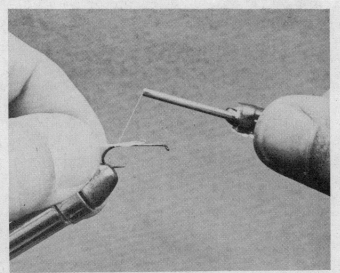

As second wrap is about to be made, move fibers into position so they are straight along the top of the hook shank. Finish this wrap, add another and the tail is complete.

Select a bunch of white bucktail hairs, even up the tips, and hold in position so that one third of the length protrudes beyond the bend of the hook. Bring the thread up to the vertical position.

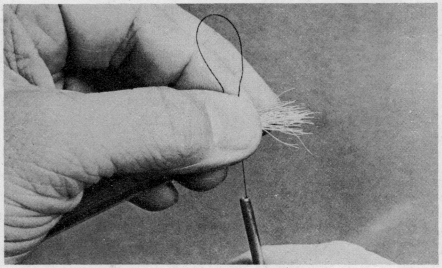

Form loop as shown by bringing thread down on far side of hook shank. Hold hair securely with left thumb and forefinger and pull loop down around hair. Make sure bucktail lies on top of hook and doesn't twist around shank. Another loop or two will hold the bucktail and you can relax your grip on it.

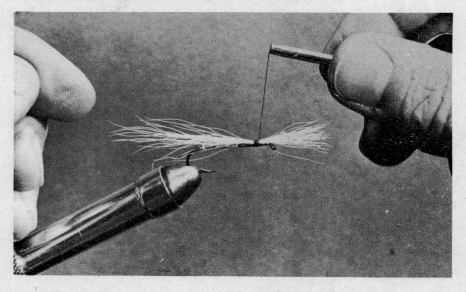

Hair will be on top of the hook if performed properly. Make several more wraps forward of the original two or three to complete the wing. Trim the excess hair extending beyond the hook eye.

There is a choice of several models, so let your pocketbook be your guide. They will all do the job and all will last a lifetime.

Scissors: These may seem to be an insignificant item in your kit, but as you progress in fly tying, you will find yourself becoming very opinionated in favor of this little tool.

Scissors should be small for convenience of handling, should have very fine points and, above all, must have sharp blades. You will find a great many operations that require delicacy in cutting and selective snipping, where you want to cut one thread or one fiber and not its neighbor. Keep a second pair of heavier scissors for cutting hairs from skins and other such operations which might cause the finer pair to become dull.

Hackle Pliers: These are really a type of forceps that operate under finger pressure. They will be used mostly to grasp the tip of a hackle feather during a winding operation in making the fly. You will find other uses, however, in the wrapping of delicate materials, spinning a dubbed body, and other lesser holding requirements. If you select a single pair for all-around use, it should be the steel type with the longer nose.

Bobbin: The bobbin is a thread holder that merely makes tying easier. You may find a mind-boggling selection. While most tiers have a preference, you will certainly be satisfied with the bobbin you select from those available. As time progresses and your experience increases, you will probably form definite opinions. When you reach that point, you can get one that appeals to you. None of them costs a great deal of money.

Bodkin: This is a needle with the blunt end imbedded in a convenient handle of wood or plastic. Many tiers find a hatpin satisfactory, but these are too short for my taste. There are

Instead of bucktail, you can tie in hackle as part of a streamer fly. Four hackles are used in this illustration (two on each side). The tying procedure is the same as you would use for bucktail or any other material.

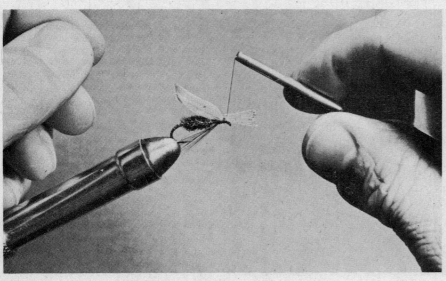

Wet fly wings consisting of duck quill segments are tied in using exactly the same procedure as outlined for bucktail or hackle.

Select a wood duck or mallard side feather and strip back the lower, fuzzy fibers.

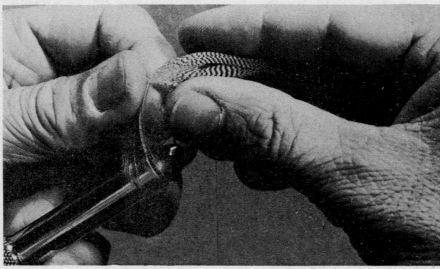

Cut the center stem out about one-half way down and fold the two halves of the feather together so that back sides meet

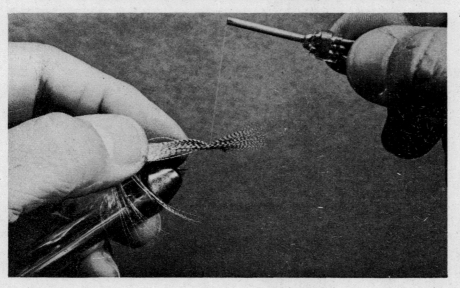

Tie these fibers in behind the eye of the hook, after measuring to assure that the length of the wing will slightly exceed the length of the hook shank. Use the bucktail wing procedure. Note that the wings extend beyond the eye of the hook in this step.

endless uses for this sharp-pointed tool. It will prove invaluable for picking out a hackle fiber that accidentally got caught under a thread or when applying head cement in small droplets (the final operation in tying a fly).

With this basic set of tools, you can tie any of the known fly patterns or — after you learn the fundamentals — you can create your own flies. Where you work becomes a matter of household convenience. In an apartment, you'll probably have to settle for temporary space on the kitchen table or a corner of another room. That means cleaning up after each session and storing your equipment until next time. Fly-tying gear can be stowed in a variety of ways. You'll find that an old tackle box or tool chest may be just the thing to house the vise and other gear when not in use. Even a plastic shoebox or sweater box can serve as an equipment keeper.

If space is not a problem, set up a tying bench where it won't be disturbed. A small table (2 by 3 feet) is ideal, providing you can clamp your vise on it and an outlet is nearby for the lamp. An old desk is often the answer, and you can use the drawers to store the materials that become part of every fly tier's inventory.

The most difficult aspect of learning this fascinating pastime is to become familiar with the great variety of feathers and furs used to make the various flies. Tying instructions list the materials for each pattern, but you should try to gain a basic knowledge of the more common ingredients. One way is to purchase a kit of materials. Each item will be labelled and, although the quantity is limited, you'll have an opportunity to recognize the different materials.

You'll need an assortment of hooks in different sizes, some thread, and head cement. The best advice

Separate fibers into equal wings with bodkin point. With your fingers, hold first the left and then the right wings. Using a "figure 8" motion, run tying thread diagonally between the wings in both directions, front and rear.

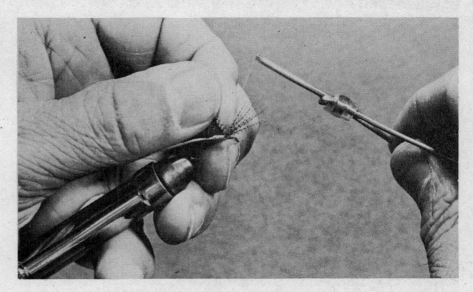

Grasp all fibers with the left thumb and forefinger, pulling them back into a vertical position. Make several turns of thread around the hook shank and against the front of these fibers to hold them in a vertical position.

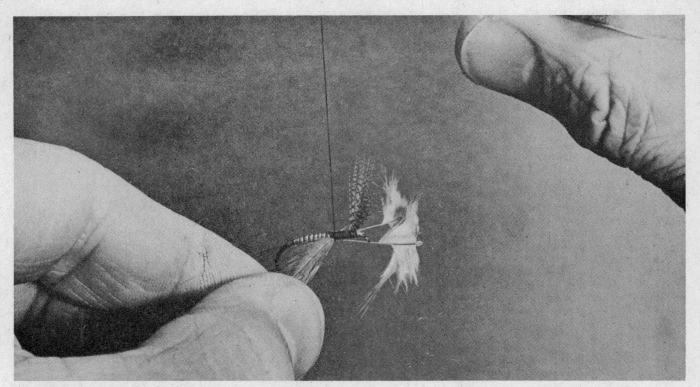

Select two hackle feathers with fiber length equal to the length of the hook shank and remove the fibers from the lower third of each. Hold both together with the front (or good) sides facing the hook eye. Tie in beneath the hook, just in front of the previously prepared body.

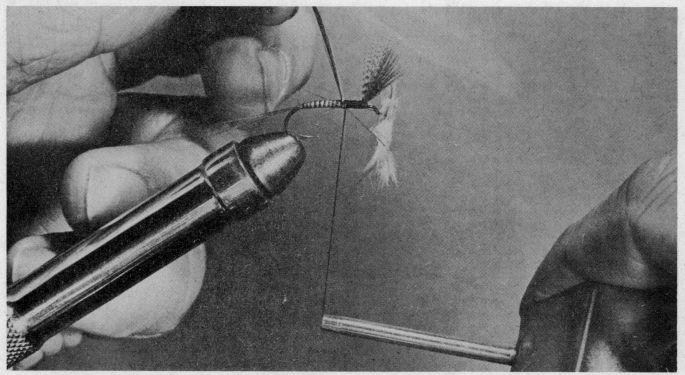

After 3-4 turns of thread, the feathers should be securely in place. Grasp tips and make a half-turn over the top of hook shank as shown. Then, take a turn of thread over the stem of the feathers to secure them in this vertically angled position. Hackles are now properly positioned to proceed with the wrapping.

anyone can offer is to start slowly and build as you gain experience. Otherwise, you might spend a lot of money on things that have little use. Select a few fly patterns as a beginning. Then, obtain the necessary materials and learn to tie them. As you expand the number of patterns you can tie, you will also be adding other materials to your inventory. Before you know it, you'll accumulate a fair supply and gain an understanding at the same time.

There are books available on fly tying materials and on techiques. No matter where you live, you can probably locate an experienced fly tier, if you try, who can give you invaluable help in identifying materials.

Limited space has prevented me from embarking on a lengthly discussion of fly-body construction. This is really the simplest part of the tie, and materials such as tinsel, chenille, and floss are usually wrapped around and around the hook and tied down. Dubbing takes a bit of practice; it is a technique with fur bodies that you should learn to round out your skill.

As you study each of the following photographs, remember that you are looking over my shoulder as I perform each operation. When you begin to fish with the flies you tied and a trout inhales one, you'll experience the greatest thrill in angling.

Grip the rear hackle with the hackle pliers and make one turn in place. Make the second turn, angling forward toward the wing and make a third turn right behind the wing. This will leave an open space in the center of these wraps. If any feather remains, make a turn or two in front of the wing and tie the hackle off with several turns of thread.

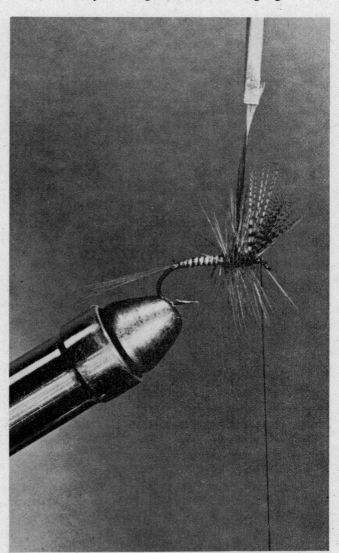

Hold second feather with hackle pliers and make a turn, angling forward into the space left in the previous operation. Make two turns in this space. If any feather remains, make turns in front of the wing and tie off.

TOOLS AND TECHNIQUES

Why Not Try Party Boats?

by Milt Rosko

Take a group of fifteen to forty people from all walks of life, put them on a comfortable, seaworthy boat, send them off fishing together for a day or night, and they're certain to have a fine trip, and often many fish and fish stories in the bargain!

Such is party-boat fishing, a phenomenon that has experienced tremendous growth in recent years on the Atlantic, Pacific and Gulf coasts. What has caused the increased interest in party-boat fishing? Perhaps it's the camaraderie aboard the boats, the lack of need for a reservation, the economy when compared to many other types of fishing, or the prospects of having a safe hull under you and a professional skipper at the helm taking you to the fishing grounds. Naturally, the idea of making a good catch has contributed a great deal, too. Party boaters consistently dock with excellent catches, ranging from small bottom-feeders to some of the greatest gamefish.

I've fished from party boats that sailed from tiny creeks and big harbors along the coast, as well as from remote villages and bustling cities. There were tiny seaports along Maine's rugged, rock-studded coast that provided fine codfish and pollock sport. Sailing from New York City produced bluefish and school bluefin tuna from the waters of the Atlantic. Aboard San Francisco boats in the cold Pacific, we scored with striped bass and king salmon. Down in the warm waters off Ensenada, Mexico, we caught variety beyond counting at the offshore Todos Santos Islands. Variety was the byword in the Gulf, too, from Gulfport, Mississippi, and other ports of call in Florida, Alabama, and Louisiana.

The equipment used by party-boat anglers from each area varies, depending upon local conditions and the species being sought. But this need not be a deterrent to a beginner; most party boats have quality tackle available at a nominal rental charge. Many newcomers use rental equipment for a few days on the packets and, once they find they're enjoying the sport, they usually select gear suited to the type of fishing they're going to do.

In my travels, I always carry a versatile party-boat outfit for each member of my family, since we do a great deal of this type of fishing.

The rod I've found well suited to most party-boat fishing measures seven feet in length, with the tip section joined to the butt at the reel seat. This breaks down to a tip section measuring approximately five-and-a-half feet, which isn't difficult to transport. The rod has a stiffish-action, which I've found essential in most party-boat fishing, because at times I may have to use upward of twelve ounces of sinker weight to get my bait down where the fish are feeding.

An exception to the stiffish-action rod is when you fish with live anchovies as bait from the party boats of Southern California. Here, a slightly longer, softer tip is essential.

Almost any fist-retrieve, name-brand, salt-water boat reel capable of holding approximately 200 yards of 30-pound test line will be more than adequate. It should have a smooth functioning drag that will relinquish line under desired tension, permitting a fish to take line smoothly. The drag minimizes the chance of a line break.

Monofilament lines are by far the most popular on all three coasts, with 30-pound test the favorite. Actually, 30-pound is slightly heavier than is really necessary, but most anglers prefer this test because it is more durable, and less apt to wear quickly if it occasionally rubs across the bottom of the boat or tangles with the lines of others. If, however, the boats on which you sail are not crowded, you can use 20-pound test with ease, and may find it superior. Its finer diameter offers less water resistance.

Bluefish are the most popular species sought by the Middle Atlantic party-boat chum fleet. Milt Rosko landed this beauty on a chunk of butterfish bait drifted back in a chum line of ground menhaden.

As a result, you can use lighter-weight sinkers and feel the bite of a fish more readily, because the lighter line is apt to be perpendicular to the bottom.

There are some areas, however, where I've observed a lot of dacron line in use, and I've used it myself. Up in Maine, where anglers employ 12- to 16-ounce diamond jigs for codfish, pollock, cusk, and fish in water ranging from 150 to 200 feet deep, dacron is preferred. It simply doesn't have as much stretch as mono. Dacron also finds favor along the sections of the Gulf coast where party packets head many miles offshore to fish the broken, irregular coral patches in deep water. Red snapper and grouper are the targets. The same is true in the Pacific Northwest, where rockfish and lingcod are the targets and are fished for in 300 or 400 feet of water, with a sinker weighing over a pound, and anywhere from four to six hooks and baits on the rig.

Terminal rigging varies from port to port, but the standard high-low rig is without question the most popular on all three coasts. (I suspect you could score while using it for most any species that is a bottom feeder.) As its name implies, this rig has one high hook and one low hook, and usually is made of heavy, stiff monofilament with a loop and swivel at one end and a sinker snap at the other. Running out at right angles near the top and bottom of the rig are swiveling arms to which you attach your snelled hooks and their accompanying 12- to 24-inch leaders. Thus, you have one hook directly on the bottom, and a second hook anywhere from 18 to 36 inches or more off the bottom. A bank-style sinker is favored with this rig, and may range anywhere from one to twelve ounces, or even a pound or more in weight.

Still another popular rig from the Carolinas south to Florida along the Atlantic and then west along the Gulf

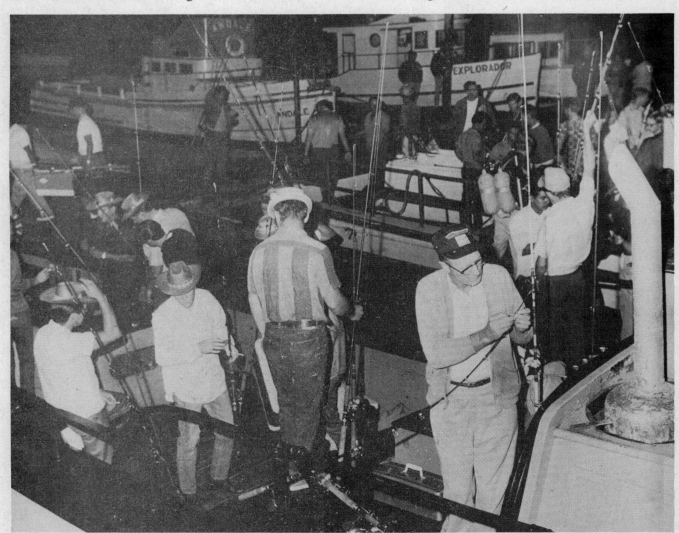

These party boat anglers busy themselves rigging up before sailing from Ensenada, Mexico, for the fishing grounds located at the Todos Santos Islands. The boats chum with live anchovies and catch a wide variety of species at the kelp beds.

to Texas is a single-hook bottom rig. Simply slip an egg-shaped sinker with a hole through its center onto your line, then tie a barrel swivel to the end of it — which permits the sinker to slide on the line — and finally tie in your leader and hook. This rig is especially popular when inshore fishing, and when fishing around coral or other bottom debris where a two-hook rig would be likely to snag frequently.

Used on the Pacific coast, and gaining popularity for chumming on the Middle Atlantic and Gulf coasts is perhaps the simplest party-boat rig of all. You merely tie your hook directly to the end of monofilament line, and add a rubber-cored sinker of desired weight, placing it about two to three feet from the hook. This rig works extremely well in shallow water, or when you are drifting your bait at intermediate levels. It is almost always used when chumming with and baiting with live anchovies on

the Pacific. Along the Middle Atlantic, it is used extensively while chumming with ground menhaden for bluefish, school bluefin tuna, Atlantic bonito, little tuna, and oceanic bonito.

The selection of hooks varies considerably. Speaking in general terms, the Atlantic and Gulf coast anglers use larger hooks on a species-for-species basis than do their counterparts who fish from party packets on the Pacific. This may be because Pacific coast anglers lean toward live baits; to accommodate them, they use hooks that border on being small, so as not to impair the swimming and mobility of the small baitfish such as the anchovy.

But large or small, I've found that the Beak or Claw style hooks are by far the finest types to use for most party-boat fishing situations with natural baits. These hooks are designed with long, curved points that are offset. Even a delicate bait isn't ripped when placed on a

The *Big Mac* is about to depart for the fishing grounds located off Oceanside, California, on a twilight chumming trip to the kelp beds.

hook of this type. The hooking capabilities of the Beak or Claw are far superior to most other styles, which is why I use them wherever I go. Of course, I select a type within these styles, depending on the species I'm seeking. If I'm after weakfish or spotted seatrout, I use a fine-wire Beak or Claw style hook, simply because these species have very delicate jaws and with a heavy-wire hook I'd lose too many fish. But, when heavyweight grouper are my target, I use the heaviest wire models made, for these heavyweights simply would straighten a fine-wire hook. With bluefish, king mackerel, and other toothy species, I use long-shanked models rather than those with standard shanks. The fish is less apt to bite through the line with a long shank if you're tying direct, and you won't get your cable or wire kinked if you use a leader of this material.

Although many anglers make up their own rigs, and others buy them aboard the packets, many ready-made basic bottom rigs are available in tackle shops that will serve the needs of the angler quite well.

It is difficult to recommend specific hook sizes. While I've seen such recommendations, they can often be misleading. If half-pound sand porgies are your quarry, you certainly wouldn't use the same size hook that you would

for two- to three-pound shad porgies. Ditto when inshore fishing for one-pound winter flounders versus being offshore after the five- to six-pounders caught in the open ocean. Seek the counsel of the party boat skipper or deckhand. They'll be glad to tell you the predominant size of the species being caught, and the best size hook to use.

On a party boat, you won't have the luxury of the skipper and deckhand taking care of your equipment; as a rule, they'll be too busy. Therefore, it's important to learn how to tie knots properly to attach your terminal rigging. Also, keep your hooks sharp. Hooks are the cheapest item you use. By taking the time to file them needle sharp, your chances of hooking fish will be increased.

There's no need to concern yourself with what bait to use aboard the party boats, because the bait will be supplied. Naturally, the skipper will take special pains to ensure that he has the best bait aboard for the species being sought. There's always a plentiful supply, too.

If you're new aboard the packets, ask the advice of the deckhand about baiting your hook. Many newcomers do it carelessly. Some make the mistake of placing too large a bait on the hook; consequently, they get many

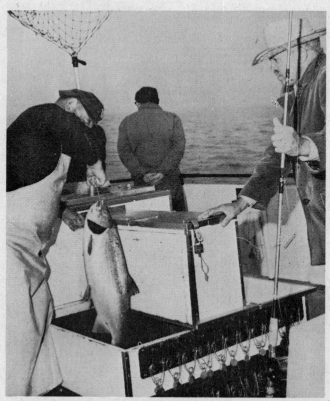

The boats sailing from Sausalito and San Francisco in California fish offshore for king and silver salmon. This fine king salmon struck a rigged anchovy bait sent into the depths via a cannonball sinker rig and trolled at the 30-foot level.

The sand bass helps to fill the bags of many California party boat anglers.

strikes from small fish, but fail to hook them, simply because the fish can't get the bait into its mouth, let alone get hooked.

Party boats basically do three types of fishing: bottom fishing, chumming, and trolling. During the course of a season in excess of eighty percent of the fishing is bottom fishing, in which an angler sends his baited rig down to the bottom and waits for a strike. Approximately fifteen percent of the fishing is done with chum: either small live fish such as anchovies, or ground fish, such as menhaden, popularly called mossbunker. Very little trolling is done from party boats — less than five percent of the fishing time expended, the exception being salmon trolling on open boats in the Pacific, a limited amount of tuna and bonito trolling along the Middle Atlantic, and some albacore trolling in the far reaches of the Pacific.

Most party boats post a notice at the dock notifying customers what the boat will be doing. Bottom fishing boats usually stick exclusively to luring fish from the bottom, while chum boats often will troll until several fish are hooked, then quickly establish a chum line to hold the fish around the boat.

I began party-boat fishing when I was a seven-year-old.

Early one morning my dad and I sailed from Shark River in New Jersey, and I succeeded in catching a prettily hued weakfish on a strip of fresh squid bait drifted along the bottom. Many people begin party-boat fishing in this way, although some start not as youngsters, but as adults looking for a way to enjoy the outdoors, meet people and catch fish.

While it may sound easy, the more you fish aboard the packets, the more you will come to respect bottom fishing. The idea that you simply drop a baited rig to the bottom and immediately begin to haul up fish soon fades. You quickly realize that concern, patience, and knowledge combine to develop skills so that veteran anglers can catch bottom feeders when others fail to score.

This challenge of learning the techniques that will catch a hundred or more species from our coastal waters is what has made party-boat fishing so interesting to me. Given the choice, I'll often forego gamefishing on a private boat to join the regulars on the packets, particularly when I'm visiting an area where I haven't previously fished from party boats.

Each species takes a bait differently, but there's still no set pattern that you can follow. It does pay to note characteristics, however, and, by anticipating a strike

Not only do grouper provide exciting sport for party boat anglers, but they're a fine table fish.

Many Gulf coast anglers drift out a whole pilchard at intermediate depths instead of fishing on the bottom. This lucky angler landed a beautiful little tuna, popularly called bonito along the Gulf of Mexico.

from a particular species, you can know the best way to react. As an illustration, the tautog in the Atlantic, the sheephead of the Gulf, and the sheep-head of the Pacific all strike a bait very quickly, and will clean a bait from a hook with their sharp teeth in an instant. It has often been said that when fishing for them, you have to lift back with your rod tip to strike them even before they take the bait! This points up the importance of striking immediately. If you hesitate even a second, you'll miss the strike and lose the bait.

With other species, quite the opposite holds true. Take the summer flounder of the Atlantic, the southern flounder along the Gulf, and the Pacific halibut. If you strike immediately when the fish takes the bait, you'll invariably pull the bait away from the fish. All of these flatfishes usually take the bait and hold it securely between their teeth before finally mouthing it. This takes patience on the part of the angler. You hesitate immediately upon feeling the flatty pick up the bait, lower your rod tip until the line comes taut, and then lift back smartly to set the hook.

Ah, ha, lift back smartly, maybe that's the key? Always strike hard. Not so. The winter flounder so plentiful and popular along the Middle and North Atlantic coast has a soft, rubbery mouth, and it is extremely small. If you lift back smartly you'll often pull the bait right out of its mouth. Here, the key is to hesitate a moment when you feel the strike, do not lift your rod tip at all, but just begin reeling. As the bait begins to move in the flounder's mouth, this winter bottom-feeder invariably applies additional pressure to hold onto the bait and the hook will set with ease.

With some species having a soft mouth, such as the weakfish and southern seatrout, applying too much pressure on the strike, or fighting it with too much drag pressure, will rip a big hole in the fish's jaw, and you'll lose your quarry. Just lift back firmly with your rod tip, and have the drag set lightly enough so that if the fish is a big one and wants to take line it can do so without excessive pressure.

Try this approach with the many groupers and snappers of our tropical waters, and you may find that you just won't put a fish in the boat. You've got to exert maximum pressure, both on the strike and during the subsequent battle. This is necessary to keep the fish from gaining sanctuary beneath a rock or coral ledge, or from

Her Majesty II is typical of the Gulf coast party boat. Anglers board on a first come, first served basis, and usually concentrate their efforts fishing for red snappers and groupers on the bottom.

cutting your line on the many obstructions, most of which will be sharp. As soon as one of these species pulls down hard, yank back just as hard, keep your rod tip high in the air, and begin a merciless pumping. This should consist of lifting your rod tip as high as you can and then dropping it quickly. You reel as you drop the tip to take in line and then lift again, repeating this procedure until you get the fish well up and away from the bottom.

Perhaps the most sporting fishing you'll experience aboard the packets is chumming for gamefish. From a reading of my angling logs, I find I've caught several dozen of our finest gamefish while chumming. Included along the Atlantic coast were bluefish, striped bass, school bluefin tuna, little tuna, oceanic bonito, and Atlantic bonito. Aboard Florida drift boats — a name applied to party packets in many parts of the south — I've scored

The long-finned albacore is perhaps the most-prized species sought by West coast party boat anglers. Milt Rosko beams approval upon landing a 35-pound specimen on a live anchovy bait. The boat sailed all night to reach the fish, which were located 90 miles offshore of San Diego.

with king mackerel, Spanish mackerel, dolphin, blackfin tuna, jack crevalle, barracuda, and a lot more. Chumming turned the trick in California and Mexico, with such noteworthy adversaries as yellowtail, white sea bass, albacore, school bluefin tuna, Pacific bonito, and Pacific barracuda.

The species that move into a chum line of small, live baitfish, or ground fish, or chunks of fish, are numerous, and can really give you a start when they leisurely swim through the chum line and inhale your bait.

Often, I improve my score by observing anglers who are consistently doing better than me. I also try to analyze why I'm catching more fish than others not doing as well. Between the two, I've picked up a lot of ways in which to improve my score.

Fish can be attracted to a party boat by dropping food into the water and permitting the current to carry it. As the fish get a taste of the meal drifting along, they follow it to its source, where they will ultimately spot your baited hook, and hopefully take it.

The key to presenting your bait to a fish is to do so as naturally as possible, whether it be a live anchovy, chunk of butterfish or menhaden, or a whole pilchard. I usually keep my reel in free spool and permit the current to carry the bait along naturally, just as it is carrying the chum. In this way, a hungry fish moving along picking up pieces of chum ingests the bait without any hesitation.

Usually I tie my hook directly to the end of the monofilament line, bait up, and let the bait drift back into the chum line. Should toothy adversaries such as bluefish or king mackerel be the quarry, I may use a short stainless steel wire or cable leader about six or eight inches long between the line and hook to keep these fish from biting through.

As my bait drifts out, if I fail to receive a strike, I simply reel it back in and start all over again. Unfortunately, many anglers quickly tire of this approach. They let their bait drift out, lock their reel in gear and let the bait hang listlessly in the current. In a swift current, the bait will be ballooned towards the surface and invariably spin, while the chum settles and drifts along beneath the bait, and this is where the fish will be.

To keep my bait deep, (usually the fish will be deep in the chum, rather than above it) I use a rubber-cored sinker, which is easily attached to the line. Years ago I used clinch-on sinkers, but found these frequently nicked the line. While fishing aboard the West Coast party boats, I was was introduced to the rubber-cored models (which are now available with a plastic core); since then, they're all I use for weight while chumming.

With your reel in free spool, let a fish mouth the bait and move off several feet. This happens quickly, and

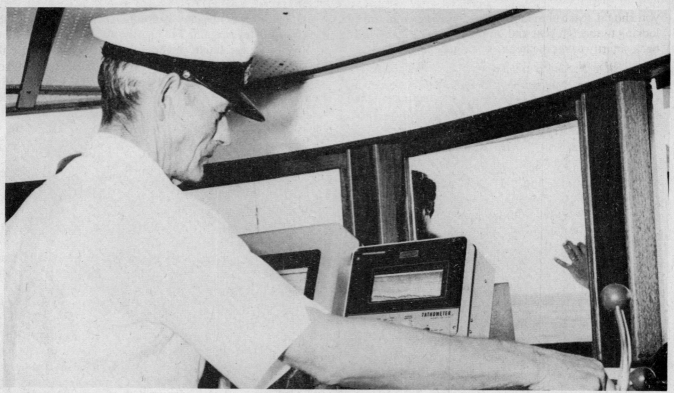

You'll find that most party boats are equipped with modern electronics to help locate fish. Often this makes the difference between success and failure.

A San Diego party boat takes aboard several netfulls of live anchovies before heading for the kelp beds. Anchovies are used as chum to attract a variety of species.

you should react immediately by lowering your rod tip, locking the reel in gear and, as the line comes taut, lifting back smartly to set the hook. Then just hang on!

If you're aboard a packet trolling to locate fish, or if it's a salmon-trolling boat along the Pacific Northwest, the skipper will usually dictate the terminal tackle to be used. In many cases, they even supply it, so there's little need to worry about the specifics. I found it best to watch and learn.

When it's time to head in, you'll hear three blasts on the boat's air horn, and it'll be up with the lines and a pleasant sail home. Most boats have a "big fish" pool or jackpot. Everyone who enters contributes a dollar, or maybe five dollars. The lucky angler who catches the largest fish of the day can come home with a sizeable prize in the bargain. Frequently, the jackpot will tentatively change hands several times as one angler's fish outweighs another's on the balance, until the deckhand makes the rounds of everyone. The final determination is made by the skipper. I've even seen fish of identical weight, with both fortunate anglers agreeing to split the jackpot.

Camaraderie, competition for the biggest fish of the day, fresh air on the open ocean, and a sack full of fine eating fish — all these combine to make party-boat fishing what it is. It's a great way to relax surrounded by people whe were casual acquaintenances when you sailed, and are fine friends a few hours later as you reach dockside.

The summer flounder is popular with party boat anglers along the Middle Atlantic coast. Hesitate when you feel the strike, giving the flatty ample time to take the bait before you set the hook.

Pacific mackerel often swarm into the chum line by the hundreds. They provide exciting sport and are great for the youngsters.

Fishing Artificial Lures

by Edward W. Keats

The best fishing lure ever designed is the one you have confidence in at the moment. If you honestly believe that a lure will catch fish, you'll fish it harder and manipulate it with greater skill to confirm your thinking. Too many users of artificial baits become mechanical casters, tossing the offering casually and cranking it back with little concern. There is the eternal hope, of course, that a fish will strike, but not much thought goes into the speed of retrieve or the method.

Fishing artificial lures is an art and it must be developed through experience, experimentation, and dedication. It is far better to fish a bait enthusiastically for a half hour than to make meaningless presentations over an entire day. You work a lure with feeling and every motion is tailored to enhance the action. The exciting objective of using plugs, spoons, bucktails, spinnerbaits, and other lures is fooling a fish into believing it's the real thing. To do this effectively, you must understand the habits of the species you seek and develop an approach that will trigger a response from the fish.

Recognize from the beginning that there is more than one way to fish any lure. The retrieve that worked so successfully yesterday or this morning might be passé now and you'll have to revise your retrieve if you expect to continue to catch fish. No lure presently on the market is a cure-all for angling ills. Sometimes lures work and at other times you'll go fishless. Beginning anglers are obsessed with the idea that a new lure might make the difference, and they are forever asking other fishermen what they are using. The lure fished by someone else might be a clue, but it isn't the answer, unless you know how to fish it properly.

It's easy to become a lure collector. All of us have a feeling that a new lure might do the job, and so we plunk down our cash in the fervent hope that we have found a treasure. Lures must first catch the fisherman before they ever get the chance to catch a fish. Remember, however, that it is extremely costly to design, test, package, and market a lure. Every offering certainly has caught fish or it would never find its way to the market place. The trick is to find those lures that will work for you.

If you meet a tournament fisherman or someone with a reputation for having caught a lot of fish, ask whether you can peek in his tackle box. No doubt you will see a lot of artificial lures, but you'll also be surprised that he doesn't have the wide variety you might expect. Every veteran has his favorite lures, and he'll have an ample supply in various sizes and colors. He won't, however, have every bait sold in the local tackle shop. As a rule, when you find a fisherman with an extensive supply of a few models, you can be certain he knows what he is doing. That's the man to ask.

It's not always the lure, but how you work it that produces fish. That's why it is important to limit your selection at first and learn how to handle each type of artificial. The angler who can work wonders with only two types of lures is far ahead of the enthusiast who insists on buying one of everything and never tries to retrieve any lure correctly.

Fish are attracted to a lure because of sound, flash, vibration, the general appearance, or a combination of these factors. Except on a dark night or in areas of very poor visibility, the final attack on any lure depends on sight: the fish sees it and hits it. There's been much written about imitating or matching natural foods, but this isn't always a requisite. A lure must behave in the same manner as the real thing, but it doesn't have to be an exact replica.

Lake trout prefer a deep-running lure.

Although this tackle box is full, there are only a few basic lure types in it. The rest are duplicates.

Your job is to retrieve the offering so that it *appears* to be something good to eat. When you are near the water, spend some time watching minnows or other baitfish. Study schools of small fry and note their behavior. The "flash" of a minnow is quick and it is subtle. An injured bait seldom makes a big commotion, but it does seem to struggle. These are actions you want to imitate.

The more you can observe fish behavior and motivation, the better your chance of fishing a lure to perfection. A fish, for example, must make the decision as to whether to strike or reject. It may be a reflex action, but your quarry does have a choice and that choice can go either way. Fish undoubtedly consider the amount of energy expended for the value received. That's a tradeoff. If the fish wants the food badly enough, it will follow for a great distance. Largemouths that have been feeding might not want to chase a lure very far from their lie. Trout in a fast stream would use up too much energy if they had to barrel after every offering that moved beyond their lie.

Some fishermen believe that when predators pounce on a school of baitfish, the gamefish opens its mouth and swims blindly through the bait, ingesting fish after fish. It doesn't happen quite like that. Researchers tell us that predators must isolate their prey and run down a single baitfish. That's not always easy in a shimmering mass of silver baitfish. The moment a school becomes disoriented or there are stragglers, gamefish can pick them off easily.

Very often, the fish you want to catch are below their prey waiting for the right moment to single out a victim.

It is also easier for a predator to spot something that looks different than the rest of the fish. That's one reason why a lure cast into a school of bait and retrieved usually brings a strike. Actually, you have helped the fish to isolate its prey by pulling the lure out of the school; because it looks somewhat different, the fish can strike it easily.

To be successful with a lure, you must know everything about it and how it will respond to the various rod manipulations you can impart. On a shallow, clear flat you can watch the lure, but most of us don't fish that type of water very often and so we have to rely on knowledge and memory. You must be able to picture what your lure is doing every instant it is in the water. The best way to learn this is to practice with the lure in a swimming pool or make short casts in shallow water where you can observe the action.

If you are jigging a bucktail vertically, you should know how far it moves when you lift your rod a foot, two feet, etc. You should also be aware of how deep a crank bait will run when you retrieve it rapidly, slowly, and anything in between. In short, you must know the movements of every lure so that you can picture mentally what is taking place under the water.

No one can remember all of these characteristics about every lure on the market, so it is best to start with a few basic designs and master those lures. If you pick general types, you can handle a variety of fishing assignments with the same lure and catch more fish than if you changed baits often without really knowing how to work any one of them.

An artificial lure that is successful will boast a delicate balance and unique action. The originator of a particular bait usually spends a great deal of time and plenty of money perfecting his creation. He's concerned with balance, hook placement, hook style and size, and a number of other things. Imitations are often cheaper, but the quality control is lacking and the action might not be precisely the same. It can be a foolish economy to spend a few cents less for an imitation.

Each lure you buy should be tested in a pool or with a short cast that enables you to observe the action. Nevertheless, some lures will work better than others, even though they are made by the same manufacturer and are supposed to be identical. Veteran anglers take the time to "tune" a lure. They make a cast or two and check to see that the lure is running true. Sometimes, a lure will track to one side or the other, and the bait can be tuned by moving the eye (where you attach snap or line) to one side or the other.

Except for a minor adjustment to make the lure track straight or, in the case of a spinner or spinnerbait, to straighten the arms when they become bent, it is best to fish a lure as it comes from the box. Eventually, as you become increasingly familiar with a given bait, you may want to experiment and modify it, but that should be left to those who have fished it a long time.

If a lure is worth tying on your line, it deserves a fair chance in the water. Some fishermen can go through a tackle box of lures so quickly as to defy the imagination. They make one or two casts, decide the lure isn't going to catch fish, and change to something else. Before you give up on any lure, you should go through several variations of retrieve. Each cast should be fished enthusiastically and you should be able to picture a fish behind your bait about to engulf it. That can give you the impetus to work the lure the best way you can.

Unless you've seen it happen, it can be difficult to understand how finicky some fish can be about a retrieve. Not long ago, Bill Dance and I were fishing for largemouths in Mississippi using fat plugs. He caught a bass about three pounds, then a two-pounder, and finally a third fish in a matter of a few minutes. I hadn't had a bump. While he was scoring, I tried to match his speed of retrieve and watched him as closely as I could. We were using identical baits, so it had to be something I was doing or wasn't doing.

He told me that he was pausing for a second after every half dozen cranks and that the fish would hit as soon as he resumed the retrieve. I changed tactics and he was right. The point is, however, that a variation as minute as a one second pause can make the difference between catching fish and not catching fish.

That's not the only time a very minor adjustment made a major difference. A friend and I were fishing off the shrimp docks in Key West, Florida one night for baby tarpon. We had a fly rod and a plug rod and alternated between fish. I had no trouble hooking fish on fly, but only my friend could score on the small plug. It's frustrating when you're in that situation and, no matter how hard you try, you just can't detect what he's doing.

Finally, I asked him. He teased me for awhile, but he did confess. Every few seconds, he wiggled his rod hand slightly as he continued the retrieve. Immediately, it made sense. That brief wiggle caused the plug to "flash" and that's all it took to catch a fish. So, before you give up on a bait, try several variations. One of them could be the answer you were seeking.

Sometimes, you can impart too much action to a lure. Another friend was with me on a snook fishing trip to Central America. He's an extremely competent fisherman and worked his lure in what appeared to be an effective manner. From talking to one of the local guides, I learned that a straight retrieve produces more fish for some reason, so I tried it. All one had to do was cast and crank the lure back, resisting the temptation to make it wiggle, dance, dive, or anything else. After I got the first couple of hits, my friend was instantly convinced, changed his retrieve, and joined the fun.

When you can see a fish follow your offering without striking it, you can rationalize it the first time. If this happens again, you can bet that something is wrong. Either your retrieve should be changed or the plug isn't acting right or there's another problem. Some fish may be curious, but when any denizen chases a lure, it has one thought in mind. If you know a fish is stalking your lure and it doesn't hit right away, start to vary your retrieve. Slow it down, speed it up, but *do something*. The longer a fish follows an artificial, the less chance you have of getting a strike. First, try taking the lure away from the fish by speeding it up.

Northern pike and other species have a habit of tailing a lure right up to the boat and then slamming it at about the time you're ready to lift it from the water and make another cast. In those situations, sweep your lure in a figure-8 pattern alongside the boat before you pick it up. It could make a difference in fish hooked.

It may be more fun to watch the explosive strike of a gamefish that has just zeroed in on a surface bait, but you will catch more fish on lures that work underwater. When you select a basic assortment, include a few topwater lures for those pleasurable times when fish will come to the top, but concentrate on medium-running lures, darters that work just under the surface, and heavier offerings that will bounce bottom.

If your lures cover every zone from bottom to top, you can tackle most situations. Remember to limit your selection until you learn to fish the ones you have. Some lures are extremely versatile and can handle a number of chores. Among these are spinnerbaits, bucktails, lead-heads, and even the plastic worm — if you modify the rig.

It's hard to believe that a fish can rid itself of a plug with three treble hooks, yet it happens all the time. Most anglers don't feel it necessary to sharpen the hooks when there are trebles, but you'll find it is worth the time. Even if the plug has never been used, take a file or hone and put cutting edges along the point of each hook on the treble. With a little practice, you can do it rather quickly, and it will mean many more hookups. After all, if it didn't make a difference, you can bet that the top anglers wouldn't take the time to do it.

Speed of retrieve and type of retrieve can be critical, but the direction of retrieve can be equally significant. There are times when fish will ignore a bait moving in one direction and clobber it if it comes the other way. In salt water, a fish feeding into the tide expects his meal to be swept along by the tidal flow. Surf fishermen some-

A simple assortment of plugs can produce many different types of gamefish.

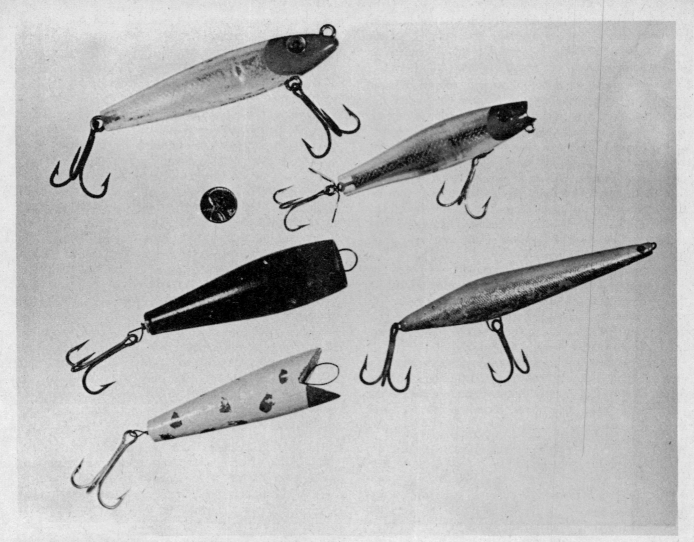

These plugs are particularly effective in salt water.

times discover that a lure worked parallel to the breakers does better than one cast seaward and retrieved shoreward. On a jetty, newcomers want to reach the horizon with their casts, yet more fish are taken by carefully placed presentations along the rocks. That is where the bait hangs out and that's where the predators lurk.

Along a dropoff, fish sometimes prefer a bait that moves from deep to shallow, but don't be surprised if the fish will only hit lures that are worked from the shallows toward the depths. If you're fishing weedbeds for pike, bass, or other species, casts that parallel the front of the weeds can be more productive than those fished outwards from the weeds. Predators often lie in wait at the edge of cover to ambush unsuspecting baitfish. A lure that parallels the cover is an easier target than one that takes off for deep water. If you don't start your retrieve near the fish, it would have to chase the bait to the right or left for a considerable distance.

You can vary your presentation when fishing a stream. The usual approach is to cast across or a quarter downstream, let the lure swing around in the current, and then bring it back. You can gain a different action and another direction when you cast upstream and work the lure down toward you. Keep in mind that fish face upstream.

If you're working a shoreline for bass, cast well beyond any obstruction instead of playing a game of accuracy by trying to drop your offering right on target. The effect you want to achieve is to have the lure swim by the cover, not hit the fish on the head. If you cast beyond the target, you can fish the back, one side, and the front with a single cast.

Many fishermen pass up prime territory when they cast to partially visible trees that have fallen in the water. The tendency is to cast to the branches that can be seen, ignoring the trunk of the tree and the portion that lies submerged. A better technique is to cast as far as you

Shad have small mouths and prefer tiny lures moved near the bottom.

You'll catch more fish if you learn to work a few basic lures effectively.

can and work the lure right along the entire length of the tree, covering the submerged portion as well as the branches that you can see. In fact, when you become skillful, you'll learn to vary the depth of the lure to follow the contour of the tree, letting it sink deeper at the outset and then working it shallower as you reach the front.

There's a lot of theory involved in trolling a lure. The two major factors are the depth of the offering and the distance behind the boat. Sometimes fish want the lure close to the boat; at other times, they won't hit it unless it's a considerable distance astern. An angler who sets his trolling lines and then wanders aimlessly without adjusting them is missing fish. Trolling is no different than casting. There are many variables — you must experiment until you start catching fish.

If you're fishing more than one line, each should be at a different depth and have a different lure. Change lures frequently unless you know that a certain one will produce, and adjust the distance astern. At the same time, speed can be important. You may start with the slowest speed that will give the lures the proper action and then speed up occasionally until you find the combination.

Steering a straight course can also be an invitation to failure. Work in and out over different depths and, if there is a current, try trolling with it, against it, and across it. All of these things can make a difference.

Most gamefish can see color during the daylight hours. There are times when a lure of one color will catch fish and another one won't. It's questionable how fussy fish really are about color under most situations. You should, however, offer them a choice of dark or light. In dark-colored water or during periods of low light levels, fish can actually see a dark color better than a light or bright color. The topwater bass fisherman often has more success in the evening with a dark plug that is silhouetted against the lighter sky.

Size is generally more important in the choice of lures than color. If there is a particular baitfish that is abundant, you might want to approximate its size in your choice of lures. Fish will often specialize for feeding efficiency if a certain bait is plentiful and ignore other offerings. They gear themselves to that food and that's all they want.

When you can't get a hit on a size that is similar to the average baitfish, try a slightly larger size. Experiments have shown that fish will sometimes strike a bigger bait when they are satiated with smaller food.

Perhaps the one mistake beginning anglers make repeatedly is the tendency to force a fish to eat what they want it to eat instead of offering an imitation of what the fish really wants. If, for example, a fish doesn't want to come to the surface, there's little point in fishing all

Always carry more than one of your favorite lures. If your line breaks, there will be a spare bait in your tackle box.

Bluefish are favorites of saltwater anglers because they'll strike a wide variety of artificial lures.

day with topwater poppers. When a gamester prefers a slow-moving target, it's not going to change its strategy to pursue a speeding lure. The trick is to discover what the fish want and then give it to them. They have to make the decision; you can't make it for them.

Topwater enthusiasts often claim that they would rather take one fish on a surface bait than a half-dozen down deep. That's a matter of personal choice, but there are a few points about fishing topwater that could make a difference. The amount of noise you make with a popper or chugger can either serve to attract fish or send them scurrying for safety. You must experiment. Loud pops in shallow water may be devastating to a fish, but the same commotion in deeper water could bring fish up to look around.

There'll be days when a steady noise is better than a loud sporadic one and other times when the reverse is true. Oldtime bass fishermen still adhere to the theory that a topwater lure should be fished very slowly. There may be merit to this, but many accomplished anglers are beginning to believe that this wastes too much time and doesn't put more fish on the stringer. They work their lures much faster, covering more water in the process.

It should be obvious at this point that there is no preferred method of working a lure and no bait that will solve all your problems. If you take the time to learn how to fish each bait properly and to the fullest extent of its capabilities, you'll catch more fish. Try each lure first to see what it can do. Then, fish it seriously and pretend there is a fish behind it every second it is in the water. You'll find it is better to fish a lure correctly for a short time than to cast it methodically hour after hour. A successful artificial lure fisherman depends on skill, not luck.

SPINNERBAIT & WORM:

BASSING'S DEADLY DUO

by Stan Fagerstrom

The contemporary American largemouth bass angler is a more effective fisherman than he used to be. Part of his success may come from better equipment. Mostly it's because he's been able to cash in on the tremendous amount of bass fishing research conducted during the professional bass fishing contests now so popular from the South all the way to the far corners of the Pacific Northwest.

Don't misunderstand. I'm not launching into a dissertation on the merits of fishing contests. Frankly, they aren't my bag. A man would be a fool, however, not to take advantage of the angling truths they reveal. Let's examine one of those truths which becomes a little more apparent with each passing year.

Suppose you were to accompany me to the annual Bassmasters Classic which the prestigious 175,000-member Bass Anglers Sportsman Society will sponsor at some mystery lake in late October. None of us would know where we were going when we climbed aboard a chartered jet to take us to this "World Series of Bass Fishing." Before that jet ever took off, I could name two lures that every one of those contestants would be using much of the time in the hope of nailing down the $15,000 top prize.

What lures will they be? They are the plastic worm and the spinnerbait: two lure types which collectively probably put as many fish in live wells and on stringers around this country as any other ten lures you could name—all lumped together.

I do not suggest that the bass man should limit his lures to these two types. For myself I don't, and I think it would be a mistake for anyone who did. Part of the

A plastic worm and a light slip sinker can be one of the most effective bass lures. Author Stan Fagerstrom proudly displays a deep-bodied fish that was fooled by a worm.

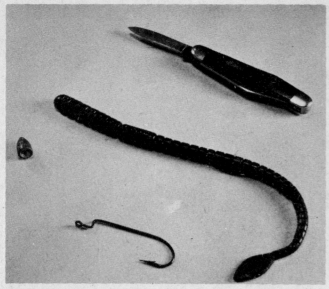

To rig a weedless worm "Texas Style," you need a slip sinker, hook, plastic worm, and knife.

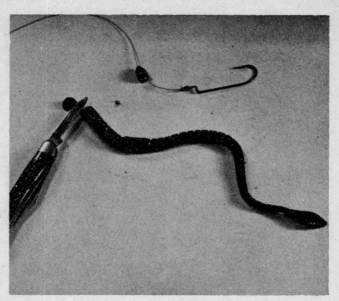

Slip the sinker on your line and attach the line to the hook using a strong knot. Cut the tip of the worm so that the sinker will fit snuggly.

fun and fascination of bass fishing is selecting the right bait for the right time and place. There's no single lure which will always get the best results and that includes the plastic worm and the spinnerbait. But those two artificials are just as dependable as anything you are ever going to find. This has been proven over and over again in the face of some of the keenest competition and toughest conditions bass fishermen have ever known.

Let's look first at the spinnerbait. The name itself is a bit misleading. Lots of bass fishermen call any artificial lure a "bait." The first time I heard the name spinnerbait was among bass fishermen down South many years ago. The term stuck and now you hear it around New York, in Minnesota, Iowa, or way out West where I hang my own fishing hat.

The spinnerbait looks like a spread-out safety pin with a spinner on one end and a hook on the other. That's an over-simplification, of course, but in the early days, before these lures were readily available, some of us really did fashion spinnerbaits out of large safety pins.

Just what is it that makes this lure so highly effective? For one thing, it can be used over a wide range of fishing conditions. The spinnerbait is a tremendous lure to fish in open water off the edge of cover. Drop a spinnerbait next to an old log, a clump of brush or a pile of rocks, let it sink to the desired depth, then give it a couple of quick flips. Get a good grip on your rod before you do.

You don't have to restrict spinnerbait fishing to the edge of cover, although it's the best way to start. Many

makes can be fished right through hazards that would hang up most lures before they could be retrieved three feet. The reason they can is the long metal arm to which the spinner or spinners are attached. This arm serves as a weed guard. Once you learn how to handle one of these lures, it can be brought back through brush and will darn near climb trees.

You can fish a spinnerbait right down on the bottom. I often use a Bushwhacker that way in the fall of the year and during the cold water of winter. Then you can let the spinnerbait sink and work it along just fast enough to make the blade slowly flip over as it thumps its way back to the boat.

Hang around where bass men gather and eventually you'll hear them talking about "buzzing" these lures. The process really isn't very mysterious. The lure is reeled back fast enough to keep the blade working right up next to the top, sometimes breaking water, but more often bulging the surface as it comes racing back just out of sight.

There's something about a fast retrieve with the spinnerbait which sometimes makes a bass madder than hell. Old lunker lip has never been known to have the best disposition and those mean eyes of his look like he's been snakebit when they spot a spinnerbait streaking away from the territory he has staked out for his own. Never overlook spinnerbait buzzing if you're operating along the edge of heavy pad cover. I like to keep my boat 30 or 40 feet out from the edge and pitch the lure into the little pockets and indentations one invariably finds in the pad fields. Don't let the lure sink. The fast

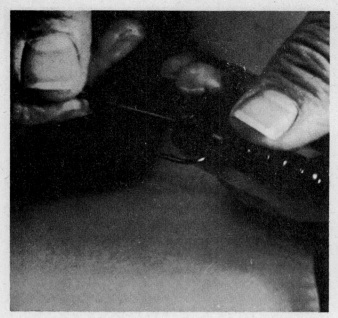

Insert the hook through the head of the worm and bring the point out about one-quarter inch down in the body.

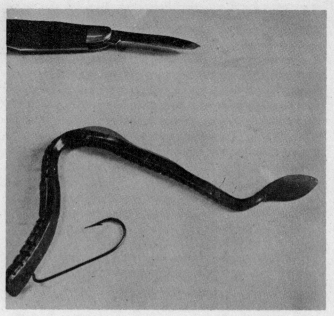

Pull the hook through the worm until only the eye of the hook remains in the worm.

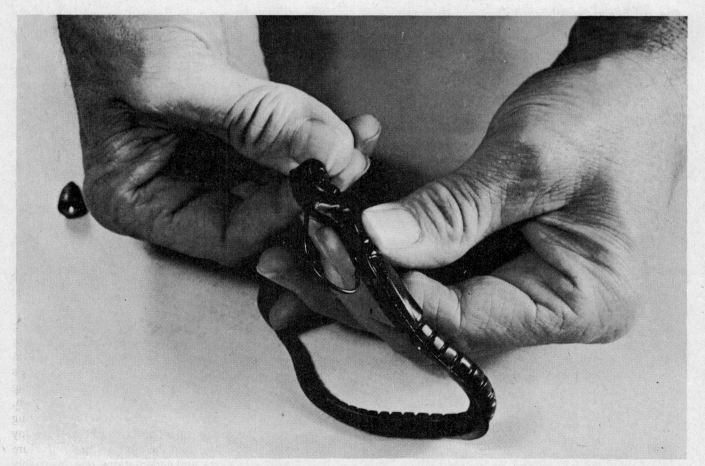

Push the point of the hook into the worm, making certain it does not go all the way through the plastic body. The result is a deadly weedless lure that is among the most effective bass catchers.

retrieve reels are a great help in keeping a spinnerbait up where it must be for best results with this fast action technique.

Not all spinnerbaits have those long metal arms I mentioned. A couple of my longtime favorites are the Scorpion and the Tarantula. One day I pitched a yellow Scorpion next to an old piling in one of our Pacific Northwest lakes. It dropped about four feet before I flipped it away. Wham! The seven-pound buster that latched onto it almost pulled my rod out of my hands. I landed that fish, cast again and—blooie. This fish went five pounds. I moved down a couple of more pilings, made another cast, and k-a-w-h-o-p: another seven pounder. I was so fired up by that time I had to run to shore to get my nerves back in their sockets.

I can't give you scientific evidence on exactly why the spinnerbait is so effective, but I can provide proof of what I'm saying. Bass fishermen who have followed my writing in regional and national publications over the years know I'm a believer in keeping written records of every trip made and every fish caught. It doesn't take long, once a fellow disciplines himself to do this, before he's developed his own fishing facts. I'm starting my 22nd year of such record keeping. The spinnerbait has taken more fish for me over that period of time (and I didn't start using it until the early sixties) than any other single type of lure among the couple of hundred I carry in my favorite tackle box.

I can tell you how I watched Bobby Murray walk off with top honors in the first Bassmasters Classic held at Lake Mead, Nevada, in 1971 using a white-skirted, quarter-ounce Aggravator spinnerbait. That's when the lure really started to take hold. Don Butler, Tulsa bass angling whiz, came right back the next year to win first place in the 1972 Classic held at J. Percy Priest Reservoir near Nashville, Tennessee. Don carved his name in the bass fishing hall of fame using his own S.O.B. spinnerbait. That's short for Small Okiebug.

I was down in Alabama in 1974 when Tommy Martin stepped up to the Bassmaster Classic winner's stand to accept a check for $15,000. Tommy proudly displayed the lure that had caught most of his fish. It was a half-ounce Weed-Wader spinnerbait. In fact, four of the top seven finishers in the 1974 Classic used the same lure to outdistance most of their competition. I could go on and on.

No modern bass fishing outfit is complete without a selection of spinnerbaits. When I say selection I refer to blade sizes, skirt colors, lure weights, and lure types. It's the wise bass man who struggles to keep from letting his own preferences constantly dictate the lure he should throw. Let the fish decide. Use a quality snap at the end of your line and change spinnerbaits until you find the color, the size or the blade combination which produces.

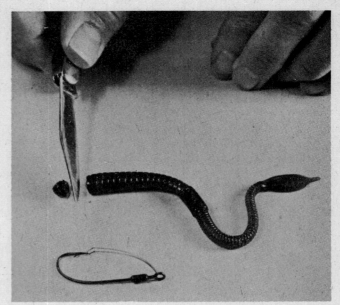
Another way to rig a worm is with a weedless hook. Begin by cutting off the rounded portion of the head.

Rest assured that's not going to be the same day after day and in lake after lake.

After I had great results with a chartreuse spinnerbait in South Carolina a few years ago, I came home expecting to really clobber the bass in my home lakes with the same color. I don't think I've managed to take a dozen fish out of old Silver yet on chartreuse. My home lake gives up most of her bass to yellow, black or brown.

Siltcoos Lake down on the Oregon coast is another of my Pacific Northwest favorites. My top colors in spinnerbaits there have been white or purple. The last time I fished in Alabama it was chartreuse again. And so it goes. Try different spinnerbaits in your own lakes, and it won't be long before you begin to get an idea of just what colors the fish prefer most. Even after you begin to get some definite opinions on what might be most effective, don't start using a spinnerbait of one pattern to the exclusion of all others. Do that and you'll soon find yourself in an angling rut from which it will be extremely difficult to escape.

Spinnerbaits are now available with hammered blades or with special colored finishes. Some anglers even paint their blades black for use in mid-summer night fishing. I personally prefer to use big, bright tandem blades when the water is murky or off color. I'll switch to the smaller, darker hues and single blades when the water is clear and clean.

The spinnerbait has only one hook. Make sure it's needle sharp. The best and most efficient way of doing that is to carry a small file of good quality right in your tackle box. Just a couple of licks with that file, always

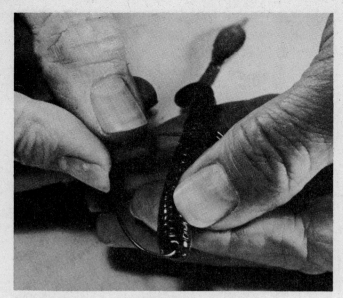

Carefully thread the worm on the hook.

The finished worm should look like this.

working toward the point, and your spinnerbait will be ready when you are.

The second half of the deadly duo is the plastic worm. I doubt that any other artificial lure has been cussed or discussed more than these plastic imitations. Few lures have caused more frustration—or caught more fish.

Show me a guy who really knows how to handle a plastic worm and I'll show you a bass man who is long on patience and who spends more time on the water than the average plug pitcher. Why do I say that? Because one doesn't learn how to use a plastic worm overnight. No lure is harder to develop confidence in than the plastic worm. And, as any experienced lunker lover will agree, until you develop confidence in a lure you aren't going to get many fish with it regardless of how hard you work. Someday, somebody a lot smarter than I am will come up with an explanation of the relationship between confidence in a lure to the number of fish caught. It's there just as sure as I'm punching this typewriter, but I don't pretend to understand all I know about it.

Earler in this article I stressed that you should not limit yourself to just one or two lure categories. I stick by that statement, but I'll contradict it to some extent with regard to the plastic worm. Use the plastic worm exclusively until you truly get the feel of the thing. If you don't go with the worm all the way, the chances are good you'll never master the technique. It's slow fishing, especially in the early stages before that confidence begins to come along.

The worm is another lure which can be fished under a great variety of circumstances, an advantage which undoubtedly has added to its popularity. Most fishermen, even those with considerable experience, rarely think of a plastic worm for shallow water. Yet it can be deadly there.

One of the lakes I fish has lots of shallow pad fields. I have a seven-foot worm rod and an open faced reel loaded with 12-pound test line. This seven-foot stick is sufficiently long with enough flexibility to let me pitch the plastic worm without any additional weight. The line I use on the open face spinning reel is sufficiently small in diameter to allow me to cast thirty feet with no special effort.

I ease through these pad fields with great caution, pitching that unweighted worm about thirty feet ahead of the boat. Now and then I've found bass, some of them darn nice ones, in almost every one of the pockets back in those fields. When I do, I have a picnic with that worm, and I'm not fishing in water more than three feet deep most of the time.

When I fish in shallow water like this with the unweighted worm, I always employ a weedless hook and use a snap at the end of my line. The snap gives just enough weight to take my worm down slowly; having it there makes changing from one lure color to another simple.

My sentiments about color as it applies to plastic worms is the same as I described for spinnerbaits. Why sweat it? Why argue about it? Doesn't it make better sense to let the fish decide? Of course it does! It's all right to have favorite colors. Mine are purple and black in that order. But in no way am I going to stick with

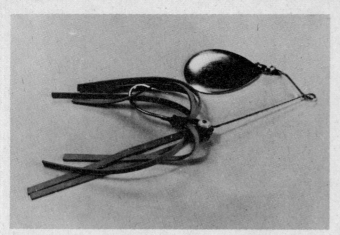

The short arm and large blade of the Tarantula account for big bass.

either one, cast after cast and hour after hour, if something doesn't happen. Change is the name of the game in bass fishing; if you don't already know that, it's a fact you'll discover one day.

In fishing tough cover the plastic worm really comes into its own. I spent a day fishing a bunch of old downed trees and brush with Rayo Breckenridge, a bass-fishing pro from Paragould, Arkansas. Rayo won the 1973 Bassmasters Classic when it was staged at Clark Hill Reservoir in South Carolina. What a pleasure it is to watch that old boy handle a plastic worm. I find myself at a loss for words to tell you exactly how he does it. I do know I caught myself setting my own rod aside from time to time just to watch him as he eased that worm through brush and limbs most of us wouldn't throw into at all. You could sense that Rayo knew exactly what that worm was doing. It was almost as though he was painting a picture with a paint brush. His movements were definite yet delicate, deliberate but almost dainty. And I know darn well some of those bass he caught that day were just as surprised as I was when he would suddenly

Here's one rig the author uses in shallow water. The snap at the head makes it easy to change worms and also provides a little bit of additional weight to take the worm down.

slam back on that short worm rod he uses and they'd have a number one hook pinned through their ugly jaw.

No, I didn't make a mistake when I said number one hook. The day I was with him Rayo was using a six-inch worm and a small worm hook. Incidentally, many of the top professionals use fairly small hooks with their plastic worms. They've discovered they get more hits that way.

Tom Mann, a lure maker from Eufaula, Alabama, has earned a top reputation among professional fishermen. I remember what Tom told me when I had dinner with him and his attractive wife, Ann, the final night of the 1971 Bassmasters Classic at Lake Mead.

"Tom," I said, "those fish were tough to come by out there today, and you were one of the few pros who got a limit. How'd you do it?"

The extended arm on this twin-bladed model makes it particularly weedless.

"The fish were hitting short," he said. "I cut a strawberry-colored worm down to about four inches and used a number two hook, an eighth-ounce slip sinker and a six pound test line. Whenever I felt a fish, I'd tighten up and then hit 'em as hard as I could."

Don't expect to get as many big bass if you stick to the smaller worms. I'm not saying a lunker will never smack a small worm. However, my records and research prove to my complete satisfaction that there is a relationship between the size of the lure you hang on the end of your line and the size of the bass you are going to take out of the water.

I recommend the small worm—especially for the beginner—because it's the one that's going to get the most fish for you, especially until you get the hang of how to use it.

What is a small worm? Six inches is a good start. Get a supply of that size in various designs and colors and go fishing. Leave the rest of your lures home. Give yourself a dozen trips with those worms as your exclusive bait, and you'll wind up a more effective fisherman than you've been before.

Let me give you one tip that will be of great help in learning how to operate the worm or to add to your techniques if you aren't already using it. Whenever you're fishing around cover, try to find something that worm can crawl over. Maybe you're around an old tree with the limbs sticking out of the water in different directions. Position your boat so you can cast over and beyond the cover. Now work the worm back slowly by alternately raising and lowering the rod tip until you feel it touch one of those limbs. Crawl it ahead, letting it creep up on the limb. Now let it tumble forward and drop over. When you feel that lure start to drop free, get a good grip on your gizzard. That's when all hell is most likely to bust loose. This approach, pulling the worm up on an obstruction and letting it fall forward, is one of the most important single points you can ever add to your bag of worm-fishing tricks.

Pay particular attention to the methods pictured in this article on rigging the worm. They are tried and true. Remember when you work with the worm, you are again dealing with a one-hook lure. Remember, too, that if you are using the popular "Texas Style" rigging, the hook must be driven all the way through the body of the worm and then into the tough tissue of the bass's mouth before your fish will be solidly hooked. That's another argument in favor of the small file I mentioned.

I've dealt at length with the effectiveness of bassing's deadly duo. Let me leave you with one final thought. If these two lures are so great by themselves, isn't it

One of the best offerings for trophy bass is a spinnerbait dressed with a plastic worm.

possible that a single lure combining some of the qualities of each might be equally deadly? You can answer that one with a clear and emphatic "yes."

One of the best big bass lures anyone can pack in his tackle box is a spinnerbait with a plastic worm trailer. Note that I said "big bass." I don't think this is something which has dawned on many bass fishermen. But it is a fact. My own research indicates I won't get more bass with the trailer, but the odds are much greater of taking a real lunker.

For years I've used pork rind with spinnerbaits. The reason is because I consistently take bigger fish when I do. I'm finding the same thing is true of the plastic worm trailer. Last season some of the very best bass action I had came on a yellow-skirted spinnerbait with a yellow Tiger Tail plastic worm trailer. The Tiger Tail is a six-inch worm with just one little crook in the hind end. Drop the combination into the water alongside your boat, and watch what happens. Up front the blades of the spinner are whirling and vibrating to provide sight and sound. The plastic worm with that fluttering little tail is swimming along behind. Look at it yourself. You will know without casting the thing that it's going to catch fish. Give it a whirl this season and see if it doesn't up your score, especially on larger bass.

In a way I envy the bass man who has never worked with the spinnerbait or plastic worm. He's got an opportunity to open the doors to some of the best bass action he'll ever enjoy once he masters the techniques necessary for one or both. Most of the time if you can't get your share of fish using bassing's deadly duo, there just aren't many bass around to be had!

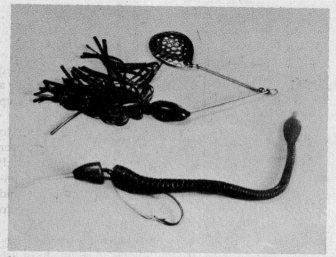

No two lures account for more bass than the spinnerbait and plastic worm.

Emergency Repairs for Fishing Tackle

by Bub Church

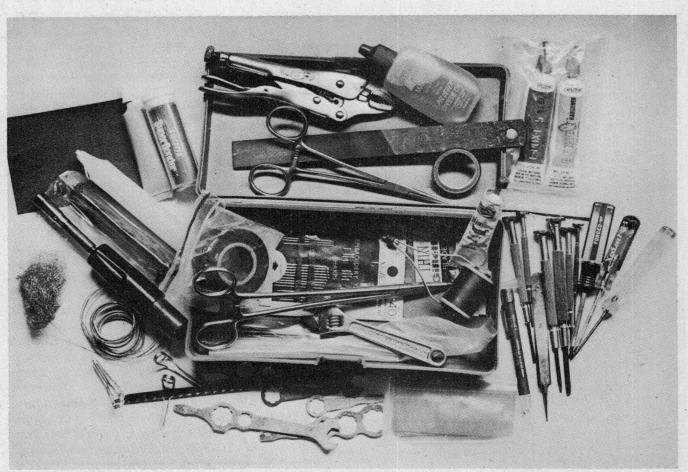

It's amazing how much can be crammed in a small box if you take the time to fit each item carefully. This emergency repair kit measures 8 inches by 4 inches and has been used in many parts of the world.

With solder and a tiny torch, you can make a number of repairs.

Spare parts for reels and extra drag washers are "must" items and should always be carried with you.

Murphy's Law, probably formulated by a fisherman by the name of Murphy, warns that if something can go wrong, it will. He was probably thinking of fishing tackle when he uttered his famous statement.

His thesis can be expanded easily. Anyone who has pursued the piscatorial pleasures for any length of time knows that the longer the distance from the source of spare parts or replacement items, the greater the chance of a malfunction. You can almost bet that if you're in one of the remote camps where the fishing is legendary, a rod or reel will immediately cease to give you service.

Tackle problems aren't limited to fishing hotspots in the obscure corners of the globe. They can occur only a short distance from your home during the couple of hours you are at a local lake before going to work or when you are enjoying a day on a party boat offshore.

Most breakdowns aren't as serious as you might suspect, especially if one studies the situation carefully, uses some common sense, and has the necessary tools and spare parts at hand to achieve the required emergency repairs. In the field, it it not always important to restore the broken tackle to its original condition. Instead, the primary objective is to get the equipment back in service with a minimum of effort.

There is no substitute, of course, for preventative maintenance. Rods and reels should be inspected and cared for after each trip. In spite of your best efforts, however, things are going to go wrong and, even though you are not a skilled mechanic or a craftsman in a rod building plant, you can still fix your tackle. Whenever you go fishing, you should always have at least one backup outfit with you. If you are traveling a considerable distance, you might want several rods and reels plus duplicate accessories. Nevertheless, even with extra tackle, you will want to put your

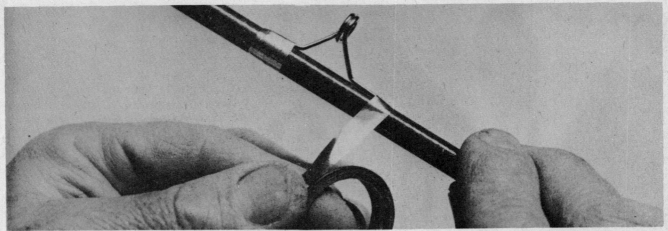

Although any type of tape will work in an emergency, Mylar tape is strong and has stretch, enabling you to wrap a guide neatly. In the field, it's better than using a bobbin to wind the guide on.

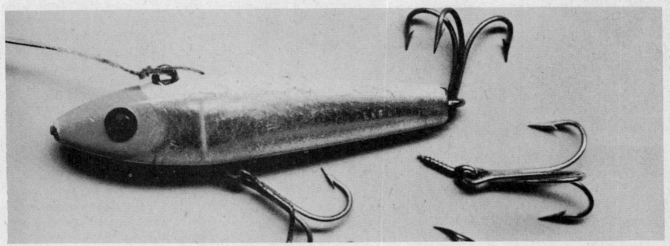

If you carry replacement treble hooks for your favorite plugs, you can put them back into service quickly. Trebles with open eyes can be put on with pliers; then the old hook can be cut off.

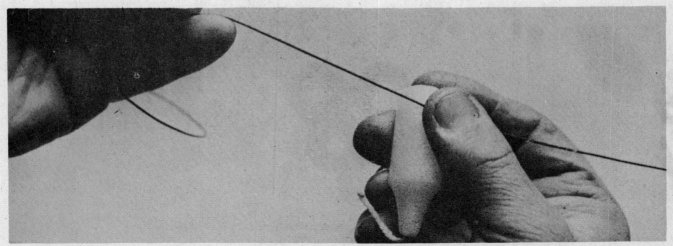

That candle that you carry for an emergency is parafin and will do wonders in dressing flyline that won't float. Drag the flyline across the candle and wipe off the excess with a cloth or your hand.

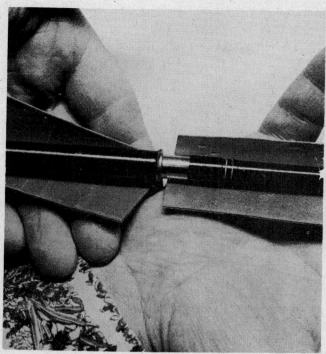

When you've tried to separate a ferrule and can't, grip the rod with two pieces of rubber tape as shown. It can make a difference. If that fails, wrap the tape around the rod and something's gotta give.

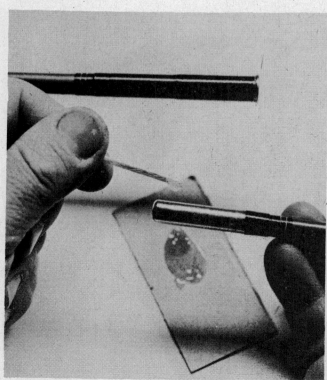

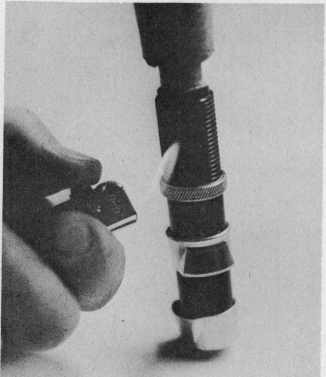

If you are plagued with a loose ferrule while fishing, take a little epoxy and glue the male section in the female section. You'll be able to fish with the rod and the ferrule will have to be replaced anyway when you get home.

Miracle sticks can also be used to replace a ferrule, tiptop, or reel seat. Heat the stick (top photo), apply it to the rod, and let it cool. Then, apply heat to the reel seat (ferrule or tiptop) and slide it on (bottom photo).

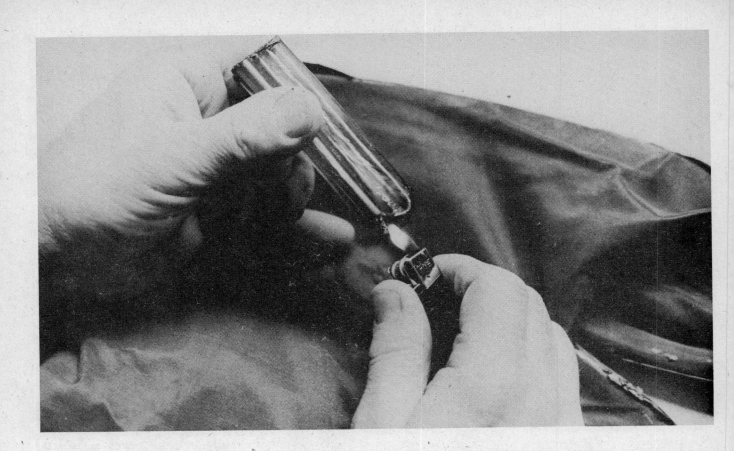

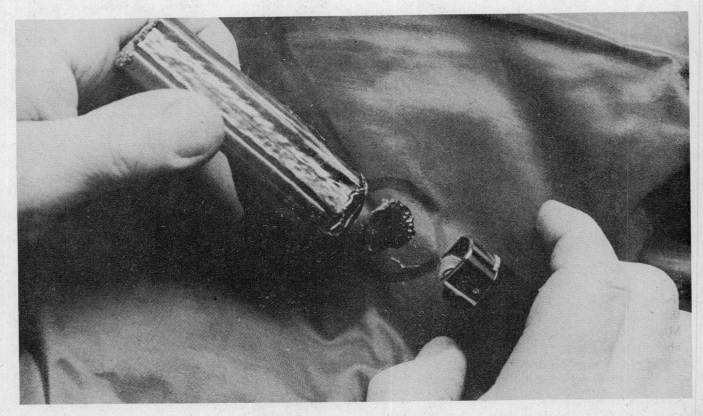

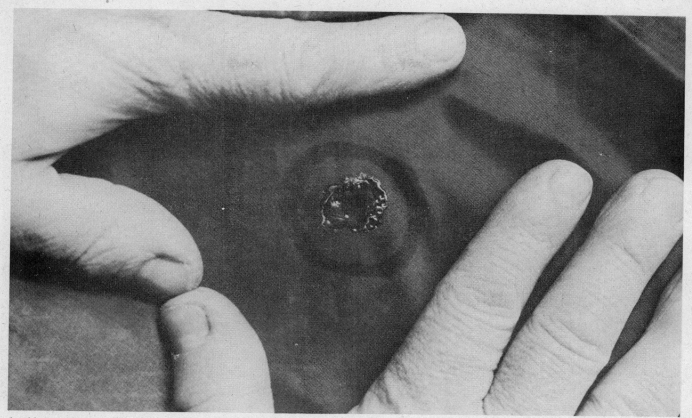

Leaking waders are the nemesis of many fishermen. They can be fixed easily and effectively with today's adhesives. Heat the patch and dab it over the tear or hole. The finished patch will probably be stronger than the original boot or wader material.

primary outfit back in working order.

The place to start is with a tackle repair kit. There is no universal formula that applies to all anglers or all situations. Experience will help you to build your own, but you might get some ideas from the one I carry. This kit is always ready to go and I never "borrow" a tool from it. Whenever I go fishing, I automatically pack it, knowing that the needed parts and tools are inside the box. No matter whether you do your fishing around the corner or around the world, your tackle repair kit will be the most valuable item you can pack.

The trick is to make the kit effective, yet to keep it small enough so that it will not take up much room. Mine is tailored to fit in an unbreakable plastic box that is 8 inches long and only 4 inches wide. In addition, I always carry a pocket knife and a pair of fishing pliers in a holster on my hip. Both of these tools are very handy.

It is amazing how many tools and parts you can cram into a small space. You may have to jockey the contents several times before everything fits, but you can cover major breakdowns with the items you pack in a small box.

The two most probable requirements are the ability to take mechanical equipment apart and put it back together again and a method for gluing or taping something that breaks. The balance of the tools in the kit fill a variety of other needs on somewhat of a random basis.

In addition to the pliers on my hip, I carry a pair of vise grips in the kit. There are also hemostats and needle holders which are really miniature vises. Tweezers (jeweler's and scientific) will hold delicate parts. A small adjustable wrench can be a blessing when you have to remove a nut. It also sense to include the wrenches that come with each reel you own. They don't take up much space, and they will fit the reels precisely.

You can never have enough screwdrivers, but the box is small. For reel repairs, you'll find a set of jeweler's screwdrivers invaluable. Add one small driver with a larger handle and one small Phillips screwdriver. A larger handle will give you leverage if a screw is pitted or corroded.

A small hacksaw blade can be a lifesaver, and you might want to consider a fine file. My own needs dictate splicing wire for dacron line, hollow tubes for tying the nail knot, bait rigging needles, regular sewing needles, and a fly-tying bobbin with thread. Don't forget lubricants such as reel oil.

In the field, when something breaks, you will have to tape it to-

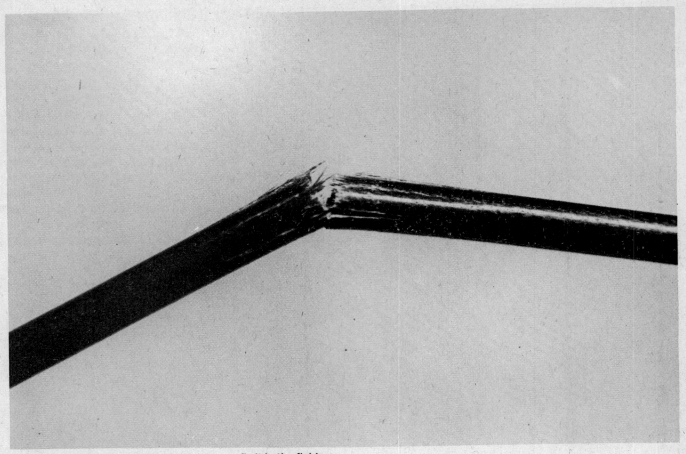

If you break your only fiberglass rod, you can fix it in the field.

gether or glue it. Space-age adhesives have made this job much easier, and it pays to carry a variety of glues with you. Five-minute epoxy can be used for a number of tasks. A rubber-based cement such as Pliobond is more flexible and has other uses. The new Miracle sticks that can be heated with a flame will repair countless items. And, there are other adhesives such as Loctite for screws or nuts which keep backing off or the Super Bonder that will glue practically anything in seconds.

You'll need at least two types of tape: vinyl electrical tape for most jobs and some silver Mylar tape for putting on rod guides if they happen to fall off or the windings are cut. I also carry a rubber tape that I use in unloosening two parts that are stuck. You can also tape some wide duct tape to the outside of your repair kit.

If you need it in the field, it's there and can be peeled off easily.

Without critical spare parts, all the tools in the world may not help. If you break a guide on your rod, you can fashion another one from a safety pin or paper clip. However, there are flexible foot tiptops available that can be used as guides or as tiptops. These will fit a number of different size rod blanks. If your tiptop breaks, all you have to do is tape one on and you can continue fishing.

Any reel repairman will tell you that certain parts are more likely to fail than others. On spinning reels, you can bet on bail springs. Plug reels may require a new pawl; you might have lost a centrifugal brake. If spare parts came with your reel, carry them with you at all times. You can also buy parts separately and it pays to have an adequate supply in your

emergency kit. If you fish for heavy-weights with light tackle, you must already know the importance of a smooth working drag. Usually, all that is necessary in the field is to replace drag washers that have become worn or glazed. Always carry an extra supply.

An emergency repair kit is a highly personal item that seems to grow and grow. Each time you are in a situation and don't have the proper tools or parts, you will feel inclined to add them to your kit when you get home. Perhaps you'll tote a few extra things with you, but over a period of time, the kit will become balanced and remain at a manageable size. You will certainly use all the available space in the box. But use it you will, ultimately finding you have to fix the hinges to keep it from bursting its seams.

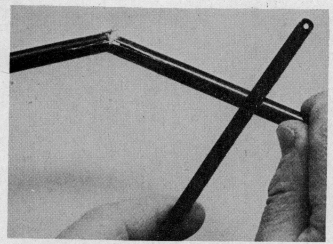

Using a hacksaw blade or other cutting tool, cut a section of rod in front of the break.

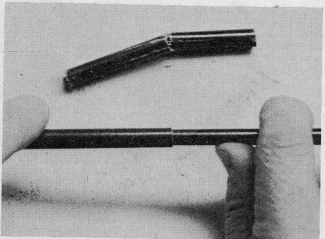

The trick is to make the tip section fit in the butt section. You may have to do it in stages to achieve proper fit.

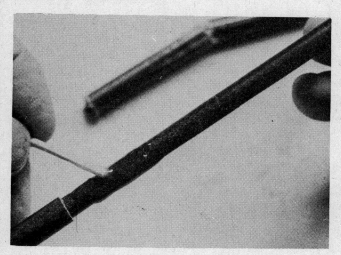

Mix some epoxy and coat the tip section with this glue.

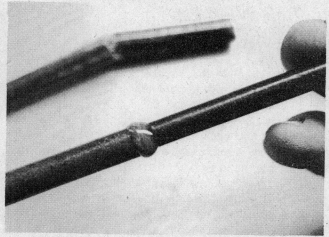

Insert the tip section into the butt section. Wipe off any excess glue that has squeezed out.

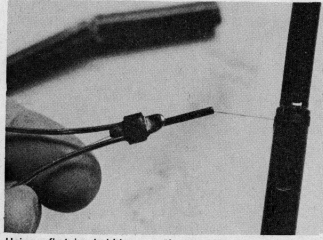

Using a fly-tying bobbin, wrap the outside of the butt section for an inch or so to strengthen the repair.

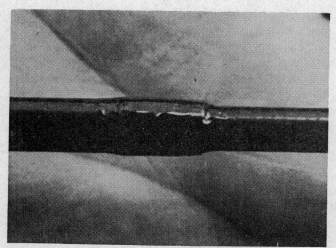

Put epoxy over the thread and over the spot where the rods join. The strength of this repair will amaze you.

TOOLS AND TECHNIQUES

A PAGE FROM THE PAST:
Using Antique Rods, Reels and Lures

by Bob Whitaker

Easing into a cactus-studded cove on Arizona's San Carlos Lake, I speculated on what lure an angler might have tossed in 1926 as he worked the same bassy shoreline of what then was a brand new Gila River impoundment.

A flurry of surface excitement at the far end of the cove brought me back to reality and indicated bigmouths were slashing into schools of threadfin shad — a favored food of Arizona largemouth bass.

Picking up a stubby, 60-year-old antique casting outfit, I lobbed a battered cedar plug smack into the melee. A bass smashed the lure almost instantly. With fumbling fingers, I tried to set the hook, hand levelwind the line, avoid slack, and still outslug three pounds of fighting bass.

"I never saw a big bass pop out of the water so fast," chided my partner, Gene Henry. "What were you more afraid of losing: the fish or the lure?"

"I'll admit to this," I replied shakily. "I now have far greater respect for those oldtimers who had to levelwind line with their fingertips, while tending to all the other essentials in getting a bass up to the net!"

Gene and I are fishing-tackle collectors. We picked this spring morning in 1974 to test whether ancient brass reels, steel rods and forgotten old wooden lure patterns could still take bass as effectively as they did a half-century before.

Our 15-foot bass boat didn't hold a single tackle item less than 40 years old as we launched near Mohave Point and began probing the first brushy cove. In fact, some of our collection of reels dated back 100 years and a few priceless lures were in the 70-year class. All this made the test authentic.

Inside creaky metal and leather-covered tackle boxes, we had a prize assortment of handmade Meek, Talbot, Milam, and other famous non-levelwind casting reels of the past. Lure trays displayed an extinct collection of wood and metal baits.

We decided on this unique experiment one evening at my home in Phoenix, while Gene and I were timing handle spins on a pair of ageless veterans. This once was considered the final test of quality in buying a casting reel. The longer the spin; the better the product.

"Let's make San Carlos the battleground and see if these outfits still can cut the mustard," I suggested, counting the seemingly endless handle spins of a 90-year old Meek & Milam. "The reservior has a booming population of bass this year, and it also was a bass-fishing favorite back in Depression years."

Gene grabbed the bait like a hungry bigmouth, and we began setting ground rules for the test.

"We'll limit ourselves to reels without levelwinds, vintage steel or wood rods, and use only glass-eye lures that no longer are in production or made in modern plastic versions," outlined my partner.

We decided to make it a two-day adventure and schedule the trip during quiet weekdays. This would ensure conditions more closely matching those an angler might have found rowing into the same cove in the late 1920's.

Two weeks later, we had our camper parked along the gravel shoreline of this excellent Arizona bass reservoir, located some 100 miles southeast of Phoenix. In soft pre-dawn light, I nervously rigged a 5-foot "Luckie" brand tubular steel rod. The rod had wire-wrapped agate guides and carried a 1926 catalog price of $3.75. Attached to the nickel-plated reel seat was my prize Meek

Lineup of old reels traces baitcasting development. Top row: (l to r) Talbot Ely, Shakespeare Professional, Meek #3, Beetzel (early flip-out style level wind, patented in 1916), Shakespeare double-track levelwind (1902). Bottom row: hard rubber and silver Abbey & Imbrie, unknown brass reel, with drag button on top (circa 1870), Meek & Milam (1870's), Gayle (with 1898 date engraved with owner's initials), and a Winchester #4256.

Blue Grass #3 (the number denoted the size) — as smooth a running reel as was ever made. The Blue Grass was built by B.F. Meek, one of the original Kentucky watchmakers who helped develop multiplying gears and invented a host of other features found on baitcasting reels sold today.

My Meek was loaded with 20-pound braided nylon. This was our only break with the past. Anglers of that era had yet to discover nylon, generally relying on braided silk or even linen. Earlier lines were made of woven horsehair. Nylon was developed shortly before World War II, inspired in part by Japanese threats to cut off America's silk supply.

Gene and I decided to schedule our adventure during late spring so we could jump overboard in the warm desert impoundment and retrieve any irreplaceable old lure that might get hung in the brush.

Studying the shelving gravel shoreline in the first cove, I plucked a South Bend Woodpecker lure out of the tackle box. This topwater plug was described in a 1925 catalog as being a concave-collar "fishgetter." The wooden collar imparted a gurgling sound as the cigar-shaped plug was jerked across the surface. It listed for 85 cents. Surprisingly, fishing lures are one item in the economy that haven't soared in price over the past 50 years.

Gene dug deep in his rusty box and came up with a weird-looking bass fooler called the Vacuum. This lure was listed in a 1918 South Bend catalog as a surface bait designed "with alluring power due to unusual shape and curves, which causes a wave to pass over the wings." The Vacuum resembled the power unit of a Hoover sweeper and came in a choice of white, dragonfly or frog colors.

My partner's casting outfit consisted of a black-enamel, tubular steel rod of unknown make in the same popular 5-foot length of the 20's. It had three sections, joined by brass ferrules. Guides were agate, with a stirrup tiptop. The "medium-stiff" action rod sold for $2.75 in a 1927 hardware catalog.

Gene's reel was a slick-running 4-Brothers Capitol model, with hard rubber end plates and German silver frame. It featured steel pivots and a single ivory handle.

After a congratulatory handshake and photographs of my first bass of the day on the red and white Woodpecker, Gene dropped his dragonfly-colored Vacuum plug next to a flooded mesquite tree. A pound-size bass charged out of the brush and sucked up the wedge-shaped lure, perhaps the same as his ancestors might have done when Coolidge was president and Henry Ford was designing his first Model A.

Gene bubbled with excitement as he released the yearling bigmouth. We continued casting and striking

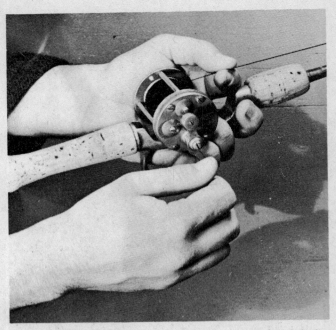

Cradling position is best for levelwinding line by hand during retrieve. Reel is a Meek Blue Grass #3. This was the most popular size for baitcasting.

smith George Snyder was fruitlessly trying to cast a minnow out to feeding bass in the Tennessee River using a simple single-action reel of the period. Frustrated, Snyder returned to his workbench and began building a fishing reel with double-multiplying gears, hoping to add distance to his casts.

Flinging bass plugs had nothing to do with Snyder's achievement. Artificial spoons didn't arrive on the scene until 28 years later when J.T. Buel began manufacturing a lure designed around a lunch spoon that he dropped in a lake and saw being attacked by a fish. Then, just before the turn of the century, James Heddon sat on the bank of Michigan's Dowagiac River and whittled out what is commonly considered the world's first artificial bass plug, initiating a mania of lure-inventing that continues to this day.

Snyder's first multiplying-gear reel essentially opened the modern era of bass fishing. Yet it wasn't fame that spurred him on. The watchmaker from Bourbon County simply wanted to get his casts out to those distant river smallmouths.

Word of Snyder's invention spread to Frankfort, Kentucky, and straight into the ears of another frustrated bass angler, Judge Mason Brown. Brown obtained one of Snyder's multipliers and brought it back to Frankfort, asking local watchmaker Jonathan Meek to duplicate it. History tells us this occurred during the 1830's; by 1840, Jonathan and his brother, Benjamin Meek, had further improved on the Snyder reel and were selling their hand-crafted multipliers for upwards of $50, a small fortune in those days.

The early Meeks were made of solid brass, but German silver later was used because of its hardness. Most reels featured quadruple (4 to 1) multiplying gears. Meek also is credited with being first to install jeweled end bearings on reels.

Ben Meek and his teenage apprentice Ben Milam joined forces in 1853 and began stamping their reels Meek & Milam. Meek later left the reel business, only to return in 1882 when he moved to Louisville. The firm continued making reels labeled B.F. Meek & Son until the business was sold to the Horton Manufacturing Company, which produced reels with the Meek name up until World War II. B.C. Milam & Son continued making bait-casting instruments until 1927. These later reels were made by his son Jonathan.

Other makers of fine fishing reels in those early years included William H. Talbot, who moved from Frankfort, Kentucky, to Nevada, Missouri, where he built some of the finest and most expensive baitcasting reels. Talbot later shifted his operation to Kansas City and continued making reels into the 1920's.

George W. Gayle was another Meek apprentice. He

bass, amazing ourselves at the way these modern bass clobbered our enameled antiques.

We caught on fairly fast to levelwinding line with our fingertips. The trick was using thumb and index finger of the same hand that cradled the rod and reel. Learning to do it without watching the reel was tricky, but essential to learn in topwater plugging.

These ancient outfits were capable of extreme accuracy. In case you are wondering why such precision tackle isn't manufactured today, the brutal fact is that a handmade Meek probably would have to sell for over $500, considering modern labor prices.

Even the cheap tubular steel rods we used had a delightful, yet different feel from either glass or bamboo. They seemed to have a stiffness that came to life when the steel rod was "loaded" with a lure. The biggest problem with steel rods was their fragility and readiness to take a "set."

It took less than a hour for us to develop pinpoint accuracy in dropping lures within inches of stumps and overhanging limbs. We couldn't have done better with any tackle manufactured today.

As the sun peeked over the eastern mountains on the San Carlos Indian Reservation, surface action slackened and we took a coffee break to ponder what lures to use next and discuss the development of bass tackle over the past century and a half.

Bass tackle as we know it today was born in the tiny river hamlet of Paris, Kentucky, where in 1810 silver-

Ancient rods and reels include Heddon 3-15 reel and Heddon matching solid-steel South Bend 5-foot rod; Meisselbach Tri-tubular steel rod; 4-Brothers reel and black enamel seam-steel rod; first South Bend anti-backlash reel (model 1131) and part reel and black enamel rod.

began building handmade reels of superior quality in 1882, with his son continuing the business through the 1940's. Other important names in the development of baitcasting reels include Abbey & Imbrie, vom Hofe, and Shakespeare.

Bass rods were limber and lengthy before the turn of the century because they were designed to toss minnows. Kalamazoo-style (overhead) casting with artificial lures called for using a shorter rod with more backbone, and these began replacing the whippy Henshall-style rods for bass fishing following Heddon's discovery that bass will hit a wooden imitation.

Greenheart and lancewood were popular for rod construction early in the baitcasting era, but began losing out in the latter 1800's to split bamboo, solid and tubular

steel. Fiberglass came along after World War II and was believed to be the ultimate rod material. Now, fiberglass is being threatened by space-age carbon graphite.

Another popular wood used in rods around the turn of the century was bethabara. In 1903, it still was proudly ballyhooed as "a famous wood for bass or bait rod use — without equal; strong, light and easy casting."

Cedar was the most common wood used in plugs. Lures then were painted in hard-enamel finish that easily chipped when the plug struck a rock or was chewed on by a northern pike or walleye.

After catching bass on a string of ancient "woodies" carrying such famous old names as the original Heddon Dowagiac Minnow (dating to about 1900), Creek Chub Wagtail Chub (1920's), Strikemaster (1929), Wilson's

Early century tackle box, with vom Hofe reel, Meek #3, Meek Bluegrass, Heddon 3-15 and Chamberlain "Hunter" reel displayed in front. Lures hanging from tackle box lid are: Heddon original Dowagiac minnow, South Bend Combination minnow, Woodpecker, Shakespeare minnow, Heddon Gamefisher, and the South Bend Vacuum.

Fluted Wobbler (1915), Heddon Gamefisher (1920), and South Bend Combination Minnow (before 1919), I hit on a possible reason for our remarkable success on these veteran lures.

"Try this for size," I asked Gene, who was caught up in the spirit of a bygone era, switching lures and scoring bigmouths on nearly every change of his battered beauties.

"You know how some brand new lures hit the market and tear up bass for a while until their effectiveness gradually tapers off?"

"Well, just suppose bass actually develop a memory bank on lures and do get accustomed to seeing certain lures in hard-pressed waters, thereby developing a resistance to them. If this makes sense, maybe the reason we are catching fish today is because we are bringing back plugs long since forgotten by the bass," I suggested.

"It's a theory to consider," grunted Gene as he popped his steel rod upward and set the hook in a two pounder. This time he was using a rainbow-colored Crab Wiggler of the early 30's.

Although neither of us took my theory to heart, one fact was clear: our glass-eyed antiques were catching bass on a par with any lure manufactured today, underscoring the fact that many modern designs closely resemble proven patterns developed 50 or more years ago.

The Arizona sun now had brightened the surface, sending bass into deeper water. I decided to switch tactics

and outfits. I slipped a Meisselbach Tripart out of its flannel bag and locked the free-spooler on the reel seat of a 60-year-old Richardson seam-welded steel rod.

Meisselbach also was a well-known early manufacturer of baitcasting reels whose greatest claim to fame was that they made quality reels at a price most anglers could afford. Even today, you occasionally see some oldtimer catching bass on a well-worn Meisselbach Takapart, Tripart, Okey or Simploreel. Meisselbach patents eventually were sold to the Bronson Reel Company, after nearly 50 years of tackle manufacturing that began in the late 1800's. The earliest Takaparts and Triparts were made in Newark, New Jersey; later models in Elyria, Ohio. In 1902 Takaparts sold for $3.75.

Studying a tray of old lures, my eyes next focused on one of the standby baits of early reservoir fishing in Arizona. This was a red and white Rush's Tango Minnow, which a 1915 magazine ad had proclaimed as having "all the wobble, dip, and dive of a minnow in action."

During the 20's and 30's, this wobbling floater-diver accounted for countless strings of bigmouths for anglers who struggled up the tortuous Apache Trail in four-banger automobiles to reach Arizona's bass-rich Roosevelt Lake.

I strung a pair of three pounders and released another in short order on the Tango Minnow, which we decided hadn't lost any of its tango.

Red and white was the most popular color combination for fishing plugs in those early years. Bass anglers felt the same about red and white in fishing plugs as Henry Ford felt about black in his Model A's. In a 1930 classic, *My Friend, the Black Bass,* outdoor writer Henry B. Hawes declared, "If there be a preference, it must be for red and white."

Although red and white isn't quite as popular today among bass pluggers, we discovered the color combo still had magic appeal for bigmouths.

Later in the day and again the next morning we returned to our classic old topwaters, while also checking out several other reels from our collections. One multiplier I particularly enjoyed casting with was a #3 Gayle, made by Clarence Gayle for Von Lengerke & Antoine in Chicago. It still bore the engraved initials of the original owner (a common practice with fine reels) and the 1898 purchase date. Other antique reels on which we took bass included an early Julius vom Hofe (patented in 1885); a solid-brass Meek that may have been one of the first this famed Kentucky watchmaker ever produced; a Talbot Ely model made in his original Nevada, Missouri, plant; an early Shakespeare stamped William Shakespeare, Jr. (before 1916); along with a hard-rubber end plate Abbey & Imbrie reel that was rated top quality in

The author took this four pounder on a Meisselbach Takapart reel and Richardson black enamel rod.

A five-pound largemouth bass such as Grandpa used to catch on tackle similar to what he used.

Dr. James A. Henshall's *Book of the Black Bass* (1885).

Most old reels in my collection were obtained from friends, local flea markets and junk shops. It isn't easy to find them anymore, because the current rage for antique collecting also extends to the memorabilia of a bygone fishing era.

The reels we used those two unforgettable days at old San Carlos sang with a harmony of precision smoothness with every cast. Fine as modern machine-made wonders may perform today, they will never surpass workmanship pridefully built into reels by those early Kentucky watchmakers. It often took a week to produce a single handmade Meek or Meek & Milam before the 1860's.

Gene and I felt a kinship with those master reelmakers of the past as we tested their tackle. We even wondered if Jonathan Meek or Benjamin Milam might have been watching from somewhere out there as we flung our battered glasseye plugs at the bass.

Our adventure proved convincingly that any good lure of yesteryear is just as effective today. It doesn't matter whether the plug is molded of plastic or whittled from aged cedar.

George Snyder set a revolution in motion 165 years ago when he finally reached those elusive Tennessee River smallmouths with a cast from the first multiplying-gear casting reel.

That era is gone forever, but Gene Henry and I recaptured it during fleeting moments at San Carlos Lake when we stepped briefly into the past and took fish on some of the finest tackle the world has ever seen.

CRICKETS, CRAWDADS & KATYDIDS

by L. A. Wilke

You get a line and I'll get a pole, honey,
You get a line and I'll get a pole babe.
You get a line and I'll get a pole
And we'll go down to the old Crawdad hole,
Honey, sugar baby mine.

You may have a multi-story tackle box filled with vari-colored alphabet lures, a set of ultra-quality rods with free-spooling reels and the most sophisticated electronic equipment available on a shining fiber glass boat. But if you really want to catch fish, there is nothing that will outclass the oldest, most dependable baits known since the beginning of time.

That's why the person who uses crickets, crawdads and katydids is called a meat fisherman!

They are the baits that were around when the Pharaohs roamed northern Egypt, through the heroic ages of the ancient Greeks and Romans. They are the baits I grew up with as a boy more than three-quarters of a century ago and which I still like.

I was so young when I caught my first fish I can't remember it. But I was told my father had baited the hook with a creekbank grasshopper and I pulled in a perch. I well remember taking my first catfish on a trotline stretched across the Colorado River in West Texas. It had been baited with a crawfish chased from under a rock near the water's edge.

The big tackle stores don't handle crickets, crawdads and grasshoppers any more, but it's a pretty safe bet you'll find them at the roadside bait shops in the proximity of a good water hole. There are some fishermen who just won't do without them.

Most of the crawfishing is in the South where, for generations, this little crustacean has been the inspiration of folksongs and stories as long as your fishing arm.

Get up old woman, you slept too late, honey,
Get up old woman, you've slept too late, babe,
Last piece of crawdad's on your plate,
Honey, sugar baby, mine.

Down South we call them crawdads, but they have other names. In the North they are known as crayfish, although sometimes they are called crawfish. In the Middle West they are occasionally identified as prairie lobsters, especially when there is a big cookout and the lobster-like crustacean is cooked with bay leaves, caraway seed and other condiments to either add to or take away the flavor of nature.

Directions for cooking them can be found in most of the outdoor cookbooks, but not everyone likes to eat crawdads. They are especially desirable in the bayou country where they grow almost as large as a lobster.

But away from the table and back to fish bait. The crayfish, is a desirable fish catcher in all the major waters of America. The smaller ones, generally found in the East from New Jersey and New York provide excellent bait for trout, bass, and other fish.

There are about 160 different species of crayfish scattered through the United States, of the order *decopda,* in the family of *Cambarinae.* The species are limited, not all being found universally.

In the underwater world, however, they are different than any other fresh-water product. First, they are ugly, with beady eyes. They are mean. They wear dirt well and, like a tractor, they can move forward or backward, or even whirl in a circle. Cornered, they back up, with their soft-shelled tail tucked beneath their body. Feeding, they move along either under or at the edge of water with long antennae-like feelers searching out food, which they capture in their pincer-like claws.

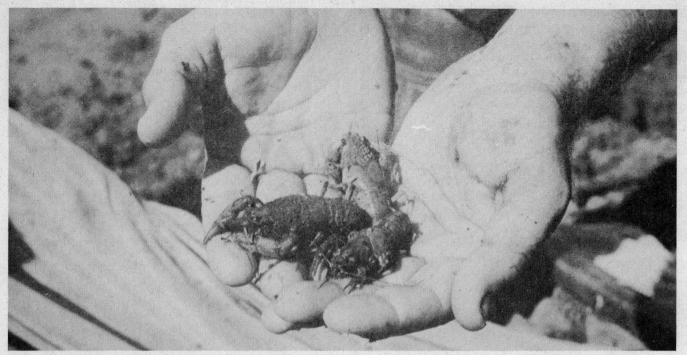

When the crawfish first come out of the muddy water, their bodies are covered with mud, which is easily washed off.

In handling crawfish, always catch them by the back "shoulders." Those pinchers can be painful.

And, when using them for fish bait, look out for those claws. They can clamp down heavily on an unsuspecting finger. If the brute is large and mean enough, it can bring blood. Women just don't like to handle them.

The most practical method of acquiring crawfish is to buy them from bait stands. Depending upon the season and supply and demand, they range anywhere from fifty cents to a dollar per dozen. If you are baiting a trot line limited to 25 hooks, a dozen will be just about right. Put a crawdad on every other hook, and the odd hooks can be baited with live perch, blood bait or chicken entrails. It has been my experience that regardless of how many hooks are baited with the crawdads not all of them will be taken by a big catfish. Like ourselves, apparently they like a variety of food, too.

There are numerous methods of putting a crawdad on the hook. When baiting trot lines for catfish, hook them through the middle of the body, just below the shoulder shell. The hook can be pushed through from either the front or the back. Or, they can be impaled like a live shrimp in salt water, by putting the hook through from either side, just back of the eyes. They don't live quite so long when hooked in that manner, but sometimes catfish are not too particular whether their food is alive or dead.

With due respect to all man-made fishing lures — and I have about as many as anyone — the crayfish is perhaps as fine a bass bait as you can get. In baiting for bass, impale the hook through the body far enough ahead of the tail section to permit movement.

Again, be selective in choosing your fishing waters. Bass eat crayfish regularly and often prefer it. It is a favorite food, especially in waters that support large crayfish populations.

Crayfish usually are plentiful during the summer in shallow water or mudholes like this one.

Crayfish are molters. They will shed their shells several times during the year. A lot depends upon the locale. Although many will be found in running streams, most of them like to sleep, eat and breed in ponds or under rocks at the water's edge.

They thrive on succulent aquatic plants and will eat some animal food, although ecologically they are dubbed as scavengers.

Although crayfish are probably cherished more in the South, they are found from one corner of the United States to the other. No one state seems to have all species. For instance, Tennessee boasts of about 20. Louisiana and East Texas perhaps have the greatest variety. Mostly, they are identified by the fishermen according to size. It takes a trained biologist to recognize the individual species, and this can be done only after long study.

Crayfish are prevalent in all the western states, accord-

ing to the U.S. Fish and Wildlife Service. The species vary according to the habitat, but small crayfish are found in all the principal streams. They are in the Snake River environs from its source near Yellowstone Park to where it joins the Columbia River en route to the sea.

On the other hand, Oregon produces some of the best eating-size crayfish, which are shipped to gourmet restaurants in Seattle.

In the Middle West, crayfish are not so numerous. For instance, of the approximately 160 different species, only six have been identified in Nebraska. There they grow to varying sizes in the meadowlands and canal systems, as well as in the rivers and lakes.

Research biologists for the state of Minnesota report several species of crayfish found in various waters, but there is no artificial production. The natural crayfish there usually have a maximum of less than 2½ inches by late

When crawfish are dumped into a holding container they are almost constantly on the move. They simply do not like confinement.

October. During June and July they range from ¾ to 1½ inches in length. Thus they become ideal baits for walleye and trout. Fishermen peel the shell off the tail and thread them on the hook for sunfish.

Crayfish are killed by pollution, which has reduced some of the population in New York, New Jersey and even as far south as Tennessee. There was a heavy die-off in eastern Tennessee several years ago. Some thirty species are found in the waters of that state, thriving in mud ponds and along the rocky streams of middle and western Tennessee.

Many live in the general vicinity of the TVA lakes. Although plugging provides most of the fishing in these lakes, there are still old-timers who use crawdads. They are a prime bait for smallmouths and their abundance helps bass to grow quickly.

Without a doubt, the greatest variety are found in the waters of Missouri, Oklahoma, Louisiana, Texas and Arkansas. There is considerable propagation in each of these states, especially in Texas and Louisiana. Extra large crawdads abound around the bayous of Louisiana and the Cajuns have learned to prepare them with all the skill to make them competitive with shrimp and lobster. Generally speaking, if the crawdad could only outgrow its ugliness, it would be considered one of the finest-tasting foods. Many women, however, turn up their noses because the crawdads they have seen are so ugly.

What you gonna do when the crawdads die, honey?
What you gonna do when the crawdads die, baby?
Sit on the bank until I cry,
Honey, sugar baby, mine!

Several species are found in the western Colorado River from one end to the other. Seems the farther south they go, the bigger they get. Some excellent specimens have appeared in the vicinity of the famous London Bridge, which was removed from the Thames River in England to Lake Havasu in Arizona.

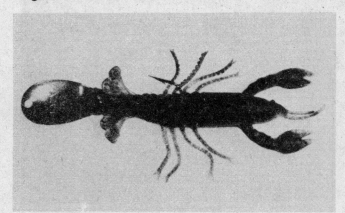

Some manufacturers make plastic crawdads.

Grasshoppers are among the most destructive insects in the world.

They also are found in much of the country traversed by the Green River as it flows from high on the Continental Divide, through Wyoming to the Flaming Gorge Reservoir, and on down to its confluence with the Colorado.

Fishermen say they are not too plentiful in the vicinity of Lake Powell, where much of the area is rock and desert.

With the building of many dams to create new reservoirs, the crawdad, which has lived in some of the small holes along West Texas streams, are even more plentiful now. Also, there are about 300,000 farm ponds in Texas. When one of those gets started in crawdads, the fishing gets better.

Some hefty ones also are found in the Rio Grande, especially through New Mexico, where a portion of the Elephant Butte Reservoir is known as "the jungle."

Farther downstream where irrigation is prevalent in the Messila Valley, they are in irrigation canals and drainage ditches. They grow larger in the vicinity of Amistad on the Rio Grande, near Del Rio, and really huge in Falcon Lake, a short way up from the Gulf of Mexico.

I heard the duck say to the drake, honey,
I heard the duck say to the drake, babe,
There ain't no crawdads in this lake,
Honey, sugar baby, mine.

Probably the only opposition to the crayfish comes from fish hatchery operators. As a rule, the fish hatcheries are located near a small running stream or other lowland property. This is naturally a good area for crayfish.

Thus it doesn't take long for them to infest the hatchery waters and to compete with the young fish for food, burrowing into the embankments or undercutting dirt dams. Biologists have found several chemicals, however, that are not harmful to the fish population, but which eliminate the crayfish.

Throughout much of the South, however, there are crayfish farms where they are cultivated throughout the year. Most of these are strictly retail outlets, but, in some parts of southeast Texas, Louisiana, Alabama, and Georgia crayfish are produced on a wholesale basis.

Some say the crayfish came along with creation, and a resemblance is found between its appearance and the first life in the world. It is interesting to note that when the world was created, there were four rivers in the Garden of Eden. The Lord had made Adam and gave him the responsibility of naming all the creatures. In time Adam got tired of sitting on the banks of the Euphrates giving names to each new creature. He was lonesome and needed help. When he went to sleep the Lord took one of his ribs and made Eve and called her Woman. Since then, man has found less time to fish!

Grasshoppers, or katydids as some of the species are identified, also were known in biblical times when they were thought to be a plague sent by God. Actually, they have been a calamity in many parts of the world, moving in by the millions and devastating crops. Right now, a study is being made in the Texas Panhandle, great farm and ranching country, to prevent another scourge as bad as the one between 1930 and 1940.

Although the earliest plague of grasshoppers, also known as locusts, is recorded in the Book of Exodus, various sections of America have been hit hard by the fish bait in disguise. When the Mormons settled in the Salt Lake area in the late 1800's, a grasshopper plague hit

This life-size hopper perched on a broken limb surveys the food below.

Grasshoppers can devastate the tender tops of grass along roads.

It's easy to catch grasshoppers with a net or by tossing your hat over them.

Cricket housing is easy to provide. Give them water, feed and an old egg carton or two to play on.

A typical commercial cricket container available in most bait stores.

there and threatened to destroy every piece of vegetation. Gulls moved in from the West Coast, however, and ate the hoppers. Understandably, a monument in Salt Lake City has been erected to the gulls.

Scientists say there are about 10,000 species of grasshoppers, katydids or locusts in the world, with some 600 species in the United States and Canada. They tell us that 50 thousand tons of grasshoppers, which is only a small portion of those alive in the United States, each day can deprive 5 million humans of food.

But with all the bad things said about grasshoppers, (or katydids or locusts) you have to agree that they provide another of nature's wonderful fish baits. All fish like them.

The largest catfish I ever took was with a huge, long-legged grasshopper as bait. The most mountain trout I've ever caught or seen caught in a day were taken with grasshoppers.

They are disdained by lure fishermen, although some artificial lure companies make imitations. Many trot-line fishermen use them on their lines and harvest such edible monsters as oversize channel, blue and yellow catfish.

Grasshoppers are so plentiful during the summer months that they have no commercial value. One doesn't have to buy them. Go into any grassy area alongside a country lane, and you'll find all you want.

Perhaps the best way is to go out at night with a good flashlight and a container. The grasshoppers will be out foraging, and you can get all the huge ones you need in a few minutes. Big grasshoppers are best for catfish and large bass. The smaller ones are ideal for bream and crappie, and will catch as many as crickets will.

Some fishermen like to remove the large and strong legs. This reduces their live action which attracts fish. But a big fish won't bother about whether the legs have been removed or not. He'll grab a mouthful and gobble.

Catching small grasshoppers for bream and trout also is easy. Quite a few bank fishermen capture them by throwing a hat or net over them, thus always having a fresh supply.

And don't ever kid yourself that trout won't go for them in a big way. Quite a few years ago, a friend and I were in Colorado. We'd worked several streams without much luck, finally stopping at one little stream, with a forlorn looking house and an old nester feeding a couple of potlicker hounds. We asked him whether there were any trout in the stream.

Several cows and calves were resting about in the shade of some scrub pine trees.

"Oh, yes, there are some good ones there, but you can't catch them this time of day," he said. "Why don't you just take a rest and about 5 o'clock when those cows go down to water you can catch some real nice rainbows." Then he explained that the cattle moving through the grass to the water's edge would chase out the grasshoppers and some of them would fall in the water. The trout knew this and would be there waiting.

"When trout are ready to feed, that's the time to catch them," he opined. And he was right. It took us less than ten minutes to limit out, and we didn't have to hide behind a tree to keep the trout from seeing us. They were intent on those grasshoppers.

Despite the fact that millions are spent each year on grasshopper-control programs, there are still plenty around for fish bait. And there is no better — especially if you want fish to eat.

Despite a somewhat similar appearance, the cricket is an entirely different insect. In fact, there are many species of crickets, too. We are most familiar with the black cricket that moves in hordes at the beginning of fall, and chirps all night to your distraction. Fish will hit this little fellow, but not nearly as well as the gray cricket, which is propagated in great numbers exclusively as a fish bait.

Although crickets also have been around since the beginning of time, commercialization only began in the late forties. At that time, the W.T. Armstrong family of West Monroe, Louisiana, wanted a better supply of fish bait and started an experiment which has grown into the world's largest cricket farm business.

Since then the business has grown until today fish-food crickets are produced by the millions on a wholesale basis. They also are instructing other cricket-hearted fishermen on how to raise and keep them alive and fresh.

Perhaps the most popular rig for cricket fishing is a cane pole, with a six-pound mono line and a small hook, backed up with a split shot and a small cork bobber or quill-type float. The hook is placed under the cricket's collar, just below the head.

While crickets are used over most of the United States, they are particularly popular in southern waters, such as Ozark streams, and in deep East Texas, Oklahoma and Louisiana. When you see a square-end, flat-bottomed aluminum or wooden boat on a lake or stream in the South, you can bet it has a carton of crickets aboard.

All marina bait houses keep crickets in stock. They are easy to care for. Mesh containers also are available, either in cardboard or plastic.

Among other large distributors of crickets are the Carter Farm of Plains, Georgia, and Selph's Cricket Ranch, Desota Station, Memphis, Tennessee.

Walt Disney immortalized the cricket by making Jiminy Cricket the conscience of Pinocchio more than three decades ago. Since then, Mr. Cricket has become the byword of all who fish with crickets today.

PIKE: THE MEAN MACHINE

by Pete Czura

A brisk north wind knifed across Ontario's Sha-buskwia Lake, nullifying the feeble attempts of an early May sun to make the day tolerable. Our bulky down jackets were grudgingly giving up precious body heat to the torturous blasts and the wind-chill factor would have convinced us to head for shore if we weren't so busy fighting northern pike.

With determined speed and fury, the pike on the end of my line had chomped down on a shiny wobbler that teasingly moved away from a weedbed. For a minute, the fish dove away from the boat and stripped line from the reel in healthy chunks. Then, with a suddenness, it reversed direction and arched through the air. Gills rattled menancingly and its head swept from side to side like a dog shaking a rat as the pike tried vainly to dislodge the lure.

Next, it headed for a patch of weeds. My line sliced through the water gathering strands of grass, until the pike finally reached the haven. I raised my rod tip and pulled back, trying to horse the fish out of its hiding place. It was a standoff for a few seconds. Then the fish stormed out and erupted in a new series of tantrums, but everything held together. A moment later I netted a 15-pound northern pike.

Action like this is typical when anglers go after northen pike, one of the scrappiest and toughest of fresh-water fish. I have fished for all kinds of gamesters from dainty panfish to the leaping sailfish during the past 50 years, but in my book, the northern pike easily wins the title as the doggonest, meanest, and savviest fish with which I have ever tangled.

Unquestionably, Canada's lakes boast the greatest populations of pike and, in some remote lakes, there are pike which have never seen a lure. However, there are many in waters in the United States which offer fine northern pike fishing. And, would you believe "Northerns in Dixieland"? It's true. Oklahoma has been experimenting with some pike stockings in selected lakes and the fish have not only taken hold, but their growth rate has been phenomenal.

In Wisconsin, northern pike reach a length of 12 to 16 inches the first year and 18 inches (or more) the second year. Oklahoma fishery biologists have proof that their fish have grown to 20 inches in six months and 30 inches in 18 months.

Some beginning anglers are apprehensive about fishing for northern pike because of the reputation the fish has gained for preying on practically anything that swims.

Jack Parry, outdoor writer from Gary, Indiana, landing a pike in Glen River, Ontario, using a spoon at the edge of the rapids.

TOOLS AND TECHNIQUES

Ed Darnell, with pike caught using cigar butt as lure.

Northerns will strike a variety of lures. This one fell for a lure made from a woman's bra.

It will occasionally take some small waterfowl, but this is rare. Pike can be caught on almost any type of lure because of their voracious appetites and their tendency to clobber anything that moves by. When they make up their minds to strike, virtually nothing will swerve them from their targets.

Superb top-water pike angling can usually be enjoyed in the spring when the pike move into the bays and inlets of lakes to spawn. Inlets deep enough to offer fish concealment are always good spots to probe. If the water is too shallow, the angler should seek out deeper holes where pike may congregate. Incidentally, pike will be spooky and hard to catch if suitable hideouts are not available. Look for them in weedy shallows which contain stands of emergent aquatic plants if the lake does not have an inlet. When fishing weedy areas, use weedless spoons with a tail of pork rind or a shallow-running plug for steady action.

The northern pike is a fish of the shallows and is very seldom taken in water more than 10 to 15 feet deep. (Oh, I know, someone will maintain, "I have caught them in deeper water" — but this is rare.) After the spawning run, they move back into the lakes and take up residence in areas which offer sanctuary from enemies and enable them to ambush prey. They often lie in wait at the edge of a heavy weed bed waiting for an unwary meal to swim by within striking distance.

Speaking of strikes, these fish tend to slam into a lure. If a pike is around, it seems to track an angler's offering like radar and, when it attacks a lure, the hit feels like a mule's kick. The very unpredictability of the pike makes any strike exciting. It can happen just as your lure plops into the water at the end of a 40-yard cast, or midway on your retrieve. The hardest one to handle is the strike near or alongside the boat. It happens so suddenly that you are caught flat footed and that's when Lunkers are missed. There's little cushion from rod and line and, even if the hooks penetrate, the sudden shock often pops the line.

On a short, missed strike, the angler will stare dumbfounded at the shredded line dangling over the spot where seconds before a giant northern pike had erupted in explosive savagery. Usually, the angler is nonchalantly ending his retrieve at that point and then is stunned when a northern storms out of the water to swipe the lure and leader, and wheels back into its domain. Veteran anglers often weave the lure in a figure 8 — just as they would for muskies — before lifting the lure from the water. It's a technique that will frequently account for extra fish.

One of the most maddening characteristics of the pike is their tendency to follow a lure right up to a boat and not take it. In plain sight, I have seen them stare at me balefully as if I had denied them their last meal. Chances of scoring right then are excellent if you get your lure in the water again quickly and jig it in a tantalizing manner. If the fish does strike, it's like watching the end of a play; all you have to do is hang on and land it — if you can.

In the spring when the ice breaks up and the water temperature is around 40 degrees or warmer, look for pike in weedy shallows, bays and coves. Best action usually occurs when the water temperature is between 60 and 75 degrees.

Dinnertime for the northern is during the daylight hours. Mornings, especially between 8 a.m. and 11 a.m. is considered one of the prime fishing times for pike. Another good period is from 2 to 4 p.m. One study indicates there is a definite rest period for pike between 11:30 a.m. and 1 p.m. However, this should not be considered a hard and fast rule, as northern pike — like most fish — can be and have been caught at all hours of day-

light. It all depends upon the mood of the fish, the seasons and latitude fished. In northern Ontario, where the days are longer in the summer, I have often caught pike around 8 to 9 p.m. The pike, however, does not feed at night.

For those of you who prefer to fish with live bait, almost any kind can be used. Large minnows, frogs and salamanders are excellent. A big 12-inch sucker usually is needed when fishing in areas containing trophy-sized fish.

Anyone who has fished for this tiger with fins while using live bait and a float will tell you that the pike's strike is intended to immobilize its prey. After hitting the bait, it will often run with it for a few yards, stop, drop it, then pick it up again head first, and devour the meal. Setting the hooks when your float first disappears is usually a mistake because the northern hasn't taken the bait well enough to get snagged. Wait for the fish to make a

Play it safe! Use a net to land northern pike no matter what the size.

Quiet bays provide an excellent setting for northern pike action. This scene is in Kississing Lake, Manitoba, famous for big northern pike.

When fishing in fast waters, retrieve your spoon slowly for best results.

second move or at least a minute or two (until you feel that the bait and hooks have been taken) before attempting to set the hook.

The northern's environment demands the use of fishing tackle capable of countering the capricious actions of this fish. Your rod must have enough backbone to slam the hooks into the bony, tooth-filled mouth and curb the fish's wild jumps. My favorite northern pike bait-casting rods are 6 feet long with relatively firm tips and plenty of reserve muscle.

The question of what line to use always starts arguments among anglers. A couple of years ago I was fishing for pike in Lake Sakakawea with Al "Frenchy" Plasair of Bismarck, North Dakota. Hubert Green, a third member of our group, had lost several good strikes. This made Al curious.

"What kind of line are you using?" he asked.

"Eight-pound test monofilament," Hubert replied.

"That's not heavy enough for the brutes here," advised Al. "Better switch to a heavier line."

"If you use less than 20-pound test line," he continued, "chances are you will lose most strikes. It's true that some anglers have caught big pike on 4- to 8-pound test line, but I'll bet my best lure that such catches were made in open water where the angler let the fish run and poop itself out.

"All of my bait-casting reels are primed with heavy monofilament line and, to prevent the fish from cutting my line with its sharp teeth, I use a 6- to 10-inch metal leader on the end of my line. With a stout rod and heavy line, I have a 50-50 chance of wrangling a pike out of weed beds."

For the spinning enthusiast, the rod should also be in the sturdy class, at least 6-feet long with a stiff- to medium-action tip. For easier casting, I prefer to use 14-pound monofilament test line.

Incidentally, if you should become bored with bait-casting or spinning for northern pike, try going after them

To land lunkers like these, the author used rod with plenty of backbone and strong line.

with a fly rod. It's a real thrill! Your best bet here is to use a stout 8½- or 9-foot fly rod and a weight-forward floating line with a sinking tip. However, instead of using a metal leader, try an 8- to 12-inch length of 20- or 30-pound test shock leader. Check your leader for nicks after every strike, and replace with a new one at once if necessary.

A few years ago, while fishing at dusk on Whitewater Lake in Ontario, I managed to trick several pike into accepting my offerings while fly fishing in a bay near our campsite. It took a while to find the right color combination, but when I presented a Gapen yellow and black hackle streamer with 3/0 hooks, I immediately got several strikes and landed one over ten pounds.

If you are a fly fishing devotee, I recommend using big salt water-type streamers and bucktails with hook sizes from No. 2 to 5/0. When fished slowly just below the surface, these flies can be very deadly. You can also use big streamers on a spinning outfit by adding a small split shot at the end of the line for casting weight.

When it comes to artifical lures which will tempt a pike to strike, the variety available is mind boggling and usually will confuse a beginning angler. However, the Dardevle and Johnson spoons are perhaps the most popular and renowned pike catchers around. The red-and-white, black-and-white, silver, and frog-design spoons generally are favored in that order. The No. 3 Mepps spinner with a bucktail is another good pike lure. Floating and diving plugs such as the Pikie, Jointed Pikie, Lucky 13, Hellbender, and Bomber are time-honored veterans. The flatfish type of lures such as Creek Chub's Nikie and Lazy Ike rank with the best. When the water is clear, use darker-colored lures for best success.

No matter which lure you offer, keep in mind that it is the *action* of the lure (generally controlled by you) that entices a pike to strike. The flash, dart and wobble of a spoon has been fooling pike for a long time. Spoons perform best in moving water. The action of your spoons can be enhanced by raising and lowering your rod tip during the retrieve. In very fast waters such as at the edge of a rapids, slower retrieves will be most productive.

Another trick is to jig your lure in an up-and-down fashion in the middle of your retrieve by raising and lowering your rod tip. Let the lure stop dead during your retrieve, wait a second or two, resume the retrieve, then pause again. Such an erratic lure retrieve often proves more irresistible than a normal, straight-in retrieve.

Pausing during your retrieve makes the lure seem to flutter like a wounded prey and this will induce a pike to go after what it feels is a crippled, easy meal. The flutter retrieve can be done with many lures.

Big northerns like this 44-incher put up great battles before giving up.

Remove your lure from inside a pike's tooth-filled mouth carefully! Wherever possible, use pliers.

In open water, play the fish by letting it fight the bend of the rod as well as reel drag before trying to bring it in.

Al "Frenchy" Plasair, of Bismarck, plays cavorting northern pike in Sakakawea Lake.

If action becomes slow, switch lures often and vary the speed of your retrieve. Once, just for the hell of it, I raced my lure back as fast as I could and, about midway in my retrieve, a northern pike busted my spoon. If you think I was courting a small fish, you're wrong. After a hectic five-minute scrap, I landed a 22-pound pike.

To illustrate more dramatically the unpredictability of northern pike and its eagerness to chomp on any lure, listen to what happened to a friend of mine.

Al Spiers, of Michigan City, Indiana, is an outdoor writer who will try anything to fool a pike. "Over the years," Spiers told me, "my cronies Ed Darnell, Ted Hill and I have caught big northern pike using odd-ball lures such as cigar butts, twisted can openers, table forks, teaspoons, and other odds and ends."

"One time," Al grinned as he recalled the incident, "I made a bet I could catch a pike with a lure made from a woman's bra. My buddies hooted at the idea, but when I landed a 10-pound pike, they glumly forked over the money."

Al admits he doesn't really know if it was the wiggle of the bra in the water that attracted a pike to strike or the perfume on it.

I'm not much of a trolling fan. Past experience demonstrates that casting covers more likely pike areas and produces — at least for me — more strikes and catches. However, if your casting arm gives out, trolling can sometimes be very productive. Use a floating-diving lure because it can be fished several ways under different conditions. Floating-diving lures are a natural for trolling. The running depth of your lure can be controlled by the length of the line you let out and the *speed* of your outboard. The faster you go, the shallower the lure will run; go slower to make it run deeper. When your lure is bumping and running just above the bottom, it performs the best and is most effective.

A couple of points to remember when fishing for northern pike: First, never try to land a fish by running your hand into its gills. If you do, you are bound to suffer some painful cuts. I have found out it pays to land *any* pike with a net, no matter how small. Also, never put your hand inside a pike's mouth to remove a lure. Instead use a pair of long-nosed pliers or hook remover for a safer job. A pike's razor-sharp teeth can damage your hand.

Don't try to scale a northern pike if you intend to eat it. Instead, remove the flesh from the skin by either filleting, or skinning. Fillets should be cut into serving-size portions and then rolled in egg batter and flour. Pike can't be beat when fried to a golden brown, especially if you dine on a freshly caught fish at a shore lunch.

Although Canada has thousands of lakes containing pike, some of the best have become devoid of pike and especially lunkers. The Indians have been given special permission to net fish in certain lakes and often fail to conserve the resource. What may have been a hot pike lake last summer, can be, by next summer, as barren as the Sahara. I know of one lake where a sixty-pound northern pike has been netted by an Indian. That's nearly 14 pounds over the world record!

For the ice-fishing clan, winter fishing for pike can be productive. In some states like Wisconsin, and Minnesota, the spearing of pike is allowed. However, many anglers are beginning to feel that spearing is not really a sporting way to take any game fish. One of the fiercest opponents of spearing is Jim Peterson, Editor of the *Outdoor News* in Golden Valley, Minnesota. Jim has

waged an annual battle with state legislators against spearing. Each year, Jim and many sportsmen try to convince the politicians to outlaw spearing, without success.

Northern pike are found in many lakes from New York through the Great Lakes region and as far west as Utah. To list all of the fine pike lakes would be impossible but here are a few worth fishing: Alaska, Lake Minchumina and the drainage into Kotzebue Sound; Nebraska, Lake McConaughy; North Dakota, Lakes Sakakawea and Ashtabula; South Dakota, Oahe Reservoir, Sharpe Lake; Minnesota, Leech Lake and the lakes around Ely; Wisconsin, the four northern counties of Douglass, Sawyer, Vilas, and Iron; Utah, Vallecita Reservoir; Oklahoma, Etling Reservoir; Iowa, Spirit and East Okoboji Lakes, Cedar River in Bermer county; Michigan, Potagannissing Bay near Drummond Island and Portage Lake entry at Keeweenaw Bay in the Upper

On surprise strikes near the boat, the advantage swings in favor of the pike.

This is the type of action you can expect when going after northern pike.

Peninsula; Indiana, the Kankakee River, east of Shelby; New York, the St. Lawrence River between Massena and Red Mills, and Sacandaga Reservoir, which yielded the current world record of 46 pounds 2 ounces held by Peter Dubuc.

Most of you, I am sure, have heard the sad stories of lost big fish, and some of you have probably bragged about "the one that got away." Would you believe it is possible to lose a pike over 25 pounds *after* it is in the boat? Don't laugh. It happened to me while fishing Manitoba's Cormorant Lake a few years ago.

On the last day of my trip, I fished in Bathtub Bay and got a tremendous strike. A husky pike inhaled my red and white Dardevle spoon, shot away and, before I recovered enough to grab the reel handles, it had taken plenty of line. After a dogged, five-minute underwater

Never reach out to grab a leaping northern pike. Let your guide net the fish.

battle, I brought the fish alongside the boat where Willie Hunter, my Indian guide, waited to net it.

When he first spotted the fish, Willie yelled, "That's a 30-pounder!" He groaned as he struggled to boat the lunker. Half of the pike flopped wildly outside the net while the head and mouth was tearing the net apart!

"Get it in! Get it in!" I yelled.

"I'm trying," Willie protested, as he barely managed to drag the still fighting fish inside the boat. Just then the spoon fell out of its mouth! What a break, I thought.

Willie dropped the angry and twisting pike onto the the boat deck and turned to start the outboard; because of high winds, we had drifted dangerously close to some big rocks.

As I sat in the bow, I watched in fascinated horror while the big fish continued to thrash around. Finally, it managed to work into the open near the gunwale. On the next flip, the fish reached the edge of the gunwale, teetered for a second and then slipped back into the water.

I felt as if I had been gut-shot. Even sadder, I didn't have my camera ready to record the scene of my big one getting away! Since that time, I have always carried a persuader — a short pool cue — to give my big catches a couple of whacks on the head the minute they are aboard!

Call it by any name, *Esox Lucius,* "snake," "jackfish" or whatever suits your fancy, you won't find another fish that can provide as many thrills as the northern pike. Once you set the hook, it has the disposition of a wildcat that had its hind end turpentined, and that's when you have your hands full with the mean machine!

Author Czura with one northern pike that didn't get away. This 27-pounder was caught in a Manitoba lake.

Shallow Water Fishing Strategy

by Flip Pallot

When you see a fish in shallow water, you immediately know three things: it is there for a specific reason, it feels insecure, and it will leave with little provocation. The search for food that isn't available or accessible elsewhere is the primary reason that will compel a fish to forsake the safety of deeper water and risk the many dangers of the flats. A fish in thin water is constantly aware of its surroundings and, if it even suspects its well-being is threatened, it will streak for the dropoff.

Sharks and other predators are always on the prowl, sometimes in water so shallow that their backs get sunburned. Smaller fish have airborne enemies and could fall victim to the talons of an osprey or the ludicrous, but effective beak of a passing pelican. The tide, itself, can be a killer if a careless feeder gets trapped by rapidly falling water, yet it is the rising tide that lures gamefish to the flats, because smaller creatures in the food chain emerge as water washes over the intertidal zone.

Fishing the shallow, tropical flats is different from any other type of fishing you have ever done. There are no analogies, no comparisons, and no training grounds. It demands total involvement and it has its own set of ground rules. You must find the fish before you can catch them; that is frequently the more difficult aspect. Unless you are a veteran at flats fishing, the best advice anyone can give you is to hire a competent guide for at least a day or two. Guide fees in South Florida average about $100 per day (two anglers in a boat) and, although guides may be expensive, they will save you precious time and help you to learn the basics of where to fish, when to fish, some of the local hazards, and protocol on the flats.

To be successful in shallow water fishing, you must be observant and you must concentrate. Before your guide takes you to the first spot of the morning, he has already considered many things that might not be obvious to you. The tide must be right and the water at the proper depth. There should be proximity to deeper water, the water temperature should be comfortable for the species you seek, and the type of bottom will help to determine the food supply available. In addition, your guide is going to be watching for general activity on the flat such as the presence of sharks, rays, mullet, other baitfish, and even birds.

If a flat is worth fishing at all, you should give it a chance to produce for you, unless you detect signs very quickly that the fish may not be there. One of these is water temperature, below the preferred level for the species you seek, especially during the winter months. Work the area for a reasonable amount of time, but if it doesn't reward you with encouraging signs, move to the next flat you planned to fish.

Silence is the key to approaching any shallow feeding area. The noise from an outboard echoes across the skinny water like a fire alarm, sending most species scurrying to the next county and making those fish that remain extremely skittish. Although electric trolling motors have gained some acceptance in recent years, their use is limited, and there is no substitute for pushing the boat with a long pole. Most of these are made from vaulting poles and feature a Y-shaped piece of hardwood in one end and a rounded or sharp point at the other. They are 16 to 18 feet in length and have a diameter of 1 to 1¼ inches.

The author holds up his world-record bonefish taken on regulation fly tackle.

Poling the boat silently against wind and tide is an art that is difficult to master, but the dividends gained will far outweigh the effort. In learning to pole, remember these basics: 1) always pole on the down-wind or down-tide side of the boat (whichever is stronger), 2) Stand as far back (fore or aft) as possible, 3) establish a "crab" angle that will allow you to track a desired course without having to make continuous adjustments, 4) keep the pole on one side of your body, shifting the position of the pole's foot on the bottom to make the boat go right or left.

Water depth determines where you should pole. Decide on the depth you want to work and then follow the bottom contours to maintain that depth. As the water rises or falls, you will have to adjust your distance, moving farther up on the flat or falling off. One excellent method is to parallel a nearby channel as the water rises and floods the flat. Choose a direction of travel that will most nearly place the sun and the wind at your back or, if these forces oppose each other, pole into the one that is less annoying.

Tide direction also will affect poling. The preferred flats species have very definite movement patterns relative to tidal flow. Generally, tarpon will move through deeper waters *with* the tide and will allow the tide to sweep them up against the shallow perimeter of a flat or bank. These fish will frequently follow the edge of the

Sea trout will take a variety of offerings and can often save the day on some shallow flats.

Captain Nat Ragland releases a permit landed on light spinning tackle.

bank down tide until the bank tapers off or they find food. If you pick the right bank, you can stake out the boat at right angles to the tide and wait for the tarpon to move back and forth in front of you.

Bonefish, permit, and redfish behave differently. They tend to swim *into* the tide, attracted by the scent of food. As the tide rises, these species will ease up over the edge and fan out over the shallows. You can intercept them by poling the down-tide edge of a flat at the proper water depth and look for fish moving up on the flat.

Another technique is to position the boat up tide from a light-colored area where approaching fish can be seen easily. Cut up a handful of shrimp and toss it on the light bottom. Then, wait for your quarry to find it and cast when you see the fish. Bill Curtis, a famous South Florida guide, perfected this technique for bonefish in Biscayne Bay and currently enjoys a 95 percent success ratio, fishing an average of 300 days each year in good weather and bad.

Flats fishing is sight fishing. You spot your target and then cast to it. Without polarized sunglasses to help eliminate the surface glare, you won't be able to see fish. When scanning an area ahead of you, concentrate on actually seeing the bottom. New anglers invariably allow surface reflections to distract their concentration. Experienced spotters have learned to ignore these and accurately read the bottom.

Never permit your scan to remain stationary unless you are concentrating on suspected movement. If the boat is being poled, remember that the bottom itself will appear to move. You are looking for distinct movement that is different from the normal flow. Keep scanning the bottom within the range of your maximum cast, but occasionally, glance beyond for other signs. You should routinely check the area around the boat, because even a pod of 100-pound tarpon can slip undetected through your visual defense network. If you suspect movement, concentrate on that spot until you can identify the object.

Once you identify a fish, you should be able to tell the species, its size, which way it is moving, whether it is a single or in a school, and if it is feeding, frightened, or something in between. Barracuda have a habit of lying completely motionless, waiting to ambush their prey. On the flats, if a fish doesn't move, you are probably looking at a barracuda. Determine which end is the one it eats with and make a cast.

Bonefish are not always easy to spot, because they move like ghosts across the flats and can be practically invisible under certain light conditions. One reason that it pays to scan way ahead periodically is that you may see a tailing bonefish. In very shallow water, when a bonefish tips down to pick a goodie off the bottom, its tail waves above the water, often reflecting the rays of the sun as it swings back and forth. These are the easiest

A topwater plug fished on tackle suited for largemouth bass enticed this nice sea trout.

The author considers big tarpon on fly tackle to be the ultimate angling challenge. This one weighed 111 pounds.

Steve Barnett admires a 14-pound snook he just caught on plug tackle.

bonefish to see, but they can be the hardest to catch.

As bonefish root on the bottom for shrimp and other crustacea, they disturb the marl, and these "muds" drift down tide resembling wisps of smoke on a gentle breeze. Redfish often do the same thing. An experienced flats angler can spot these signs easily and some can tell you how long it has been since the fish was there.

When visibility is poor, you may detect movement without ever seeing the fish. It could be a cross ripple that runs counter to the normal pattern of the water. At times, the surface seems to vibrate and this phenomenon is called "nervous water." This is one of the most difficult forms of fish spotting to master, but it is vital to locating fish on the flats. Other water movements such as "waking" are far more obvious. Fish swimming just under the surface will actually create a wake, similar to what you might expect from a very slow-moving torpedo. The water streams off the fish and you can determine direction, speed, and even where to place a lure without ever seeing your quarry.

Particularly in calm weather, some fish, including tarpon, will "lay up." They seem to be asleep and basking in the sun, but are alive, well, and often hungry. Spotting them is exceptionally difficult and you often have to resort to a technique known as color differentia-

The push pole is the favorite method of propelling a boat silently and effectively in shallow water.

tion. The fish are so hard to see that you invariably flush them before you know they are there. When you locate an area that has a lot of fish, but you can't avoid spooking them, move the boat very slowly. Scan the water carefully and if you see something that looks slightly off color from the rest of the bottom, make a cast. It's better to make 50 casts too many than to fail to make one cast.

Bonefish, redfish, and permit feed primarily on bottom-dwelling creatures such as crabs and shrimp. Tarpon, snook, trout, jacks, and barracuda feed at mid-depth and their prey is smaller fish. Lure presentation should be predicated on the feeding pattern of the species you see. An artificial must approach a feeding fish in precisely the same manner as a natural bait would be discovered. Fresh-water anglers feel it is important to present a lure or fly that imitates a natural food. Many salt-water offerings bear no resemblance to a specific food, but if your lure behaves as most normal prey would, a feeding fish should strike it willingly.

The shallower the water, the smaller the lure you can use under most circumstances. A lighter bait enables you to cast closer without spooking your quarry. For bonefish, permit, and redfish, the bucktail jig is the single most-effective lure.

I try to cast my jig three feet in front of the fish's line of movement and four feet beyond the fish. If time allows, I wait until the fish turns most nearly into the tide and then make my presentation. You want the lure to intersect the fish's line of movement as your quarry continues into the tide. This presentation duplicates the circumstances under which most flats feeders encounter their prey. As crabs and shrimp emerge from the bottom, they are sometimes swept away from their lies by tidal action. If it appears to the fish that the same thing happened to my jig, I have a better chance of getting a strike.

Once the jig is in the water, it must be retrieved to move it in front of the fish and keep it there. You don't want it to sweep toward the fish and intimidate your quarry. Instead, it should resemble food that is attempting to escape. I have learned to observe the fish closely and determine its reaction, changing the retrieve as necessary to keep the feeder interested. Too many anglers insist on continuing a retrieve pattern in spite of the fact that the fish is not responding favorably.

In sight fishing, you actually see the fish take your lure. When I am convinced that the fish has it, I set the hook immediately. If you wait until you feel life on the other end of the line, it may be too late and your offering might be out of the fish's mouth. This is particularly important when fly fishing. A fly is presented in the same basic manner as a jig, but you should wait until you can get close enough to the fish so you don't have to press. It might be only 20 feet for redfish or as far as 70 feet for tailing bonefish when the surface is slick calm.

Presentations to mid-depth feeders are more varied. You can often lure barracuda by working a cigar-shaped surface plug at reckless speed across the surface of the water. The same technique can turn on large jacks. A slower, more deliberate version of this retrieve can be very effective on snook and trout, particularly over potholes or depressions in shallow flats. By observing the reaction of the fish, you can determine the correct retrieve.

Regardless of the species, the lure will be most effective when worked at the same depth as your quarry. It should appear to be escaping. Frequently, a fish will swim right up behind your lure and follow it as it moves away from him. Vary your retrieve immediately until you elicit a strike. If you can't get a response, try a short burst of speed. Sometimes, if a fish believes your offering is about to get away, this will trigger a strike. At least, you'll force the fish to commit itself. It may eat and it may turn away, but in either case, you'll be none the worse for the effort.

Tarpon are more receptive to a slow-moving small fly at the right depth than all other lures combined. In fact, an expertly presented fly will often take most flats species when other artificials fail. There are times, however, when the normal retrieve won't work. On a hot, muggy, June afternoon, giant tarpon tracked a slow-moving fly for a considerable distance with their noses almost touching the feathers. They refused to take until I applied a short burst of speed to the retrieve. That's when the tarpon realized they really wanted the fly and would surge forward to grab it.

With bonefish and other relatively small species, presentation is 80 percent of the game, but when you fish for tarpon (and particularly with a fly), the battle first begins when you set the hook. I believe that giant tarpon on fly are the ultimate challenge in light-tackle salt-water angling. The principles of fighting a fish, however, apply to any form of light casting tackle.

Then natural panic that overcomes a fish when it is first hooked is the most effective tool you have in winning the battle. During this short period, the fish exerts more energy in less time than at any other stage of the fight. That means that you can expend less effort initially, but you must be on top of the situation quickly. If you can get up to the fish right away, it may make a fatal mistake. If you are slow and the opportunity escapes you, you're going to have to carry the fight to the fish. Many inexperienced anglers and even some veterans rely on the "wait him out" method. They put a bend in the rod and hope that the fish perishes from exhaustion before they do. In most cases, the line gives out before fish or angler. Every minute that fish is in the water, your chances of landing it diminish. It's genuinely a game of beat the clock.

My experience shows that if you don't boat most strong fish within the first 30 minutes, you may have to hang on for two or three hours. When it takes that amount of time, all the odds shift in favor of the fish.

When first hooked, most flats species will run or jump or do both in a frantic effort to get free. It takes energy to propel their bodies through the water and they use up oxygen faster than they can strain it through their gills. Your tackle can't stop a fish that has embarked on a panic flight for deeper water. That's why a very light drag on the reel is critical at this stage of the fight. The primary objective is to avoid breaking off the fish at all costs. As the fish seeks to put distance between itself and the boat, your partner should be leaning on the push pole, working hard to shorten the distance between angler and fish. That fish will never be more exhausted than it is after the first few blazing runs. If you can rush up to the fish at this time and exert maximum pressure before it gets its second wind, you will increase your chances for an early success.

In the shallows, a fish has only one dimension in which to travel. There isn't enough water to dive, so it must keep running or at least stay ahead of you. If you get up to the fish in time, you may find it tired, momentarily disoriented, and even dazed. Teamwork between angler and boatman at this moment can spell victory.

Regardless of what happens, you cannot let the fish rest. It will regain its strength much faster than you can muster your own reserve energy. Most novices merely hang on while the fight drags on for a considerable period of time. You must pressure the fish to the best of your ability and to the maximum that the tackle will withstand.

The most dangerous period with any fish is right after you lift the rod to set the hook. A fish in the shallows is going to outdistance a jack rabbit as it races for the sanctuary of deeper water. Point the rod at the fish, holding it in a smooth, *shallow* bend. This is the worst time to pressure a fish or to lean on the rod and let it double over. As soon as the fish stops running or jumping, you can change your tactics and start exerting whatever force you can.

Remember the light drag setting. You can add more drag with your hands and fingers, reserving the option of removing the drag instantly. The fight should be conducted as close to the boat as possible, but in doing so, you must keep in mind that your tackle will not be nearly as forgiving. There is less stretch in the line, and

Captain Nat Ragland lifts a beautiful permit taken on spinning tackle. The permit is perhaps the least-known flats denizen and one of the most difficult to catch.

This 10-pound redfish provided plenty of angling thrills on a flyrod originally designed for trout or bass.

a sudden surge by the fish can evoke some rather smokey dialogue if you happen to break it off.

The tackle you use should be the best available and tailored for this type of fishing. This is not the time or the place to cut corners on equipment. Rods should have adequate backbone to pressure your quarry and tips designed to cast the necessary lures. Reels must have adequate line capacity, which means a minimum of 250 yards of the line test you choose. Drags have to be unquestionably smooth. Every hook on every lure should be sharpened with a file or honing stone.

A competent flats fisherman has the skill and practice to handle any type of casting tackle. He is equally at home with a flyrod, spinning gear, or plug-casting equipment — and can use them interchangeably. I prefer to use lighter lines on spinning tackle and favor them when it is necessary to present small lures. Plug tackle is heavier (although I do carry light plug outfits) and can be used to pressure a fish.

If you enjoy the flyrod, you'll need two basic outfits on the flats. The first would handle an eight weight line and would see duty for the smaller species. Your second outfit should cast a twelve weight line; it is a fighting tool that can land big tarpon and husky sharks. Any single-action flyreel is satisfactory for the smaller rod, but you should have a direct-drive flyreel for the heavy rod. This reel has no anti-reverse and you'll find that with a little practice, you can fight a fish harder using the direct drive.

Floating grass and weeds are sometimes a problem on the flats. I have found that a slow sinking flyline is an advantage because the line will inch below the debris, and you won't be plagued with weeds. It has a second advantage of getting the fly down to fish level quicker. This can be important, especially when visibility is limited and your casts are necessarily short.

You can carry other lines in your tackle box with loops spliced on the back end. Another loop in the dacron backing on the reel can be interlocked in a matter of seconds, enabling you to change flylines to meet any situation.

Learning to fish the flats takes a measure of dedication. You can read about it, but the most vivid lessons take place on the casting platform of a skiff than can run in ten inches of water. That's when your eyes will be scanning the bottom like a radar antenna; your whole body will tingle with the excitement created by an underwater world passing in front of you. Your knees will shake as you make the cast and start the retrieve, but that's all part of the game — a game that constantly challenges the finest anglers in the world.

The cast to a cruising fish must be accurate. The lure should land about 3 feet in front of the target and 4 feet beyond.

So You Want to Buy a Bass Boat!

by Tom Gresham

The joy you get from a bass boat is directly proportional to the research and study you put in before the purchase. The right boat for you is the one that fits your needs and your style of fishing. Many decisions must be made in choosing the boat that *is* right for you.

Although they are called bass boats, these fishing machines are well suited for other species as well. It happened that the first ones were developed in the South where the bass is the most popular gamefish.

Bass boats are divided into two general types — the standard and the "pro boat." In the standard model, the seats are mounted on the floor, and you have your choice of stick or console steering. Stick steering is done by a vertical stick on the left side of the bow seat with which the angler steers the boat. Push the stick forward to turn right; pull it back to turn left.

Very simple and responsive, stick steering eliminates the steering wheel, which frequently is in the way in small boats. However, it should be limited to outboards of 50 hp or less.

The "pro boat" configuration has a raised casting-deck in the bow; some have a raised deck in the rear. Pedestal seats are mounted on these decks, with another seat and steering console in between.

Most bass boats feature padded swivel seats, some of which are adjustable for height. There should be an alternate seat position for the passenger to use when the boat is underway. On many models, the bow seat can be removed and inserted in a holder near the driver. The raised pedestal-seats are not only dangerous riding positions, but it is illegal to use them for that purpose in some states.

Size is probably the first decision to be made in choosing a bass boat. This will be determined by how and where you fish. Bass boats are designed for two anglers, but three people can fish from them.

If you stick to small waters, you may get by with a boat in the 14-foot class. Most of these have stick steering. It's very important to equip boats of this type with kill switches. The kill switch is a lanyard connected to the driver and plugged into the ignition system. If the plug should be pulled out, as when the driver is thrown overboard, the motor shuts off immediately.

For most people, however, a 14-foot bass boat is too small. The boat that fits most fishermen's needs — hence the most popular — is the 16-foot "pro boat." The larger boat has the advantages of a smoother ride, greater capacity, and is safer in rough water. It will weave through thick timber with no problems and is a very stable fishing platform.

Fishermen who need even more room or fish large bodies of water will find that an 18-footer fills the bill. Although an 18-foot boat will not negotiate a flooded forest as well as smaller boats will, most people are surprised at how maneuverable the big boats are. On large impoundments, sudden storms can turn a leisurely fishing trip into a struggle to reach shore. If you fish open water a lot, perhaps the extra margin of safety a larger boat provides should be an important consideration.

Just as the bass boat is a generation removed from the small, unstable fishing boats of fifteen years ago, the high performance or HP hull is thought by some to be a new generation of bass boats. The main advantages of the HP bass boat are increased fuel economy and a much smoother ride.

Even at top speed, a standard bass boat rides on its practically flat bottom, putting a lot of surface on the water, and creating drag. The high performance hull is a modified deep-V with a plank, or pad, running down the middle. This pad is about ten inches wide at the stern, narrowing at the bow, and projects ⅜ to ½ inch into the water. At high speeds, the lifting strakes on the hull lift the boat onto the pad where only the last 15 to 20 inches are on the water. This means that the boat is riding on a surface area of only 150 to 200 square inches. Naturally, drag is reduced tremendously. The hull design is very efficient and very fast.

To get the maximum efficiency from an HP bass boat, it must be rigged properly, but unfortunately not many dealers know how to handle the peculiarities of this high-speed creature. Most of the weight should be put in the stern and distributed evenly on both sides. The outboard should be mounted higher on the transom than usual. Even if the dealer does excellent work rigging standard bass boats, he may not know what he is doing on an HP hull. You should look for a dealer who has experience at equiping HP boats.

Some equipment considered optional on other boats is mandatory for these crafts. Power trim is vital because accelerating and high-speed running require different motor attitudes. A kill switch should be considered essential on all boats, but especially on speedsters that can approach a mile a minute. Different props will have to be tried to find the size and pitch just right for your rig. This is done by running different props while noting engine performance on the tachometer. (You *do* have a tach, don't you?) Again, you need a good dealer who will lend you props to try, or will do it himself.

The speed you can expect depends on you. For maximum speed, just put a gas tank in the boat and go. However, most of us put a lot of additional gear on and in our fishing boats; this adds weight and slows the boat. Outfitted for fishing and properly rigged with the maximum recommended horsepower motor, practically all makes and models are capable of 45 mph. Some will run 55 and better, and that's really moving!

One additional note on HP bass boats. The new owner must learn how to drive a boat all over again in order to operate one safely. Response is different and a new set of reflexes must be developed. My advice is to practice in open water first and be particularly careful on the first few outings.

Although some fishermen prefer the extra room in a boat without compartments, I like the storage space. Many bass boats come with several built-in compartments for storing and locking up equipment. The big problem until recently has been how to keep water out of dry compartments. That problem was solved by putting a ½- to one-inch lip around the opening with the hinged top resting on the lip. Not all boat manufacturers include this feature, so look for it. Discovering that a rain shower has filled your compartments with water is no fun.

Many boats have a long compartment on one side in which your rods will fit. There will be room for a lot of other things, too, but it's important that it be long enough for your longest rod (fly rods excluded). Some boats have one or several smaller compartments in addition to the rod box. Only you can decide how much storage you need.

Another type of compartment is a live well. This space for holding fish has a means of letting water in or out and an aerator for keeping plenty of oxygen in the water. Closely inspect the finish on the inside of a live well. A sloppy job means that water may leak into a nearby dry compartment or the hull itself.

Another item that is sometimes built into bass boats is a fuel tank. The advantage of a built-in is the ability to burn 12 or 18 gallons without changing the fuel line to another tank. On the other hand, the six-gallon portable tank can be carried to a gas station, but the boat can't. Probably the best solution is a built-in *plus* a portable.

Accompanying the rise in popularity of the bass boat was the application of modern technology to fishing techniques and equipment. Many of the accessories considered standard equipment now were not in existence twenty years ago.

Power trim is useful for tilting the outboard in brushy areas.

Most bass fishermen feel that the introduction of the depth finder has been the greatest advance in fishing technology. Depth finders have been used for quite some time on large boats, mostly in salt water, but these were bulky and expensive. It wasn't until the mid 60's that Carl Lowrance developed a unit small and inexpensive enough for practical use by fresh-water fishermen. Many serious anglers rank their depth finder as important as their outboard.

A depth finder enables the fisherman to "see" the bottom of a lake, and the bottom contour determines where fish will be. Regardless of whether the model is called a fish finder or a depth flasher, they all work in the same way.

A depth finder is a small sonar unit that sends sonic signals into the water by means of a transducer. These sounds travel through the water at about 4800 feet per second and, upon striking the bottom or another object, are reflected back to the transducer. The unit interprets the delay between transmission and reception and gives a readout in feet.

Most models have a circular scale with a flashing light whirling around the scale. The light flashes at the zero mark and at the depth from which the signals bounced back. The flashing is so fast that it appears to be a continuous light. There are also some models which give a digital readout and are quite accurate. They are also more expensive. In use, the finders help fishermen locate underwater dropoffs, creek channels, or anything that might provide cover for a predator fish intent on capturing a small baitfish.

The first depth finders were portable; there are many portable models made today, but the man outfitting a bass boat will probably want a permanent unit. The mount should swivel so that the finder can be read from the driver's seat as well as from the bow casting-deck.

A fisherman buying a depth finder has a choice of scales. Some units read from 0 to 70 feet, others to 100, and a few to 200. Buy the one that covers the depth you fish in regularly, but remember that the smaller the range, the more detailed and accurate will be the scale. Also, most makes have enough power to read twice around the

The standard model has the seats mounted on the floor. Note the stick steering to the left of the driver.

scale, so a 70-foot model would be good to 140 feet. Just make sure you know whether it is on the first or second time around the scale. Thus, after it has gone around, a reading of 20 feet would really be 90 feet, and so on.

Many fishermen are going to what I consider the ideal set up — two depth finders on one boat. This may sound like overkill, but it makes sense. If the transducer is mounted in the stern and the fisheman is seated in the bow, he could be 16 feet from where his depth reading is being taken.

That may seem unimportant until you consider the situation of a fisherman trying to stay right on top of a four-foot wide creek or a sharp dropoff. When the back of the boat is just right the bow could be completely off the structure being fished.

To take care of this problem, a lot of people are mounting a depth finder on the bow deck and the trans-

ducer on the hull directly below. The place to mount the transducer is inside the boat on the outside "step." A thin layer of epoxy will hold it there through any kind of pounding and it will read right through the hull if it is a single layer of fiberglass. It won't work where the hull has inside foam flotation or through wood or metal. I also epoxy the rear transducer inside the well where the drain plug is. This eliminates the bother of an outside bracket as well as the possibility that the transducer will be knocked off by a stump.

In the last few years, several recording depth finders have been introduced and are beginning to generate enthusiasm from fishermen. The recorder traces the bottom (and anything suspended) on graph paper. This visual picture of the bottom is easy to read and provides a record for later reference.

The best type is a straight-line recorder and, so far as I know, there is only one moderately priced to fit the

The pointed-nose "skeeter" boat was the forerunner of the bass boat.

pocketbook of the average fresh-water fisherman. The straight-line recorder is exactly that: the graph lines run straight across the paper. It is accurate and easy to read. The other type has curved lines on the paper and it is more difficult to read.

One problem inherent in all recorders is the amount of paper used. The common practice of leaving a flasher running all day would be impractical with a recoder, because the paper would end up filling the boat. One solution is to mount both a flasher and a recorder on the boat, using the recorder only when checking something of particular interest.

Anyone who has ever tried to paddle a bass boat very far can tell you that it's a losing proposition. The standard means of propulsion when fishing is a bow-mounted electric motor, also known as a trolling motor.

When the fisherman is sitting in the bow seat, he uses the electric to position the boat where he wants to fish. There are two methods of operation available. The hand-controlled models have the speed and on-off switch on the steering handle. The foot-controlled models are started, stopped, and steered with a foot pedal. This leaves the hands free for fishing. Which one to buy is a matter of personal preference but, if possible, try both types before deciding.

Another decision to make when choosing an electric motor is whether to get a 12- or 24-volt model. The 24-volt has more power which is important on large or heavily loaded boats. On the other hand, it requires two batteries, which means extra weight and expense. Anything larger than a sixteen-foot boat will probably require the use of a 24-volt electric motor.

In the past, anchors have been awkward to use and store, and the line frequently has gotten fouled. Now, there are several anchor systems that eliminate that worry for the modern fisherman.

The simplest is a bracket that holds the anchor over the water, and a hand winch. The bracket is mounted either on the bow or stern, or both, and the winch is mounted close to the fisherman. The winch has a release that lets the anchor free fall for getting it down fast.

There are several electric anchors available, and the

The oxygen monitor tells the fisherman where the fish can't be; thus he can avoid a lot of fishless water.

This fisherman pulls a good bass from a treetop after easing into position with the foot-controlled electric motor.

A bass boat requires a good trailer and a car equipped to tow heavy loads.

The "pro boat" configuration has a raised fishing deck in the stern. This allows the fisherman to maneuver around the outboard.

convenience they provide must be experienced to be appreciated. Most are lowered by running the winch motor in reverse, but at least one model has a drop feature, which lets the anchor free fall. This is preferable to a relatively slow-powered descent.

Some precautions are needed when using any of these anchor systems. If the anchor is suspended over the edge of the boat, it might slip from the bracket. Should this happen while trailering the boat, the anchor line could wrap around a wheel and flip the trailer. If it slipped off while running across a lake, the anchor could hang on brush or the bottom with equally disasterous results. Make sure your bracket has a strong pin holding the anchor in and be constantly alert to the possible danger.

When trailering, it is a good idea to let some line out and put the anchors inside the boat.

An electric bilge pump is almost a necessity. With batteries, fuel tanks, and transducers in the stern, it is sometimes impossible to bail water manually.

I find that more and more fishermen are equipping their boats with Citizens Band (CB) radios. Such two-way radios provide an extra measure of security in case of breakdowns or other emergencies. A call for assistance sure beats paddling five miles back to the marina.

The range that can be expected from a five-watt unit, the legal maximum, is up to 15 miles depending on atmospheric conditions and obstructions between the two parties. You can mount a permanent mobile set such as

The electric anchor is a terrific labor-saving device. This one has a strong pin holding the anchor in the bracket.

are used in automobiles, or use a walkie-talkie.

A relatively new piece of equipment that isn't mounted *on* the boat but is being carried *in* many bass boats is an oxygen monitor. This small instrument tells the fisherman how much dissolved oxygen is in the water. We all learned in school that a fish gets oxygen by pumping water through its gills, but what most of us don't know is that the higher the oxygent content of the water, the more active the fish (up to a point).

In any body of water, the oxygen content isn't the same at all points, and fish prefer the areas with more oxygen. In fact, frequently there will be areas where there isn't enough oxygen for fish to live, such as below a certain depth. Fishing in such water would be as productive as fishing in a bath tub.

The point is that all this water looks the same and without an oxygen monitor, a fisherman might fish all day in water where there couldn't possible be a living fish. The monitor doesn't tell where the fish are, but it tells where they can't be, thus eliminating a lot of fish-

The efficiency of today's bass boats frees the fisherman to spend more time in fishing.

less water.

Thus, a completely outfitted bass boat needs a lot of electrical gadgets. A single battery simply won't get the job done. One twelve-volt battery should be used exclusively for the outboard.

This will ensure that you don't get stuck in the middle of a lake with a dead battery. Depending on the equipment you have added, you will need from one to four extra batteries. Your dealer can advise you on this.

You'll need at least one battery charger and maybe two depending on how many batteries you have. Get one powerful enough to handle the big marine batteries you'll be using.

An item which some fishermen foolishly try to save money on is the boat trailer. Sometimes a cheap, lightweight trailer will be included in a dealer's package to keep the cost down. A trailer which doesn't support your boat *correctly* can ruin the hull.

The trailer should have car-size tires — 13-inch wheels are good, and 14- or 15-inch even better. They will give a better ride and last much longer than eight inch wheels that must turn eighty zillion times a mile. Guide posts on the sides with tail lights on top are worth the extra cost. The trailer is definitely not the place to cut costs.

In bass boats, it's very true that beauty is only skin deep. Visual inspection alone won't tell you what kind of materials or what level of quality went into the hull. Two boats on a showroom floor can look identical, yet one can weigh several hundred pounds more. The other boat may be lighter because of lack of foam flotation, fewer structural members, and thinner fiberglass — all of which contribute to an unsafe boat. The only bargains in bass boats will be found among the major brands. These have stood the test of time in a very competitive business. Poor products soon make their deficiencies known, and fishermen spread the word.

Perhaps the most important decision you will make is not which model or make of boat to buy, but rather the dealer to buy from. The dealer can make the difference between your boat ownership being a dream or a nightmare. Ask people who have boats where they got them and what they think of the dealership. Before buying, go to the service area and look around. Do the people look like they know what they are doing? Rigging a bass boat is quite a job and it must be done right.

After you've bought the boat and have it sitting in the garage (the family car will now brave the elements), there's still another thing to do. Sit down and fill out every warranty card and mail it right away. It's almost inevitable that something in all that gear will have a bug in it and, if you have mailed in the card, you'll be covered.

One final word: Take it easy your first time out, be safe, and leave a couple in the lake for me.

CHUMS AND CHUMMING

by Art Glowka

Chumming is the art of attracting fish to your baited hook by stimulating the fishes' senses of sight, taste, feel, hearing and smell. At one time, chum consisted entirely of chunked or ground-up aquatic creatures that were put into the water in a fishing area, in the hope that any fish close-by would swarm toward this free lunch and attack the baited hook. Today, however, sophisticated anglers are also employing lights, electrical impulses and currents, as well as sound pulsations and artificial tastes and smells as chum in their endless quest for more and bigger fish. Anglers are also becoming very conscious of the smells and odors that repel fish, and they go to great lengths to avoid such anti-chum situations.

Because various states have different attitudes and laws regarding chumming and baiting in their freshwater lakes and streams, there is more chumming done in salt water than in freshwater. Seawater is affected by tidal flow which aids the spreading of chum. Finally, saltwater fish are generally more predacious than their freshwater cousins, causing them to respond to chumming methods more quickly and positively.

Old-time anglers were a lot more knowledgeable about using chums and chumming inasmuch as natural baits were all they had with which to catch fish. Chumming declined with the advent of artificial lures, because lures not only caught fish but were simpler and cleaner to use. But today, when fishing with artificials has become honed to an exacting science, especially in the arts of ultra-light and fly-rodding, the use of chum has once more come into vogue as a way of attracting fish within the limited casting range of these techniques.

Some of the simplest and most effective chums and chumming methods are brought into play in angling for winter flounder in northeastern waters during the spring and fall migrations. These methods can be easily applied to other similar fish and fishing situations. The most elementary consists of nothing more than dragging an anchor or a chain around and around over the bottom you intend to fish. This churns up the bottom muds and all the little goodies that flounder relish. Once anchored over this spot, a supplemental mushroom anchor can be briskly raised and lowered at intervals to create the same silt cloud. A plumber's helper on the end of a long pole or even an oar scraped over the bottom will create the same effect. If there is considerable wave action and one feels lazy, an anchor or chain tied at the bow at just the right length will cause the waves to raise and lower it against the bottom to attract flounders.

The next step is to use crushed clams and mussels as chum. The simplest system involves nothing more than crushing these bivalves either singly or en masse and chucking them into the water around your fishing area or boat. Many anglers concentrate this fishy essence in a chum pot or bag. I haven't seen many old-fashioned brass chum pots lately, but a very serviceable substitute can be made by drilling three-eighth-inch holes in a one-quart plastic ice cream container. A loose-meshed bag such as an onion sack or small-load washing-machine bag makes an admirable chum sack. Rocks or other weights must be put in chum pots or sacks to keep them on the bottom. The chum pots and sacks should be shaken occasionally to loosen the juicy tidbits inside.

Since clams and mussels are often not readily available, various other substitute chums have been used on flounder with satisfactory results. Cans of cat food, salmon, sardines or mackerel are punctured and either hung over the side or put in the chum pot or sack. Sometimes extenders such as rolled oatmeal, cooked instant rice and corn meal are added to the chum to appeal to the fish's visual senses as they flutter downtide.

Recently, the most successful and contriversial flounder chum has been whole-kernel canned corn. I have yet to read or hear of a good explanation for its astounding success in attracting flounders, but I have read plenty of arguments which have raged about whether flounder can digest the corn chum they eat or if it merely swells up inside and kills the fish. Just this last spring, New York's Department of Environmental Conservation conducted a series of experiments at their Ocean Science Laboratories at Montauk, Long Island. These tests proved conclusively that winter flounder not only thrived on a diet of canned corn but statisically outgrew other flounder which were fed a normal diet.

My own experience indicates that flounder don't seem to take to corn chum as fast as they do to the more fishy types. Still if you fish an area that has been previously corned by someone else, such fishing can be very good. Real flounder fanatics paint their sinkers, dye their baits, and constantly bounce their sinkers off the bottom to attract fish.

Chumming in itself is no master key to instant angling success. But, if it is combined with a thorough knowledge of where each fish sought can generally be found, it can increase angling success dramatically. As a rule, if you chum for an hour in a good spot with no action, it might be well to move off and try another hole.

Chumming in salt water can be done best from a boat, although old-timers used to be quite successful at establishing a chum slick from shore. Probably the epitome of chum slicks were those of the old Cutty-hunk Bass Fishing Club, where the

Bonefish can be taken easily by chumming an area with pieces of shrimp or conch. Captain Cal Cochran is about to release a beauty taken by one of his customers using this method.

guides used to chum at night with lobser tails so the rich sports would have fish to cast to in the morning.

Boat chumming is most effective when the tide is actively moving the chum away from the boat. If you're bottom-dunking under the boat, then chum either has to be cast uptide far enough to reach bottom under you or else weighted in a pot or sack and dropped to where you want it. A good chumming trick to remember is to put your chum material into a paper sack along with a rock. When it hits the bottom, the bag can be jerked hard, breaking it and depositing the chum in exactly the right spot. It's always best to employ two anchors while chumming so the boat can be solidly held directly over the sweetened spot instead of constantly swinging back and forth, pushed by both wind and tides.

Catches of reef-roving species like blackfish can be increased if baited and chummed. Crushed clams and mussels seem to work best. But here, again, knowing where to fish is the primary requisite for angling suc-

cess. Chumming will merely concentrate the fish that are there.

The most successful blackfishing method I've ever used was taught to me by an old-timer a few years ago: the day before you're going to fish, gather up a bushel of clams and mussels. Crush them thoroughly either with a flat shovel on a smooth rock or in a metal tub using a baseball bat. Take these crushed hors d'oeuvres out to the area you intend to fish and carefully anchor your boat over the spot, using at least two strong anchors. Then spread the chum on the bottom around the boat. Untie the anchors from the boat and leave them there secured to a floating buoy. When you return the next morning and re-anchor, be prepared for some fantastic fishing!

Technically speaking, this is baiting and not chumming, but it is a time-honored salt-water fishing technique. Baiting, to my way of thinking, is spreading chum well before you intend to fish and then returning to reap the rewards; chumming is something you do while you're actually fishing. Many states have strict statutes against baiting in both fresh and salt water so it would be a good idea to carefully read your state's fishing laws before attempting this method.

The two glamor kings of the East and Gulf Coast fisheries are bluefish and striped bass, both of which are very susceptible to the siren song of a good chum line. Ground menhaden, also known as mossbunker or bunker, makes the best chum for both species. Bunkers are plentiful, cheap, bony, oily, relatively easy to net and snare, and are the chief forage fish in the diets of blues and stripers.

Ideally, menhaden should be ground up fresh as needed during the fishing trip. But the difficult logistics of acquiring fresh bunker and having a suitable grinding device on board forces most anglers to purchase ground bunker from a bait dealer, either frozen or semi-fresh. This isn't such a great tragedy, especially to those anglers who already know that there is nothing smellier or messier than grinding fresh

bunker chum. If purchased frozen, it must be thawed before using, since the ice crystals tend to make the fish particles float. Some chums can be purchased in frozen blocks or chunks which are put into a chum pot or bag or merely suspended over the side where the warmer water will slowly thaw and disintegrate them.

Before using bunker chum, it should be mixed with copious quantities of salt water so as to produce a thin, soupy mixture. Then, small quantities of this mixture are continually broadcast on the downtide side of the anchored or drifting boat. The secret of success is to maintain this chum slick constantly, even after fish have been attracted and are being caught. It takes determination to continue chumming while you and others are battling blues, but it has to be done.

Strangely, the best bait to use in a chum-line situation are something entirely different from what is being used as chum: for example, butterfish chunks in a menhaden slick and menhaden pieces when chumming

with ground-up mackerel. The cardinal rule of chumming is never to put your boat through another person's chum line or try to fish directly down current of his efforts. If violated, at best you can expect some well-chosen epithets slung in your direction, followed by a few large cod sinkers.

So many boats chum so regularly each day in certain popular bluefishing holes such as the Acid Water just off New York harbor, that the bluefish become conditioned to expect this food and go into a Pavlovian feeding spree when they hear the boats coming. In fact, so much bunker chum is used that many regulars shun the spot because they swear the blues themselves begin tasting like menhaden.

Clam bellies are another popular chum; tossed into deep tidal holes under bridges, they've been the downfall of countless big stripers. When I'm livelining bunkers for bass and blues, I always make it a point to continually toss overboard small chunks of mackerel or trash fish just to sweeten the water around my boat.

Grass shrimp have always been the favorite chum for weakfish and sea trout along the East and Gulf Coasts. But their availability has been spotty during the past decade. Hopefully, the recently enacted federal laws against the use of chlorinated hydrocarbon insecticides (such as DDT) will help foster large populations of grass shrimp which have been returning to the northeast. Both the weakfish and blue crabs have also been showing a strong trend toward recovery.

Collecting grass shrimp for chum and bait is a do-it-yourself proposition, since very few commercial bait houses collect and sell these tiny delicate creatures. Again, the old-time methods of working a fine-mesh seine or small trawl through shallow grassy areas will harvest

Repeated experiments with salmon show that fish are particularly sensitive to human odors in the water and will usually flee the area where the odors occur.

Captain Joe Renzo nets live mackerel which will be used for chum. Baitfish are lured into the net with small pieces of fish.

lots of shrimp. Separating the shrimp from the weeds is best done by the shrimp themselves. Place them in a shrimp can — a floating box with a fine-mesh bottom. The shrimp will tend to swim to the bottom, after which the weeds and grass are discarded. Smaller quantities can be scooped up from under and around the weeds and grasses which grow on floating docks and piers; use a small net.

Shrimp should be doled out in twos and threes in a known weakfish spot. If they seem to be swimming away too fast, pinch them before tossing overboard. Extenders such as cooked instant rice and rolled oatmeal are often added to stretch the shrimp chum. Fish attracted to the chum usually announce their presence by surface swirls. A baited hook offering can then be floated out under a bobber or just drifted out. It's good to remember that it works better if the hook is tied directly to the end of your line without any hardware.

Along the West Coast, the favorite chum is the anchovy. These are purchased live from bait boats in most fishing harbors. On the fishing grounds the anchovies are tossed away from the boat. Their frantic attempts to gain the safety of the hull triggers the feeding instincts of the tuna-like species found out there.

The large pelagic billfishes and sharks have always been chummed successfully by the traditional ground-fish methods. Recently there has been much experimenting to attract these biggies with lights, sounds, and electric currents — all with some success. It's always been known that tuna and barracuda are attracted to boats operated at certain speeds. Whether it's the throb of the engines, the flash of the props, or the wake bubbles which are the chief attractants is still a moot question. Many skippers will tow such oddities as buckets, old tires, and even logs to try to create a fish-attractant effect.

Similarly, many fresh-water anglers know that a steady trolling speed over deep water will often bring salmon, large trout, and bass right into the wake where they will strike a fly or artificial lure, often less than twenty feet from the boat. I know one fisherman who paints the prop blades on his trolling motor fluorescent and pearly, figuring that if a string of rotating cow-bell spinners will attract fish so might a slowly turning prop.

Electricity, both AC and DC, has

long been one of the fresh-water fishery biologist's chief tools for surveying fish populations in lakes and streams. Anyone who has ever witnessed large fish being drawn inexorably toward the charged probes or grids cannot doubt that electric currents of the proper intensity would successfully chum fish. Commercial shrimpers place an electrical charge just in front of their nets which makes the shrimp jump up out of the mud and be swept into them. Other experimenters have charged the otter boards of a trawl, thereby hoping to attract fish towards the net. Today some sport billfishermen are trolling electric coils and wires with dissimilar charges, confident that these electric fields will attract their quarry. These efforts are somewhat hampered by the large size of generators needed to produce sufficient current.

For many years both electric and fossil-fueled lamps and lanterns have been used successfully to attract fish by both fresh and salt water anglers. Commercial squid fishermen use flashing lights to draw squid and concentrate them around their boats. Any serious crappie angler knows that both crappie and insects are attracted by a bright light hung over the side of a boat or bridge. A productive cycle takes place: insects arrive, are burned, and fall into the water — thereby attracting baitfish which, in turn, attract and concentrate crappie right under the fisherman.

During the past few summers I've been experimenting with various combinations of lights and lanterns while night fishing for rainbow trout and kokanee salmon. Both these fish are plankton feeders, so the object of the lights is to draw as many plankton as possible under the boat. Hanging gasoline-fueled lanterns over the side was once the standard fishing technique, but I've found that floating, battery-powered,

electric "crappie beacons" are more effective. Rather than burn them steadily, these lights should be turned off at intervals; this stimulates fish in the plankton column to strike the baited hook. I've recently heard of some Florida charterboat skippers who have mounted flashing strobes under their boats and claim that they are catching more fish.

As far as I can tell, the use of sounds and lights for chumming fish in fresh water is legal in most states. Electricity is not permitted except for biological use, but there is a strong tradition about "telephoning" catfish throughout the south. Again, before using any method of chumming it would be wise to read your local fishing laws; if you have any doubt, consult your local conservation officer. Some states actively permit fishing technique that others forbid outright. Generally, those northern states whose chief game species are the salmons and trouts frown on any organic matter being put into the water to attract fish. Large trout are particularly susceptible to baiting with trash fish and entrails. Many western states even forbid use of corn as bait and chum.

Those fishes lower down on the social scale such as the panfishes, carp, suckers, and catfish are easily chummed, using various items from grocery shelves and the vegetable garden as well as many natural baits. Again, laws vary from outright "no-nos" in northern areas to the "anything goes" attitude of most southern states. Sweet taste or smell seems to be the chief criterion of a good fresh-water chum. Here is only a partial list of what will work: various cheeses, corn, cooked rice, corn meal, oatmeal, peanut butter, macaroni, the oils of anise and vanilla, peas, marshmallows, bread, and tomatoes. Many of these flavors and smells are now produced synthetically, marketed in aerosol cans, and impregnated into many fresh-water

lures. Baiting an area with cotton-seed cake, dog food, cattle feed or even over-ripe muskmelons and watermelons will draw every panfish, carp, eel, and turtle to the spot.

The use of chum while ice fishing is an effective tactic which many winter anglers overlook. Since the water under the ice is generally clear during the winter, *visual* attractants are the key. Scraped-off fish scales, crushed white eggshells, clamshells, as well as Christmas-tree tinsel will all draw panfish and trout as they flutter down through the water. Often fish will look at a winter bait for a long time before taking it, but they can be stimulated into striking if a few salmon eggs or a crushed minnow is dropped into the hole.

Chumming in fresh-water streams is a time-honored European fishing method. The English excel in the high art of using maggots and ground bait to lure coarse fish. In France, dead animals and meat are hung over streams and, when the fly maggots fall into the water, fish come running. The method works, but I must admit—it stinks to high heaven. American anglers often use the stream-chumming trick of overturning rocks or washing some bank soil or mud into the water upstream of where they want to fish. This often starts the fish feeding. Some desperate trouters often bang rocks together underwater to wake up the fish. Surprisingly, it often works.

Most anglers only consider chumming from the point of view of attracting fish, but almost as important are all the anti-chum substances which repel them. Top on the list of repellents is oil and gasoline, followed closely by insect repellent, suntan lotion, and tobacco. After coming into contact with any of these odoriferous materials, one should wash his hands with a mild soap before resuming fishing. A wet bar of soap is a messy thing to carry in a tackle box, so a better idea is to put some

Canned catfood in a homemade chum pot lowered over the side will attract flounders.

kitchen detergent in a small plastic squirt bottle. Some soaps, such as TRAK, are sold in handy plastic toothpaste tubes. In a pinch toothpaste or hair shampoo can be used — both foam and clean.

Since fish are repelled so easily by even a few parts per million of oil or gasoline in water, I've often wondered whether the various dry fly concoctions which have petroleum bases — or even the line cleaners for that matter — might often spook fish because of the smell. One of the most powerful anti-chums is the human product of protein splitting known as serine. Fish react violently when exposed to it. It can be masked by washing one's hands, but again I wonder whether wet stream and pond wading didn't repel many fish because of the body odor washed into the water. Most of the newer rubber fishing lures have artificial flavors and smells not only to attract fish but to mask human odors. Finally, since fish are so sensitive to sound, one can only be curious over what their reaction must be to the high-frequency sonic pulsations which are emitted by electronic depth recorders.

Fish themselves exude various secretions which can attract similar species or predators. The sounds and smells of a wounded baitfish are quite different from that of one swimming normally; predators use these sounds and smells to home in on their quarry. Many an angler has seen a second fish closely following alongside one that has been hooked, attracted by the bait or the odor of fright and the fluttering of the fish in trouble.

The basic techniques of chums and chumming have been around for a long time. More and more, it's becoming a science as modern anglers experiment to produce better chumming methods to catch fish.

Ice Fishing from the Bottom Up

by Charles J. Farmer

The snow under our rawhide webs crunched and whined like stale popcorn in the mouth of a hungry boy. Cold it was. Downright bone chilling. But we were told the lake trout were hitting. No cozy fireside hearth or mugs of steamy, buttered rum would keep us in doors that day. Not even the collisions of pro football pads on TV would lure us away from the ice holes. So we dressed, my wife and I, with layers of wool and nylon. We gulped hot chocolate; packed the rods, auger, skimmer and sled; and headed for our creaking, cold four-wheel drive. And the snow? How it crunched with the brittleness of minus 10° — dry, powdery cotton, the January kind!

We bored six holes off Donoho Point. Soon Kathy and I were jigging spoons off the bottom in about 15 feet of water. Action came fast, as it often does with ice fishing. Winter fish have ravenous appetites. We had forgotten the cold. Fat, sassy fish have a way of injecting almost immediate warmth into winter hands and feet. When our number reached eight (mostly two pounders), we quit for the day. Content. Thoughts switched to crispy fillets fixed that evening. They would go perfectly with a flickering fire and a balm of foggy, hot rum.

Ice fishing is meant to be something complete . . . total. The parts of the ice world — wool, snowshoes, touring skis, snowmobiles, catching, eating, savoring and talking — fit into a neat, compact winter package. Full enjoyment comes from sampling each segment. A tradition can be born like that of a north country goose hunter or a trout man who wields a deadly rod.

Ice fishing is not for everyone. It is reserved for those who enjoy challenging northern winters. It is the sport of trophy fishermen who know that the biggest fish are most often caught through the ice. Ice fishing is for the cross country skier, the snowshoer, snowmobiler, and hiker who harness ice and snow rather than reject it as a curse from winter's gray skies. Ice fishing is not a widespread virus; but once the bug strikes, the infection spreads fast, deep and permanently.

Ice fishing is naturally limited to those states and provinces where winter is long enough and cold enough to form a safe, fishable lid of ice over lakes and ponds. The northern tier of states usually has predictable, safe ice cover for periods extending from one to four months. Generally speaking, about 21 states in this country can legitimately qualify as regular ice-fishing prospects. There are some marginal areas, where exceptionally cold winters might produce prolonged ice cover and some good ice fishing. For the record, the states of Washington, Oregon, Montana, Idaho, Wyoming, Utah, Colorado, North Dakota, South Dakota, Minnesota, Wisconsin, Michigan, Ohio, Pennsylvania, New Jersey, New York, New Hampshire, Vermont, Iowa, Maine and Connecticut; and, of course, all of the Canadian provinces, can be classified as ice-fishing regulars.

The species of fish also determines ice fishing potential. Some fish like largemouth bass and catfish become relatively dormant under the ice. All trout species, pike, pickerel, muskies, walleye, bluegill, perch and burbot are active winter feeders and eager to hit live or artificial baits fished through the ice.

HOW TO GET STARTED IN ICE FISHING

There is nothing complicated about the sport, although there are some closely guarded secrets among some old timers in various parts of the country. These secrets usually involve under-ice warm springs (winter fish love to congregate at them); old river channels; deep "honey holes"; and special baits. Some of the precious secrets are legitimate and were learned after many hours of surveying the ice. But the newcomer to the sport can fare well if he keeps his eyes and ears open.

The toughest part about ice fishing is getting out and doing it for the first time. But if you enjoy winter and don't mind snow, ice and cold, then you are, without a doubt, a prime candidate for ice fishing. In fact, being a fair-weather angler does not have to be a prerequisite. I know a few hardy souls who fish exclusively in winter, through the ice. "Guess, it's just because I catch more and bigger fish through the ice," they say. And that's pretty good reasoning.

There are three basic ways to pick up the sport: reading a "how-to" article like this one in a book or magazine; first hand observation; and word of mouth. A combination of all three is a good way to avoid a lot of cold, fishless trips to new areas or new lakes.

For example, this article will give you everything you need to know about general fishing techniques, equipment, tricks, and clothing. This is the foundation of the sport. With a basic desire to try ice fishing, the "how-to" article will either stop you in your tracks or entice you to go further. A reasonable next step then, provided you live in good ice-fishing country (or have access to it) is to visit a local tackle shop. Find a store that specializes in fishing, hunting and camping gear, rather than the large discount department type.

Ask specific questions about nearby lakes that offer ice fishing. Check on the fishing regulations (a call or letter to the local fish and game department is a good bet also) and the types of fish that can be caught. Make sure the ice is safe. Try to find someone in the store who is especially knowledgeable about where to fish in local lakes; what baits to use and special jigging methods. Most tackle shop personnel will be interested if you point out that you will also be selecting some of the gear they recommend. Chances are good that this word-of-mouth investigation will have you on the ice within a week. But there is another means of investigation — personal observation.

When I was first learning how to fish Jackson Lake,

Trout on ice taken with spoon by jigging.

where I live in northwestern Wyoming, I took two rod-less trips to the lake before I wet a line. The trips were in conjunction with some wildlife photography in the area, so I had a dual purpose. I snowshoed and skied to several different groups of anglers and passed the time of day with them. Most were willing to divulge information they had about specialized fishing methods and baits. Some of them told me about areas that were productive in the morning and hotspots in the afternoon. They showed me how they rigged baits, their favorite spoons, how deep they fished, and the punch needed to set the hook into a tough-jawed lake trout. I made a rough map of the lake and pinpointed the likely fishing spots. It was easy to see that most of the fishing was centered in certain spots — known dropoffs, feeder streams and warm springs. Many of these areas had been marked in the summer.

A tackle store owner in Jackson, Wyoming, told me to fish where I saw the greatest concentration of fishermen. "Look especially for the ones with snowplanes. They are the serious ones and probably have every big trout in the lake marked." And without butting in too closely, a novice icer or one new to a lake can locate some pretty good fishing in relatively short order.

After you get into ice fishing, you will discover new areas on your own, and that enhances the enjoyment of the sport.

BASIC EQUIPMENT

After visits to the local tackle shop and having talked with ice fishermen, you will have a pretty gool idea of the equipment you will need. Your biggest investment will include basic gear that can be used in every ice fishing state in the country.

Ice augers or drills make a clean, relatively quick job of boring through the ice. They are especially good for new spots where old holes are not available. Ice spuds or chisels, made of heavy steel or iron, are fine for chiseling through an old hole or cutting an opening in thin (under 12 inches) ice. But for anything over a foot, I recommend an auger that works like a small hand drill or an ice drill that resembles a large cork screw. Both are efficent, safe tools well worth the money. If you get into fishing seriously, you may even consider a gas-powered ice auger that makes hole-boring a cinch.

Some ice fishermen, fortunately not the majority, use an axe or hatchet in a pinch. Using an axe to hack through thick ice is risky business and can be dangerous. Ice chips fly in all directions and some can sting the face and hit the eyes. And when the axe head hits the slush, a fisherman is sure to get wet.

After the hole is bored, slush from the chiseled ice and snow fills the hole. An ice skimmer or slusher, resembling a large, kitchen strainer, can be purchased to clear the hole. Large kitchen strainers themselves can be used. On cold days, skim ice is likely to form in the hole, so periodic slushing is needed. If the hole is not kept clear, when fishing with live bait, bites will often go un-detected.

An item that is most often forgotten is a short-handled gaff. Why the gaff? A lake trout, walleye, pike, or musky just bristling with sharp teeth and weighing seven pounds or more can be nearly impossible to ice without a gaff. If you try to hoist one out of the hole by hand, you will be sorry. Try to horse it up and out and there's a good chance you'll lose a big fish. By maintaining steady pressure on the fish at the lip of the hole and carefully spearing the jaw area with the gaff, you can land a trophy safely.

One other point: there is a tendency for many anglers to scoff at a gaff especially when primary targets are bluegill or perch. Remember, big fish are on the prowl under the ice. Some fall for tiny ice flies or grubs. It is a good idea to be ready, and a gaff is good insurance.

Coming under the heading of basics are ice sleds for hauling gear; stools to sit on; charcoal bucket or cat heaters; plastic bags for transporting fish; some type of blanket (for warmth and for use as a cover to see into a hole); and a tackle box of some kind.

The above items will vary greatly according to brand, design, and personal taste. But they all perform important functions.

The sled may be nothing more than a common children's snow sled. Gear can be strapped to the sled or removable wooden sides can be bolted on to hold equipment in place. The relatively cheap plastic sleds work well for hauling gear from the car to the ice holes. They are lightweight and easy to tow even behind a pair of touring skis or snowshoes. Sleds can also be used to sit on.

Quite a few ice men design their own fishing sleds for their special needs. They are relatively simple to build and can be as fancy as an angler likes. I've seen some with recessed built-in draws to hold lures, terminal gear and bait. Some have lantern stands for night fishing. Most have storage places for tip-ups, heaters, food, and extra clothing. The sled keeps gear in place. Many ardent anglers in the northern states will keep the sled fully loaded in car trunk, pickup or station wagon all year. When the urge hits, they are ready to go.

Stools of some kind are essential. They insure good positioning over the hole for positive reaction to strikes. Standing is fine for awhile, but when properly dressed, a fisherman can be very comfortable even sitting on a stool. Any small, canvas, or aluminum stool is fine for the purpose.

You can make an adequate heater by filling a bucket

Ice fishing setup includes tilt, corkscrew ice drill, and slusher. Note warm snowmobile suits.

about a quarter-full with sand and then adding some charcoal briquets (or wood) for heat. Take some charcoal fuel with you so you will have a quick source of warmth. Catalytic heaters, the models that use either white gas or propane for fuel, work well, also. A good, old-fashioned wood fire, built on the ice or shore, can do much for the spirits. Make sure however that it is legal to build open fires where you are. Be sure to use dead tree limbs, downfall or some of your own fireplace wood for fuel. Using freshly-cut, green wood is not only illegal in most places, such a fire is nearly impossible to get started.

You will never need a handy ice cooler during winter fishing and the possibilities of spoilage out on the ice are virtually nonexistent. Some anglers field-dress fish immediately after catching them, depending on the size of the fish and the rate of catch. Ordinarily, it is sufficient to clean a batch of fish after you are done fishing. Large, heavy-duty plastic bags are good for storing the fish while transporting them.

Some kind of blanket or ground cover is good to have. Blankets, nylon or canvas tarps can break the wind. They can be used to sit on. And they can be used as a "dark cloth" for blotting out daylight, permitting relatively good visibility (depending on water clarity also) through the hole and into the water. Some anglers use a dark cloth extensively. They enjoy seeing the fish below and can react better to strikes and nibbles. The sight of a three-foot northern pike toying with a minnow bait is enough to warm any ice fisherman up in a hurry.

Your old reliable summer tackle box might be fine for ice fishing. In order to save time, I have found that the box, regardless of its size, should hold ice equipment only. Having to sift through a maze of open-water gear that has no practical use on the ice, can be frustrating. You may want to purchase a smaller box and use it exclusively for ice tackle. And, of course, weight and space limitations should be considered.

RODS-REELS-LINES

Short rods, under three feet in length, are suited for ice fishing. They can be willowy or stout, depending on the type of fishing. Bluegill and perch rods, for example, should bring out the best in the fish. If, however, I'm fishing lakes where big trout, walleyes, pike, or muskies are present, I stick with a rather stubby two-footer with a medium action.

Short rods enable an angler to sit over the ice hole, or nearly so. This cuts the "stretch" time from the initial strike or nibble to the setting of the hook. And if there be one major difference in fishing technique between open water angling and ice fishing, it is the way in which the hooks must be set. Ice fishing is vertical fishing. When setting the hooks a fisherman strikes with a solid upward motion, rather than the horizontal or diagonal snap of the arms and wrists of summer fishing. The short rod aids in upward hook setting. There would be too much give or play in a spinning rod of conventional length. Tough-jawed fish like lake trout and pike are often not hooked effectively. Yet, many novices and veterans continue to use six- or seven-foot rods for ice fishing. Their usual excuse is, "Just can't seem to hook 'em today." The best material for the short rods is fiberglass.

Either a bait casting or spinning reel can be used with an ice rod, depending on the size and fittings of the rod's reel seat. I have used both types of reels with equal enjoyment and success. If there is a difference, it is that the bait casting reels seem to handle larger fish better. I have more drag control. Nothing, however, can beat the fun of catching winter bluegills on tiny ice flies with an ultralight spinning reel.

I feel that standard bait casting or spinning reels should be used in preference to reels where line has to be peeled off manually. Some ice rods come equipped with these rather flimsy reels. They can be adequate for panfish, but if you tie into a good one, you may not land him. Somewhere down the line, rod and reel manufacturers seemed to feel that a rather cheap reel could be used for ice fishing. Not true. Choose your reel as you would for summer

Rainbow trout being caught on cheese bait.

fishing, and you will have more fun out on the ice. Special jigging rods and reels equipped with a trigger device are adequate for some panfishing, but after using one for a year, I'm convinced most anglers would be better off with a standard "summer" reel and short rod. Gimmick rods and reels are not worth the risk.

Monofilament lines are fine for the ice. In fact, I believe they have the dacron and nylon lines beat. Mono lines from six to eight pounds handle panfish adequately. For larger fish, or the possibility of larger fish, line anywhere from ten to 15 pounds does the job. Remember, it is not so much the weight of fish that causes line problems as hauling the fish up through the hole vertically, jagged ice edges, and general "horsing" procedures required when landing a fish through the ice. I have also found that the heavier line is easier to work with on extremely cold days when fingers tend to become numb, and heavier line works better when rod guides are freezing. In any case, the use of fresh mono and a brand that does not hold a bird's nest coil, is important for peace of mind.

TIP-UPS, TILTS, (OR TRAPS)

Northern Great Lakes fishermen, along with anglers in the northeast, use some mechanical hook setting and signaling devices with regularity. These devices are called tip-ups, tilts, or traps.

The devices eliminate the constant vigil that a single fishing rod requires. They allow fishermen to warm themselves over a fire or in a shanty. And where legal, several holes can be fished at once with a set of tip-ups. The number of tip-ups and tilts that can be used varies from state to state. Anglers should check local regulations.

While the tip-up is indeed popular, some anglers prefer to hold conventional short rods. One angler told me that tip-ups eliminate the most exciting part of fishing: the initial bump or strike and setting of the hook. A good point. But nevertheless, tip-ups are popular, especially for bluegill and perch.

With some minor modifications, tip-ups, tilts and traps are words used to describe a device that is a complete ice fishing unit in itself. In other words, the tip-up consists of rod, reel, line and hook.

Tip-ups can be purchased commercially or made at home. Some are made to be set into a slanting notch cut into the ice in such a way that the top of the trap comes over the center of the ice hole. The line is laid out on the ice in coils that will easily unwind when there is a strike. When the fish hits, a diagonal bar or rod is pulled down toward the hole. The rod has a signal flag on one end, thus letting an angler know he has caught a fish. The most important function of the angler when using tip-ups is to make regular rounds.

Where anglers congregate, the action is usually hot.

Ice flies photographed on head of auger.

Rainbow trout fell for ice flies.

Another type of tip-up can appropriately be called a tension device. The signal rod is "loaded" by a loop in the line that sets a determined depth where the bait is fished. The loop is a tightened slip knot. When a fish strikes, it pulls down a wire release that hooks the fish and raises the signal flag on the opposite end.

It goes almost without saying that live bait is needed for tip-ups — the livelier, the better. Minnows, shiners, worms, and grubs work well. Corn and cheese — not really "live" bait — can also be effective. Some anglers impart a slight quivering motion to tip-ups while making their rounds. Lightly tapping the device with their feet or hands, often produces the necessary action for a strike.

The angler who fishes artificials — both lures and ice flies — will, of course, use the short rods already mentioned to give the necessary life to spoons, leadheads and flies. Tip-ups are a rare sight on northwestern ice waters. But without a doubt, both the mechanical hooking device and the jigging rod are both sporting in their own ways.

ICE SHANTIES AND ICE TENTS

Great Lakes fishermen make use of ice shanties or shacks to a great extent — more so than western ice anglers. The shanty can vary from a crude "tree hut"-type windbreak to an elaborate cabin-type affair, complete with wood-burning stove and bar. The main purpose of the shanty is to provide protection from the cold and wind. Elaborate shanties are usually erected on lakes that have rather long (two to four months) ice cover. Some are anchored by "ice stakes" that keep them from blowing away in the wind. Anglers will usually position the shanty over a good hole where relatively large numbers of fish congregate.

Some shanties have no floor, and holes can be located just about anywhere. Other shanties have wooden or canvas floors, with holes cut in them. The less elaborate, lighter-weight shanty can be moved to various parts of the lake manually or by snowmobile.

For the most part, shanties are homemade wooden structures varying in size and shape. Commercially manufactured ones, some from metal, aluminum and plastic, are made in the Great Lakes area. Regardless of the type of shanty, anglers should determine when it is safe enough to move the structure out on the ice. They must also use common sense in removing the shanty from the ice while it is still safe. Yes, there have been some shanties that were not removed in time and are now homes for schools of fish. It goes almost without saying that ice anglers must also use good judgment in driving any kind of motorized vehicle on the ice.

Ice tents are igloo-shaped canvas or nylon structures that can be staked to the ice (stake holes are filled with water and frozen solid). They are portable and relatively lightweight. Holes are cut in the canvas or nylon floor. They provide good windbreaks and are quite cozy when equipped with a small portable heater. But for maximum effectiveness and durability, they should be taken down after each use and not left out on a lake permanently like a shanty. Tackle shops in popular ice fishing areas usually stock commercially manufactured ice tents.

JIGGING TECHNIQUES

Just as there are warm-weather fishing methods, a variety of jigging methods exist which are successful. I will give you my method. Try it. If the method does not work for you, experiment on your own.

Most of my fishing is concentrated about one foot from the bottom. I let the lure or bait hit bottom. Then I crank the reel a few times to get my offering off the bottom. Now, pretend you have a hammer. Instead of using a quick, nail-driving movement downward, reverse the action so that your wrist and rod snap smartly upward. If that does not work, rest the lure and quiver it by shaking the rod.

Some anglers swear by the slow lift and flutter method, and this has worked for me at times. With rod in hand, raise the lure and your arm as high as you can raise them. Then drop your arm quickly. This results in the lure fluttering ever so tantalizingly to the bottom. The short ice rod will give you good jigging control and at the same time give you the needed punch in order to drive the barbs home.

LURES — ICE FLIES — BAIT

Spoon fishing has been my bread and butter for big fish. I'll work a Daredevle just off the bottom in one of the methods discussed above. Sometimes I'll add a piece of pork rind, a minnow or worm to the spoon's hooks. Or I'll attach a wire trailer equipped with a treble hook to the split ring near the end of the spoon (removing the original treble hooks). Spoons should be relatively heavy so they sink and "jig" fast. Lighter spoons tend to be flighty, and it is hard to give them good action. Spinners work well in some waters. Color combinations are an important consideration. Silver and brass are effective standbys. But talk to the locals in a new area. Some weird color combinations are often the most effective attractions for fish.

Ice flies are great for panfish and trout. Use the "quiver" jigging motion for flies. Not much up and down vertical distance need be covered. I have had trout hit stationary ice flies. In fact, when quivering doesn't work, hold the fly still. Often a fish will nail it then. Buy ice flies locally because what works well in one lake may be a loser in another lake. But one important thing to consider: ice flies can be deadly at times, often saving the day when lures and bait have failed. Have a good assortment of colors in your tackle box.

Brief mention has been made about minnows, worms, grubs, cheese, and corn. All are excellent winter baits. It is best to stick with local favorites. Chumming with cottage cheese (where legal) in an ice hole can also be an effective way of drawing fish. Try various bait combinations where more than one hook is allowed. And don't forget those miniature marshmallows. They are particularly good for trout and panfish. If still-fishing bait is slow, try jigging your offerings. Sometimes that can make the difference in catching fish.

STAYING WARM

If you are skiing, snowshoeing or hiking to your destination, go rather light. Pack extra clothes with you and put them on when you arrive. Pack warm insulated or felt-lined boots if you are wearing touring shoes. Go light to prevent sweating which will keep you chilled.

Perhaps the warmest thing you can wear is an insulated snowmobile suit and a heavy wool cap. Snowmobile boots are good foot warmers, too. Your hands and feet are your most important considerations. Bring along extra pairs of wool mittens or gloves in case one pair gets wet. An extra pair of socks does not hurt either.

Food and warm drink stokes your body's furnace. Hot chocolate is the best drink you can have on the ice; alcohol, especially in excess, is the worst. High energy foods soothe the stomach and spirit. There is nothing worse than being cold and hungry on the ice. With the right planning, you do not have to be either.

If you do not have a snowmobile suit, remember the "layered" system of wool and nylon. Next to your body, wool is warm even if it gets wet. Nylon breaks the wind. Layer your body with wool and nylon. Top the whole works off with a coat of goose down or Dacron II. Add and subtract layers according to your body warmth.

"You have to be crazy to be an ice fisherman," some of my friends say. I snicker. If they only knew. But then again, maybe it is best they don't know. Ice fishing is not for everyone, and those of us who are sane will gladly reap its benefits.

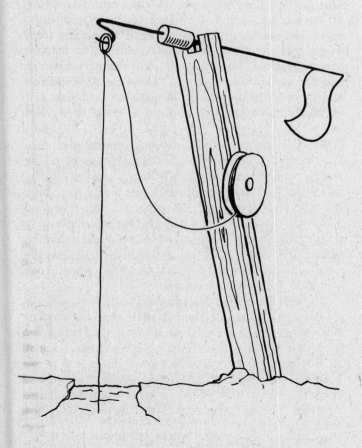

Ice fishing tilt.

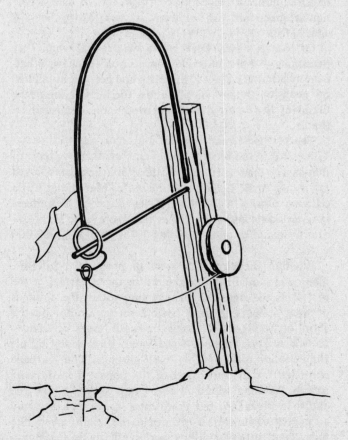

Common Tip-up with release bar and signal flag.

How Primitive Man Fished

by Louis A. Brennan

No human aim or endeavor has so stimulated the mind of man, since man had a mind, to the heights, and depths, of its cunning as the capture of fish, lots of fish, a particular species of fish, or even, as with Moby Dick, a special fish.

Of course, Moby Dick was a whale, and whales are mammals — but that is a biologist's point of view. Whatever lives in the waters of the earth and gets about in them by means of fin and tail falls under the jurisdiction of the Guild of St. Peter, the oldest profession — masculine, that is.

The first fisherman was the first man, and vice versa. The fact is in the record; one of the few facts we have of that part of the record. In the late 1950s the archaeologist Dr. Louis S. B. Leakey and his wife, Mary, dug up in Olduvai Gorge, Tanzania, Africa, a series of human-looking skulls and other bones that have since been laboratory dated at an astounding 1,750,000 to 2,000,000 years.

Whether these remains were of pre-men, borderline men or first men is an argument for the experts. For the rest of us the signs are clear. Lying within the confines of what appears to have been a shelter or hut on the shore of a long-extinct lake the fossil bones of what is known as Homo habilis were found surrounded by his simple stone tools and his fossil garbage. That garbage consisted for the most part of the bones of turtles and catfish. Nothing found in this camp suggests how the catfish were taken, but there must have been a canny strategem to it; catfish are not to be hand-picked like mussels or turtles, and they were regularly on the Homo habilis menu.

The first men to arrive in America from Asia 40,000 years ago, give or take 10,000 years, had to have been fishermen, perhaps of no great skill but certainly of long experience. In life style they were beachcombers, drifting slowly southward along the Pacific shoreline from where Asia and Alaska were once connected by land to, eventually, South America, sustaining themselves almost entirely on the fruits of the sea. These included shellfish and shore birds, the flotsam of dead sea mammals cast up on the beach and such of these as could be waylaid live.

But our earliest American beachcombers must also have possessed a simple and reliable means of taking shallow water feeders, if they were not to depend entirely on chance for their nourishment. This would have been the tidal weir, a porous dam of stones and driftwood across the entrance to tidal pools behind which fish were trapped by closing the dam when the water began to recede. If Homo habilis had a catfishing technique, the weir — a mud-dammed pool into which fish were herded — would probably have been it.

The oldest weir known archaeologically in America is a tidal weir. A more elaborate affair than the mud or stone dam types, it was a construction of posts connected by willow webbing. Remnants of this weir were found off Boyleston Street in Boston harbor, in the land of the bean and the cod. The radiocarbon dating of one of the posts was about 4000 years, no great antiquity even in America, but an indication of the ancientness of the practice.

Weirs and similar traps took more fish by tonnage in America than any other method and possibly, more than

Salmon trap used in narrow streams, Kwakiutl, Northwest Coast of North America.

all other methods combined, since they were the favored method wherever there were runs of anadromous fish, the shad in the Northeast and the salmon in the Northwest. But when Europeans made the first historic contacts with America in the 16th century, every fishing method, technique, trick and device known to them, and to us, was being employed somewhere. The only exception was dynamiting, but that had a kind of counterpart in stunning, which used the same principle of causing shock waves in the water to kill or stun.

The gamut of fishing practices included all kinds of netting and seining, with trawling between two boats, spearing, gaffing with the pronged leister or fish spear, harpooning using the retrieval line, bow shooting, angling with hook-and-line and gorge-and-line, jigging, fishing by torchlight from a boat, poisoning, clubbing, jugging, dragging, trotline setting, raking, noosing and belly-tickling. The tool materials are different today, steel hooks, nylon line, harpoons shot from a gun, etc., but no patentable improvement in process can be claimed by modern man.

In aboriginal America, as now, fishing graded from mass-production methods through the more sporting, one-on-one, man-against-fish practices to the purely recreational, like noosing and shooting with the bow and arrow. Stunning could hardly have been more than a juvenile pastime, while noosing and belly-tickling would be more feat than fishing.

Since stunning is such a simple operation one would think that it had been discovered far back in time, per-

haps as early as Homo habilis. What it requires is the right environment, a shallow, rocky stream with a piscatorial population that likes to lurk under the stones of the stream bed. The stunner, armed with a hammer of some sort, a stone or club, wades upstream whacking every rock he sees. By the time he has covered twenty yards or so, the bodies of "stunned" fish, internally injured by shock waves, will come floating up. Sizable fish can be reaped this way, if the stream affords any; minnow sizes fall victim by the hundreds and it is not unthinkable that many a meal of fish stew was the result of stunning, by youngsters no more than six or seven years old.

Stunning at least provided a bag of fish for the pot. Noosing was pure exploit. Known or reported for about 20 tribes out of about 250 scattered throughout North America in historic times, it consisted of slipping a noose over the tail of a fish and hauling it in. In some instances the noose was at the end of a line tied to a pole, as in angling; in other cases the nooser had to place the loop over the tail by hand, quite like putting salt on a bird's tail. Since this could be done only by lulling, beguiling or hypnotizing the fish, belly tickling must have been the answer.

As this is described by honest men to be found in West Virginia and Tennessee to this day who claim to have done it, the tickler enters the water quietly and eases up on a fish lazing in the shade of an overhanging rock or bush. The target fish, undoubtedly believing that the tickler is only another fish, allows its underside to

New England Indians night fishing.

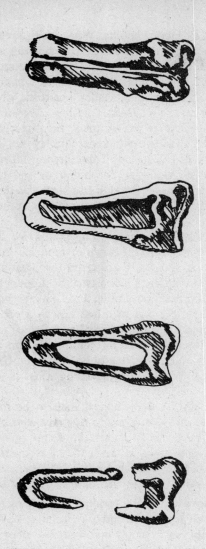

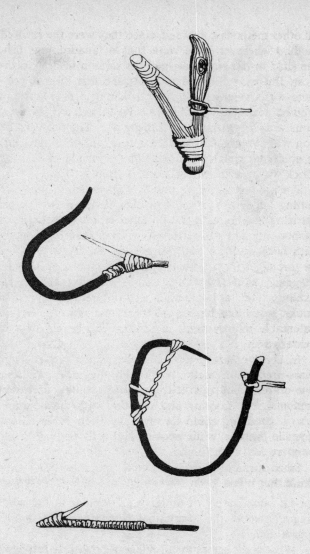

Steps in making a fishhook from a deer toe bone.

Fishhooks of wood and bone.

be gently stroked with the fingertips. The stroking produces a state of ecstatic languor or a trance or a short circuit of the reflexes and the fish can be handled, to its own destruction, if that is the intent of the tickler. The soothing effect of stroking on the sympathetic nervous system has, by the way, been demonstrated on creatures presumably as insensitive as the lobster.

Shooting fish with the bow and arrow could not have been anything but a sport of the skill-displaying, show-off kind so dear to the heart of the aboriginal warrior-hunter. The bow and arrow appears very late in American prehistory, about 2000 years ago in the Southwest, and about 1000 years ago in the Northeast, a mere 700 years before the arrival of Europeans in that region. As fishing gear it could, therefore, never have had much significance, and the fact is that fish were nothing more than a different kind of target, a problem of aiming in the sight-deceiving medium of water.

Angling with a single line and hook or gorge falls somewhere between recreation-sport and serious subsistence gathering. For the production of bulk for diet it is far down the list of efficient methods. In one instance only was it a necessity in which no other method would serve. That was in winter fishing through holes in the ice. In the upper Midwest archaeologists have discovered a series of stone tools along the shores of lakes that can only be interpreted as axes for chopping out fishing holes in the ice. Such fishing would have been for supper, not for fun.

When the fish hook first began to be used is not certain from the archaeological record and it will probably never be known. Bone fish hooks of conventional design were made perhaps 5000 years ago, but these were undoubtedly only translations into bone of hooks made of wood or thorn, of bird or animal claws. The U-shaped hook with point and barb cut out of a deer long or meta-

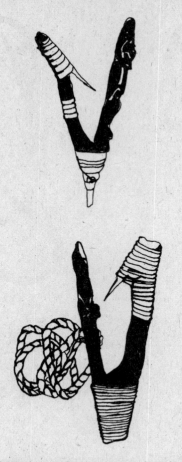

V-shaped halibut hooks used by Indians of Northwest Coast of North America.

podal bone, rarely of antler, was popular in the whole region east of the Mississippi beginning at least 4000 years ago.

What complicates the problem of how early fish hooks were used is a technical argument about fish hooks and fish gorges. The hook is defined as the device intended to be taken by the fish so that it catches him by the mouth. The gorge is defined as a kind of bait-holder intended to be swallowed and taken into the stomach from which it cannot be disgorged.

The earliest archaeological fish hooks are composite specimens; that is, they are made up of two pieces, the stem or shank, a slim-rod-like length of bone or wood slightly larger than a kitchen match, to which the line is attached, and a second rod-like length, shorter and pointed, which is tied to the shank at an acute angle in a V, and which serves as the hook or impaler.

There are good, experimental reasons to believe that, because the attachment of the two pieces would also be weak, and would act as a hinge, that the composite hook would not hold a bulky fish by the mouth. It must therefore have been intended as a gorge; the bait being held in the V and the whole swallowed by the striking fish, with the loose, moveable "hook" component finding lodgment in the stomach as the fish tried to regurgitate it. There are students of this surprisingly involved but minor problem who believe that many artifacts of the one-piece kind called fish hooks because of the shape are really bait-holding gorges.

Those artifacts that are correctly called gorges at all times are simple, bipointed two-inch lengths of bone with a hole in the middle for the attachment of the line. Any tug on the line after the bait had been taken would set one or the other of the pointed ends in the stomach or gullet. Some species at certain times of the year would probably strike the gorge even if it were unbaited.

Given the low, uncertain production of single-line, single-hook tackle, its very existence in prehistoric American contexts leads to the conclusion that aborigines enjoyed angling. With no laws prohibiting the use of any method or kind of gear, they invented and regularly used hooks and gorges. There did occur that exigency, winter icing, which would have mothered such an invention, but it would be almost dehumanizing to insist that Indians never felt the nerve-end tingle of playing some of the monsters that must have been in pristine

Haida "black cod" hooks.

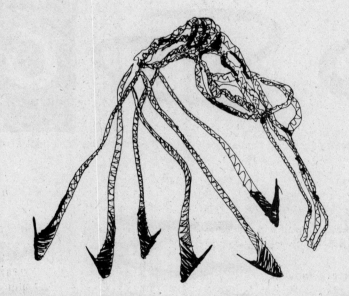

Sharp-angled hook of the type commonly used for codfish, and also for salmon-trolling.

Halibut hook; the U-shaped shank was steamed and bent into shape.

Nootka type, used in offshore trolling for salmon.

Halibut hook.

(Left) J-shaped bone hooks **(Center)** Typically shaped bone hooks **(Right)** Bone hooks of "V" shape.

(Left) Bone hooks **(Center)** Four typically shaped copper hooks **(Right)** Four abalone-shell hooks.

(Left) Multipointed hooks **(Center)** Top, composite bone hook; center, locust twig with thorn; bottom, ivory shank with copper point **(Right)** Composite hooks, wooden shanks and bone points.

streams. After all, there were so many other ways of taking fish for pure nutrition.

The jig of many hooks is known from Alaska only and is probably a late import from Asia. The trotline is not mentioned in the literature on aboriginal fishing but it would not have left any specific traces except under the most fortuitous circumstances. The one argument against its use by Amerinds is that it would have required the manufacture of a long line; a tedious chore which might have been considered unnecessary in view of the many other ways there were of catching several fish at a time. But in my youth along the Ohio River, the oral tradition was that trotline fishing "went back to the Indians."

Suspending short lines with hooks from a float either tethered or set adrift in a pool may also have been aboriginal in origin. It is called jugging in some areas because of the use of jugs for floats. Indians, if they used this method, would have used inflated bladders or sewn skins. Both of these were used off the Northwest Coast in conjunction with harpoons in the hunting of sea turtles and large sea mammals, such as whales and walruses. This is hardly proof of "jugging" but the use of floats in fishing, or water-hunting if you insist, was known in the New World.

Spears, leisters, harpoons, and clubs had dual purposes: as fish-kill weapons in harvesting fish trapped in weirs or otherwise impounded or herded, and as direct fishing implements. There are many natural situations, such as fish having to cross shoals or struggle up rapids where cast or thrusting implements could be very profitably used. The one created situation where they came into play was night fishing, where a torchlight set in the bow of a boat attracted fish irresistibly. So deadly is torchlight fishing that there probably would not now be a fish left in fresh water anywhere were it not universally prohibited by law. If it could be shown that Homo habilis controlled fire it could be posited that this was the way he could have lured fish into shore waters shallow enough for clubbing or stoning.

Nets, including seines, are the most versatile of all fishing gear; they can be used for any species of fish and they are quickly portable. The weir is fixed in one location, and fish must reach it by tidal action or by driving; the net goes where the fish are. Net weights or sinkers, usually crudely notched pebbles — though they may be grooved by abrasives and shaped into possibly effigy forms — have been found all over America; apparently there were no people who fished who did not use one form of net or another, from gill nets and dip nets to 40-foot-long trawling nets and casting nets, though these seem to occur only along the Pacific coast and may have arrived late from Hawaii.

Nets were of the first order of importance, equal to hunting weapons, from the extreme Northeast, across Canada and into Alaska. The scarcity of edible plants in this territory made steady catches of fish a necessity; with nuts entirely absent from the evergreen forests and agriculture never possible, smoked fish was the winter-keeper staple. Although the territory is not overly endowed with fish resources, fish were proportionately exploited more heavily there than, perhaps, in any area outside the salmon region of the Northwest.

Which is not to say that nets were thought not worth the effort elsewhere. There is another evidence of their use, beyond the occurrence of net sinkers. Very early on in the manufacture of ceramic pottery, which began about 3000 years ago in the Northeast, the potters began to treat the outside and sometimes the inside surfaces of their vessels with netting. In some cases the netting was wadded up and dabbed against the surface; in others, the pattern of reticulated cords and the knots of a stretched-out net show clearly in the baked clay. It would appear that potters used scraps of discarded netting somewhat as housewives now use old curtains for dust cloths. This kind of evidence of nets, found mainly along the Eastern seaboard, does not, however, date the earliest use of nets; it dates only this secondary use.

It is surprising how much of the fragile physical evidence of fishing gear has turned up archaeologically; the Boyleston Street weir, a 42-foot trawling net, scraps of netting, gorges and hooks. But there is one fishing method for which no evidence will ever be found, so that we will never know how old it is. This is fish poisoning, historically known to have been practiced by Indians in the Far West, in the Southeast and along the rim of the Caribbean, in Mexico and Central America.

Some 20 species of plants were used, with the buckeye and the devil's shoestring favored in the East and the soaproot and turkey mullein in California. A kind of elixir was made by steeping the mashed buckeye, which contains cyanide, or the stems and leaves of plants in something other than cooking vessels and spreading it over the waters of a sluggish stream or still pond. The poisoned or narcotized fish floated up to the hands of the gatherers.

Ethnographers, who draw their conclusions from observation or historically recorded information, tend to place poisoning low on the list of fishing methods. Unless qualified, this may be a misreading. Too often repeated, poisoning would soon render a fishing ground devoid of fish. More probably, the custom was to do a poisoning session at some time when a large take was wanted, for example in the fall to harvest for smoking and winter keeping. Thus, though only a once or twice a year event, the poisoning project may have been of great importance in an aboriginal band's economy. If the acorn crop had failed — and such failure would hit deer and turkeys as hard as man — the harvest of a fish poisoning session could be crucial to survival.

For an omnivore like man, fishing is an inevitability, as inevitable as picking berries or hunting deer. With two million years to solve the problems of taking fish in estuaries, in running streams and lakes, in shallow water and deep, it is no wonder that all possible methods were discovered for all existing circumstances. Throughout human history some period of the life of nearly every human being must have been vitally dependent on fish food. In the temperate zone there can be little doubt that at the tag end of winter, with winter stores depleted and the game thin and hunted out and the greens season weeks away, fish were the only food to be had in sustaining quantity. Probably even now, we do not know all the tricks of the prehistoric fisherman's trade.

Only about five per cent of the surface of North America is water-covered — by lakes, ponds, rivers and tributary streams. By reason of that beneficent medium, however, this five per cent was more productive of food per acre than any area of vegetation and the animal life it carried, even an area ten times that size. Amerinds made their way in the New World by fishing as well as hunting and were equally knowledgeable about both. In truth, today's fisherman and hunter are the heritors of a proud tradition the roots of which are firmly lodged in the dim and distant past.

Salt Water Bottom Rigs and Baits

by Vlad Evanoff

Salt-water anglers who fish from party or head boats, private boats, rental skiffs, docks, piers, bridges, jetties, and even from the surf, use many different kinds of bottom fishing rigs and an assortment of natural baits.

The type of rig you use will depend on the species of fish you are seeking, where you are fishing, and the natural bait you will be using. Some fish feed right on the bottom and want a bait lying on the sand, mud, shell bed, or rocks. Others feed a foot or two off the bottom, while still others may want a bait presented at a mid-depth.

You can buy many kinds of "ready-made" bottom rigs in almost any coastal fishing tackle shop. Some of these are good, but others may have too much hardware or may be too expensive. Some commercially tied rigs may have the wrong hook style or wrong size. The snells or leader material may be too thick or too weak, too long or too short, or too low or too high on the fishing line.

Some of the best bottom fishing is found around obstructions and broken bottoms — piles, rocks, coral, mussels, sunken wrecks, weeds and kelp — consequently many bottom rigs are lost or broken off. By tying your own rigs you not only save money, you can also tailor the rig to your exact specifications and needs. Most "regular" or "pro" bottom fishermen are pretty fussy about their rigs and prefer to tie their own.

To tie various kinds of bottom rigs you need nylon monofilament, cable or stainless steel wire, hooks, sinkers, three-way swivels, spreaders, snaps, snap-swivels, and fish-finders.

The hooks usually used for bottom fishing include the flounder or Chestertown, blackfish or Virginia, Carlisle or Pacific Bass, Sproat, Cod, Beak or Eagle Claw, and O'Shaughnessy. Most of these will range in sizes from No. 1 to 8/0 or 9/0 and can be bought economically in boxes of 100.

Sinkers for bottom fishing include bell or dipsey, oval or egg, round or ball, bank, diamond, and pyramid. These range from an ounce or two up to 16 ounces. Occasionally, for fishing in very deep water or strong currents you may need even heavier ones.

Although there are hundreds of different kinds of bottom rigs used in coastal waters, a few are basic and most popular. After you have learned to tie some of these rigs, you can easily create other versions to suit your local needs and preferences.

Basic Bottom Rig Called the "deep-sea" rig on northern party boats, this simple rig is used for porgies, sea bass, blackfish, and cod in northern waters. In southern waters you can use it for croakers, spot, sheepshead, grunts, snappers, and other bottom fish. It consists of a snelled hook or a hook on a short leader tied a few inches above the sinker. The quickest and simplest way to do this is to tie a loop on the fishing line and then add your snelled hook. You can also use a three-way swivel or cross-line swivel or some kind of spreader to help keep your hook away from your fishing line and prevent tangles. If you want a two-hook rig simply add a second hook above the first one.

The length of the snell or leader holding the hook will vary. So will the distance it is tied above the sinker or from the other hook. For small fish such as porgies or sea bass, you can use shorter snells and tie the hooks closer to the sinker, but for cod or pollock you should use longer snells and tie them higher up on the line. And, of course, the size and style of the hook you use will also vary according to the fish you are seeking and its size.

Flounder Rigs These rigs are used to catch winter flounders. In the past, many anglers have used wire or plastic spreaders with two hooks for these fish, but in recent years with light spinning tackle and other light outfits, they have found all this hardware and extra weight

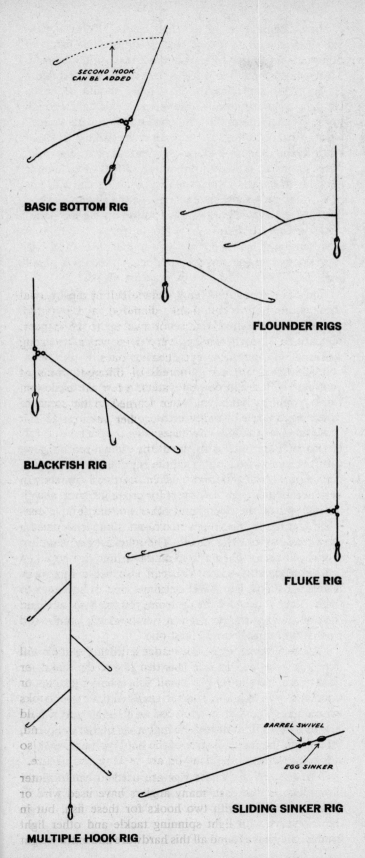

BASIC BOTTOM RIG

SECOND HOOK
CAN BE ADDED

FLOUNDER RIGS

BLACKFISH RIG

FLUKE RIG

BARREL SWIVEL

EGG SINKER

SLIDING SINKER RIG

MULTIPLE HOOK RIG

unnecessary. You just tie a single Chestertown hook on a foot-long snell a couple of inches above the sinker. You don't even need a three-way swivel, but can tie the snell directly to the line. To make a two-hook flounder rig, you can tie another hook to the snell or leader of the first one at about the middle.

Blackfish Rig   The blackfish rig is similar to the two-hook flounder rig except that the second hook is added on a shorter snell to the middle of the longer one. This rig can also be used for croakers, sheepshead, and many other bottom species. Both the blackfish and sheepshead are notorious bait stealers and, with two baited hooks, you'll have to reel in less often. You can also use two different baits. One can be a fiddler crab and the other one can be a tough piece of conch or clam, which is hard for a fish to steal.

Sliding Sinker Rig   The sliding sinker rig is a very popular bottom rig in southern waters and is widely used from party boats, drift boats, small boats, piers, and bridges. An egg-shaped sinker with a hole running through it is the key. The sinker is slipped on the line above a barrel swivel and the leader and hook are tied to the other end. The length and strength of this leader and the size and pattern of the hook you use will depend on the tackle and the fish sought. It can be used for bonefish, permit, grunts, snappers, small grouper, or any other fish that takes bait from the bottom. If you leave some slack in your line, a fish can take the line freely without feeling the weight of the sinker.

Fluke Rig   This rig is used for summer flounders or fluke and features a leader anywhere from 2 to 3 feet long. Tie a Carlisle or Pacific Bass long-shanked hook to the end of the leader. Sizes from 3/0 to 5/0 are best for small fish, while 6/0 or 7/0 hooks can be used for the big doormats. To hold the strip of squid or baitfish more securely, many anglers like to tie a second smaller hook near the eye of the larger one and impale the bait on both hooks. You can also buy ready-made two-hook fluke hooks in many coastal tackle stores. The leader and hook should be tied a few inches above the sinker when fishing over mud, sand or gravel bottoms. In rocky areas, you can tie it somewhat higher on the line.

Multiple Hook Rig   The "multiple hook" rig is popular for whiting or silver hake in northern waters. Use Carlisle or Aberdeen hooks in sizes from 2/0 to 5/0, and tie one above the other until you have four or five on the line. Silversides or spearing, sand eels or strips of fish can be used as bait for the whiting. The same rig with smaller hooks can also be used for smelt, mackerel, herring, and other fish that travel in big schools and feed near the bottom. When tying this rig, attach the snells and hooks to the line or leader with loops and knots rather than with hardware.

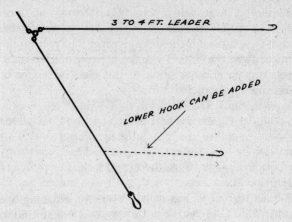

HIGH LEADER RIG

3 TO 4 FT. LEADER

LOWER HOOK CAN BE ADDED

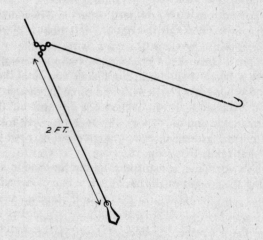

2 FT.

COD-POLLOCK-TILEFISH RIG

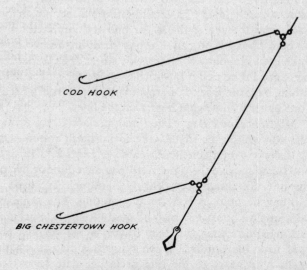

COD HOOK

BIG CHESTERTOWN HOOK

COD-SNOWSHOE FLOUNDER RIG

High Leader Rig The "high leader" rig is a good one for fish such as striped bass, weakfish, bluefish, and other active fish that often swim and feed off the bottom. Tie the hook from 3 to 4 feet above the sinker and add a leader of the same length. The sinker should be heavy enough to hold bottom in the current, but light enough to move when lifted. This rig can be baited with a sandworm, strip of squid, shedder, soft crab, shrimp, or small baitfish and bounced along the bottom with the tide. After letting it out about one hundred feet or so, reel it back in slowly and repeat the process. You can add another hook on a short snell just above the sinker to catch bottom feeders while waiting for action on the top hook.

Cod-Pollock-Tilefish Rig Hooks from 7/0 to 9/0 are used with this rig for big cod and tilefish. You can use skimmer clams for cod, pollock or hake. A small whole squid or cut fish can be used for tilefish.

Cod-Snowshoe Flounder Rig When fishing in waters that contain both cod and snowshoe flounders, you can use this combination rig. On the bottom snell tie a big No. 4 Chestertown hook a few inches above the sinker. Then, about two feet above this hook, tie a cod hook on a longer snell or leader. The cod hook can be baited with a half or whole skimmer, while the lower hook should be baited with thin slivers of clam or with the stringy mantle of a skimmer.

Sinker Release Rigs When fishing on the bottom for tarpon or other gamefish that leap or make long, fast runs, or when using very light tackle and you want to get rid of the sinker, the two "sinker release" rigs shown here can be used. In the top one you tie a barrel swivel on the end of the line, then add the leader and hook. Then you tie on the sinker on a short dropper to one of the barrel-swivel eyes. This line should be very weak so that it will break when a fish leaps or runs.

The second rig starts off with a barrel swivel, and leader and hook, but here an egg or oval sinker is tied to the barrel swivel with soft wire. Make only a loose turn or two so it stays on while fishing, but comes off when a fish leaps or runs.

Striper Drifting Rig The striper drifting rig shown here is a good one to use when drifting from a boat in tidal rivers, bays, inlets, and off the beaches. Tie a small three-way swivel about 8 or 10 inches above a one- or two-ounce sinker. Then, tie a 30-inch leader and a No. 2/0 or 3/0 hook to the eye of the swivel and attach your fishing line to the remaining eye. Bait the hook with a whole sandworm.

Surf Bottom Rigs Surf anglers fishing for striped bass, channel bass, weakfish, kingfish, whiting, and bluefish use the two surf bottom rigs shown. The top one is the "fish finder" rig which makes use of a fish-finder gadget (or you can substitute a large size snap-swivel

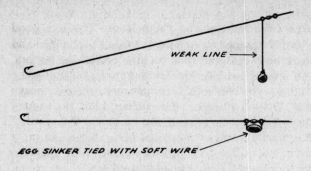

WEAK LINE →

EGG SINKER TIED WITH SOFT WIRE

SINKER RELEASE RIGS

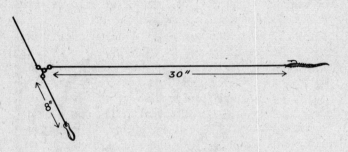

← 30″ →

8″

STRIPER DRIFTING RIG

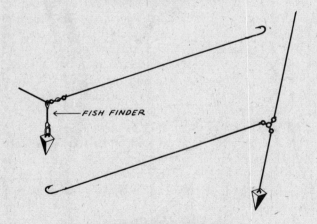

← FISH FINDER

SURF BOTTOM RIGS

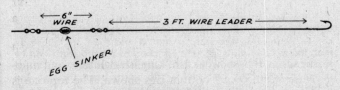

← 6″ WIRE → ← 3 FT. WIRE LEADER →

EGG SINKER

GROUPER RIG

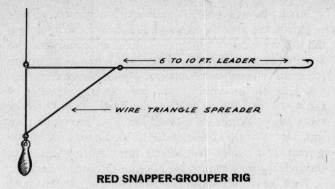

← 6 TO 10 FT. LEADER →

← WIRE TRIANGLE SPREADER

RED SNAPPER-GROUPER RIG

instead) which has an eye through which the fishing line runs. Then tie a barrel swivel on the end of the line to act as a stop for the sinker sliding up and down. Now attach your leader and hook to the other eye of the barrel swivel. The leaders range from two to four feet long. Hooks will vary according to the fish sought and its size. Usually Eagle Claw and O'Shaughnessy patterns are favored for surf fishing.

The standard surf rig makes use of a three-way swivel tied a few inches above a pyramid sinker. Next the hook is tied to the three-way swivel. This leader can vary from 14 to 36 inches, depending on the fish sought. If there are bluefish, sharks, or other sharp-toothed fish around, use nylon covered cable or stainless steel wire for leaders on both rigs.

Grouper Rig The grouper rig can be used in shallow and moderate depths. First, attach a barrel swivel to the end of the line, then a short length of stainless steel wire (about 6 or 7 inches). Now, slide an egg sinker on this wire and then add another barrel swivel to the end of the wire. To complete the rig, tie on a three-foot wire leader and the hook.

Deep Water Rig When fishing for red snappers and grouper in deep water, this rig is the favorite. Use a triangular spreader made from heavy wire. This has three eyes, one on each point of the triangle. One eye holds the sinker tied right up close. The eye extending out holds the leader hook. Because red snappers and even grouper may shy away from this hardware you should use a 6- to 10-foot leader. Tie your fishing line to the remaining eye on the wire spreader.

SALT-WATER BAITS — How to Hook Them

You can use many different kinds of salt-water baits with the rigs described above. It depends on the fish you are seeking, the waters you are fishing, and what the fish want on a given day. How you hook these various baits is important, because a bait should be hooked to stay alive, remain securely on the hook, and be presented in an attractive manner to the fish.

When using a whole sandworm for striped bass or weakfish, the best way to hook it is to run the hook into the worm's mouth and then out about an inch away. Use a small No. 2/0 or 3/0 hook for this. When using worms for small fish such as flounders, porgies, blackfish, croakers, kingfish, or whiting, use only about a quarter of the worm and thread this on the hook. Two, three or more whole worms on a hook are more attractive than just one. When surf fishing for striped bass with bloodworms, you can pierce two or three worms just once through the middle with the hook so the ends wriggle.

With the popular skimmer clam, you can use the entire insides for big cod, striped bass, black drum or channel bass. For small cod, pollock, haddock and hake, cut the clam into two or three sections. For fish with small mouths such as porgies and blackfish, a small piece on a hook is enough. For snowshoe flounders or sea flounders, cut the clam into narrow slivers or use the stringy mantle and pierce it two or three times.

Many kinds of crabs can be used for bottom fishing. Small, hard green crabs are used for blackfish. Fiddler crabs can be used for blackfish and also for sheepshead. Hermit crabs make fine bait for bonefish, permit, sheepshead, snappers and blackfish. Small, hard blue crabs are used for tarpon and permit. Big blue crabs can be used for black drum, channel bass and grouper.

Hard crabs can be hooked by running the hook from the underside out through the top shell. With fiddler crabs, you can remove the big claw and insert the hook in the hole that is left. After you remove a hermit crab from its shell, run the hook through the entire body and into the soft tail section. Soft-shell and shedder crabs can also be used for many fish. You can wrap these soft baits around a hook with thread or rubber bands.

The big edible shrimp make great baits in southern waters for many fish. When hooking a live shrimp, run the hook through the hard part of the head, taking care not to hit the dark spot inside the body. Another way to hook a live shrimp is through the tail, running the hook from the underside and out through the top. For small fish, you can use only the tail section after peeling off the hard shell. Thread the hook through the entire tail.

The natural squid is one of the most versatile baits you can use for many salt-water species. A small, whole squid can be hooked by running the hook through the tail and body and then through the head or eyes. A big, wide, long strip of squid makes a good bait for cod, pollock, bluefish, striped bass, and channel bass. A long, narrow strip of squid can be used for summer flounders or fluke in combination with a live killie or a dead baitfish. And a tiny piece of squid on a hook can be used for many of the smaller bottom species.

When using dead baitfish such as spearing, sand eels,

shiners, pilchards or herring, a quick way to hook them is to run the hook through both eyes. A more secure way and better method to hook the fish is to run the hook through both eyes and then into the body near the tail.

When using live baitfish such as killies, mullet, pinfish, and others, you can hook them through the back for still fishing. When drifting or slow trolling, hook the baitfish through the upper lip or both lips.

And finally, you can cut a fillet from almost any small fish and use it for cod, pollock, tilefish, red snapper, grouper, channel bass, bluefish, weakfish or sea trout. Pierce the fillet two or three times with the hook so it stays on securely. You can also cut a chunk or small steak from a thin fish and put it on the hook by running the hook through the meat twice. For small fish with small mouths you can cut the fish into tiny pieces and use these for bait.

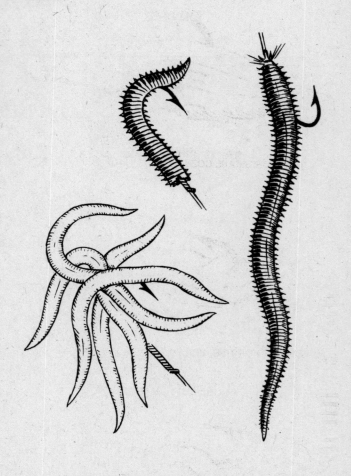

When hooking a whole sandworm for striped bass or weakfish run the hook into the worm's mouth and then out about an inch below the mouth. A small section of a sandworm can be threaded on the hook for fish with smaller mouths. When using bloodworms, just pierce the worm once through the middle so the ends wriggle. For striped bass, two, three or even four bloodworms on a hook make a more attractive bait.

FOR BIG COD, STRIPED BASS, BLACK DRUM

FOR SMALL COD, POLLOCK, HAKE

FOR PORGIES, SEA BASS, BLACKFISH

FOR SNOWSHOE OR SEA FLOUNDER

HOOKING SKIMMER CLAMS

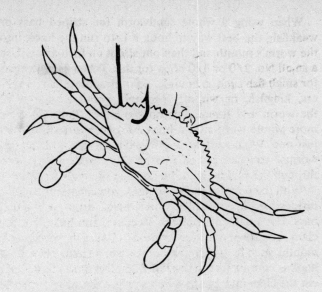

HOOKING HARD SHELL BLUE CRAB

You can tie the best bottom rig in the world and use the best bait you can get, but you also have to know how to use these rigs and baits effectively. Here are some bottom fishing tips that should help you get more bites, and hook and catch more fish:

Monofilament line can be used in shallow and moderate depth when bottom fishing, but in deep water dacron line will be better because it has less stretch. The smaller diameter of the line enables you to use less weight and put more line on your reel.

It is very important to use a sinker that will hold bottom when anchored or drag along the bottom when drifting. In shallow water and weak tides you can use lighter sinkers. In deep water and strong tides you need heavier weights. When drifting with little or no wind or tide, use lighter weights. On windy days or in strong tides, you'll need heavier sinkers. Conditions may vary during the day or in different spots, so you have to keep changing sinkers as required.

The general rule is to use big baits if you want big fish. A smaller bait will catch more small fish, but it is quickly stolen by the small fish, and the big ones don't get a crack at it. A big bait also gives you more fishing time on the bottom, because you don't have to reel in as often to check your bait.

Once you locate a good bottom-fishing spot, throw over a marker buoy with a line and weight to mark the spot. Then you can anchor near it, or drift past the same spot as long as the fish keep biting.

A drifting boat usually produces better than an anchored one, especially when the fish are scattered or the fishing grounds are spread out. You cover more territory and always present the bait to new fish. And drifting gives your bait more movement and action.

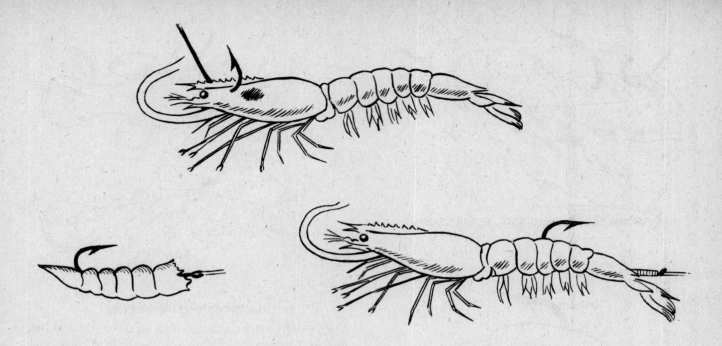

One way to hook a live shrimp is through the hard part of the head, but don't hit the dark spot inside the body. Another way to hook a whole live shrimp is to run the hook from the under-side of the tail and out through the top. For small fish, you can use just the meat from the tail and thread it on a hook.

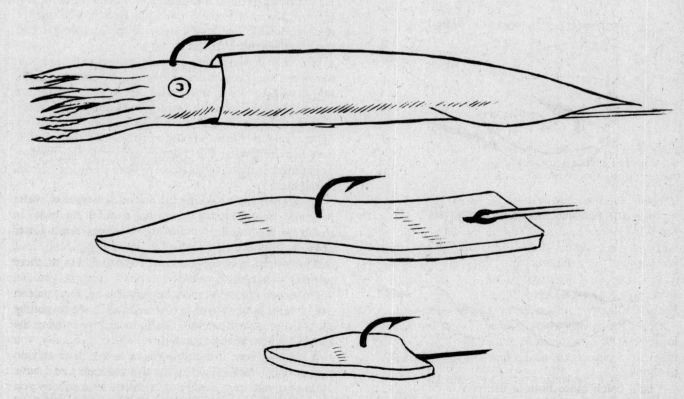

A whole, small squid can be hooked by running the hook through the body twice, then through the head or eyes. A big strip can be hooked twice, while a small piece can be hooked once.

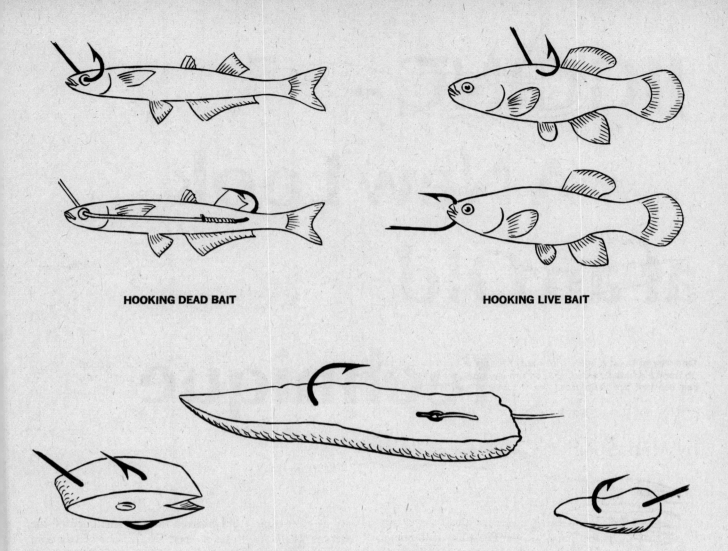

HOOKING DEAD BAIT

HOOKING LIVE BAIT

You can cut a fillet from almost any small fish and use it for cod, red snappers, grouper, tilefish or pollock on a bottom rig. Hook the fillet two or three times so it stays on well. You can also cut a chunk or small steak from a thin fish and put that on the hook as shown. For small fish you can cut a small piece of fish and use it on a hook.

Using two different baits on the same hook often gets more action than just one bait. Such "cocktails" offer the fish a choice and also enable you to use one tough bait and a softer one. If the softer bait is stolen or lost, you will still have the tough bait left on the hook.

Most bottom species will grab a slow-moving bait, but some prefer a bait which is lying still on the bottom or hanging still while suspended above the bottom.

One trick to use when drifting for bottom fish is to lower your rod and even let out some line if you feel a nibble or a bite. Then, wait a few seconds before you set the hook.

You'll catch more bottom fish if you chum an area before or during the fishing. Crushed clams, mussels, crabs, shrimp, and ground-up fish can all be used. You

can also use canned dog or cat food. In shallow water you can simply scatter this chum around the boat. In deeper water put it in a mesh bag or chum pot and lower it to the bottom.

If your sinker or rig gets hung up on the bottom, there are a few things you can try to release it. First, you can let out slack line, then reel in and pull hard. Or, you can try moving your rod to the left and right while pulling on the line. If you are in a boat you can try moving the line to the opposite side and then pull on it. Finally, you can grab the line and pull hard, releasing it quickly so that it snaps back. If you still can't get free, you'll have to break your line. Tighten your drag as much as you can, lower your rod so it faces the line, and pull hard until it breaks.

JIGGING – A New Look at an Old Technique

by Mark Sosin

There are so many fish stacked vertically over the wreck that the graph paper on the recording fathometer looks as if someone just spilled a bottle of black ink all over the tracings. A cloud of amberjack has formed that ominous "blotch" on the face of the machine and even the babies in the bunch will pull the needle on any scale to at least 40 pounds.

As you watch your two-ounce bucktail plummet out of sight in the crystalline tropical waters and invade enemy territory, it is perfectly normal to question your own sanity. In less than a minute, you're going to be belly up to the gunwale or standing spread-legged on a casting platform desperately struggling to retain your grip on a slender shaft of fiberglass that is beginning to resemble an inverted "U". The rod tip is tickling the surface of the sea, while the butt digs deeper in your gut, forcing you to grunt as you try to draw a breath.

Ignoring your mental reservations and realizing that it is too late to have second thoughts (because there is no way to recover your lure), you begin to pump and reel. The strike is vicious. Line streaks off the reel with author-ity as your quarry crash-dives for the sanctuary of the depths. It's going to be at least a half hour of barroom brawling with that unseen animal before the battle ends (assuming you land the fish), and you're going to curse that critter a hundred times as your muscles ache and sweat collects in random puddles. To the inveterate deep jigger, however, this is pure pleasure and a way of life.

The technique of probing every layer of water with a jig is one of the most effective fish-catching methods in the light-tackle angler's arsenal. A handful of specialists in South Florida have worked overtime to refine this valuable art on the salt water scene, yet the entire pro-cedure is equally valid in fresh water. If you ever have an opportunity to watch a man like Blake Honeycutt of Hickory, North Carolina, work a Hopkins Shorty #75 along a submerged creek bed, you'll be convinced that vertical jigging can be the answer to catching largemouths under certain conditions. It also does the job on striped bass, whether they're off the coast or locked in an im-poundment. The basic approach works on lake trout, and it will produce other trout species in lakes where the fish

Large grouper like the one the author just landed will inhale a bucktail readily and offer a tough angling challenge on light gear.

White, mylar-dressed arrowhead bucktails can be jigged effectively when stripers are concentrated during the late fall.

are deep. Crappie and walleye fishermen have been using jigs for a long time, so they don't need any encouragement.

Learning to work a jig is not difficult, but — like any other facet of fishing — it takes practice until you can begin to master some of the intricacies. Those anglers who have bounced jigs off a variety of bottoms soon develop a feel and eventually manipulate that hunk of lead and hair like a puppeteer handling his charges.

The major advantage of vertical jigging is simply that you cover every tier from the bottom to the surface. If you seek a single species, this enables you to scout the entire range of its habitat until you locate your quarry. On the marine scene, it permits you to fish for a number of species at the same time. A jig worked at the floor of the sea will produce bottom dwellers, but as the offering moves toward the surface, it enters the territory of the pelagic species.

Most light tackle jigging is done in water depths up to perhaps 200 or 225 feet. There are a few veterans who might, on occasion, probe deeper, but you're at the limits around 35 fathoms. In lakes, depths would naturally be much shallower.

Normally, experienced jiggers prefer to fish around some form of structure. It might be a reefline, wreck, or an offshore hump in salt water, and possibly a creek bed, brush pile, or sudden rise in the lake floor in fresh water. There are times, however, when you might try a stretch of water that doesn't have any distinguishing features, but is known to harbor plenty of fish. One clue can usually be gleaned from trollers. If they are plodding back and forth in an area, you might want to drift through and jig it. At times, species such as striped bass and bluefish will feed ravenously on the surface and then disappear. Often, they remain in the area, coming topside in flurries of activity and then diving again. That's a good time to work a bucktail or metal by jigging from the bottom to the surface.

Unless the water is particularly shallow, avoid the temptation to cast. As long as the boat passing overhead won't spook your quarry, the water is deep enough for vertical jigging. That's the toughest concept to accept. The majority of anglers feel they can cover more territory and catch a greater number of fish by casting. There are times when they may be right, but I think you'll discover more situations when working the lure straight up and down is the answer. The lure seems to have a better action when it is retrieved vertically.

The trick is to allow the boat to drift over the area you want to fish and simply drop the jigs right over the side and free spool them until they hit bottom. If you don't feel the jig strike bottom, you can usually tell by watching the line because it will go slack for an instant. Of

Working a bucktail over a North Carolina wreck produced this nice cobia for Joel Arrington on spinning gear. Note the short butt on a rod designed for jigging.

Deep jigging near Diamond Shoals produced this bluefish. Jigging rods feature short butts to aid in fighting the fish.

course, if you're fishing a creek bed channel, you'll probably use the electric motor to keep the boat positioned and to follow the intricate turns the creek might make.

It doesn't take long to recognize when the boat is drifting correctly, and you soon begin to feel uncomfortable when you can't get the right type of drift. Not long ago, I was fishing the oil rigs off the Louisiana Coast; the skipper was so skillful at handling his boat that he insisted on holding us in one position just off the platform even though the current was reasonably strong. He had never seen deep jigging before and it took some explaining before I could get him to ease up to a platform, throw the boat in neutral, and let the current carry us away. The moment he modified his boat handling, we couldn't stop getting hits and catching fish. Before that, it was a slow pick at best.

No rules in fishing can be perfectly rigid, and there are exceptions to this one, as well. When wind, tide, current, or a combination of factors moves the boat so fast that you can't get a jig down to the bottom easily, the trick is to cast up current and let the lure settle. By the time the boat has reached the spot, the jig should be right below you.

There are other subtle approaches. If you are working over a wreck, reef, hump, or other type of structure in salt water where the fish are big and the tackle is light,

you want to gain every advantage. Whenever possible, drifts should be made parallel to the structure or from shallower to deeper water. If the boat moves from deep to shallow, your line could inadvertently be dragged over obstructions and be cut, or the fish can burrow on the backside of the structure and you have no chance of getting them out.

The basic method of retrieve is nothing more than rhythmically lifting and dropping the rod tip, causing the jig to climb and then nosedive. You can learn this in a few minutes, but the refinements take longer. Sophisticated enthusiasts picture mentally what their lure is doing at all times. They develop a sense that tells them the approximate depth at which the lure happens to be at any given moment, and they are more often right than wrong. It is this intense concentration coupled with desire that brings the best results.

Veterans often use one form of retrieve near the bottom and then vary the motions at mid-depth to appeal to other species. If you get a hit close to the bottom but the fish isn't hooked, put the reel in free spool after one or two more lifts with the rod and drop right back to the target. Frequently, you can elicit a second strike. Many bottom dwellers aren't going to climb very high to get the lure, so you'll want to put it in the productive zone quickly.

At mid-depth in salt water, you are dealing with pelagic species and it isn't quite as simple. My own preference after a missed strike is to continue the retrieve for a few more feet. If nothing happens, I may drop back 20 or 30 feet and then begin the retrieve again, working the jig right to the surface.

In fresh water, you often find suspended fish that will maintain their position at a given depth. Crappie do this and so do bass and other species. You can use a counting technique to find that depth. Until you locate the concentration of fish, you might want to retrieve from the bottom to the surface. When you hook a fish, drop down and let the lure go to the bottom. Jig it a few times. Then, turn the reel handle five times and jig some more. If you don't hook a fish, crank five turns again and jig. Continue the procedure until you get a hit. Then, you can lower the lure to the bottom, wind up the right number of turns, and hook a fish.

To the majority of anglers, all leadheaded bucktails appear to be the same, and minor variations of head shape or dressing are normally ignored. The jigging enthusiast learns early in the game, however, that head shape can be critical and that all bucktails are not identical. The configuration of the lead actually determines how the lure will perform in the water. Most specialists tend to prefer jigs that have a knife edge on one side or that are shaped like an arrow. They try to avoid bucktails that are rounded on all sides when they have to probe deep.

Equally important, if you were to suspend the bucktail from a loop of monofilament, the lure should automatically assume a 45-degree angle (approximately) with the horizontal. Try this test with a number of different bucktails and you'll discover that most of them will rest parallel with the ground when they are suspended. A lure with a tapered edge that normally hangs at a 45-degree angle is going to cut through the water erratically when you lift the rod or when it falls freely. Other bucktails merely follow an up-and-down course, failing to produce the extra action.

The weight of the lure depends on the tackle you select, the depth of the water, and the amount of wind or current you must counter. The best approach is to use the lightest lure that will get to the bottom reasonably quickly. In water up to 200 feet deep, using 15 pound test monofilament line I seldom find it necessary to use more than 2¼ ounce bucktails. If you insist on heavier line, however, you're going to require lures that weigh four ounces

This outfit is tailored for jigging. The reel boasts a manual pickup that will rotate under pressure and the rod has plenty of reserve power. The strength of the rod lies between the reel and the first guide.

Charlie McCurdy is pleased with this huge jack crevalle that fell for a jig over a Key West wreck. The plug tackle is only slightly heavier than most anglers would select for large-mouth bass.

or more to do the same job. Of course, when you fish fresh water, most of the jigs you use will be much lighter and your tackle will also be more yielding. One thought you might want to remember is that you may happen upon a situation where the use of a heavy bucktail in relatively shallow water can turn big fish on. I can't tell you why it happens, but there are occasions when the crashing of a heavy jig bouncing on the bottom gets an immediate response.

For marine use, I prefer white bucktails dressed with Mylar. Nylon skirts also work well and are particularly valuable on fish with sharp teeth, but, in my judgment, there is no substitute for deer tail. Other colors will also work, yet I have always favored white, and it is probably the choice of most veteran offshore jiggers.

It always pays to play the percentages regardless of the type of fishing you prefer. It's no different with jigging. Many of us add a plastic worm to the hook of a bucktail. This is the same worm worshipped by largemouth bass anglers. Color of the worm is a matter of personal choice, but my two favorites are a pearly white or a middle green. Some of the new twist-tail worms add a beautiful swimming action to the bucktail. All you do is thread an inch or so of the worm on the jig hook and let the worm trail behind the dressing on the lure. You can also use a variety of other materials, but I tend to believe that some addition to the hook produces more fish. With smaller bucktails, you simply cut the head end of the worm.

Tipping a jig with natural bait is another technique that can be deadly. On smaller jigs, you may want to add a piece of shrimp or a strip of squid. For deep water work where the fish get husky, a whole balao hanging from the hook will catch its share of fish. You'll discover that early and late in the day when light levels are low in the depths, a tipped jig produces far more fish than a plain bucktail. Some anglers favor metal instead of buck-tails for jigging. Diamond jigs and hammered metal jigs such as the Hopkins are excellent in many waters. Perhaps one reason that bucktails are used in some places is that a lot of lures are lost to fish you will never see; it's just cheaper to sacrifice the leadheads.

Light tackle jigging centers around plug tackle or spinning gear and, in salt water, many of the rods are custom constructed to incorporate the necessary features. New rod blanks have recently been introduced in the marketplace that offer a combination of lightness and strength. A jigging rod must have tremendous back-bone to lift a fish once it is hooked. If the rod doubles over and the tip collapses, you'll never get your quarry to the surface. For openers, the rod you select should be able to lift five pounds of weight off the floor with the

The formidable dentures on big snapper and other species often dictate the use of heavy mono shock leaders or wire.

Although they are not always as effective as jigs, spoons can often be worked vertically and will produce fish. This striper found the fluttering action of a spoon to be particularly appealing.

weight tied six inches from the tiptop and still have plenty of reserve power.

Plug rods for salt water use are usually seven feet long with a short butt. Unless you were raised in country where these rods are popular, it will take a little time before you are willing to accept the short butt. Its advantage is that the rod stays close to your body, making it easier to fight a good fish.

Tailored jigging rods have a relatively stiff tip that seems to dip slowly as the rod with jig attached is lifted. Then, the tip tends to spring upward almost flipping the jig through the water. It's a subtle action, but it can make the difference in catching fish. Looking at the rods from the other side, you don't want a fast tip or soft tip that will collapse easily. Otherwise, the tip will absorb all the action you are trying to impart to the lure.

Sometimes, a slightly longer spinning rod adds to the lifting power, but again, a short butt will prove more comfortable in the long run if you expect to tackle big fish. The rod may be 7½ or even 8 feet long, but it won't have an extended foregrip or butt. If you haven't seen one, you might suspect that the rod maker didn't know how to build a spinning rod of that length. It is meant for a specialized purpose, however, and does the job.

For smaller fish and shallower water, you can increase your choice of rods. Lake-bound anglers often find the so-called "worm rods" to be effective jigging sticks, because the tips are relatively stiff and the rods have backbone. There are also going to be times when you jig with small lures and ultra-light tackle. As long as the rod will work the jig and has the backbone to lift a fish, you're in business.

The greatest shortcoming of most casting reels is the drag system. The mass of fishermen fail to understand the need for smooth drags and therefore they don't demand the necessary performance from the manufacturers. Almost all of the sophisticated deep jiggers searching for heavyweight denizens modify the drags on spinning and bait-casting reels either by changing the material of the drag washers or, in some cases, having someone make or modify parts. I mention this in the hope that you will study the performance of your reels carefully and keep the drag in top working order.

To lift a fish out of the depths or to stop a fish from reaching cover in shallow water, you must apply maximum pressure and that is only possible when the mechanical drag performs smoothly. Any jerkiness or erratic behavior in the drag will cost you a fish. It's easy to recognize a properly performing drag. When you hook a fish and it is taking line, the rod tip should arch over and remain relatively stable. If the rod tip is bouncing up and down, the drag will be jerky. The ultimate drag

The bucktail jig is one of the deadliest lures on the market. Here, Bob Stearns admires a husky jack crevalle he took on a light plugging outfit with 12-pound test line and a white bucktail.

is one that will yield line without undue starting pressure on a fast-running fish and again when your quarry barely exerts enough pressure to turn the spool.

Spinning devotees must also inspect the rollers on their reels. Many will not turn under the pressure of a fast-running fish, and the line will be dragged across them. If a roller is made of tungsten carbide, it will chew up monofilament line faster than any other material in use today. That's why many jigging fans convert their spinning mills to manual pickup. The bigger manual rollers usually perform well with minimum maintenance.

The breaking strength of the line you select should be tailored to the fish you seek, conditions under which you must fish, and your own angling skill. From a sporting standpoint, 15-pound test in salt water is a good choice. You may want to go lighter for smaller species. However, if you choose to go heavier, you'll need more weight in the lure to reach the same depth.

Lines should be inspected frequently and changed when necessary. The tendency is to get by with an old line; when you are applying maximum pressure, such a marginal line will cost you fish. Because of bottom

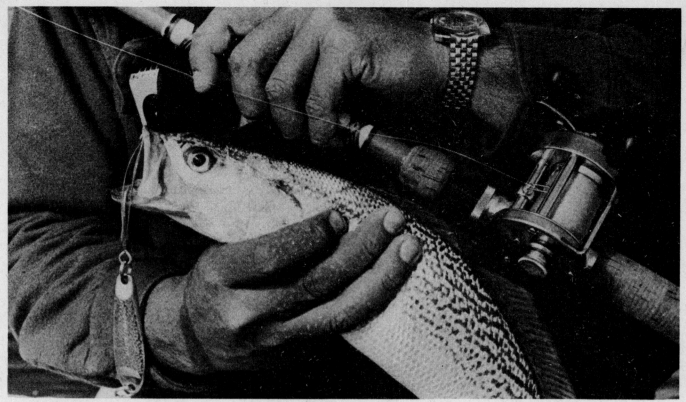

You can jig in shallow water as well as deep. This nice weakfish hit a small Hopkins in 15 feet of water.

Jigging around brush piles and dropoffs in fresh water impoundments will produce striped bass like this beauty about to be netted in Oklahoma's Keystone Reservoir.

A spoon worked vertically proved the nemesis for this trophy lake trout on Snowbird Lake, North West Territories. Jim Thurston is about to remove the lure and release the fish.

of the lure sometimes gives the edge to the fish and enables it to get rid of your offering. Jig hooks are frequently heavy-gauge wire and that makes it more difficult for the barb to penetrate the jaw of a fish. Use a file or hone to sharpen every jig hook before you use it. The trick is to create cutting edges. Hold the hook by the bend with the point on top and facing away from you. A few forward strokes with a file or hone toward the hook point will do the job. Make sure the file is at a 45-degree angle to the hook and work one side and then the other.

Beginners believe that the moment the barb is planted, they can use the reel as a winch and crank their quarry to the top. This might work on small fish, but it's suicide on the huskier critters that call the depths their home. You'll find that most fish hit a jig as it is falling. Usually you'll start the next lift and feel the fish there, but the strike actually took place on the fall. The first step is to set the hook by lifting the rod in a series of short, sharp, upward jabs. Then, hang on. If there is any size to your quarry, it will respond in panic and take line from the reel. There's little you can do to stop this initial onslaught. Once the fish pauses, however, it's time to go to work.

The technique of fighting a fish is to pump it slowly to the surface, using your rod as a lever and your reel only to recover the controlled slack you created by pumping. Generally, the boat will be right over the fish and your job is to lift. With a fish that stays up on the surface, you can pump rapidly, but an animal that sulks in the depths must be moved slowly. Start with the rod tip at or near the water and lift the rod slowly and steadily. As the rod reaches a little above a 45-degree angle with the horizontal (measured from the butt), lower the rod tip quickly and reel in at the same time. The secret is not to create slack line. That means you must develop rhythm so that you recover the line at the same rate that the rod tip is dropping. As soon as the rod is near the water, start to lift again and repeat the procedure. There will be times when you are in a standoff and can't move the fish, but you must keep trying. And, once you get a fish coming your way, don't stop pumping. Keep your quarry coming until it dives again or it's on the surface.

Jigging can become an addiction as soon as you realize how valuable the technique can be in a variety of situations. Most fishermen, however, ignore it because they don't understand its value. When you have taken your share of fish with this method, you will always think in terms of using a bucktail or metal jig, and you will search for areas where fish may be concentrated. The most important ingredient in jigging is confidence. The moment you gain it, you will have discovered a *new* way of angling life.

obstructions, lines often become frayed near the lure. Periodically run your hand over this portion and, if you feel any nicks, cut the line back and re-tie your lure.

Fish can fray a line close to the bottom and, for that reason, it's a good idea to use a shock leader. The combination you choose depends on where you are fishing, but there are guidelines you should follow. Ultra-light jigging for crappie won't require a shock leader, but any fish with teeth or abrasive mouths will dictate the use of heavier mono or even wire. At sea, it is common practice to use about six feet of 30- to 50-pound test mono attached to your 15-pound test mono. Then, if the fish have teeth, you can add a short section of heavier mono or wire. You'll find that mono will produce more fish than wire when used as a shock leader. The reason for the length of 30-pound to 50-pound mono is to hedge against the fish rubbing the line against rocks, brush, or other objects down below.

Even though the strikes can be savage, it is not always easy to hook a fish on a jig. For one thing, the weight

Smallmouths

by Don Marco

Among anglers who fish for both species, the smallmouth black bass is cherished much more than its cousin, the largemouth. There are many who claim that the bronzeback strikes with greater fury, fights harder, and is tougher to fool with artificial lures or natural baits. All fish are individuals and, although one can generalize about traits and tactics of a species, there are exceptions to the rule.

In most places where smallmouths are abundant, a three pounder is bragging size, a four pounder is considered a trophy, and a five pounder will produce enough conversation to keep the old potbelly stove glowing a warm red long after the last log has turned to ashes. The majority of fish average between a pound and two, but they are tough little competitors and very popular with anglers of every persuasion.

The world-record smallmouth weighed 11 pounds 15 ounces and was taken from Dale Hollow on the Tennessee-Kentucky border back in 1955. By comparison, the record largemouth came from Montgomery Lake, Georgia, in 1932, and pulled the needle on the scale to 22 pounds 4 ounces. Dale Hollow still yields some of the largest smallmouths and there are many aficionados who believe that a new world record will eventually be caught from that lake.

Originally, smallmouths were native to the Ohio River system and Lake Ontario. Historians tell us that transplants followed the pattern of railroad development. As steam locomotives pressed across the rapidly growing network of tracks that began to span our land, smallmouth bass enjoyed a free ride in many of the water tenders that were vital to the performance of the iron horse. In fact, that's how this great gamefish found a home in the Potomac. When the Baltimore and Ohio Railroad finally developed a route over the Alleghenies, smallmouths hitched a ride in some of the water tenders, encouraged, of course, by engineers and firemen who had enjoyed the wonderful sport offered by these tough gamefish.

Today, many states boast a smallmouth population; they are even found on the West Coast from California to Washington. The best smallmouth waters, however, are still in the Eastern half of the United States and range from the Canadian border to Florida, across the top of the Sunshine State to Mississippi, and then northward again. If I had to pick one state for trophy-sized fish, Tennessee would get the nomination. The Tennessee River system has been a haven for smallmouths, and lakes such as Pickwick, Dale Hollow, and Center Hill are top choices. Wilson Lake on the Tennessee River in Alabama is prime territory, and Kentucky's Lake Cumberland also rates an emphatic nod.

Beginners sometimes have difficulty in identifying a smallmouth, because coloration can vary with the habitat. The typical smallmouth is brown to bronze in color and has darker vertical markings on its sides. The largemouth is greenish-black and has a dark horizontal stripe or markings. On a smallmouth, the mandibles of the jaw only extend to the center of the eye, while those on a largemouth usually reach beyond the eye. All black bass have a single dorsal fin, but the dorsal on a largemouth is almost separated in the middle. A smallmouth's dorsal dips in the center, but not as much.

Bronzebacks prefer slightly cooler water temperatures than bigmouths and they are also found in clear streams. Stream fishing for smallmouths is pure delight and you will find the greatest number in waters flowing from one to four knots. They tend to congregate around riffles and in rocky stretches, offering a perfect target for the fly fisherman or the casting enthusiast who enjoys ultra-light lines and small lures.

A fish that lives and feeds in a current will take up a lie where it doesn't have to expend much energy to maintain its position, yet close enough to the flow so that it can feed effectively. Smallmouths follow this pattern. That's why they will be stationed behind or in front of obstructions such as rocks, fallen trees, or other debris that has fallen into the stream.

Study the habitat carefully and try to determine where the zones of "dead water" occur. This might be behind a big rock if the boulder tapers back, but when the rock has a vertical front, dead water will pile up ahead of the rock. Stream fish seldom move very far to get their food. That's why an offering has to be right on target and follow the natural flow close to the lie of the fish. If a smallmouth, for example, had to pursue its meals halfway across the stream, it would expend more energy than the food was worth.

Some rivers have slick glides that pass over rocks or develop right behind low dams. A fish can rest out of the current, rising quickly to inhale a morsel that is swept over the top. One way to fish these glides is to work a surface plug or a popper upstream. Let it swing below the holding area and then twitch and pop it gently toward you, as if a small baitfish were caught in the current and was trying valiantly (if somewhat unsuccessfully) to make headway against the force of the water. Although largemouth anglers sometimes favor loud pops with a surface offering, smallmouth fishermen believe that they do better with a steadier, but muffled commotion.

Many specialists feel that it is important to keep popping a topwater lure in a stream situation. They argue that the current sweeps the lure downstream and, if you only worked the bait occasionally, it would pass over a lot of fish without offering any action to entice the quarry. Keep in mind that any fish in moving water only has a very brief time in which to decide whether to take or reject a bait.

Underwater lures and spinners are excellent smallmouth artificials. The best have a short stroke and create

Roland Martin is about to release a nice Minnesota smallmouth taken in late June when the fish were over the spawning beds.

a lot of vibration. Usually, smallmouths are deep and a lure that sweeps over the rocks while hugging the bottom can do an outstanding job. If you fish spinners, resist the temptation to cast them across the stream and let them swing around. A better method is to make the cast upstream and then work the lure back toward you. It takes practice to develop the timing necessary. The blade should barely turn and the lure has to dust the bottom without hanging up. Colorado blades are the best for this type of fishing because they will create flash and vibration at a slower rate of retrieve than any other spinner configuration.

Smallmouths can be finicky feeders and they are also sometimes difficult to fool. If you run a series of comparative experiments, you'll convince yourself that lighter lines and finer diameter leaders account for more fish. In faster water, you can get by with lines or leaders up to 8-pound test, but, as the current slows, you have to go much lighter to be consistently successful. It is not uncommon to fish smallmouths with four-pound test line and equally fine fly leaders.

As a general rule, the bigger the stream or river, the larger the smallmouth you can expect to catch. Small waters hold diminutive fish. Another interesting sidelight for the fly fisherman is that more big fish will be taken on poppers than on streamer flies. No one has been able to explain why, but continued observations confirm it. The same flyrod outfit that you use for trout will work well for most smallmouths. Poppers should be small, but capable of creating a lot more commotion than you would suspect if you use size as the only criterion. The tail of the popper should be tied in such a way that it does not foul on the cast. If a hunk of hair or a hackle on a fly or popper wraps around the bend of the hook, you can be certain that a smallmouth will reject the artificial.

The trout fisherman can often extend his season by switching to smallmouths. Stream fish begin to feed selectively just as trout do when there is a hatch. They will concentrate on the small insects floating by, and it is not uncommon to take upwards of 30 smallmouths in an evening's sport. They'll rise to a dry fly or take a wet fly just under the surface. If you watch a particular beat,

Smallmouths are tough competitors on light tackle and must be played carefully.

you'll see them dimpling the surface as they feed on the hatch.

Most anglers who have become addicted to smallmouth fishing, dream of the odd moments when they can fool a trophy-sized fish. It doesn't happen all the time, but the personal rewards will outweigh the effort involved. And, there usually is considerable effort. A bragging-size fish varies in different parts of the country. In Minnesota, for example, a four pounder may elicit smiles of approval from envious fishermen, but on Dale Hollow in Tennessee, the same fish would hardly be noticed. There, a bronzeback would have to weigh at least seven pounds to be worthy of the "ohs and ahs."

Billy Westmoreland grew up on the shores of Dale

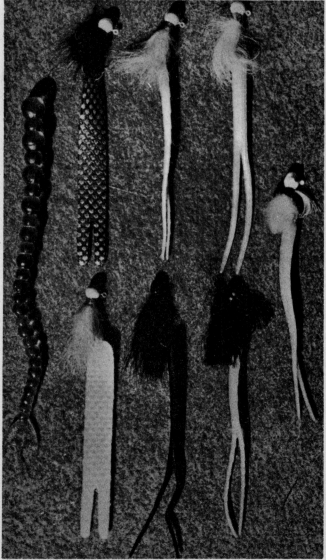

Tiny bucktails with porkrind or artificial tails are an excellent smallmouth bait, especially late in the season when the water is cold.

Hollow, and his knowledge of smallmouths and their life styles is almost legendary. You can learn more in a day aboard his boat than you can plodding along on your own for years. You'll suddenly discover that Billy's theories run counter to everything you have heard about smallmouth fishing. His credentials include a 10-pound smallmouth, but he has lost several fish at boatside that he believes would have been new world records.

Every smallmouth angler knows that his quarry prefers rocky terrain. Even in a lake, the moment you see rocks or gravel along the shoreline, visions of smallmouth form a mental picture. In fact, you'll probably offer a comment to your partner about the possibility of taking a bronzeback. Billy claims that smaller fish might prefer the rocks, but the husky smallmouths spend their days (and nights) over a basically clean bottom. At least in Tennessee, you won't find them near gravel or weeds. The trophy fish will be over red clay, mud, or shale.

Researchers determined a long time ago that smallmouths grow fastest and largest in lakes that harbor an abundance of crawfish. That doesn't mean that you can't catch big fish in other waters, but your chances are better if you concentrate on those lakes that have plenty of crawfish.

Unless someone shows you the areas known for trophy smallmouths, there's a good chance you would pass them up simply because they don't look "fishy." Most of us try to read the waters and apply our knowledge to the habits of the species we seek. The problem in lakes like Dale Hollow is that reading the water goes against everything we ever learned. Billy will tell you to picture a farm sitting on a hillside. There will be pastures, cornfields, and some land that is too rocky to taste the plow. The natural tendency would be to concentrate on the rocky areas. The fish are over the cornfields and the pastures.

The best habitat centers around gently sloping points that extend from the shore into deep water on both sides. This enables the fish to change depth, remain near the bottom, and have the sanctuary of deep water all around. Steep banks that plummet into the lake will drop off sharply underwater and your chances of finding fish diminish. When you read the shoreline, look for flat hills that ease down to the shoreline. You'll probably see a mud or clay bank that doesn't look too exciting, but to the trained eye, it will signal smallmouth habitat.

Largemouths tend to migrate at times and they will suspend when water conditions are right. Smallmouths spend most of their adult lives in a limited area, and they insist on staying on the bottom. You won't find them suspended in a lake.

There's a brief period during the spring when once-in-a-lifetime fish move into shallow water to feed. It hap-

Billy Westmoreland, the legend of Dale Hollow, holds up a stringer of respectable smallmouths. The smallest fish is 3½ pounds, the largest is 6 pounds.

pens rather suddenly when warm rains in late March or early April start to boost the water temperature. Fish can appear in a few feet of water almost overnight, but they will spawn and move back into deeper water when lake temperatures reach the upper 50's or low 60's. A number of factors contribute to how shallow the fish will feed. Cover is very important and you can bet that there will be a direct route to deeper water.

The most steady angling for big fish starts in mid-October and continues well into January on Dale Hollow and similar lakes. When the water temperature drops below 58 degrees, the lake begins to "turn over" and that's a signal for the fish to move in on the sloping points. If fishermen make any mistake, it is in working too shallow. Smallmouths might move up to the 15-foot level on rainy days or during periods of marginal visibility, but most of the time they are hugging the bottom in 18 to 35 feet of water.

Clear lakes like Dale Hollow have proven to be the nemesis of many anglers. Heavier lines favored by large-mouth fishermen have no place in water where you can count the change from a dollar bill at 20 feet. The answer is light lines, matching rods, and small lures. Not only does this make sense because of the water conditions, but you must also consider that smallmouths are finicky and can easily be alerted if the offering is not presented properly. It may go against the thinking of the dedicated bass angler, but lines testing 4 pounds or 6 pounds can make a difference. Make sure that you use a rod with enough backbone to lift a fish, but with a softness in the tip that will be forgiving and cushion any sudden shocks.

There isn't much margin for error when you are using light lines and that means that the reel must have an exceptionally smooth drag. Over open bottoms, you don't have to concern yourself with a bronzeback crocheting the line in a sunken bush or going under one side of a

Smallmouth bass are an excellent target for the fly fisher-man. This beauty was taken in southern Canada.

A tiny plug worked near the spawning beds proved the down-fall of this husky smallmouth.

Ultra-light tackle and lines testing 6 pounds or less are the answer in clear lakes. Observe the typical smallmouth coloration on this 5½ pounder.

TOOLS AND TECHNIQUES

log and out the other. The fish is going to run and you must resist any efforts to snub your quarry up short. It is better to set a light drag on the reel and, when you need more drag, use the fingers to apply it by cupping the spool of a spinning reel or exerting thumb pressure on a bait-casting outfit.

Big fish don't make a habit of chasing lures very far. When a smallmouth reaches wall size, it merely wants to inhale a goodie that foolishly swims too close. Your target isn't about to sweep its powerful tail in a series of strong beats for any reason other than danger, so it prefers its meals to move slowly. There are exceptions, of course, and we have all enjoyed vicious strikes from these great fish, but you will consistently catch more fish on a bait that moves slowly.

Over the years, Billy Westmoreland has experimented with virtually every type of lure. He has settled on three favorites: a tiny jig with porkrind that he makes himself, a small plastic grub, and a tail spin lure. The best tail spin he has found is the Spinrite (now manufactured by Uncle Josh), followed closely by Tom Mann's Little George.

You can't cover much territory with the lightweight jig and rind, but it is deadly once you have located the fish. Billy reasons that most anglers impart too much action to this lure and that the only reason for giving it any action at all is to enable it to fall again. Bass hit the lure as it is falling. This may occur on the cast (and that's why it is necessary to tight line it as it falls) or when you lift the rod tip to work it further down a slope. Don't retrieve the lure all the way to the boat and don't raise the rod tip very much. You can figure that a half-inch tip movement will work the lure about a foot, and you don't want to pass up productive territory.

All of these lures are effective on smallmouth. The fish prefer miniature offerings to larger baits.

When you catch your first big smallmouth on a tailspin, you're going to be surprised. The tendency is to overfish it and to impart action that is not necessary. Learning to work the lure properly isn't difficult, but it does take a little practice. Your goal is to let the lure fall on a controlled line, and then inch it along the bottom with just enough speed to keep it from hanging up. When you cast, watch the line closely and keep most of the slack out of it. If the line is too tight, the natural sinking rate will be affected and you won't catch fish. Watch the line closely. If it stops short of the bottom or you detect even the slightest pull on the line, take in the slack quickly and set the hook.

Assuming that the lure has reached bottom without a strike, you begin the retrieve by flipping your rod tip slightly to insure that the spinner blade is turning. Then, crank the lure toward you with a slow, steady retrieve. Don't worry about twitching it or flicking it. Just keep cranking. Until you hook a fish, you won't believe that any smallmouth would hit a lure moving like that — but it happens. If you're working it right, you should be able to drop your rod tip and the lure will touch bottom within a count of two or three. Unless your tail spin is that close to the bottom, you'll be fishing out of the strike zone.

Sometimes, the lure merely stops as if it has hung up on an obstruction (and that could be the case). Take the slack out of the line if there is any and set the hook as fast as you can. Big smallmouth sometimes stop a lure cold. You'll experience other strikes that are unmistakable and strong, but in this type of fishing, you can't take a chance.

Compared to a bronzeback, the largemouth bass is fearless and doesn't spook very easily. You can move in on old bucketmouth and bombard the fish with lures. It doesn't work that way with smallmouth. The fish are skittish; even in 30 feet of water. If there is a hidden failing in this type of fishing, it is the tendency to discount the wariness of these fish. Smallmouths in Dale Hollow and similar lakes won't tolerate any disturbances. You must approach the area silently and fish carefully.

Once you run the boat over the fish (even in 30 feet of water) or let a heavy wake sweep across the area, you can forget the spot for the day. A better approach is to spend the first day scouting territory. Use your depth sounder and locate the spots that should hold fish. Take notes and be certain that you know how to approach the area from a direction that will enable you to shut down before the boat passes over the fish. Billy Westmoreland comes in from the back side of a cove slowly, and then uses the electric motor to work deeper on a sloping point.

Usually, you don't have to make long casts to catch fish, but smallmouth fishing in clear lakes is the exception. Here, the preferred technique is to cast as far as you possibly can. Most of the time, you'll work a point from shallow to deep. Make a series of long fan casts into deeper water, let the lure sink to the bottom, and retrieve it up the slope of the point. It is much more difficult, of course, to fish from deep to shallow, because it takes a talented touch to keep the lure just off the bottom.

If you hook and lose a fish or two, the school might ease off into deeped water, and you'll have to rest the spot for at least a day and maybe two or three. It doesn't pay to fish the same spots everyday, anyway. Billy follows a game plan and rests each spot for several days between fishing trips.

Unless an angler has spent considerable time on the shallow, tropical flats and has observed fish behavior, it is hard to convince him that movements in the boat can spook fish. It happens, however, and smallmouths in deep, clear water will respond to movement in the boat. That's why Billy insists on keeping a low profile, restricting movements and noise as much as possible, and wearing clothing that blends into the background, instead of something like a white shirt that can magnify the slightest twitch. You might doubt his word, but he'll quickly tell you that you'll catch more fish if you are careful about these things.

Regardless of their size or where you catch them, smallmouth black bass rank as one of the world's greatest gamefish. When you are fortunate enough to boat a trophy, it seems to mean more than a stringer of largemouth bass. Perhaps that's what smallmouth fishing is all about.

Wading the Waters

by Alex Chenoweth

Aside from the practical aspects of reaching certain lies that would otherwise be inaccessible and presenting a fly or lure in a realistic manner, wading a stream can have an esthetic quality that contributes to angling enjoyment. When you're in the stream with the swift current elbowing all around and the hurried sound of rushing water plays its melody in your ears, you literally become part of the environment. In fact, even if a particular spot can be worked better from the bank, it is often difficult to resist the temptation of slipping into the water.

Effective wading combines a knowledge of how to approach fish with streamside safety. The clumsy angler who insists on plowing through the water like a bull moose during rutting season will only alert more fish than he will ever catch. Even minor carelessness such as grinding gravel underfoot, kicking loose rocks, or creating excessive mud that is carried downstream has its effect on fish and fishing.

There are serious considerations as well. Fast-moving water can be treacherous, especially when the footing is impaired by slime-covered rocks or soft spots that grab a foot and make it difficult to take another step. It's easy to walk in over the tops of hip boots or waders. And it can be truly dangerous if you are swept off your feet and carried downstream through boulder-strewn rapids.

Although they are more expensive initially, waders are a better investment than hip boots. Boots are simply too

With properly fitted waders, you should be able to place one foot on a chair comfortably. Too many loose folds of material are quite as bad as a tight fit.

limiting, and you tend to spend more time worrying about whether you can negotiate a particular stretch of stream than in actually fishing. There are exceptions, of course. Hip boots are worthwhile for youngsters and senior anglers, simply because they are a limiting factor. The wearer recognizes that he can't get too far out before he gets wet, so the tendency is to stay in shallower water. Naturally, safety for youngsters who might become venturesome or older fishermen who might probe beyond their capabilities is a primary consideration.

Most waders are advertised as chest-high; these are the ones to get. Waist-high waders are a compromise over hip boots. Some makers turn out a product that come right up under your armpits, while other chest-high waders reach only the middle of the rib cage.

You have a choice of boot-foot waders in which the boot or foot is an integral part, or stocking-foot waders that are used with separate wading shoes. There are advantages to each, and any decision should be based on personal preference. If you must walk long distances, however, you'll find that the stocking-foot wader with wading shoes is more comfortable. If you'll be putting them on and taking them off frequently, boot-foots are the way to go.

The soles of your boots or waders are important. Standard models offer a ripple-type sole which are designed for all-purpose use. If you wade rocky streams, felt soles would be a better choice. There are also other soles now made that work well on slippery bottoms.

When you are being fitted for a pair of waders, it is important to get the right size. If there are too many loose folds of material, the waders will be uncomfortable and will wear out quickly. The Converse Rubber Company, one of the largest manufacturers of waders, recommends that you should be able to put one foot on an ordinary chair with the other foot on the ground. If the waders feel comfortable and are not pulling with your foot on the chair, the fit is correct.

As you walk to the stream, you should be safety conscious. There might be a number of deadfalls in the woods, and it is important to either walk around them or to cross them carefully. If you stand on a log, it could collapse under your weight and injure you. When you walk along the bank of the river or brook, remember to stay back a ways. For one thing, you won't spook as many fish, and another, the bank won't collapse under your weight. Undercut banks can cause problems you may not always recognize. A good clue is to study the current. If the main force sweeps into a bank, you can almost bet it is undercut.

When you're going to fish a stream for the first time, it makes sense to study your surroundings before you enter the water. Take advantage of any high points that

Felt soles are better for rocky bottoms, but regular ripple soles have an advantage on a muddy bottom. Felt-soled wading sandals can be slipped over the regular soles to convert them temporarily.

It's best to enter a stream where the water is shallow and the current isn't swift.

If you start to lose your balance, push as much of your fishing rod as possible underwater. The cushioning effect will help to steady you.

With the handle at a comfortable height, a wading staff should be long enough to touch bottom.

will give you a view. You should be looking for two things: spots that could hold fish and the general course of the water. Try to identify the deeper holes and the faster runs. Get an idea of what is upstream and downstream from where you intend to start. By learning to read the water, you'll not only gain the advantage from a safety standpoint, but you'll also catch more fish as a result of not plodding through where you should be fishing.

There are various opinions on how to fish any body of water. Keep in mind that fish always face into the current. It may be easier wading downstream, but you have a better chance of approaching fish undetected if you work upstream. On big rivers, this is not nearly as important as it might be on small creeks. You'll also find that if you stay in shallower water and keep a low profile, you can sometimes do better.

Some fishermen become so absorbed in wading that they lose sight of its purpose. You are merely positioning yourself so that you can present a bait, fly, or lure to a fish. If you remember nothing else, think before you walk. Study the spot and then move directly into position. If you are using a flyrod, be sure you have room for your backcast whenever possible. In fact, you should even decide which side of the stream to wade, and that can be predicated on whether you are a right-handed or left-handed caster.

When you wade upstream, any silt or mud you kick up will be swept below you by the current. However, if you work downstream, the disturbed silt will be moving in front of you. Also, any fish hooked on an upstream wade will come down toward you without disturbing other fish in the pool. That's not going to happen if you catch a fish below you.

Pick the best possible place to enter the water. The ideal is a gravel bar or a shallow point that offers the convenience of getting set before taking the force of the current. The least desirable is a steep bank that falls off into fast-moving water. That should be your last choice, but if there are no alternatives, use caution and study the setting before you slip into the water.

Wading can be best described as an extremely slow dance in which you move your feet one at a time, planting one securely on the bottom, then dragging the other up to the first. There may be variations, but that's the basic step. Concern yourself with one foot and don't worry about the other.

The secret is to keep all of your weight on the foot that is solidly placed on bottom that you have tested. Move the other foot forward and probe for a foothold. Wiggle the foot around to make sure it is secure. When the second foot is nestled on the bottom, transfer your weight and drag the back foot up behind. Then, repeat the procedure. There are times when you can simply walk in the water, but these are limited to shallow conditions without any current. You'll find that by moving one foot at a time, you can approach fish much more quietly and you won't fall into a deep hole so readily.

Whenever you wade, you always run the risk of getting wet, but you do want to prevent yourself from pitching forward or having your feet slide out from under you. In a rock stream, either of these accidents could be dangerous. While you are fishing, make certain that your feet are not parallel and your back is not to the current. Instead, place one foot upstream or downstream from the other so that you have some balance and the ability to shift weight with or against the current.

Crossing a stream should be done with planning and care. If you have a choice, select the fording area. It might be a shallow spot or perhaps it is a place where boulders help to break up the current. Usually, it is better to cross on more of a downstream diagonal. You want to avoid the tendency to try to walk directly across, only to find yourself suddenly being bounced downstream with the rushing water.

A wading staff can prove to be an invaluable tool. They are available in tackle shops or you can make your own from an old ski pole or a fiberglass rod blank. The staff should be lightweight, should float, and should have a brush hook on one end and a thumb grip on the other. Most have a length of line and a clip that hooks to the fishing vest. You can often locate a stout stick that can be pressed into emergency service. The tendency is to carry a wading staff that is a little short. Make sure it is long enough for deeper water.

In a current, the wading staff should be planted on the upstream side. It's a third leg and it will enable you to lean into the current instead of away from the rushing water. The trick is to plant the wading staff in the bottom, use it to help support you, place one foot firmly on the bottom, and move the other foot up. Then, re-plant the wading staff and follow the same procedure.

As you move across the current, your body will be sideways to the water. It is creating the least possible resistance. When you stop to fish, you will tend to turn and that means that the current could hit you broadside, pitching you forward. Even the sudden jolt of turning and being hit by more water can throw you off balance. You'll also discover that a strong current striking you around the knees can be more tricky than the same current where the water is deeper.

Frequently, an angler eases out in the stream with no problem, fishes a particular lie, and then decides to return to the bank. The instant he tries to turn around, he realizes he's in trouble, and it is not a comfortable feeling. The *only* way to turn is upstream. If you attempt a 180° turn downstream, you might get wet.

You can be swept off your feet if you turn your back on the current in knee-deep water.

By studying a stream, you can pick your course before crossing. Here, the angler uses available rocks to help break the current.

Use a wading staff on the upstream side. It should be firmly planted before you move your feet.

A wading staff is really handy in such a situation, but if you take your time, you can still turn around without one. Lean into the current wherever possible, and don't allow the current to knock you upright or the slightest bit downstream. It's often a slow process to plant one foot and then the other, but it is the only way to do it. You must start with the upstream foot and continue to move only that one while you press your weight against the downstream foot. Eventually, your feet become reversed and the upstream one now moves downstream.

The fishing rod in your hand can help in an emergency. Lay the tip and as much of the rod as possible on the water in front of you and push on it. You'll find that the water offers a cushioning effect and the rod will help you to maintain your balance. If you have a fish on at the moment, just the pressure of the fish can be an aid in keeping your feet. It really doesn't take much tension to do the job. In fact, you can cast the fly or lure in a shoreside tree and, by keeping a tight line, use that to help steady you.

Years ago, anglers lived with the fear that air would be trapped in their waders if they fell in the water, and their feet would be lifted over their heads. It has been proven by experts that you can't turn bottoms up if you are wearing waders. The worst that could happen is that you would float like a log if air did get trapped.

It's important to wear a rather tight belt on the outside of your waders to prevent water from pouring in if you do take one step too far. A belt will help to hold the water to a trickle. (You're already wet, so don't worry about a little more water.) If the water is relatively still, merely walk out of it. You may need a swimming stroke or two

A tight line can be a steadying influence when crossing a stream. You can have a friend hold one end or even cast into a tree limb if you're in an emergency situation.

with your hands to get back up the sides of the hole.

Most problems occur in fast-moving water and, although you can't really know how you will react until it actually happens, there are a number of suggestions that are worth remembering. As in any other emergency, try to remain calm and survey the situation. You have at least a reasonable amount of time.

In a current, you're going to go downstream, so don't fight it. Angle for the nearest shore or an island. Your first task is to get back in water in which you can stand. Often you can do this by walking on your tiptoes and bouncing along at an angle. If you can't keep your head above water by walking on your toes, use your arms to swim or paddle. In a very strong current, try to grab anything while you are being swept along. It might be a tree limb, a root, a rock . . . anything.

A number of anglers are now carrying inflatable devices just for this kind of emergency. They attach easily to fly vest or waders, and you either pull a lanyard or squeeze them for inflation. If you have a wading staff, remember the brush hook on the other end. It can help you reach out for an object that you might be passing.

Problems sometimes occur when a fisherman takes chances and presses his luck to reach an out-of-the-way spot. If in doubt, don't take the risk. There will be other places to fish that you can get to without wading up to your armpits.

If you take the time to study any stretch of water before you start to fish, you'll be able to locate the fish easier, and your chances of getting caught in the current or stepping into a deep hole will be minimized. Just remember when you're in the water to dance across the bottom slowly — one foot at a time.

Never step out of the water on a log. You can lose your balance and slip off backwards.

If you have to negotiate a barbed-wire fence, remove fly vest and outer clothing. Slide under the bottom strand on your back.

Tricks That Take More Panfish

by Jerry Gibbs

Back in the days of scratchy, wool bathing trunks when I was learning about sunfish, my father would row our family out to a special boulder that poked above water on a public lake. Just off the big rock, the bottom dropped sharply and there were always bluegills nearby.

Our simple methods on those trips consisted of dropping little hooks over the side baited with slightly moistened, doughy white bread. It took me a while to realize why we usually ended up with more and larger fish than the other folks who fished around the rock, even though most of them had fancier tackle (which meant rods that sported reels). Almost everyone fished with a bobber set firmly in place on their lines and never moved it all day. Sometimes it didn't matter, but when the water was clear and it was hot summer weather, the big bluegills were down in the deep water. Our dough baits drifted down to them. Things haven't changed much today.

Even in the spring when nesting bluegills crowd the shallows and sock anything that moves overhead, the big fellows will be deeper. Sometimes, they won't even be close to their smaller kin. You'll find them off a bottom hump or off a finger of land from a shore point that has the right bottom conditions for spawning, or that has the proper combination of ingredients — shade, cover, food, oxygen — to keep them around awhile. A bluegill is big if it stretches from the tip of your longest finger to over your watchband when you lay it in your palm. It's an excellent gamefish on light tackle and you needn't feel guilty about keeping it, because sunfish of all kinds reproduce with extreme success and often crowd out larger sportfish.

Whether you call them bream or sunnies, bluegills spawn around April in warmer climes and May through June in the north. If extreme crowding exists, spawning occurs later and sometimes not at all. There are often several spawns in a year. Bluegills need a sandy or gravel bottom for successful spawning, and that's your key to locating the fish early in the year. If water drawdowns eliminate the proper spawning area (especially before the first spring spawn), the fish will try nest making in muck. They'll go so far as to burrow down over their heads out of sight in silt and mire, and their spawn will die.

I have never found large bull bluegills shallower than two and one half to three feet deep during spring spawning. More likely, they will be four to six feet deep. When the water is clear, shadows from clouds or birds scudding across the sun will send bluegills fleeing from their nests. Shadows cast by an angler will do the same — so a cautious stalking approach is always in order.

The larger fish are often suspended at the edge of the first dropoff if a pond or lake has one. On bowl-shaped lakes, bluegills will favor bars and weeds. Whenever you locate smaller fish along a point or underwater bar extending from shore, search the fingers or secondary offshoots of the main formation. Often, these drop down faster into deep water, and the larger fish like them for that reason.

In summer, the bigger bluegills behave like bass, taking advantage of submerged creek channels in lakes. If you can locate a channel near a rise in the lake floor or a point extending offshore, fish the area carefully. Work into the channel and up the other side. During hot weather, many anglers say that the "brim" aren't biting. These anglers are still fishing the way they were in spring. That's the time to look for fish in water that's 10-20 feet deep, and sometimes as deep as 30 feet.

One method of finding bluegills in bowl-shaped lakes is to drift in small boat, looking for weedbeds that will usually hold the fish. If it's not too windy just a touch

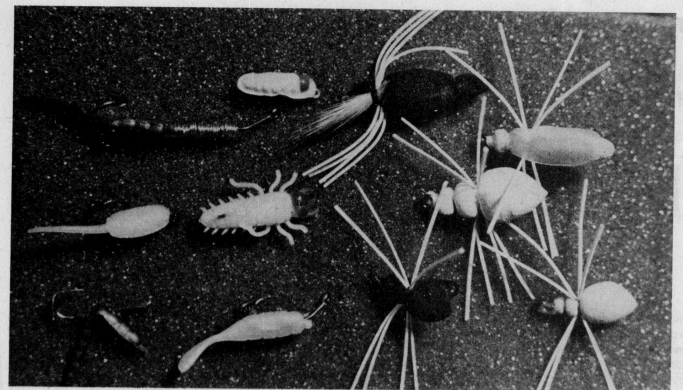

This selection of foam bugs and solid plastic grubs will entice a variety of panfish.

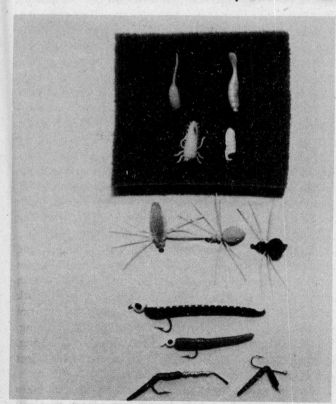

Plastic grubs (top), foam spiders, and mini worms are all good panfish lures.

with the oars, or an electric motor, will keep you drifting on course so you can fish a pattern across the lake. When you've finished a drift, head back upwind, cut over and drift through another section. Your lures or baits should be fixed so you have one near the bottom and another at middle depth. When you hit fish, toss over a marker buoy. Because large bluegills do not school as tightly in the warmer weather as they do in the spring, you'll probably catch more by working in a wide circle around your marker.

In summer, bluegills often suspend in deep water around mid-lake weedbeds. If oxygen becomes depleted at lower levels, bluegills, or any fish for that matter, will be forced closer to the surface than they would prefer. In such cases, they'll stick very tightly to shade-giving cover of any kind. As a lake cools and turns over in autumn, the fish will begin to go deeper. Increased oxygen will permit this.

In small lakes or ponds, the larger fish just don't have a lot of room to stake out separate territory from their little brothers. You can sometimes pick up good-size bluegills in a pond you thought contained only smallfry by weighting your bait or using a heavier lure that will quickly sink the offering past the little fish which normally school above the big bulls.

Three types of tackle are best suited to bluegills and most panfishing: fly, ultralight spinning, and canepoles.

Tiny poppers should be worked slowly by vibrating and swimming them over the surface.

Outstanding panfish flies. Top row, left to right: bees, ant and hopper. Second row: woolly worm, beetles. Far left: bivisible deer fly. Lower right grouping: wet flies and nymphs. Upper left: muddler and royal coachman streamer.

Left: double and single bladed Indiana shaft spinners, some trimmed with flies or fly+worm. These are excellent on bluegills, redbreast sunfish. Crappie jigs, right, will also take redear. Mini safety-pin type spinners (bottom) are great for perch.

The latter is most effective during the spring, in shallow lakes, or where schools of fish are known to be located. Using flyrods or spinning tackle you locate fish more quickly. Canepoles from 10 to 14 feet are deadly machines for dropping delicate live baits into cup-size pockets in the weeds.

I like a flyrod which measures 7½ to 8½ feet for panfishing, and I choose the longer stick if using natural bait or poppers. An extremely willowy ultralight spinning rod is right for casting natural baits, but I prefer a stiffer rod when using artificials. I never use monofilament over six pound test, and usually, my panfishing line is four pound.

Most fishermen think of poppers when they talk about flyrod lures for bluegills, and these can be excellent in the spring or during later spawning periods. Poppers are most effectively worked by vibrating or slowly swimming them along in stop-and-go fashion rather than popping them. Dry flys in white, green, yellow, black, and brown are another good choice. Precise patterns are not required. Hook sizes should be 10 to 12. Although I love surface action, I probably catch more bluegills on sunken flies throughout the entire year. The best bluegill pattern for me is a bucktail streamer with a white or cream body ribbed with tinsel. The wings are black over green over yellow or orange. You can put a red tail on, but it is not necessary. The head is black tying thread. Tie it on a No. 8 streamer hook. The Mickey Fin, Black or Gray Ghost are also quite effective streamers on No. 8 hooks.

Slowly-worked nymphs are excellent bluegill flies. The best colors are black and white, white, brown, and gray. White, plastic mousies or other white imitation grubs or pork rind flicks can be put on your streamer or nymph hooks. Often, they trigger action when bluegills are very fussy.

Foam bugs in green or white with white rubberband legs work well when fished as a wet fly. The closed cell foam will not sink, so you must clamp a weight about 12 inches ahead of the bug.

If you're interested in catching a lot of fish, it's hard to beat a double-bladed Indiana shaft spinner with No. 1 or 2 silver blades trailing a No. 8 hook trimmed with pork rind. This is basically a lure for your spinning outfit, but it can be cast with a fly rod. Other good spinning lures include a small surface plug with the aft hooks removed. Tie in a 12-18 in. piece of mono where the hooks were, and then attach a nymph to the end of the mono. Dart the plug on the surface to attract fish. The nymph will rise and fall with provocative undulation. You can also swim a sinking fly this way using a casting bobber — one of those clear plastic, weighted or water-fillable models. They're available in teardrop or sphere shape. A casting bobber will also enable you to throw

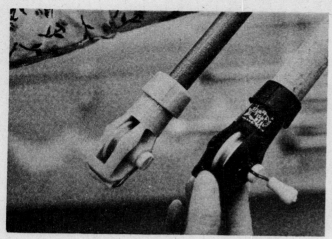

Though most canepoles feature a fixed length of line, these incorporate a caged reel at the butt. The pole telescopes.

Jig fly behind spinner or fly before spinner is an extremely effective lure for big sunfish, perch, crappie, redear and smallmouth bass, too.

Casting bobbers, from left: spring clip-on, weighted with eyes in each end, water-fillable for weight, round weighted with fixed eyes.

surface flys with spinning gear. Attach your drys 15-18 inches below the bobber. Twitch the bobber gently to give your flies a skittering motion across the surface.

The best natural bluegill baits are earthworms, crickets, small hoppers, and katydids. Use a No. 8 long-shank fine-wire hook like the Aberdeen. Commercial dough-type panfish scent baits also work well. When bluegills are shallow and you have to place a bait some distance away (you can fish quite close when the fish are deep), a bobber is effective. The casting bobber and standard sliding or ball bobbers are good when there's a little water movement. For still water, I like the stick or natural porcupine quill bobbers.

Redbreast Sunfish

Known sometimes as a robin or yellowbelly throughout its range, the redbreast sunfish is one of my favorite panfish. It is at its best in rivers where it'll put up a really fine scrap.

Redbreasts eat crustaceans, minnows, and insects. Depending on the available forage, little silver spoons, small single spinners, plain pork strips, tiny plugs, dry flies and wet flies in light and dark colors will take them. You can also catch them at times on poppers. The silver, double-bladed, pork-trimmed, Indiana spinner I use for bluegills, however, is most productive.

In lakes, look for redbreasts around rocky formations and outcroppings if weeds or brush are not too distant. Other good places include areas where timber extends into the water, and at covemouths with gravelly or rock bottoms. In rivers, redbreasts nest in the slower currents behind boulders. They also make nests in rocky pockets near shore to escape the main current. If a river contains smallmouth bass as well as redbreasts, look for the sunny in areas with slower pools than those a smallmouth would use. They won't be where the bottom is muddy and water nearly still. Just out of the fast water in rocky pools is a typical redbreast hangout, as are ledges and caves formed by boulders or outcroppings along shore. Like bass, redbreasts prefer some protection from bright light, so it does not pay to fish in exposed areas unless there is some depth to the water.

Redbreasts can be extremely shy at times, especially in clear rivers. This means using fly leaders at least nine feet long, and mono line in the 2-4 pound class. In shallow water don't try fishing for robins closer than 25 feet from your position.

Redear Sunfish

The redear makes its home in the South, where many folks who fish for him don't even know him by that name. You might be better off inquiring about the shellcracker fishing through most of its range.

There's a belief among some anglers that redears won't touch artificial lures, but this isn't so. Small weighted streamers (sometimes called fly jigs), and light spinners are fine lures for shellcrackers. Weighted bee flies, ants, and chenille-body bugs in black, brown, green, and gray work, too. Use a sinking tip or sinking head fly line for these baits except in spring when the fish are on shallow beds. You can even take this fish on poppers during a limited time in spring.

Natural bait will probably catch more redears over the long haul. And, if you are just starting in fishing for redears, spring is the best time. Because so many anglers fish for this species in the early season, it's easy to locate the top spots. Anglers through the South crowd the redear beds when the water temperature rises above 70 degrees. They use freshwater shrimp, shelled snails, earthworms, white grubs and catalpa worms, impaled on No. 6 or 8 hooks, eased down from long canepoles. An 8½-foot fly rod will also work.

Redears feed primarily on fresh water mollusks, and they like snails best. Shells are ground by special teeth located in the fish's throat. The name shellcracker is accurate. After the shellcracker bedding period, some anglers grind a mixture of shrimp, snails, worms, and the like, putting the stuff into a cheesecloth sack or one of those chum cans used by flounder fishermen. The concoction is lowered over the side of the boat to hold fish in the area or lure them in if they weren't very close to begin with. This method is best later in the season when redears are loosely schooled on dropoffs. Make sure it's legal where you fish. Redears frequent large open waters and do not choose weedbeds as thick as those favored by bluegills. If the main lake water is rough, look for your shellcrackers in bays with depths from 18 to 30 feet during the warm weather.

Crappies

Once, when I was without a motor and the only boat I had left was a beatup plywood pram with an outrageous 12-letter name painted on its transom, I realized my timing was very bad. The crappie season was upon us and I had promised my wife Judy a fishing trip. Somehow I coaxed Dave Kemp, who was and is an understanding fishing crony, to tow us out to an area near where he planned to plug for largemouth bass. As we nosed into a quiet bay I yelled for Dave to cut us loose. He untied us and powered over toward the shore while I put together some minnow-with-bobber rigs. We were just inside the bay mouth where an underwater bar ran out from shore. The bait fish rode from 24 to 18 inches off the bottom.

I began rowing slowly in a wide circle, pausing frequently to give the minnows a rising and falling action.

After awhile, my rod dipped and I dropped the oars, set the hook once and gently brought the first fish in.

"What do you have," Dave called over.

I showed him.

"Calico, eh. Get some more."

We did. After anchoring quietly fore and aft, we proceeded to make up for a long winter without open water.

Whether you call them calicos, or speckled perch, black and white crappies are on the most popular list just about anywhere you go in this country. Trolling with or without a motor is one of the best methods for locating schools of this great-tasting panfish, especially during the hot weather.

In spring you'll find crappies closer to shore near heavy cover. Many anglers make their own crappie hotspots by sinking brushpiles in various sections of a favorite lake. The whereabouts of these spots is usually closely guarded. Shallow bars that run off shore can also be good drawing places for crappies in spring if they have some form of cover on them.

A white marabou jig is one of the all-time, top crappie lures. Using a light spinning rod, make a short cast into the shore-side brush, or over sunken bars and brushpiles. Allow the jig to sink nearly to the bottom, then begin hopping it back, letting it free fall between each upward hop. These jigs are from 1/16 to 1/32 of an ounce and I don't recommend their use in water over ten feet deep.

When crappies move deeper later in the year, look for them by working out into water adjacent to the areas in which you found them in spring. I like to work the dropoffs at the ends of long points, especially if there is good brush there. Crappies are notorious fish for suspending, particularly over the deepest part of the lake or over a sharp dropoff such as a river channel. If you have an electronic depth finder you can see the crappie schools hanging usually from ten to 30 feet deep.

When they don't have the luxury of depth, as in many southern ponds and lakes, crappies will head for bottom. In such cases look for spots that differ from the surrounding general bottom makeup; a hard spot, hump, or brush. Check mouths of feeder streams that enter any small shallow lake.

In warm weather, if you have no depthfinder, try trolling with several rods rigged with baits that ride at different levels. Troll the type areas already mentioned. When you locate a school, toss over a marker buoy, back off and start fishing. You'll probably be fishing vertically in water over ten feet. Use spoons or jig spoons of up to ½ ounce. Jig them up, letting them flutter back a little, and then bring them still higher, working this pattern all the way back to the surface.

Extra small live minnows fished on No. 6 Aberdeen hooks at the proper level, catch a great many crappies

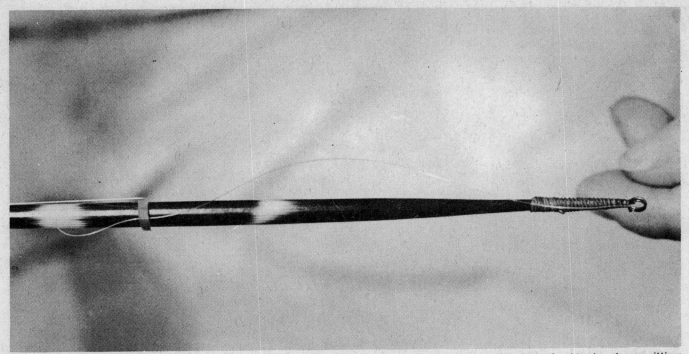

Natural porcupine quill float is shown with proper rigging. When hook is set, mono loop pulls free of rubberband, permitting quill to run free.

every year. You can utilize a bobber when the fish are shallow. When deep fishing with a minnow, clip a weight 12 inches up from the minnow to get the bait fish down.

You can fish a variety of natural baits to cover different depths by tying three or four snelled hooks along the main line, about 15 inches apart. Stiff leader material instead of soft mono will keep the snells from twisting. A heavy silver jig of ⅝ to 1 oz. at the end of the line will get this rig down fast.

Black crappies like clearer water but more cover than whites which are more frequently caught in the South. The white crappies are found in larger schools than the blacks.

It pays to play crappies gently, because their tender mouths will tear if you try to hustle them in as you might a largemouth bass.

Yellow Perch

The only problem with these fish is their armor-like scales, and that's no problem if you forget about scaling them. I started skinning my perch a long time ago and wouldn't think about a scaling job again. But you've got to catch them before cooking them and, at times, these seemingly easy-to-hook panfish can be exasperating. The trouble usually stems from their ability to spit out a bait quickly. This is why I usually trim all my artificial lures with a little flag of rough fish belly or, where legal, perch, pickerel, or bluegill belly. The perch is best.

In spring these fish will be out from shore in lake arms or coves usually associated with heavy weeds. They also frequent midlake islands and channels between shore and islands. Even along a rocky shoreline, if there are weeds not too far out, you are likely to find perch.

The lures I usually use for perch are gold-headed, barred yellow feather jibs, gold single-bladed spinners, brass or gold finish spoons. For bait, I prefer minnows or worms at the end of spinners.

Perch, like other fish, will move deeper in summer. During periods when I must fish deep, I often switch to a fairly large jig — larger than perch will normally take — and use it primarily as an attractor. I hop the jig where my live minnow lines are streamed suspended by floats. A school of perch will normally give up the attractor and head for the minnows.

The slip sinker rig, made famous by Al Lindner (called the Lindy Rig), is ideal when perch are ten to 20 feet deep, feeding near the bottom. Basically the rig consists of a flattened, bent bank sinker known as a walking sinker, a barrel swivel and clip to prevent the weight from riding down over the hook, and a snelled hook. You crawl and lift the weight over the bottom, pausing frequently. A fish that takes the bait (use minnows or worms) will be able to pull it through the sinker with no resistance. If you keep a tight line you'll be able to tell in an instant what's happening, and you'll set your hook quickly.

Dick Frohs demonstrates casting bobber to enable spin fisherman to use a fly.

A few crappies for lunch that were taken on streamer fly in spring around close-to-shore rubble.

This survey would not be complete without some mention of my little friend the rock bass. On dreadful days when fishing unsuccessfully for smallmouth or other fish, Old Rocky has had positive reaction by waking my dulled brain and refocusing my attention so that I did not miss a larger sportfish. While drifting along half asleep, I've been jarred awake by its crashing strike — unbelievably hard for such a little fellow. It may take a big surface Rapala his own length, or a lipped diving plug, a spinner or live bait. It won't fight too long, but it hits like a ton and smashes around for a bit and it's a great fish to please the kids. You'll find them near shore in rivers, hiding around rocks, rubble, and gravel. It'll take flyrod poppers well, or about anything else it things it can do in.

After you bring the little red-eyed mobster in, let him go home again. It usually takes the fellow six or seven years to grow to nine inches.

I use one chief method for preparing all panfish. Kids like it. I like it. Even people who normally don't care for fish like it.

You'll need fillets which have been cut into small chunks. Dip the pieces in milk, then roll them in flour that's spiced with Italian seasoning. Drop the fillet pieces into a Dutch oven filled with 425° (or barely smoking) cooking oil. When the pieces float or are golden brown, they're done. Let them sit on paper toweling. Sprinkle them with garlic salt if you like; then enjoy.

Panfish were named for a reason. They're great on the table and in most instances you are performing a conservation service by harvesting them in goodly quantities. In addition they provide some of the most relaxing fun you'll find in sport fishing.

The Amazing Catfish

by Russell Tinsley

The catfish family is widespread and abundant. You can catch the whiskered critter from California irrigation canals to Iowa rivers, Oklahoma impoundments, and even the sluggish bayous of the Deep South. In fact, there are few warm-water streams and lakes in any part of the country where the catfish, in one shape and size or another, is not found.

Availability is the prime reason it is prized by anglers. The catfish is also delicious tablefare, and there are those who consider it to be the best. Thousands are raised on farms and sold commercially for food. The cat isn't a flashy fighter like the black bass, or a selective feeder like the trout. The light-tackle purist might not comprehend or appreciate the methods used in catfishing, but millions of anglers from youngsters to senior citizens find untold pleasure in catching this fresh-water denizen.

As someone once observed, you don't have to be crazy to be a catfish fisherman, but it helps.

The catfish fisherman's ritual includes being dirty from spading worms, red-eyed after sleepless nights of fishing, and smelling like a garbage dump outcast after handling malodorous stink baits. There is no fishing quite like it.

Catfish are found throughout the world, numbering from several hundred upwards of 1,000 different species, depending on which authority you accept. Here in the United States there are seven species: channel catfish, blue catfish, white catfish, flathead catfish, black bullhead, brown bullhead, and yellow bullhead. But, because of their many aliases, you may not recognize any of these names. Perhaps you know it as the fork-tail cat (channel catfish) or yellow cat (flathead) or a mud cat (bullhead). Practically every region has its catfish sobriquets.

The American Fisheries Society lists 24 freshwater catfish species, but most, like the madtoms and stonecat, are diminutive fishes only a few inches in length.

Identification of the seven popular species can be difficult. Sometimes a small bullhead, for instance, can be mistaken for a flathead. Both the channel and blue catfish have deep-forked tails while the others are rounded or only slightly indented. To distinguish between a channel cat and blue catfish, look at the anal fin. A blue's is almost straight along the edge and contains 30 to 36 rays; a channel cat's anal fin is slightly rounded and contains from 24 to 29 rays.

As for the others, a flathead has 12-15 rays, the white catfish 18-24, yellow bullhead 23-27, brown bullhead 17-24, and black bullhead 17-24. Since three — white catfish, brown and black bullheads — have almost identical ray counts, one must depend on other identification. The white catfish more closely resembles the channel cat than it does a bullhead, although the channel catfish's tail is more deeply forked. The sharp spine on the brown bullhead's dorsal (back) fin is very stiff, while that of the black bullhead is weakly barbed.

Despite the species differentiation, the locations where they are found, and what they are called, the collective catfish family provides a lot of entertainment for a large number of anglers. This is an adaptable fish which often inhabits waters unsuitable for other species. It has a high tolerance for mud and pollution.

The catfish will eat almost anything whether the food is dead or alive, meat or vegetable, and virtually everything else not covered by these definitions. A cat feeds both by sight

Catfish prefer shady river pools such as this.

TOOLS AND TECHNIQUES

Wade-fishing a small river after catfish.

and smell. It probably has a better-developed smelling or tasting apparatus than any other fish. Tests have shown that catfish can home in on food from several feet away even in muddy water with this uncanny ability to smell or "taste." Yet a catfish has no nose per se; its ultrasensitive taste buds are distributed along the whiskers (called barbels). A cat has eight of these appendages: one long pair protruding from each corner of the mouth, much like a handle-bar moustache; two more growing near the nostrils, and four trailing beneath the chin.

Remarkably, a catfish can survive even without eyes. One caught last year from a small lake in Daingerfield State Park in northeast Texas had only skin covering the areas where its eye sockets should have been. The blind channel cat hadn't prospered. It was 18 inches long and weighed only a pound and a half. Normally a channel catfish that long would go better than four pounds.

Fishing for catfish can be as simple or complex as the angler wants to make it. This crowd pleaser is caught by youngsters sitting on the shore holding willow poles fitted with cotton-cord line, by anglers in the most sophsticated boats and using the most expensive rods and reels, and even on unmanned trotlines with their many hooks lined up like obedient soldiers.

They are caught by running natural baits through river riffles or by dropping an earthworm or grasshopper into an eddy or beside a brushpile! You can also succeed by putting baits directly on the bottom and leaving them there until a catfish wanders by, or you may choose to fish in diminutive creeks, big rivers, natural lakes, manmade impoundments, and even in farm ponds. There are few places where catfish do not thrive. Every dyed-in-the-wool catfish fisherman had his favorite hotspot, and he will conceal its location with a cover-up that would make Watergate appear to be small time. Curiously, the catfish fisherman tends to be more secretive than other anglers.

Finding the right place to fish is basically a matter of experimentation. It's a process of elimination that involves prospecting many different places until you find that magic spot where catfish are both present and cooperative. Unless conditions change drastically, such spots have a special "chemistry" which attract catfish, and they will produce over and over, year after year. That is why a fisherman will do anything to keep from divulging the location of such a spot.

There are some places, however, too public to be kept secret. Below Conowingo Dam on the lower Susquehanna River in Pennsylvania, fishermen often crowd elbow to elbow along the walk to dangle baits into the swift tailrace waters in which catfish congregate. The Missouri River of southern South Dakota and northern Nebraska below the Fort Randall Dam attracts its share of anglers. Lake Livingston Dam in Texas (not far from Houston), Pickwick Dam in Tennessee or, for that matter, any of the other dams along the Tennessee River have all earned reputations as catfish hotspots.

Among the places where catfish are found, however, a huge impoundment probably is the most unreliable, mainly because the fish are scattered. Most big-lake fishermen put juglines or trotlines or droplines (limblines, if you prefer) near or in the mouths of tributary streams. Catfish like a current and, while you might not always find them directly in the moving water, they will be hanging along the edges waiting for something edible to come drifting by. A prime time to try for catfish is just after a heavy rain, when a flooding stream empties food-rich muddy water into the impoundment. They become active.

The list of baits that take catfish is lengthy. It includes — among other things — earthworms, grasshoppers, minnows, shad, sunfish, mussels, aquatic salamanders, frogs, hellgrammites, tadpoles, cut bait, coagulated blood, chicken entrails, shrimp, leeches, eels, mice, beef liver, marshmallows, clams, rancid meat, nostril-searing commercial concoctions, and even other catfish. The flathead catfish is the gourmet of the clan, preferring something alive or at least fresh without any odor. Trophy-sized flatheads (and even big blue cats) weighing more than 50 pounds are often caught on live bullheads as bait. Some fishermen use baits for these huge brutes that most anglers would be glad to catch, such as a carp or a freshwater drum weighing two pounds or more. These live baits are put on No. 9/0 hooks attached to lines stout enough to slow a runaway submarine.

Do some investigating in your area and determine which baits are most popular. The salesman at any fish-bait outlet can tell you. If in doubt, use common earthworms or night-crawlers. I've never been to a place yet where catfish wouldn't go for a gob of juicy worms.

Worms are universally popular, but that doesn't mean they are always the best. I was fishing for channel catfish on a spring-fed river near my central Texas home using worms for bait. After catching only a few small

Lots of kids learn to fish by catching bullheads.

throw-back cats on the garden hackle, I switched to gizzard shad (caught in a nearby reservoir and frozen). The new bait produced more than a dozen nice-sized cats before the day was over.

Another time on another river worms weren't working. When I rendezvoused with a friend downstream later, he showed me several husky channel cats he'd taken. He said he couldn't coax a nibble on worms and only started getting action when he tried jumbo yellow grasshoppers. The 'hoppers were everywhere in the tall grass along the river and obviously were the catfish's primary food source at that time.

If one bait is not producing, don't

hesitate to try something different. It might be more pleasant to use natural baits, but there are occasions (especially in the summertime) when malodorous commerical baits, made from blood and ground-up fishes among other ingredients, will catch more catfish. Such dough-like substances should be fished on a small treble hook (No. 10 or no larger than No. 8), in a ball slightly larger than a grape. A special treble with a springlike coil of wire around the shank is best; the bait will otherwise wash off a conventional hook even in still water.

My favorite fishing is with rod and reel on a small- to moderate-sized river, using natural baits such as hellgrammites, worms, frozen shrimp, or grasshoppers. The trick is to put the bait into fishy-looking spots where cats are apt to be lurking. Among the best are below riffles, slicks behind rocks, an eddy in the river bend, and wherever debris has turned the current and washed out a hole. Sometimes I put the bait directly on the bottom, but there are situations when I use a float and swim the bait through an area where I think cats might be hanging out. There are no hard and fast rules. Try one system and then the other. If you fit all the pieces of the puzzle together — the right bait at the right place with the right technique — you'll catch fish.

I use the basic fishfinder bottom rig: a hook (No. 1/0 or 2/0) tied to the end of my line with a slip sinker. The line is passed through the hole in the egg-shaped slip sinker before the hook is added. Push the slip sinker about a foot up the line. Add a tiny split-shot or pinch-on sinker below it to keep the slip sinker from sliding down against the hook on the cast. When a catfish picks up the bait, the line runs freely through the sinker and there is no resistance to alert the fish. You also will have a better "feel" and can tell precisely when to set the hook. The size of the sinker will depend on the water flow. Use just enough weight to keep the bait stationary alongside or in the current.

My floating rig consists of a No. 1/0 hook, a small pinch-on sinker to keep the bait down, and a plastic snap-on float. When using this setup, I periodically vary the depth. Usually, catfish remain near bottom, but sometimes they might be suspended about halfway up or actually might be foraging near the surface if they are after grasshoppers or other insects.

There are many variations and most will work, but you can get by only with these two rigs. I seldom change.

Your tackle, however, should be matched to both the quarry and the conditions. Fishermen after big cats often use salt-water spinning or casting outfits. If you elect to fish in swift tailrace water below a dam, an extra-heavy sinker is needed, the rod must have backbone, and the line must be strong. When fishing small rivers, however, you can use light tackle. A spinning or casting outfit with line testing eight to ten pounds is a good choice. On this outfit, even a pound-sized specimen can put up a good protest, yet it will subdue a cat of ten pounds or more if you know what you are doing and don't panic.

Many catfish are taken on plain, vanilla canepoles, especially where the water isn't too deep. Don't be ashamed to admit that you enjoy dunking a chunk of rancid meat from the end of a whippy canepole into a sluggish stream to tempt a bullhead. Despite the advancement of angling techniques and the acquisition of sophisticated equipment, there still is a bit of boy (or girl) left in all of us, and we enjoy the nostalgia of leisure-fishing for ugly bullheads.

All catfish are delicious to eat, but they also have a way of inflicting revenge on any careless fisherman. Those sharp spines in the dorsal and pectoral (front) fins are as lethal as small icepicks and are fortified with poison glands at the base. A stab wound not only is immediately painful, but the spot will swell and hurt for days. From my experience, the little cats with straight-pin spines are most dangerous of all. Handle with care.

Cleaning a catfish is easy. On a small cat just cut the throat and bend the head back until the spine snaps. You can dispatch a large catfish by running the point of a sharp knife blade between the eyes into the brain cavity. Make two vertical slashes through the skin just behind each gill cover (for a big cat with tough skin you might also need to cut straight back along the backbone). Grip the cat in the gills with one hand and with the other, grasp the skin with a pair of skinning pincers or pliers and peel it off.

There are many ways to prepare catfish for eating, but my favorite is to fry and serve them with hushpuppies and slabs of sweet white onion. Mmmm, delicious!

Catfish prefer warmer water than most fish, and they begin to get active in late spring. They will continue to cooperate through the summer and on into the fall until the water temperature drops. Some of the better catches are made at night, particularly in the summertime, and they seem to bite best when there is little or no moon. Often they go on a feeding spree just before the moon comes up.

Numerous catfish are taken after nightfall on stationary lines: a trotline perhaps, or a jugline, dropline or throwline. A trotline is nothing more than a long line anchored or tied at either end with short lines (called stagings) tipped with hooks scattered along this main line. A jugline is a floating jug (a sealed plastic bleach bottle will do) and a line dangling below with a baited hook. Some juglines are anchored with a weight held by a light-test line tied to the float. When a catfish gets hooked, a sharp tug will break this line so that the fish can pull the jug about until it becomes exhausted. Some fishermen use no weight and allow the jugs to float freely, following in a boat and watching for a float to give the telltale bob which indicates a hooked fish. A dropline (limbline) is tied to an overhanging branch, hanging straight down into the water, with a sluggish current perhaps moving the bait back and forth to give it a lifelike motion. A throwline is similar, only longer. It is tied to the bank with a hook and heavy sinker, and the bait is pitched into or near the current. If possible, it should be tied to a sapling that will "give" so a cat can't twist off or break the line.

Where legal, a sunfish is a popular bait for big catfish.

Grasshoppers are hard to beat when cats are feeding.

The method you select will depend on personal choice and state regulations. Most states have restrictions that should be checked before setting a trotline or jugline.

Although catfish are widely distributed and they will go for a variety of baits, they can be as finicky as other fishes at times. Some days they cooperate; some days they don't. Like most fishing, it is a guessing game.

If you want surefire fishing however, try a commercial fish farm. There are many of these farms throughout the South; they not only raise catfish to sell, but most will also permit fishing. You pay so much per pound for what you catch.

Or, you might follow the example of my veterinarian friend, Dr. C. H. Richey, who built his own catfish-fishing hotspot. Richey, like many city dwellers, bought a small plot of land just outside Austin in central Texas. On this acreage he constructed a pond and stocked it with catfish. His modest venture is comparable to a home vegetable garden. It's simply for his own pleasure and to effect economies. He raises catfish, catches them on sport-fishing tackle, and eats them, saving money over the cost at the market.

You hardly can beat a deal like that.

Surf Casting Today

by Frank Woolner

Surf fishing in America has undergone considerable change since the days when it was pictured as a challenging of North Atlantic combers by men armed with long rods, heavy revolving spool reels, and block tin squids. That vision remains; while it is true in some areas, there has been a healthy and progressive evolution.

Surf casting is the business of casting fresh baits or artificial lures from an open ocean beach to catch game fishes. Nowadays, there can be no single choice of a tackle combination because all of the various disciplines are used in their proper places.

Moreover, while traditional surf casting was born on the North Atlantic coast from New England down through North Carolina's Outer Banks, and was first primarily employed as a means to harvest striped bass, channel bass, bluefish, and weakfish, it has now become a nationwide and worldwide sport devoted to catching a tremendous variety of game fishes. The gear is important and easily described.

First, if only in order of seniority, there is the classic, conventional, high surf outfit — which has now been challenged by the bright Young Turks of spinning. Today, fixed spool is far more popular than its predecessor, yet one must not leap to a hasty conclusion. No tackle combination is all-purpose.

Admittedly specialized, nothing is better than the time-honored conventional rig when it is necessary to throw a heavy artificial lure or an even heavier bait-sinker combination to maximum distance. This is high surf at its classic best, yet any modern practitioner will argue that the big gun is only part of a weapons system. There are debits and credits.

A long, relatively stiff surf rod which will measure an average of 10 to 11 feet from butt to tiptop and is calibrated to throw lures or bait-sinker combinations rang-ing three to eight ounces or more, is a heaver. It is designed to cast for distance and then set heavy wire hooks at maximum range. It is a poor "fighting rod," because of its stiffness, but it has to be stiff in order to throw the apple. Consequently, lines must be beefed-up to about 30-pound test in order to guarantee success with fish that might well be rendered unto possession with a third of that muscle — *if* you could reach them.

Revolving spool is less trouble-prone than the more delicate fixed spool winch, yet is requires an educated thumb. This technique must be mastered through practice; a school held in ill-repute by moderns. Basically, it is a two-handed extension of inland bait casting, differing only in that one doesn't turn the reel on its vertical axis during a cast, and the more popular squidding models never feature a worm gear to lay line. This is done with a left thumb, and enthusiasts often suffer a livid groove in that member!

Lines may be monofilament or braid. Mono is almost always chosen for bottom fishing because it presents less water resistance than braid. Braid is easier to control, so it is favored by some night rovers. Nylon, dacron and micron braids are currently most popular, but the trend is toward round mono for general use. Flattened or "ribbon monofilament" pleases a few specialists because it is a superb casting line: its Achilles heel is a tendency to twist and, for that reason alone, should *never* be used on a spin-casting reel.

In view of the fact that more people now use spinning gear in preference to *conventional,* an argument might be made for a change in definition. The word endures only because squidders of the late 40's resisted those fixed spool "foreign devils," calling them yo-yo's and less complimentary things. Most of the old crocks have experienced a change of mind, since spinning has brought a

On a warm summer afternoon surf casters wear everything from Bermuda shorts to the traditional northern waders.

new dimension to an ancient skill. (It should be noted that purists of both persuasions still wrangle about how many angels can dance on the head of a pin, forgetting that the angels themselves have little regard for useless dogma. We'd better be practical.)

Spinning has been called "the system that does it all," and that's reaching. Charitably, fixed spool is more versatile than any other single system, yet the outfit is supreme only in its limited sphere of efficiency. If that sounds familiar, it should, since it applies to every tackle combination yet invented.

Initially, spinning is easy to learn. After ten minutes of instruction, any duffer is able to throw a lure far enough to catch a fish. That's a primary reason why fixed spool has conquered the world of angling. It's a good thing, and yet it introduces a shadow of delusion. Great spin-casters are quite as sophisticated in their approach as any champion of high surf conventional or fly casting. One must examine credentials.

Spinning was developed in Europe, and its mandate was the throwing of light lures attached to light lines. Nothing has changed! Fortunately, in modern surf casting the trend is toward light tackle. Only on a few specific seaboards must a heavy bait or lure be thrown to maximum ranges, and then one goes to the time-honored conventional. It is simply a matter of choosing a weapon suited to the game.

In high surf, the spinning gear can be anything from a one-handed outfit armed with spiderweb line, up to the 14-foot rod loaded with 20-pound-test mono in a frustrating attempt to challenge conventional. It is best in the light to medium balance and, until the line-makers do better, 18-pound test should be rated heavy. Beyond that, casting is sharply handicapped

Rod length remains a matter of controversy. Tournament aces feel that in heavy spinning, there is no profit in using an ultra-long stick: one of 10 or 11 feet is sufficient. Always the open-faced reel is preferred for marine work and, since spring-activated bails remain trouble-prone, manual pick-up is favored for true bull-baiting. Where the outfit is a light to medium combination, then the spring-activated bail is no handicap.

For high surf adventure, where a lure or bait must be cast to a considerable distance, the two weapons systems — conventional and spinning — are paramount. Either can be, and are, scaled up and down. In the former, one progresses from the bait casting rod to big surf sticks. Spinning can be anything from ultra-light to the big heavers armed with bucket-sized reels. Each is ideal within its sphere of efficiency. None prove to be all-purpose.

In addition, there is the fly rod — rarely advocated for surf casting, but nonetheless highly effective under certain conditions. When species like the striped bass take to feeding right in the suds, then a big fly-casting outfit (say a Number 9 or 10) throwing streamer flies or popping bugs can be the royal road to riches.

In addition to proper tackle for the job at hand, several items of equipment are essential, although some are regional requirements. For example, chest-high waders are mighty comfortable where waters are cold, yet would be an abomination in the tropics. Away down in South Florida or on the spectacularly beautiful beaches of Baja California, tennis shoes and long pants are better for wading. The long pants are not chosen for warmth, but to prevent painful sunburn and, in some cases, to guard against the stinging tentacles of jellyfish.

Boot-foot waders are excellent on a sand beach, and treacherous where the form calls for rock-hopping or clambering over jetties. There, some sort of steel-studded sandals or ice-creepers provide enough bite to prevent dangerous spills. Be advised that the "felts" of inland trout and salmon fishermen are worthless: they simply do not grip on the weed- and slime-coated rocks of the sea rim.

Unless surf casting is a tropical thing, a foul-weather

Spincasters search for striped bass in a Long Island surf.

Frank Woolner's big fly rod and Hal Lyman's one-handed spinning rig are equally effective for close-in sport at an inlet.

jacket is a must. Make it a tough and waterproof parka type sans full-length zipper or buttons. There should be a drawstring at the waist, not an elasticized cord. Lacking this, the foul-weather top must be secured at the waist by a tight belt so that there will be no inundation when a wave slams home. Many use the U.S. Army web belt, available at any military surplus outlet; it is tough and efficient and its brass eyelets may be used as hangers for a lure container, a club, or a folding gaff.

Where night fishing is the norm, traveling surfmen usually prefer a miner's headlamp slung around the neck instead of positioned on a hat. Penlights are excellent, since they can be tucked into an inside shirt pocket and kept out of trouble until needed to pick out a backlash or remove the hooks from a game fish. Gasoline and propane lanterns turn the trick when surf casters use bottom baits at one location over a period of time.

Incurables among the addicted feel underprivileged without beach buggies for transportation over remote dunes far from the black-top. Extremely popular from New England down through Cape Hatteras, the buggy has become a status symbol, sometimes a luxurious camp on wheels, more often a small and nimble four-wheel-drive machine fitted with outside rod racks, built-in tackle boxes, and lots of duffle space. The ultimate, often seen on Cap Cod, is a family caravan consisting of one big live-in coach-camper or walk-in truck fitted with all the comforts of home (including TV), plus a smaller "chase car," plus a trailered surfboat!

Possibly the finest of all buggies for basic transportation out in the blue is a modern four-wheel-drive station wagon fitted with soft, oversized tires: such a vehicle will carry anglers and their gear over the mushiest and roughest of outback tracks.

To beginners all of the ocean looks alike: it is simply blue or jade-green sea stitched by the white horses of curling breakers. To them the tides are enigmatic and the winds perplexing: yet they should know that in order to be successful one must learn to "read" this elemental mixture. Sun-bronzed old surfmen do it almost by rote, absorbing a multitude of subtle hints completely lost on a tyro.

First, it is necessary to gear one's life to the tides. During any 24 hours there are two floods and two ebbs, each encompassing approximately six hours. Since the tide is influenced by the attraction of the moon, and since the lunar day is nearer 25 than 24 hours, a progressive variation occurs. These comings and going are accurately plotted on tide tables, give-aways at a majority of coastal tackle shops and gasoline stations.

It is an old rule of thumb that surf casting is always best from "two hours before, to two hours after the top of the tide." Don't bet on it. Obviously, a flooding tide covers sloping beaches and flats that were high and dry at the ebb, thus allowing game fish to cruise in through sloughs and gullies to frolic and feed. On some beaches there is no better directive.

However, where a coastal creek or estuary is pouring its wealth into the sea during a falling tide, then practically all of the ebb is likely to be productive. That's because the outward-bound water carries with it a smorgasbord of crustacea and other succulent bait. Game fish line up just outside the portals of such a banquet hall.

Tides, abetted by winds, create swirling rips at specific points, often where a thumb of land juts out into the ocean. There, bait is tumbled helplessly in the clashing waters and, again, predators enjoy a Roman holiday. This furious maelstrom of current will occur, depending on location, at the peak of ebb or flood. It won't happen at high or low slack.

Wind direction must be taken into account. Roughly, an inshore gale will drive bait shoreward and, if there is sufficient depth for game fish to follow, they'll be there.

Heavy, conventional gear caught this Cape Hatteras channel bass for Charley Whitney.

If a shelf is very gradual, then an offshore wind boosts the long cast necessary to reach a productive bar. High winds from one quarter may "dirty" the water with torn weed or suspended sand, while just around the next headland it guarantees fruitful clarity.

Look for "live water," moving of sufficient depth to harbor both bait and predator. High slack and low slack are least productive, since all of the sea creatures welcome such periods to rest and charge their batteries. Salt-water angling, and particularly surf casting, is all movement and fury — not like Ike Walton's melody of tranquility.

It will be, almost always, a business of casting bottom baits or artificial lures. "Almost always," because there are occasions when healthy eels and other swimming goodies such as herring or menhaden can be live-lined from shore with marked success. The great trick is to identify forage most in demand during a particular slice of time and space.

This naturally varies, and types of baits are legion. Sand bugs may do for pompano on Florida's eastern coast. Maybe it will be ghost shrimp or pile worms for corvina and surf perch in the Pacific. Trophy stripers engulf seaworms, squid, crabs, clam-flesh and a number of other offerings. It is necessary to study one's chosen quarry and trigger its appetite.

Terminal tackle is no big thing. Usually it consists of the sliding sinker or "fishfinder rig," maybe a basic sinker and fixed leader, a hi-lo combination in which two hooks are positioned at different levels, or a fishfinder with the leadered hook buoyed by cork barrel floats to keep it above trash-fish and crab level. Use monofilament leaders on soft-mouthed species, and wire for the sharp-toothed legions.

Sinkers are job-rated: invariably the edged-pyramid type in sand or soft mud, and the rounded dipsey or bank on rocky or coral bottom. There are hosts of sinker variations, yet major requirements are still efficiency in holding and resistance to fouling. A weight should be no heavier than that which is practical in a given current and on a specific ground.

Successful bait-men prefer to hand-hold their rods, yet often there are long waits between bites, so the sand-spiked rod holder is indispensable. Make it a rugged type, one that can be well anchored. Lots of fine tackle combinations, plagued by too tight a striking drag, have been hauled into the deep six.

One short word about hooks, important! The finest sell for a pittance, so it is disastrous to cut corners. Use the very best in size ranges designed for the species sought. An 8/0 may be fine for a huge channel bass, but it won't catch many corvina, surf perch, or flounders. Today the claw or Eagle-Claw bend is difficult to beat

One of the largest channel bass ever caught on fly, a 37-pounder. The angler is Claude Rogers of Virginia Beach, Virginia.

in bottom fishing with bait.

Once upon a time, as all good stories begin, the surf caster who considered himself a purist used nothing but block tin squids. Sometime shortly after World War II a new aristocracy appeared, and these were plug casters. It's all pretty ridiculous, since great surfmen employ whatever is most efficient. There are burgeoning families of lures, plus a host of variations. Each can be, at a moment in time, just right.

In the high surf, today's nonpareils are plugs and metal squids — the latter a casting version of the time-honored spoon. There are beefed-up spoons that are marine cross-breeds, heavy enough to cast effectively, yet broad-beamed enough to provide seductive action on the retrieve.

Never have surf casters had so grand an assortment of excellent artificial lures. There are about nine basic plug types ranging from surface poppers and sliders through top-water swimmers, mid-level wigglers to deep-diving marvels. There are "stick-baits" and mirror-sided artificials that require rod action to come alive. We enjoy a brand-new family of soft plastic offerings. Choose those manufactured by the reputable old firms, and they'll catch fish.

Bucktail jigs, plus the new lead-heads that incorporate soft plastic bodies instead of feather or deer-hair dressing, must be considered. It is true that the bucktail is a special-ist's weapon, yet — once mastered — it may well be the deadliest lure ever designed for marine angling. This hunk of lead and hank of hair or plastic can be trolled or cast. It intrigues almost every game fish that will hit a moving target: it is a cinch to throw and it can be used at any depth other than on the surface film.

The trouble with bucktail is the very fact that it must be "fished"! You don't just throw it out there and reel it in as you can with a plug or squid. The lead-head may be Murder, Incorporated, when cast up and across a strong current, then bounced through in a half-circle swing. It is equally deadly when worked rapidly with the "Florida Whip" retrieve: fast reeling interspersed with switches of the rod tip. It is excellent on night or day tides, some-thing that may also be said for the plug, but not so often for the metal squid or spoon, both of which are better in daylight hours.

Return to that often-suspect "rule of thumb." Usually — and speed of retrieve is always geared to the species sought — a lure used during the night hours is brought back at approximately half the speed of that same bait worked during sunny hours. Slow it down. Practically dream it along. Change the pattern only when it fails, because then you must be an opportunist and experiment.

Since America's rush to the sea shortly after World War II, there has been no dearth of good literature about the tactics of successful surf fishing, yet there is a tremendous gap between academic instruction and the real thing: primarily the feel of it, the tug of tidal cur-rents, the little things that later seem so easy, like master-ing ice-skating after a multitude of spills.

Reading the beach is easy, if you know how. You go there at flat ebb and, wearing polarized glasses, search for the now-exposed sloughs and cuts which will be the

Bunny DiPietro of Buzzards Bay, Massachusetts, uses an ultra-light spinning outfit on the Cape Cod Canal.

highways of the ocean when the tide comes flooding in. You note the locations of "black spots," the mussel beds or anchored weeds that will shelter forage later and will vector in trophy game fish. Every creek mouth or inlet is carefully plotted. One must watch the development of rips at certain stages of tide. All of these things will be valuable later.

Finally on site, with the wind keening and the surf crashing ashore, there are other highly important clues. Bird action, for example. Anyone, other than a complete dolt, understands the situation when a tremendous gag-gle of terns, gulls, or maybe pelicans circle widely and go dive-bombing into a maelstrom of surface-breaking fish. A canny regular will also mark the flight of a single tern that circles tightly and obviously sees something beneath the living ripples.

On some species, the tip-off will be a sudden, blos-soming slick on an otherwise ruffled surface. A tight little swirl may be the first indication of a feeding spree. When the light is right (and this is a moment to treasure until death do us part), one may even see surf-feeding warriors sliding right through the hearts of emerald combers. Nothing is so indicative of the inshore battler's tremendous power.

Surfmen forever study bait. If any one species of forage is abundant, that one may well prove the pièce de résis-tance. It works day or night, incidentally. If certain little goodies come flipping up on the beach at midnight, then it is reasonable to assume that they have been harrassed by something big and toothy in the second wave. Match the hatch!

Listen! Even above the booming crash of arriving combers and the grating slide of shell and sand in undertow, one can hear the pop or slap of a feeding gamester.

Use your nose! Certain game fishes, such as the striped bass (which smells like thyme), the bluefish (cut melon), and the channel bass (an acrid, almost chemical odor), can be located by the living scent they exude. This is a fact often discounted by beginners, but all regulars know that it is true and they often predict the catching of a fish before any lure is presented. Melville's whale hunters did the same thing.

So you throw it way out there, flip the reel into gear and start a retrieve calulated to hoax the wariest of game fishes. The strike, if all connections are as tight as they should be, is both sudden and solid. Now you're "in," and lots of things can happen.

To begin with, in high surf, you're splashing in and out of the suds, getting belted by an occasional wave that seems to come from nowhere, trying to maintain a precarious footing and keep the tip up. You worry about being cleaned-out, and it's a dangerous thought.

Try to remember that tight drags lose more fish than any other single factor. Doggedly resist that human impulse to tighten up, because, if you do, then you're going

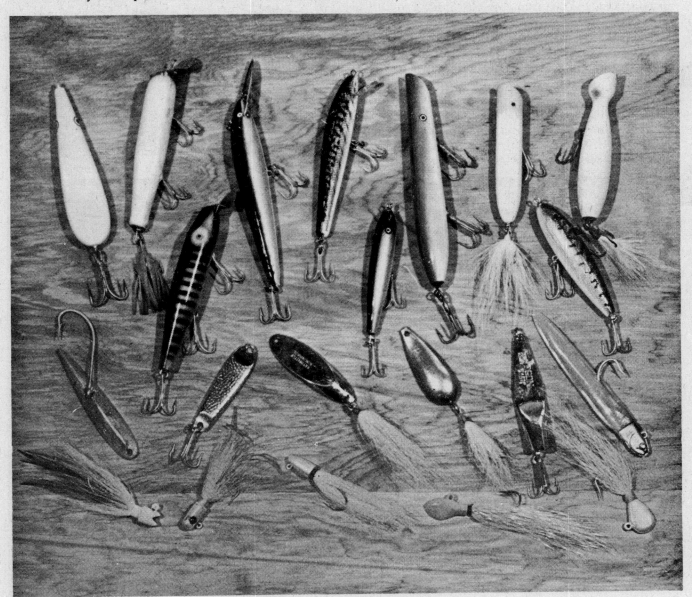

Some of the lures currently favored by surf casters on American coasts.

TOOLS AND TECHNIQUES

A picket line of spinning and revolving spool enthusiasts works a point.

Ralph Gray, Frank Woolner and Hal Lyman with a catch of North Carolina weakfish caught on bait-casting tackle in the surf.

to pop a line and lose a trophy.

Let him run against medium pressure, fighting the spring of the rod. There'll be plenty of time to pump and reel later, even to manipulate the brake after some of this tiger's stripes have faded. In the beginning, be tight and be careful. You *can't* stop him cold, but you *can* wear him down. It isn't babying, it's just prudence until the tackle tells. He'll turn.

Now, on the way back, put the boots to him! It is always wise to whip a game fish as rapidly as possible, within reason. A tedious and long drawn-out battle allows the keyholing of hooks and subsequent escape. At the same time the fish is given an opportunity to rest. Finally, if release is contemplated, your quarry will be close to death at the end of a long fight. Who needs it?

Beaching any surf fish is an art in itself, one too often botched. These trophies are lost to tight drags and to inept landing tactics. It's surf, remember? There will be powerful ground swells smashing ashore with enough force to lift a medium tank. Immediately after each comber bursts into spray on the shingle, there'll be a back-rush of receding water, often called undertow. It will be tremendously powerful.

In the morning's first light a couple of spin-fishermen head for the beach. Their rods are the medium-weight racket heavers that have proved to be most effective.

A surfman's job is to ride his quarry ashore on a wave, to maneuver so that pressure can be applied to coincide with the advancing ground swell's force. Always bring them ashore on a crest.

But, be particularly alert at this point. If the fish retains some hidden reserve of energy he may turn and dig in just before the ground swell slams home. Split seconds later the surging backwash will be his ally, not yours. Beginners panic and try to hold — and beginners part lines then and there.

Proper operational procedure is to accept a momentary Mexican stand-off, to drop the tip and rush toward the surf line, keeping all conections tight, but exerting no undue force on this prize which is being washed back with the undertow.

Play is again, Sam! Ride him ashore on the next wave. Then, while he's flopping high and dry on the shingle, practically spent, grab the leader and drag him higher! Or, if there's a lust for fishflesh on the table, belt him with a short club or hook a gaff's point into his gills.

Surf casting is a hard, rough business, but some think it the most satisfying of all sea sport, if only because an angler goes in alone with no skipper or mate to advise him, with no weapon other than a long surf stick and a basic understanding of the forces at work. In this wonderful age of sophisticated electronic aids, big boats and team effort, a surfer remains — one man against the furious sea.

He goes in alone and nobody shares his triumph or disaster.

Frank Woolner with heavy surf rod shouldered. The "trigger" under the reel is favored by a lot of old stagers who started with plug-casting tackle.

SHARK!

by Jerry Kenney

It wasn't a very large shark — a mere pup about two feet long — and the angler hauled the writhing thing out of the water without much effort and then grabbed it by the tail. With the hook still imbedded in its jaw, the beast snapped into a U-turn, stretched its tiny three-inch-wide mouth into something the size of a bear trap and clamped down on the fisherman's forearm.

In the hospital later, after torn muscles and tendons were sewn back together and 38 stitches embroidered his mangled flesh, the fisherman was still shaking his head in disbelief. It was six months before he could shake hands.

Just a little mako shark, about 20 pounds, the kind that make wall trophies that people admire more for their beauty than their alleged ferocity . . .

You should have seen the big mako Charlie Nappi had on a line for three hours a few years back off Montauk Point. All that time it acted like it was possessed, rocketing through the air, turning cartwheels, splashing down in giant geysers of foam.

It would bolt up again, a twisting mass of blue and silver fury, the head beating from side to side and that hideous, muscular mouth agape, exposing a mangle of pearly spikes.

When it wasn't jumping, it was running wildly across the surface on its tail like a torpedo out of control. All that time the action was 100 to 200 yards from the boat, but then Nappi's rod arched sharply downward. Line smoked off the reel and it was going straight down and down until the arching rod snapped straight out and the line, tight as a bowstring, went limp.

Nappi's outburst at what he thought was a busted line was understandable. He was still sounding off when an explosion occurred 15 feet from the boat. I had tossed an empty five-gallon bait can over the side and 15 seconds later it blased into the air on the nose of this writhing mako torpedo. Up the beast went, rolling, twisting, the head whipping back and forth.

We watched stunned. It seemed the shark was a hundred feet directly overhead, toppling in the slow motion of our fright. It started down and then the sickening thought struck: It could land in the boat; it might go right through the bottom of our 24-footer; it didn't take much to imagine what else it could do.

The shark missed the boat by 10 feet, and the splash almost swamped us.

Sharks have landed in bigger, stronger boats and the results are almost always devastation. One skipper tried beating the beast with a club without effect. He took out a shotgun and blasted a six-inch hole through the shark's head, taking his chances with a boat leaking from gunshot holes rather than one that surely would have been torn to bits.

Some experienced shark hunters think sharks actually try to come aboard. Did that mako of ours — which we landed, by the way, and it was 299 pounds — really aim at that tin can? Who's to say? Ernest Hemingway, who loved fishing for sharks but hated their guts, once said: "The mako will deliberately leap at a man in a dory who has hooked him."

A native Solomon Islander once told me that a shark never dies until the sun sets. In some Pacific islands the people made the shark a god and sacrificed human beings by feeding them to the deity.

Another group in the Pacific would capture a shark and crucify it. They'd nail it to a board and send it out to sea to die under the glaring sun. Some present-day shark hunters have been known to ruthlessly massacre them in hideous ways, but not always without retaliation. Even beheading does not always stop this marvelously simple organism from biting at everything within reach. The fishermen who have been mangled by bodyless shark heads are too numerous to count. After losing their heads sharks have been seen swimming away to be devoured by their comrades.

They prefer to feed on fish and mammals that swim slowly or have been injured, but their diet can include anything that floats or might be dumped in the sea. Cinder blocks, shoes, bottles, tin cans, burlap bags and in one case a tire, have been found in their stomachs. It is a diet that makes a shark easy to attract.

In Florida, shark fishing is often done from the beaches, but in the Northeast it's almost entirely from boats. A good sturdy boat is a wise first choice of equipment. Tackle can be any medium-weight rod, reel and line that might be used for big cod, bluefish and striped bass. A rig tested at 50-pound strength can land almost any shark a fisherman will run up against except the real giants. John Casey, a fisheries biologist with the National Marine Fisheries Service in Narragansett, R.I., caught a 1,500-pound white shark on an old codfish rig with 40-pound test line.

A strong, three- or four-man crew is indispensable along with an arsenal of clubs, meat hooks or gaffs; wire clippers, knives and a gun. The chum that best attracts sharks is ground menhaden, mackerel or any of the tunas, all of which are oily. As the oil slick spreads, a shark will turn toward where the smell is strongest and follow it to the boat like an eager beagle hotly purusing the fresh trail of a cottontail.

Often a dorsal fin zigzagging up the slick is the first sign of action, an eerie sight to see for the first time. The shark will swim up to the boat, circle within view and seem to single you out with cold, malevolent eyes. You thank God for the sturdy boat under your feet because you know that if it ever sank you'd be right on top of the menu. But that chum slick is just whetting the shark's appetite. Chunks of fish and baited hooks soon catch his eye and he may attack, circle, bump or slowly inhale the offering. That's when to strike, to sink the hook deep into the jaw.

One school of thought holds that a shark should be allowed to swallow the baited hook deeply before striking. But a gut-hooked shark eventually winds up dead whether he's caught or escapes. And a growing new school of shark hunters isn't out to kill sharks but only catch them for the sport and release them when the fun's over. There are exceptions. Some fishermen want shark trophies or a mounted small shark. The mako is not only a trophy; it yields delicious steaks too.

Fighting a shark, a novice fisherman may feel safer strapped into a chair like a murderer in the death house with the rod, perhaps as thick as a broomstick, strapped to the chair: The only way a shark can pull him overboard is to tear the chair right out of the deck.

That's not shark fishing. Most fishermen use medium weight tackle and stand up for a toe-to-toe battle. They wear a belt with a cup for the rod butt so it won't gouge out their insides. Sometimes a shoulder harness is attached to the reel so the angler can rest his arms during what can be an hours-long battle. But an unwritten law says shark fishermen don't sit down.

The crew is tense when the sharks start to arrive. They're hoping for a mako, the great fighter, but any shark will do. To the inexperienced eye, most sharks look alike but the mako is an awesomely beautiful acrobat, while the long, lean blue shark fights in wide circles around the boat. The homely sand shark and the bulldogging duskies and porbeagles do their fighting way down deep and rarely come to the surface until exhausted.

The great white shark, with a well-established reputation as a man-eater — as has the mako, tiger, porbeagle and hammerhead — has unbelieveable brute strength. The hammerhead has to be the most bizarre-looking beast man will ever see in the ocean. Its normal swimming pace is faster than most sharks and, as the name suggests, the head is somewhat like a hammer, the eyes set like beacons on the wing tips. Circling, it looks like a vulture gliding in the sky waiting patiently to pounce on its prey.

For all their differences, though, sharks have a common dislike for the annoyances inflicted on them by fishermen and none submits willingly. So the angler tied into a shark is off on a merry chase around the boat, climbing over gunwales, up around the bow, down the other side, across the cockpit and around again and again. He'll struggle a half hour to gain 50 yards of line and then in 10 seconds the shark will rip off 100 yards. This kind of give and take can last for hours.

When the shark tires, the real excitement is just about to erupt. Then it'll take two, sometimes three strong men to finish up the job. From the hook in the shark's jaw a 10-to-15-foot piano wire leads to the line. One man must grab the wire with a gloved hand — and make sure it never loops around his hand.

There's no telling what a shark will do when he sees the boat. Some attack or bite into it, others roll up in the wire and most get a second wind and explode into a mass of foaming fury. That's when fingers and even hands disappear, if not from the shark's jaws, then possibly from the looping piano wire. From there on, it's hand to hand. The flying gaff — a foot-wide meat hook that disconnects from the shaft once sunk into the shark — is set in the area of the gill, and this spurs the beast on another break for freedom. The jaws snap at everything within range and the tail slashes with the weight of a steel girder.

Dodging the tail and jaws is one thing, but the flying hardware — gaffs, hooks, wire and other UFOs — is something else. The trick is to get a rope around the shark's tail and hoist it high enough to lash it to one of the stern cleats of the boat. With the head lowered a shark is sometimes paralyzed and quiet unless another shark comes around and starts a battle that can tear loose the boat hardware. If the beast is over 150 pounds, attempting to pacify it with a club of any size is useless. Even a 50-pounder seems immune to blackjacking.

Not even the so-called harmless sand shark can be counted on as harmless. Two fishermen in Delaware Bay caught one which bit into their 12-foot boat and shook it like a rattle before breaking loose and leaving a row of ivory spikes embedded in the planks.

Nor need a shark be provoked. A 200-pound dusky shark tore the exhaust pipe off a sport cruiser and almost sank it 12 miles off the Jersey coast. A giant white shark rammed a sturdy 40-foot charter boat off Montauk with such force that the skipper swears it would have smashed a smaller boat to bits. Eventually they subdued the monster with two harpoons and a rifle. It was 17 feet long and weighed 4,500 pounds.

Hunting sharks that size is like taking on a tiger with a pair of chopsticks. The best defense is an honorable and rapid retreat.

Shark hunting as a sport is only about a dozen years old. Commercial fishermen chased them back in the '40s and '50s for their tough hides and livers rich in Vitamin A. But synthetic methods of producing the vitamin all but collapsed the industry. One or two are still operating off Florida, and one firm, Ocean Leather at Newark, N.J., processes hides which come mostly from South America and Mexico.

Probably the first real shark hunt in this region began back in the summer of 1916 in New Jersey. Three swimmers were killed by sharks and another lost a leg. Three of these incidents occurred 11 miles inland in Matawan Creek. The community turned out with pitchforks, harpoons, shotguns, knives and even rakes. With dynamite they killed two sharks, but the real culprit wound up in a fisherman's net in Raritan Bay.

It was an 8½-foot white shark that weighed only 250 pounds, but in its stomach was the shinbone of a youngster (a boy had his leg torn off two days earlier), ribs from an adult and 15 pounds of human flesh.

It's a far cry from shark hunting today though. One of the biggest hunts may be the Bay Shore Mako Tournament, which is held off the South Shore of Long Island every June. One year, in two days of fishing by about 150 boats, more than 1,000 sharks were captured. Other hunts are held at Montauk and Shinnecock on Long Island, offering prizes up to $1,000 for the biggest catches.

This kind of fishing is taking the Atlantic Coast by storm. Shark hunters are getting out in everything from rowboats to yachts and they're getting dumped, bumped, attacked and bitten, losing hands, feet and fingers, getting legs broken by swinging shark tails, and even being frightened to death.

Conservationists are so uptight about the depletion of lions, tigers and such that big-game hunting on land is becoming a shameful sport. But there aren't many shark lovers around and the ultra-conservationists haven't yet come to their rescue. Shark hunting has all the excitement and danger of stalking any dangerous land animal. What's more, it's relatively inexpensive and easily accessible to anyone along the coast. The declining numbers of marlin, tuna and swordfish also have popularized the shark as a quarry.

The origin of the shark is hard to trace because sharks have no skeletal bones, and the only remains seem to be fossilized teeth and jaws. But the beast probably dates back about 300 million years to the Devonian period.

Each spring and summer sharks of all species start migrating northward as the sun warms the ocean. They arrive in our waters from the coast of South America, the Caribbean, the Gulf of Mexico, the Florida coast, the Sargasso Sea and as far as 2,000 miles east in the Atlantic. Trailing schools of bait fish, they have a constant supply of food. Then they lurk generally eight or more miles offshore but, when bait fish move in closer, follow to within 100 yards of the beach.

Some fishermen shoot the shark, and if it is particularly large or obnoxious, bullets may be the only solution. Next to going into the water with the shark, the stupidest thing a fisherman can do is bring it into the boat. Even dead sharks bite. The recommended procedure is to tow a shark behind the boat tail first. This is supposed to drown them. Some are left for hours in the hot sun and this is supposed to kill them. Bullet holes through the head should do it, and a shark hanging by the tail out of water for six hours ought certainly be dead.

But a 300-pound blue shark we caught off Montauk at 9 one morning hung tail high until 3 p.m., then was towed 20 miles tail first and finally was hoisted on a scale just as the sun was setting. Until then I had forgotten the Solomon Islander's superstition that sharks never die until sundown. This guy lunged towards the west, tearing inch-thick strips out of a nearby telephone pole.

Casey, the fisheries biologist, believes that such ferocity can only encourage shark hunters. "It's hard to combat the reputation these creatures have, and a lot of people figure the more sharks we kill the safer the oceans will be and we'll all be better off," he said.

"Right now we happen to have a great supply of sharks, and their population is certainly underexploited. We are going to see commercial fishing for sharks expand in the Northeast. It's a question of when rather than if."

Shark meat has been a big item in Europe and the Orient for years. Mako can easily pass for swordfish, and it often does, on the American market. Other species find their way to market disguised as gray fish, white fish and sea scallops. The common dogfish shark has a big following even under its own identity. Fulton Fish Market handles more than 100,000 pounds of doggies every year.

Shark fishing, in other words, is not what Oscar Wilde said of fox hunting: the unspeakable in pursuit of the inedible. In fact, if we can believe Orientals and certain South Pacific islanders, there's more than one sensation to be had from catching the shark. Shark fin soup, they say, is an aphrodisiac.

BOOKS FOR ANGLERS

by Robert H. Boyle

The literature on fishing is the richest and deepest of any sport in the world, but because of the abundance of titles it can be confusing to fishermen unacquainted with the field. In an effort to bring order out of chaos, here is a critical list of books to serve as a guide for anglers, be they interested salt or freshwater, jigging or fly-tying, trout, black bass or tarpon. All the books are in print at this writing.

The most single comprehensive work on the entire subject of angling is *McClane's New Standard Fishing Encyclopedia and International Angling Guide.* Edited by A. J. McClane, the angling editor of *Field and Stream,* the *Encyclopedia* is a hefty work of 1156 pages, and it is expensive: $40. It includes life histories of important species of fishes, fresh and saltwater, excellent color plates of flies, first-rate articles on aquatic insects, advice on where to fish in the United States and abroad, and much, much more. The *Encyclopedia* also offers a lengthy bibliography helpful to readers who want to explore the finer points of almost any subject. Although the entries are arranged alphabetically from Aawa to zooplankton, the book suffers from lack of an index. Still and all, four stars.

While McClane looks at fishing from the angler's point of view, Mark Sosin and John Clark take the opposite tack in *Through the Fish's Eye,* a superb study of why fishes act the way they do and how the angler can take advantage of their instincts and behavior patterns. Sosin is an angling writer, Clark a biologist with a thorough knowledge of ichthyology, and together they have written the best book of its kind. Back in the 1930s the late Brian Curtis wrote his *Life Story of the Fish,* now available in paperback from Dover. Not as fishing-oriented as the Sosin and Clark study, Curtis's book is well worth buying and consulting. It also reads extraordinarily well; Curtis was a talented writer who had the ability to put the findings of science into clear and often amusing language.

Of course, fishes are products of their environment, and the angler who wants to take a look at the larger scheme of things in ponds or streams is advised to turn to either H. B. N. Hynes' *The Ecology of Running Waters,* or Dr. George W. Bennett's *Management of Lakes and Ponds.* If you want to know how many largemouth bass you can expect to find in a pond or what happens when largemouths are stocked with warmouths, read George Bennett, who recently retired as chief of the Aquatic Biology Section of the esteemed Illinois Natural History Survey. The Hynes book on streams must be read to be believed: it is a comprehensive and critical review of the world literature on the biology of streams and rivers and deals at length with such subjects as aquatic insects, the fishes of running water and the ecological factors affecting them. One has to be somewhat hipped on the whole subject of fishes and the worlds they live in to read Hynes or Bennett, but if you are the kind of angler who really wants to get to the essence of things, buy them both. There are tremendous amounts of information distilled in these books, information you can't get anywhere else.

Good books on saltwater fishing are unknown to many saltwater fishermen. A pity, because there are a couple of gems. *Fishes of the Gulf of Maine,* by Henry B. Bigelow and William C. Schroeder, is a classic. My definition of a classic is any book that becomes staple bathroom reading. My copy, originally published as a bulletin of

the U. S. Fish and Wildlife Service, is dog-eared, tattered, annotated in pencil, and the spine is held together by red electrician's tape. Fortunately for fishermen, *Fishes of the Gulf of Maine,* has been reprinted in hard covers by the Museum of Comparative Zoology at Harvard. If you are an East Coast saltwater fisherman, buy it and read all about striped bass, bluefish, weakfish and other coastal marauders. If the book has one fault, it is the title. The book really deals with fishes from Delaware to Canada.

Back in 1928, the U. S. Bureau of Fisheries published a similar work by Samuel F. Hildebrand and Schroeder, *Fishes of Chesapeake Bay.* Long out of print, it commanded a premium in the rare book market. The Smithsonian Institution has now reprinted a revised edition.

The best all-around book on the "how to" of saltwater fishing is Frank Woolner's *Modern Saltwater Sport Fishing.* The editor of *The Salt Water Sportsman* magazine, Woolner deals with rods, lines, leaders, lures, trolling, natural baits, surf casting and other related subjects. Saltwater fishermen interested in the evolution of the sport and the people who developed it, such as Ernest Hemingway, Michael Lerner, Frank Woolner and others, are advised to read George Reiger's *Profiles in Saltwater Angling.*

Individual species of saltwater fishes are treated in various books. Worthy titles that come to mind are Milt Rosko's *Secrets of Striped Bass Fishing,* Frank T. Moss's *Successful Striped Bass Fishing,* and Henry Lyman's *Successful Bluefishing.* For a look at all the species, see Edward T. Migdalski's *Angler's Guide to the Saltwater Game Fishes,* which covers both the Atlantic and Pacific Coasts. (Equally well done is a companion volume by

Migdalski, *Angler's Guide to the Fresh Water Sport Fishes of North America.* The two Migdalski books are often overlooked, but they are basic to any angling library.) In recent years, saltwater fly fishing has boomed in popularity, and two books of interest are Kenneth E. Bay and Hermann Kessler's *Salt Water Flies* and Lefty Kreh's *Fly Fishing in Salt Water.* Kreh is also the author of another recent book, *Fly Casting with Lefty Kreh.* If the title seems immodest it is not; Kreh is a master in the field. Kreh and Mark Sosin are also the authors of a lavishly illustrated book, *Practical Fishing Knots,* which goes into the intricacies of splicing and popular knots from the nail knot to the Bimini twist.

Like *Practical Fishing Knots,* there are several other "how to" books that cover both salt and freshwater fishing. In a class by itself is C. Boyd Pfeiffer's *Tackle Craft,* the ideal book for the fisherman who wants to make or repair his own rods, plugs, spoons, plastic worms, jigs, and goodness knows what else. This is a book that will not only save you money but also give great enjoyment if you like to work with your hands. Highly recommended for all anglers.

For all the popularity of spinning (in either fresh or saltwater), there is little on the overall subject except for a helpful book by Norman Strung and Milt Rosko, *Spinfishing, the System that Does It All.* Although the subtitle is somewhat overblown, this is a handy book to have. Anglers who think they know it all would do well to read it, and it is just the book to give a novice fisherman or anyone starting out. The most common question put to an experienced angler by parents is, "My boy wants to go fishing. Is there any book that will tell him how?" The answer is *Spinfishing.*

Jigging is the deadliest art of fishing known. For all its effectiveness, jigging has not received the attention it deserves except for two books devoted to the subject. First and foremost is *Bait Tail Fishing,* by the late Al Reinfelder, a brilliant angler who was in charge of product development for Garcia. The title is a misnomer because *Bait Tail Fishing* is really about jigging, and Reinfelder tells readers how to jig in very practical terms. A great deal of thought and experience went into *Bait Tail Fishing,* and it is highly recommended. There is a good little booklet, *How to Fish with Jigs,* by Lacey E. Gee and Erwin D. Sias, which gives advice on rods, reels, line, ultra light, the jigs for various species of fishes, mainly freshwater but some salt, plus information on how to make jigs.

Trout fishing has a large literature, but here are selected titles. Paul R. Needham's *Trout Streams* is a classic study recently revised and updated. It is technical, but reading is easy and profitable. *The Stream Conservation Handbook,* edited by J. Michael Migel, is written in popular style, and any fisherman who wants to see those streams we have left protected or improved is advised to consult it. The *Handbook* fills a gap long neglected.

W. E. Frost and M. E. Brown's *The Trout* is a scientific work. Although the book deals with trout in Great Britain, there is much for the American angler to absorb on such topics as age and growth, the food of trout and the physical environment. Less detailed but American-angling-oriented is Cecil E. Heacox's *The Compleat Brown Trout,* which has short chapters on stream tactics and management. The Kamloops trout is native to the Kamloops region of British Columbia, but that did not prevent Steve Raymond from writing an excellent book,

Kamloops, about the species. Doubtless of marginal interest to most fishermen, *Kamloops* is cited here because it is a thorough work and reading it may stimulate new thoughts in the mind of the serious trout angler.

The standard work on trout fishing is *Trout,* by the late Ray Bergman, which probably has sold more than 100,000 copies since it first came out in the 1930s. Obviously *Trout* has much to offer readers, but it is beginning to show its age around the edges. A more up-to-date book is *Trout Fishing* by the late Joe Brooks. Another Brooks, Charles E., has written *The Trout and the Stream.* Although Charles Brooks has fished mainly in the West, his book should prove stimulating to anglers in other parts of the country. Brooks knows his rivers, insects and fishes, and he also knows the scientific literature. There is just something about the whole approach of the book, written in Dutch-uncle terms, that says it is going to become a standard.

Newcomers to fly fishing are often put off by the arcane talk that abounds. For the angler too shy to ask questions, try *Fly-fishing for Trout, A Guide for Adult Beginners* by Richard W. Talleur, the fly fishing equivalent of *Spinfishing* mentioned previously.

The salmons belong to the same family of fishes as the trouts, and the best overall book on the natural history of Atlantic and Pacific salmons is Anthony Netboy's *The Salmon, Their Fight for Survival.* A resident of Oregon, Netboy travelled to Europe and Japan to gather material, and his book belongs in the library of every serious fisherman. Not angling oriented, *The Salmon* is nonetheless highly recommended. For the angler, Joseph D. Bates' *Atlantic Salmon Flies and Fishing* is thorough and informative.

Fly tying grew out of trout fishing, and it is a craft or art that every fisherman should learn. You can learn more in an hour at the bench with an experienced fly-tyer than you can from books, but books definitely have their place. In fact, they are invaluable references because it is impossible for anyone to keep all the patterns and techniques in his head at one time. The best basic book is J. Edson Leonard's *Flies,* which has been a standard for years. A handsome new book by Poul Jorgensen, with photographs by Irv Swope, *Dressing Flies for Fresh and Salt Water,* goes from the elementary to the advanced. Another excellent book is *Art Flick's Master Fly-Tying Guide,* with contributions from such masters as Dave Whitlock and Ted Niemeyer, and Eric Leiser's *Fly-Tying Materials* is a must for the addict. A classic in the field is Art Flick's revised *New Streamside Guide to Naturals and their Imitations.* Other books of merit are Vincent Marinaro's *A Modern Dry Fly Code,* strong on terrestrial insects such as beetles and grasshoppers, the late John Atherton's *The Fly and the Fish,* Doug Swisher and Carl Richards' *Selective Trout,* which focuses on "no hackle" patterns, and Ernest Schwiebert's *Nymphs.*

So-called "black bass" are the most popular sport fishes in the United States, but the number of good books available is not large compared to trout, possibly because there is a certain snobbery, or tradition if you will, connected with trout. Publishers apparently presume bass fishermen are illiterates, an error of the worst sort, but despite the lack of titles there are some good ones.

The bass professionals who fish on the BASS circuit all learned from the Arnold Palmer of the BASS circuit, Bill Dance, who has written a couple of books, including *Practical Black Bass Fishing,* with Mark Sosin. Other books of note are Grits Gresham's *Complete Book of Bass Fishing* and Byron Dalrymple's *Modern Book of the Black Bass.* In some parts of the country, walleyes rank right up with bass, and the interested fisherman should read *Walleyes and Walleye Fishing,* by Joe Fellegy, Jr.

One of the charms of angling literature is that there are books that defy classification. The titles listed here can be read for history, inspiration or amusement. There is Edward R. Hewitt's *A Trout and Salmon Fisherman for 75 Years,* Charles Ritz's, *A Fly Fisher's Life,* John McDonald's *Quill Gordon,* and any book by Roderick Haig-Brown, such as *A River Never Sleeps.* Sparse Grey Hackle's *Fishless Days, Angling Nights,* is both an interesting look at Hewitt, George La Branche and Theodore Gordon and a witty account of the vagaries of angling. Mr. Hackle, the *nom de peche* of Alfred W. Miller, also wrote the commentary for *Great Fishing Tackle Catalogs of the Golden Age,* edited by Sam Melner and Hermann Kessler, which should be read by fishermen seeking the Rosebuds of their youth way back when Abercrombie & Fitch boasted the slogan, "Where the blazed trail crosses the boulevard." Nick Lyons has written a couple of funny, yet occasionally wistful books, *The Seasonable Angler* and *Fishing Widows,* and Lyons also had edited the best anthology available, *Fisherman's Bounty.*

Finally, Arnold Gingrich, the man behind the scenes at *Esquire,* has written *The Joys of Trout,* really a gossipy inside account of who's who in trout, and *The Fishing in Print,* his own very special and occasionally outrageous tour through five centuries of angling literature.

Cook What You Catch

by L. James Bashline

If most of us added up the cost of our fishing tackle and then threw in the additional expenses of each fishing trip, we'd find that the price per pound of fillets in the freezer would be frightening. Supplementing the family larder with angler-caught fish is a mighty poor yardstick for measuring fishing success. Yet, in these days of continually rising prices, the fish we do bring home should be utilized.

There isn't a fresh water fish that can't be prepared to please the most discriminating of gourmets. All of the bass and trout are excellent. Walleye pike are outstanding and even the sometimes scorned northern pike is fine fare when properly filleted. Yellow perch, rock bass, bluegills, and crappies aren't called panfish for nothing. Deep-fried catfish are magnificent and the anadromous shad and salmon are the basis for some terrific eating adventures. Even the imported European carp can be treated in ways that will excite the most sophisticated taste buds.

With the exception of small trout under twelve inches in length and very small panfish, most connoisseurs of fish agree that filleting is the first step in the route any fish should take through the kitchen. Still I'd better amend that right away. The *very* first step is proper boat or field care of the fish you intend to eat.

For the wading angler, the old rattan or willow creel is about the best thing that has ever been invented. These bulky affairs are miserable to carry, but they do keep trout and small pan fish in reasonable good condition for a few hours. Ideally trout—and any fish for that matter—should be eaten the same day they are caught. As Ted Trueblood once said, "Fish are better if they are cooked with the wiggle still in the tail." Sound advice but seldom followed. If the fish are to be kept for twenty-four hours before eating, clean them as quickly as possible and place them in the refrigerator or on a bed of ice, but not in ice water. Keep them out of any water if at all possible.

On a boat, you should have ice in the fish box or in a portable cooler, if the weather is at all warm. Place them *on* the ice, not in it. Since I don't like to fillet fish that have stiffened in an awkward position, I dispatch all fish before depositing them in creel or fish box. A knock on the head with a small billy or section of broom handle usually does the trick. With large saltwater species such as blues or stripers, this sometimes requires a pretty good whack. When dispatched, the fish will stiffen in a straight position and be much easier to fillet.

It's surprising to note how many fishermen do not fillet their fish. They either don't know how or are afraid to try, especially when their buddies are looking on. Almost every fisherman knows someone who can fillet fish. Spend some time watching him.

A table fork is helpful when operating on small fish . . . here a crappie.

Peeling off the skin with the help of a table fork.

Every fish filleter I know loves to show off this talent and, with the proper knife, anyone can do a passable job. The knife is extremely important. It must be sharp—very sharp—and ideally should have a thin, flexible blade.

Just about every tackle shop in the nation sells serviceable fillet knives. One of the best is the Rapala. It comes in three sizes, from the tiny trout blade that is just five inches long to the jumbo salt-water size. The in-between model is perfect for most fresh water fish and salt water species that weigh up to about seven pounds. Case makes a well designed fish skinner and so do the Queen people. There are a number of other suitable knives on the market for this purpose. Just be sure the blade is slightly curved and not too hard. If a lot of filleting is called for, the blade should be touched up frequently. A very hard piece of steel resists quick sharpening. A hunting knife and a fillet knife are two different things. They are not readily interchangeable.

There are a number of *right* ways to fillet, but all of them wind up with

A thin, flexible blade is needed for lifting out the rib cage bones.

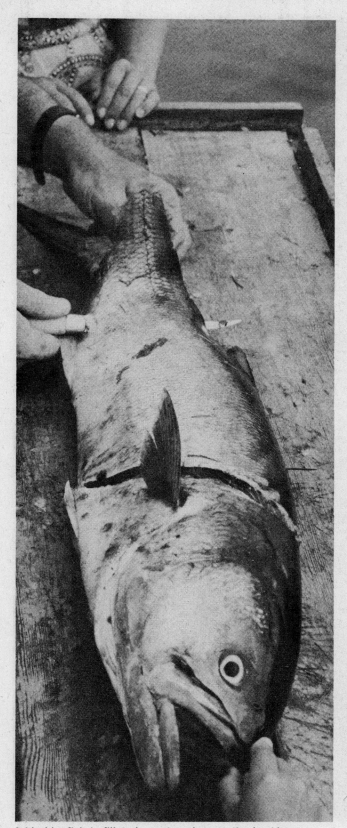

A big bluefish is filleted . . . stay close to the backbone.

Peeling the skin.

Whole fillet is removed. Next step is to remove skin.

the same basic result: a skinless, reasonably boneless fillet. The photographs show one way to handle most fresh and salt water fish. Make the first cut just behind the gill covers. Cut all the way to the backbone, *but not through it*. A slightly rough board is the best filleting base. Holding the tail down with one hand (or a table fork for small fish), slice into the fish just ahead of the tail. Allow the knife to find the backbone again and follow it forward, see-sawing just a bit. Stay as close to the backbone as possible without cutting into it. Go forward until the blade meets the first incision. You now have one fillet removed. Turn the fish over and do exactly the same thing on the other side.

All that's left on the carcass is the backbone and the head and tail. Lay the fillet on the board with the skin side down and cut into the fillet just ahead of the tail end. Allow about a half inch of meat to remain on the tail section. Cut to the skin *but not through it*. Press forward at about a fifteen-degree angle and the knife will slide beneath the flesh and ride along the inside edge of the skin. As the knife moves forward, grasp that little end of meat and pull gently with the free hand, wiggling the skin back and forth slightly. Don't force it! If the knife is sharp it will coast along smoothly and the skin will slip off cleanly with no meat sticking to it. With the tip of the knife, trim off the rib cage bones that are still hanging on to the now-skinless fillet. It sounds easy and it is. Like any other skill involving the use of a knife, it merely requires a little practice.

The northern pike and the American white shad require a bit more artistry. The pike has a row of floating Y-shaped bones that require an extra pair of incisions to remove. A substantial portion of meat will be lost if you choose to remove these bones, but they are large enough to find easily when eating. I usually leave them alone. With shad, it's a matter of patience. As mentioned earlier, most fish filleters love to show off their skill. Well, they all do *except* those who fillet shad for a price.

These experts are the crown princes of the fish filleting world, and it takes more than a friendly smile to induce them to reveal their secrets. In a shad fillet there are two rows of single bones that are not attached to the backbone. Removing them is a real art. For this reason, many shad are relegated to the garbage can after the photos have been taken. This is a shame because the shad is one of the most delicately flavored fishes in the

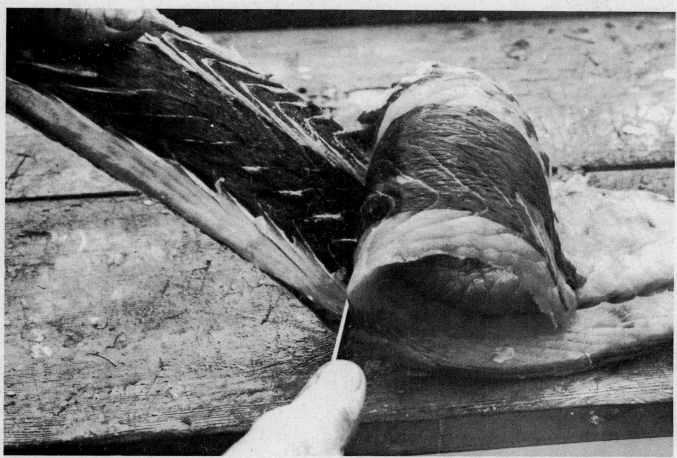

One bluefish fillet coming up.

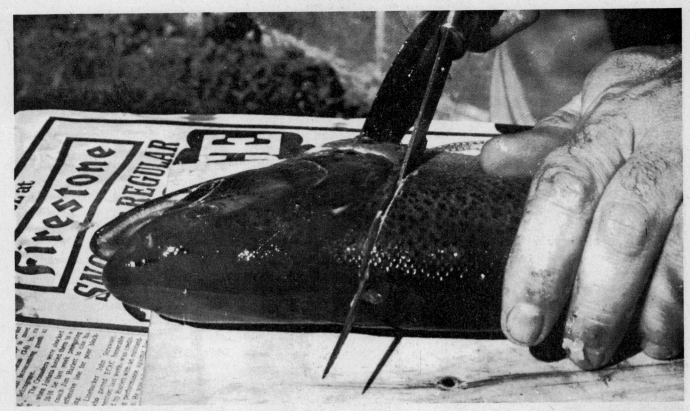

Filleting a coho.

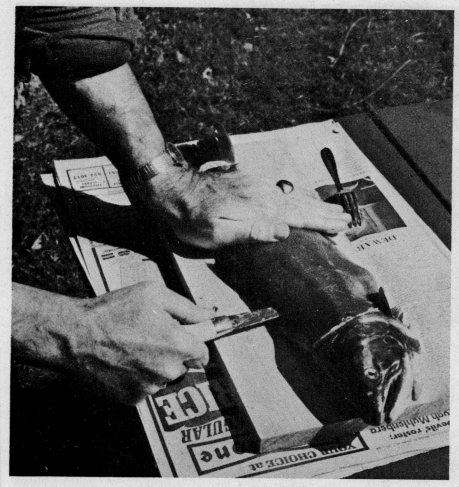

world. The bones can be felt in the fillet but are difficult to see. To take them out requires two cuts per row of bones; as with the pike, some meat will be wasted, but the results will be worth it. It's practically impossible to remove all the bones from a shad fillet. Sauteed in butter, the white shad makes amends. It is absolutely magnificent. Incidentally, professional shad cleaners charge about 50¢ per fish.

Although I fillet most fish over twelve inches and some that are under, a whole trout or panfish under seven inches long can be broiled, poached or deep-fried to perfection. With small trout the cleaning process couldn't be simpler. Just open the fish from vent to gills and, grasping the gills, pull everything out to the rear. It should all come with one motion.

The only chore remaining is to insert a thumbnail underneath the thin membrane that lies along the backbone and strip out the blood line. Dry the trout with a paper towel, and it's ready to go. Remove the head if you wish. I allow the head to remain, because it makes the fish lie straighter in the pan while cooking. Besides, there is a choice morsel of meat on the back of the head and another on each cheek.

Small panfish can be treated in much the same way, except it is necessary to scale the fish. Do this before you remove the entrails. (It makes it easier to hold onto.) If you are inside and don't want scales flying all over the kitchen, do it in a pan of water, completely immersing the fish and the knife.

Whole fish may be poached or

baked with the skin on, but be sure to remove it before serving. If the skin is removed while it's still warm, it will peel off easily. And do remove it in a hurry. Fish skin is the only thing that really tastes "fishy," and it gets worse as it cools.

When freezing small whole fish such as trout, bluegills or perch, it's best to freeze them in water. Disposable, wax-coated milk cartons are ideal. Put as many fish as will fit into the carton and fill it up with water. Set it in the freezer and allow it to freeze solid. The blocks of fish and ice can then be removed and wrapped in freezer paper for longer storage. If you have plenty of milk cartons, it's okay to leave the fish in those containers. For larger whole fish or fillets, dry the fish thoroughly with paper toweling and wrap with Saran wrap. This seals out the air and freezer odors. Around this inner container, wrap a layer of freezer paper and seal well with masking or freezer tape. In a deep freeze, fish fillets will last about four months before taste is affected. In the freezer compartment of a refrigerator, about six weeks is the maximum. In super-cold commercial freezers fish will last much longer.

To thaw fish, allow them to remain at room temperature. If you are in a hurry and the fish are sealed in a package, place the container in cool water to thaw. Never allow the bare fillets to sit in water. They will become a soggy mess.

Practically all fish can be smoked. Some fish are better for smoking because of excess oil in the flesh. Some of these are salmon, lake trout, bluefish, mackerel, and large brook, brown and rainbow trout. Small fish can be smoked whole; for larger ones, fillet as described and cut into chunks about three inches square.

The basic brine for smoking is made of equal parts of salt and white (or brown) sugar. Use about a cup of each in enough water to cover

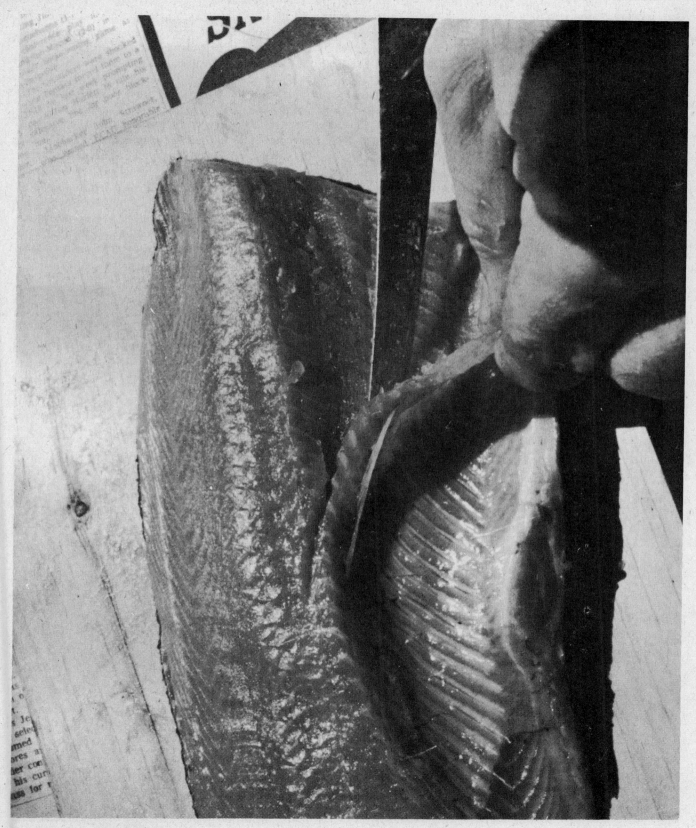

Removing rib cage bones.

three pounds of fish. I add a bay leaf and a teaspoon of freshly ground peppercorns. Allow the fish to pickle in the brine overnight and then dry at room temperature once they are removed from the brine. If you own a custom-made smoke house or know a friend who does, so much the better. In case you don't (and most of us don't), you should purchase one of the little electric smokers that are advertised in dozens of outdoor supply catalogs. Mine happens to be a Little Chief, but all are very similar. They are nothing more than aluminum containers with a tiny electric hotplate at the bottom. Place the fish on the inside wire racks and fill the small pan with wood chips.

Special hickory chips come with the smoker. If you like the meat a shade on the soft side, eight hours of smoking with a couple of pan refills will do the trick. If you prefer the fish a bit more firm, twelve hours of smoking will add even more smokey flavor. Put the dog outside! This is really prime hors d'oeuvre material. Extra hickory chips can be ordered from the smokehouse maker. I've tried about every sort of finny creature in my smoker and I've decided that salmon are the best from fresh water and bluefish is the best salty species. But nearly all fish are excellent when smoked including the lowly carp. Smoke a carp for one of your finicky friends, and he will camp on your doorstep.

Fresh fish are a valuable source of protein and, while I'm not a nutrition expert, I have noticed that citizens of fish-eating nations such as Iceland and Portugal and those natives from the South Sea Islands certainly do seem to maintain great general health. I'm not sure about fish being "brain food", but if you properly take care of your catch and then enjoy it on the table, you'll *think* you're smarter!

Rolling fillets in cracker crumbs . . . "Orville style."

Crappie fillets.

Some Basic Fish Recipes

Although these recipes were originally created for the species mentioned, there is no hard and fast rule. They can be juggled around and tried with other fish. The same bouillon listed for poached salmon may also be used for trout and a number of other fish. The same is true of the sauces.

Poached Salmon

Atlantic or Pacific salmon are equally good poached and, of course, so are the transplanted cohos and chinooks of the Great Lakes. Begin with a whole salmon if you have a roasting pan big enough. It may be necessary to cut off the head but it will look more elegant if you bring the entire fish to the table. Guests are guaranteed to "oh" and "ah." Pour enough water into the pan to cover the fish. Into the water, add one stalk of celery cut up in chunks, one scraped carrot, one medium onion, one bay leaf, and a cup of dry white wine—Chablis is perfect. Bring the mixture to a boil and allow to simmer for ten minutes. Wrap the fish in cheesecloth and immerse into the boiling bouillon. When this is bubbling well, set a timer for ten minutes. At the end of that time, check with a toothpick or a clean broom straw. If the pick or straw will penetrate the meat, it's ready to eat. If not, allow to simmer for two or three minutes more. Unwrap the cheesecloth and lay the fish on a long heated platter. Peel off the skin and discard. Leave the head on, if possible, and garnish with lemon wedges and parsley.

For the sauce, combine a cup of mayonnaise with a half cup of prepared mustard. Add the juice of a lemon and a teaspoon of dried dill. Mix well and add a small dollop to each portion. Continue to drink the chilled Chablis.

Walleye Fillets, Orville Style

This is a great fried-fish recipe first served to me by a meatpacker from Saskatoon named Orville, of course. It works as well for any lean fish such as striped bass, black bass (small and large mouth), yellow and white perch.

Dip ice-cold fillets into a half-and-half mixture of beaten egg and evaporated milk (both also should be cold). One egg and ¼ cup of milk will take care of six fillets. Coat thoroughly and then roll in cracker crumbs, crushed into powder. Lay the coated fillets in a skillet where a half-and-half mixture of butter and cooking oil has been brought to a sizzling condition. The cold fillets going into the hot skillet create an interior steaming effect that cooks the fish clear through in a matter

of four minutes on a side. Serve fillets with this simple tartare sauce recipe:

Tartare Sauce — Combine 1 cup of mayonnaise with 1 chopped sweet pickle, 1 teaspoon chopped onion, 1 teaspoon prepared mustard, ½ teaspoon each of chervil, tarragon and minced parsley, and a dash of garlic powder.

Since this is a Saskatchewan creation, the best thing to drink with it is redeye. This national drink of the central Canadians is nothing more than half tomato juice and half beer poured together. It's great with fried fish.

Bluefish Cakes

A heap of bluefish are brought back to docks all along the east coast, and a steady diet of broiled bluefish can become tiresome. Not that broiled bluefish isn't great eating, but here's a variation on that technique: Poach the fish in the same bouillon given for salmon, except poach a bit more fish than you'll need at one sitting. For the cakes, combine three cups of flaked bluefish with one tablespoon each of finely chopped onion and parsley, and one teaspoon of white vinegar. Melt five tablespoons of margarine in a saucepan and blend in five tablespoons of flour, ½ teaspoon of salt, and a generous sprinkling of freshly ground pepper. Add 1½ cups of milk slowly to the saucepan and cook until thick. Mix well with the fish combination and chill for a couple of hours. Separate into twelve cakes, dip each into slightly beaten egg, and roll in one cup of fine, dried bread crumbs. Fry in a half cooking oil, half margarine mixture until the cake is hot clear through — about ten minutes on each side. These are great fish cakes; they have a taste something like crab cakes. I've been told that some restaurants have been known to mix bluefish in with their hardshell crab cakes and no one is ever the wiser. Bluefish cakes are top seafood fare.

Fish Salad

Here's another dish you can make with almost any sort of leftover poached fish. On a large platter, arrange a bed of lettuce leaves. In the center, pile the chunks of fish. Surround these with wedges of avocado, tomato, hard-boiled egg, and celery and cucumber stalks. Pour the following dressing over the whole concoction and sprinkle with paprika:

Dressing

Blend until creamy ½ cup mayonnaise, 2 tablespoons prepared mustard, 1 large package of softened cream cheese, ¼ cup of poaching bouillon, and a dash of celery salt, tabasco and curry powder.

This makes super summer eating. I have made this salad with trout, pike, salmon, striped bass, bluefish, grayling, and halibut. All were great. For a variation, a few shrimp, a spot of crabmeat or lobster can be added. Nothing else is needed with this meal except a loaf of hot bread or some fresh rolls and, of course, a good bottle of dry white wine.

Whole fish and large fillets are also delectable eating when baked. The trick here, as it is with all fish, is to avoid overcooking. The process is easy but the timing is critical. Over-cooked fish of any kind taste like sawdust. An oven temperature of about 450 degrees is just about right, and 10 to 12 minutes per pound is usually sufficient. Fillets will take about 15 minutes. Since ovens vary considerably in their temperature settings, test frequently with a fork. If the meat flakes easily, it's done.

Baked Trout with Vegetables

Line a large baking dish with foil. Dry the fish thoroughly with paper toweling to remove the slime, both inside and out. Stuff the trout with 2 large chopped onions, 1 chopped green pepper, 2 chopped tablespoons of parsley, and 1 chopped large tomato. Salt and pepper the stuffing liberally and dot with 1 tablespoon of butter. Close the opening with toothpicks or skewers, rub the whole fish with butter and place in a preheated 450-degree oven. Bake 10 to 12 minutes per pound, basting with melted butter frequently.

Either whole or filleted striped bass, salmon, pike, large black bass (over four pounds), and trout are good fish for baking.

The number one and two deep-fried fish in my estimation are catfish and crappies. They are both very lean fish and are the best for the batter-dipped, hot-grease treatment. A deep cast-iron skillet is perfect for such an operation. Any cooking oil will do an admirable job; some prefer peanut oil while others like lard.

Deep-fried Crappie

Wipe ice-cold fillets with toweling to dry them and cut into serving pieces. Roll each piece in flour seasoned with salt, pepper and a dash of seafood seasoning. Then dip the fillet in a mixture of beaten egg and water. Next coat the fish with finely crushed bread crumbs. Place the fillets in a frying basket, just a few at a time, and fry at 370 degrees until their coating is golden brown. Drain and serve immediately with lemon wedges.

Two important details should be remembered when deep frying. The grease must be super hot to seal the outside coating in a hurry. This retains the moisture and flavor of the fillets and prevents the grease from penetrating the end product. Second, have the fillets chilled or else very fresh. Warm soggy fillets will not deep fry satisfactorily.

Angling Classics

Cat-Fishing in the Ohio River

John J. Audubon

It is with mingled feelings of pleasure and regret that I recall to my mind the many pleasant days I have spent on the shores of the Ohio. The visions of former years crowd on my view, as I picture to myself the fertile soil and genial atmosphere of our great western garden, Kentucky, and view the placid waters of the fair stream that flows along its western boundary. Methinks I am now on the banks of the noble river. Twenty years of my life have returned to me; my sinews are strong, and the "bowstring of my spirit is not slack;" bright visions of the future float before me, as I sit on a grassy bank, gazing on the glittering waters. Around me are dense forests of lofty trees and thickly tangled undergrowth, amid which are heard the songs of feathered choristers, and from whose boughs hang clusters of glowing fruits and beautiful flowers. Reader, I am very happy. But now the dream has vanished, and here I am in the British Athens, penning an episode for my Ornithological Biography, and having before me sundry well-thumbed and weather-beaten folios, from which I expect to be able to extract some interesting particulars respecting the methods employed in those days in catching Cat-fish.

But, before entering on my subject, I will present you with a brief description of the place of my residence on the banks of the Ohio. When I first landed at Henderson in Kentucky, my family, like the village, was quite small. The latter consisted of six or eight houses; the former of my wife, myself, and a young child. Few as the houses were, we fortunately found one empty. It was a log-*cabin*, not a log-*house;* but as better could not be had, we were pleased. Well, then, we were located. The country around was thinly peopled, and all purchasable provisions rather scarce; but our neighbours were friendly, and we had brought with us flour and bacon-hams. Our pleasures were those of young people not long married, and full of life and merriment; a single smile from our infant was, I assure you, more valued by us than all the treasures of a modern Croesus would have been. The woods were amply stocked with game, the river with fish; and now and then the hoarded sweets of the industrious bees were brought from some hollow tree to our little table. Our child's cradle was our richest piece of furniture, our guns and fishing-lines our most serviceable implements, for although we began to cultivate a garden, the rankness of the soil kept the seeds we planted far beneath the tall weeds that sprung up the first year. I had then a partner, a "man of business," and there was also with me a Kentucky youth, who much preferred the sports of the forest and river to either day-book or ledger. He was naturally, as I may say, a good woodsman, hunter, and angler, and, like me, thought chiefly of procuring supplies of fish and fowl. To the task accordingly we directed all our energies.

Quantity as well as quality was an object with us, and although we well knew that three species of Cat-fish existed in the Ohio, and that all were sufficiently good, we were not sure as to the best method of securing them. We determined, however, to work on a large scale, and immediately commenced making a famous "trot-line." Now, reader, as you may probably know nothing about this engine, I shall describe it to you.

A trot-line is one of considerable length and thickness, both qualities, however, varying according to the extent of water, and the size of the fish you expect to catch. As the Ohio, at Henderson, is rather more than half a mile in breadth, and as Cat-fishes weigh from one to a hundred pounds, we manufactured a line which measured about two hundred yards in length, as thick as the little finger of some fair one yet in her teens, and as white as the damsel's finger well could be, for it was wholly of Kentucky cotton, just, let me tell you, because that substance stands the water better than either hemp or flax. The main line finished, we made a hundred smaller ones, about five feet in length, to each of which we fastened a capital hook of KIRBY and Co.'s manufacture. Now for the bait!

It was the month of May. Nature had brought abroad myriads of living beings: they covered the earth, glided through the water, and swarmed in the air. The Cat-fish is a voracious creature, not at all nice in feeding, but one who, like the vulture, contents himself with carrion when nothing better can be had. A few experiments proved to us that, of the dainties with which we tried to allure them to our hooks, they gave a decided preference, at that season, to *live toads.* These animals were very abundant about Henderson. They ramble or feed, whether by instinct or reason, during early or late twilight more than at any other time, especially after a shower, and are unable to bear the heat of the sun's rays for several hours before and after noon. We have a good number of these crawling things in America, particularly in the western and southern parts of the Union, and are very well supplied with frogs, snakes, lizards, and even crocodiles, which we call alligators; but there is enough of food for them all, and we generally suffer them to creep about, to leap or to flounder as they please, or in accordance with the habits which have been given them by the great Conductor of all.

During the month of May, and indeed until autumn, we found an abundant supply of toads. Many "fine ladies," no doubt, would have swooned, or at least screamed and gone into hysterics, had they seen one of our baskets filled with these animals, all alive and plump. Fortunately we had no tragedy queen or sentimental spinster at Henderson. Our Kentucky ladies mind their own affairs, and seldom meddle with those of others farther than to do all they can for their comfort. The toads, collected one by one, and brought home in baskets, were deposited in a barrel for use. And now that night is over, and as it is the first trial we are going to give our trot-line, just watch our movements from that high bank beside the stream. There sit down under the large cottonwood tree. You are in no danger of catching cold at this season.

My assistant follows me with a gaff hook, while I carry the paddle of our canoe; a boy bears on his back a hundred toads as good as ever hopped. Our line — oh, I forgot to to inform you that we had set it last night, but without the small ones you now see on my arm. Fastening one end to yon sycamore, we paddled our canoe, with the rest nicely coiled in the stern, and soon reached its extremity, when I threw over the side the heavy stone fastened to it as a sinker. All this was done that it might be thoroughly soaked, and without kinks or snarls in the morning. Now, you observe, we launch our light bark, the toads in the basket are placed next to my feet in the bow; I have the small lines across my knees all ready looped at the end. NAT, with the paddle, and assisted by the current, keeps the stern of our boat directly down stream; and DAVID fixes, by the skin of the back and hind parts, the living bait to the hook. I hold the main line all the while, and now, having fixed one linelet to it, over goes the latter. Can you see the poor toad kicking and flouncing in the water? "No" — well, I do. You observe at length that all the lines, one after another, have been fixed, baited, and dropped. We now return swiftly to the shore.

"What a delightful thing is fishing!" have I more than once heard some knowing angler exclaim, who, with "the patience of Job," stands or slowly moves along some rivulet twenty feet wide, and three or four feet deep, with a sham fly to allure a trout, which, when at length caught, weighs half a pound. Reader, I never had such patience. Although I have waited ten years, and yet see only three-fourths of the Birds of America engraved, although some of the drawings of that work were patiently made so long ago as 1805, and although I have to wait with patience two years more before I see the end of it, I never could hold a line or a rod for many minutes, unless I had — not a "nibble," but a hearty bite, and could throw the fish at once over my head on the ground. No, no — If I fish for trout, I must soon give up, or catch, as I have done in Pennsylvania's Lehigh, or the streams of Maine, fifty or more in a couple of hours.

But the trot-line is in the river, and there *it* may patiently wait, until I visit it toward night. Now I take up my gun and note-book, and, accompanied by my dog, intend to ramble through the woods until breakfast. Who knows but I may shoot a turkey or a deer? It is barely four o'clock; and see what delightful mornings we have at this season in Kentucky!

Evening has returned. The heavens have already opened their twinkling eyes, although the orb of day has yet scarcely withdrawn itself from our view. How calm is the air! The nocturnal insects and quadrupeds are abroad; the bear is moving through the dark cane-brake, the land crows are flying towards their roosts, their aquatic brethren towards the interior of the forests, the squirrel is barking his adieu, and the Barred Owl glides silently and swiftly from his retreat, to seize upon the gay and noisy animal. The boat is pushed off from the shore; the main-line is in my hands; now it shakes; surely some fish have been hooked. Hand over hand I proceed to the first hook. Nothing there! But now I feel several jerks stronger and more frequent than before. Several hooks I pass; but see, what a fine Cat-fish is twisting round and round the little line to which he is fast! NAT, look to your gaff — hook him close to the tail. Keep it up, my dear fellow! — there now, we have him. More are on, and we proceed. When we have reached the end many goodly fishes are lying in the bottom of our skiff. New bait has been put on, and, as we return, I congratulate myself and my companions on the success of our efforts; for there lies fish enough for ourselves and our neighbours.

A trot-line at this period was perfectly safe at Henderson, should I have allowed it to remain for weeks at a time. The navigation was mostly performed by flat-bottomed boats, which during calm nights floated in the middle current of the river, so that the people on board could not observe the fish that had been hooked. Not a single steamer had as yet ever gone down the Ohio; now and then, it is true, a barge or a keel-boat was propelled by poles and oars; but the nature of the river is such at that place, that these boats when ascending were obliged to keep near the Indiana shore, until above the landing of the village, (below which I always fixed my lines), when they pulled across the stream.

Several species or varieties of Cat-fish are found in the Ohio, namely the Blue, the White, and the Mud Cats, which differ considerably in their form and colour, as well as in their habits. The Mud Cat is the best, although it seldom attains so great a size as the rest. The Blue Cat is the coarsest, but when not exceeding from four to six pounds, it affords tolerable eating. The White Cat is preferable to the last, but not so common; and the Yellow Mud Cat is the best and rarest. Of the blue kind some have been caught that weighed a hundred pounds. Such fishes, however, are looked upon as monsters.

The form in all the varieties inclines to the conical, the head being disproportionately large, while the body tapers away to the root of the tail. The eyes, which are small, are placed far apart, and situated as it were on the top of the forehead, but laterally. Their mouth is wide, and armed with numerous small and very sharp teeth, while it is defended by single-sided spines, which, when the fish is in the agonies of death, stand out at right angles, and are so firmly fixed as sometimes to break before you can loosen them. The Cat-fish has also feelers of proportionate length, apparently intended to guide its motions over the bottom, whilst its eyes are watching the objects passing above.

Trot-lines cannot be used with much success unless during the middle stages of the water. When very low, it is too clear, and the fish, although extremely voracious, will rarely risk its life for a toad. When the waters are rising rapidly, your trot-lines are likely to be carried away by one of the numerous trees that float in the stream. A "happy medium" is therefore best.

When the waters are rising fast and have become muddy, a single line is used for catching Cat-fish. It is fastened to the elastic branch of some willow several feet above the water, and must be twenty or thirty feet in length. The entrails of a Wild Turkey, or a piece of fresh venison, furnish good bait; and if, when you visit your line the next morning after you have set it, the water has not risen too much, the swinging of the willow indicates that a fish has been hooked, and you have only to haul the prize ashore.

One evening I saw that the river was rising at a great rate, although it was still within its banks. I knew that the White Perch were running, that is, ascending the river from the sea, and, anxious to have a tasting of that fine fish, I baited a line with a cray-fish, and fastened it to the bough of a tree. Next morning as I pulled in the line, it felt as if fast at the bottom, yet on drawing it slowly I found it came. Presently I felt a strong pull, the line slipped through my fingers, and next instant a large Cat-fish leaped out of the water. I played it for a while, until it became exhausted, when I drew it ashore. It had swallowed the hook, and I cut off the line close to its head. Then passing a stick through one of the gills, I and a servant tugged the fish home. On cutting it open, we, to our surprise, found in its stomach a fine White Perch, dead, but not in the least injured. The Perch had been lightly hooked, and the Cat-fish, after swallowing it, had been hooked in the stomach, so that, although the instrument was small, the torture caused by it no doubt tended to disable the Cat-fish. The Perch we ate, and the Cat, which was fine, we divided into four parts, and distributed among our neighbours. My most worthy friend and relative, NICHOLAS BERTHOUD, Esq., who formerly resided at Shippingport in Kentucky, but now in New York, a better fisher than whom I never knew, once placed a trot-line in "the basin" below "Tarascon's Mills," at the foot of the Rapids of the Ohio. I cannot recollect the bait which was used; but on taking up the line we obtained a remarkably fine Cat-fish, in which was found the greater part of a sucking pig!

I may here add, that I have introduced a figure of the Cat-fish in Plate XXXI. of my first volume of my Illustrations, in which I have represented the White-headed Eagle.

— from *Ornithological Biography* (1835)

Ktaadn Trout

Henry D. Thoreau

Ambejijis, this quiet Sunday morning, struck me as the most beautiful lake we had seen. It is said to be one of the deepest. We had the fairest view of Joe Merry, Double Top, and Ktaadn, from its surface. The summit of the latter had a singularly flat, table-land appearance, like a short highway, where a demigod might be let down to take a turn or two in an afternoon, to settle his dinner. We rowed a mile and a half to near the head of the lake, and, pushing through a field of lily-pads, landed, to cook our breakfast, by the side of a large rock, known to McCauslin. Our breakfast consisted of tea, with hardbread and pork, and fried salmon, which we ate with forks neatly whittled from alder-twigs, which grew there, off strips of birch-bark for plates. The tea was black tea, without milk to color or sugar to sweeten it, and two tin dippers were our teacups. This beverage is as indispensable to the loggers as to any gossiping old women in the land, and they, no doubt, derive great comfort from it. Here was the site of an old logger's camp, remembered by McCauslin, now overgrown with weeds and bushes. In the midst of a dense underwood we noticed a whole brick, on a rock, in a small run, clean and red and square as in a brick-yard, which had been brought thus far formerly for tamping. Some of us afterward regretted that we had not carried this on with us to the top of the mountain, to be left there for our mark. It would certainly have been a simple evidence of civilized man. McCauslin said that large wooden crosses, made of oak, still sound, were sometimes found standing in the wilderness, which were set up by the first Catholic missionaries who came through to the Kennebec.

In the next nine miles, which were the extent of our voyage, and which it took us the rest of the day to get over, we rowed across several small lakes, poled up numerous rapids and thoroughfares, and carried over four portages. I will give the names and distances, for the benefit of future tourists. First, after leaving Ambejijis Lake, we had a quarter of a mile of rapids to the portage, or carry of ninety rods around Ambejijis Falls; then a mile and a half through Passamagamet Lake, which is narrow and river-like, to the falls of the same name, — Ambejijis stream coming in on the right; then two miles through Katepskonegan Lake to the portage of ninety rods around Katepskonegan Falls, which

name signifies "carrying-place," — Passamagamet stream coming in on the left; then three miles through Pock-wockomus Lake, a slight expansion of the river, to the portage of forty rods around the falls of the same name, — Katepskonegan stream coming in on the left; then three quarters of a mile through Aboljacarmegus Lake, similar to the last, to the portage of forty rods around the falls of the same name; then half a mile of rapid water to the Sowadnehunk dead-water, and the Aboljacknagesic stream.

This is generally the order of names as you ascend the river: First, the lake, or, if there is no expansion, the dead-water; then the falls; then the stream emptying into the lake, or river above, all of the same name. First we came to Passamagamet Lake, then to Passamagamet Falls, then to Passamagamet stream emptying in. This order and identity of names, it will be perceived, is quite philosophical, since the dead-water or lake is always at least partially produced by the stream emptying in above; and the first fall below, which is the outlet of that lake, and where that tributary water makes its first plunge, also naturally bears the same name.

* * * * *

As we poled up a swift rapid for half a mile above Aboljacarmegus Falls, some of the party read their own marks on the huge logs which lay piled up high and dry on the rocks on either hand, the relics probably of a jam which had taken place here in the Great Freshet in the spring. Many of these would have to wait for another great freshet, perchance, if they lasted so long, before they could be got off. It was singular enough to meet with property of theirs which they had never seen, and where they had never been before, thus detained by freshets and rocks when on its way to them. Methinks that must be where all my property lies, cast up on the rocks on some distant and unexplored stream, and waiting for an unheard-of freshet to fetch it down. O make haste, ye gods, with your winds and rains, and start the jam before it rots!

The last half mile carried us to the Sowadnehunk dead-water, so called from the stream of the same name, signifying "running between mountains," an important tributary which comes in a mile above. Here we decided to camp, about twenty miles from the Dam, at the mouth of Murch Brook and the Aboljacknagesic, mountain streams, broad off from Ktaadn, and about a dozen miles from its summit, having made fifteen miles this day.

We had been told by McCauslin that we should here find trout enough; so, while some prepared the camp, the rest fell to fishing. Seizing the birch poles which some party of Indians, or white hunters, had left on the shore, and baiting our hooks with pork, and with trout, as soon as they were caught we cast our lines into the mouth of the Aboljack-nagesic, a clear, swift, shallow stream, which came in from Ktaadn. Instantly a shoal of white chivin (*Leucisci pulchelli*), silvery roaches, cousin-trout, or what not, large and small, prowling thereabouts, fell upon our bait, and one after another were landed amidst the bushes. Anon their cousins, the true trout, took their turn, and alternately the speckled trout, and the silvery roaches, swallowed the bait as fast as we could throw in; and the finest specimens of both that I have ever seen, the largest one weighing three pounds, were heaved upon the shore, though at first in vain, to wriggle down into the water again, for we stood in the boat; but soon we learned to remedy this evil; for one, who had lost his hook, stood on shore to catch them as they fell in a perfect shower around him, — sometimes, wet and slippery, full in his face and bosom, as his arms were outstretched to receive them. While yet alive, before their tints had faded, they glistened like the fairest flowers, the product of primitive rivers; and he could hardly trust his senses, as he stood over them, that these jewels should have swam away in that Aboljacknagesic water for so long, so many dark ages; — these bright fluviatile flowers, seen of Indians only, made beautiful, the Lord only knows why, to swim there! I could understand better for this, the truth of mythology, the fables of Proteus, and all those beautiful sea-monsters, — how all history, indeed, put to a terrestrial use, is mere history; but put to a celestial, is mythology always.

But there is the rough voice of Uncle George, who commands at the frying-pan, to send over what you've got, and then you may stay till morning. The pork sizzles and cries for fish. Luckily for the foolish race, and this particularly foolish generation of trout, the night shut down at last, not a little deepened by the dark side of Ktaadn, which, like a permanent shadow, reared itself from the eastern bank. Lescarbot, writing in 1609, tells us that the Sieur Champ-doré, who, with one of the people of the Sieur de Monts, ascended some fifty leagues up the St. John in 1608, found the fish so plenty, "qu'en mettant la chaudière sur le feu ils en avoient pris suffisamment pour eux disner avant que l'eau fust chaude." Their descendants here are no less numerous. So we accompanied Tom into the woods to cut cedar-twigs for our bed. While he went ahead with the axe and lopped off the smallest twigs of the flat-leaved cedar, the arbor-vitæ of the gardens, we gathered them up, and returned with them to the boat, until it was loaded. Our bed was made with as much care and skill as a roof is shingled; beginning at the foot, and laying the twig end of the cedar upward, we advanced to the head, a course at a time, thus successively covering the stub-ends, and producing a soft and level bed. For us six it was about ten feet long by six in breadth. This time we lay under our tent, having pitched it more prudently with reference to the wind and the flame, and the usual huge fire blazed in front. Supper was eaten off a large log, which some freshet had thrown up. This night we had a dish of arbor-vitæ, or cedar-tea, which the lumberer sometimes uses when other herbs fail, —

"A quart of arbor-vitæ,
To make him strong and mighty,"

but I had no wish to repeat the experiment. It had too medicinal a taste for my palate. There was the skeleton of a moose here, whose bones some Indian hunters had picked on this very spot.

In the night I dreamed of trout-fishing; and, when at length I awoke, it seemed a fable that this painted fish swam there so near my couch, and rose to our hooks the last evening, and I doubted if I had not dreamed it all. So I arose before dawn to test its truth, while my companions were still sleeping. There stood Ktaadn with distinct and cloudless outline in the moonlight; and the rippling of the rapids was the only sound to break the stillness. Standing on the shore, I once more cast my line into the stream, and found the dream to be real and the fable true. The speckled trout and silvery roach, like flying-fish, sped swiftly through the moonlight air, describing bright arcs on the dark side of Ktaadn, until moonlight, now fading into daylight, brought satiety to my mind, and the minds of my companions, who had joined me.

—from *The Union Magazine* (1848)

A Fatal Salmon

Henry William Herbert

It was as fair a morning of July as ever dawned in the blue summer sky; the sun as yet had risen but a little way above the waves of fresh green foliage which formed the horizon of the woodland scenery surrounding Widecomb Manor; and his heat, which promised ere mid-day to become excessive, was tempered now by the exhalations of the copious night-dews, and by the cool breath of the western breeze, which came down through the leafy gorges, in long, soft swells from the open moorlands.

All nature was alive and joyous; the air was vocal with the piping melody of the blackbirds and thrushes, carolling in every brake and bosky dingle; the smooth, green lawn before the windows of the old Hall was peopled with whole tribes of fat, lazy hares, limping about among the dewy herbage, fearless, as it would seem, of man's aggression; and to complete the picture, above, a score of splendid peacocks were strutting to and fro on the paved terraces, or perched upon the carved stone balustrades, displaying their gorgeous plumage to the early sunshine.

The shadowy mists of the first morning twilight had not been dispersed from the lower regions, and were suspended still in the middle air in broad fleecy masses, though melting rapidly away in the increasing warmth and brightness of the day.

And still a faint blue line hovered over the bed of the long rocky gorge, which divided the chase from the open country, floating about it like the steam of a seething caldron, and rising here and there into tall smoke-like columns, probably where some steeper cataract of the mountain-stream sent its foam skyward.

So early, indeed, was the hour, that had my tale been recited of these degenerate days, there would have been no gentle eyes awake to look upon the loveliness of new-awakened nature.

In the good days of old, however, when daylight was still deemed to be the fitting time for labor and for pastime, and night, the appointed time for natural and healthful sleep, the dawn was wont to brighten beheld by other eyes than those of clowns and milkmaids, and the gay songs of the matutinal birds were listened to by ears that could appreciate their untaught melodies.

And now, just as the stable clock was striking four, the great oaken door of the old Hall was thrown open with a vigorous swing that made it rattle on its hinges, and Jasper St. Aubyn came bounding out into the fresh morning air, with a foot as elastic as that of the mountain roe, singing a snatch of some quaint old ballad.

He was dressed simply in a close-fitting jacket and tight hose of dark-green cloth, without any lace or embroidery, light boots of untanned leather, and a broad-leafed hat, with a single eagle's feather thrust carelessly through the band. He wore neither cloak nor sword, though it was a period at which gentlemen rarely went abroad without these, their distinctive attributes; but in the broad black belt which girt his rounded waist he carried a stout wood-knife with a buck-horn hilt; and over his shoulder there swung from a leathern thong a large wicker fishing-basket.

Nothing, indeed, could be simpler or less indicative of any particular rank or station in society than young St. Aubyn's garb, yet it would have been a very dull and unobservant eye which should take him for aught less than a high-born and high-bred gentleman.

His fine intellectual face, his bearing erect before heaven, the graceful ease of his every motion, as he hurried down the flagged steps of the terrace, and planted his light foot on the dewy greensward, all betokened gentle birth and gentle associations.

But he thought nothing of himself, nor cared for his advantages, acquired or natural. The long and heavy salmon-rod which he carried in his right hand, in three pieces as yet unconnected, did not more clearly indicate his purpose than the quick marking glance which he cast toward the half-veiled sun and hazy sky, scanning the signs of the weather.

"It will do, it will do," he said to himself, thinking as it were aloud, "for three or four hours at least; the sun will not shake off those vapors before eight o'clock at the earliest, and if he do come out then hot and strong, I do not know but the water is dark enough after the late rains to serve my turn a while longer. It will blow up, too, I think, from the westward, and there will be a brisk curl on the pools. But come, I must be moving, if I would reach Darringford to breakfast."

And as he spoke he strode out rapidly across the park toward the deep chasm of the stream, crushing a thousand aromatic perfumes from the dewy wild-flowers with his heedless foot, and thinking little of the beauties of nature, as he hastened to the scene of his loved exercise.

It was not long, accordingly, before he reached the brink of the steep rocky bank above the stream, which he proposed to fish that morning, and paused to select the best place for descending to the water's edge.

It was, indeed, as striking and romantic a scene as ever met the eye of painter or of poet. On the farther side of the gorge, scarcely a hundred yards distant, the dark limestone rocks rose sheer and precipitous from the very brink of the stream, rifted and broken into angular blocks and tall columnar masses, from the clefts of which, wherever they could find soil enough to support their scanty growth, a few stunted oaks shot out almost horizontally with their gnarled arms and dark-green foliage, and here and there the silvery bark and quivering tresses of the birch relieved the monotony of color by their gay brightness. Above, the cliffs were crowned with the beautiful purple heather, now in its very glow of summer bloom, about which were buzzing myriads of wild bees, sipping their nectar from its cups of amethyst.

The hither side, though rough and steep and broken, was not, in the place where Jasper stood, precipitous; indeed it seemed as if at some distant period a sort of landslip had occurred, by which the summit of the rocky wall had been broken into massive fragments, and hurled down in an inclined plane into the bed of the stream, on which it had encroached with its shattered blocks and rounded boulders.

Time, however, had covered all this abrupt and broken slope with a beautiful growth of oak and hazel coppice, among which, only at distant intervals, could the dun weather-beaten flanks of the great stones be discovered.

At the base of this descent, a hundred and fifty feet perhaps below the stand of the young sportsman, flowed the dark arrowy stream — a wild and perilous water. As clear as crystal, yet as dark as the brown cairngorm, it came pouring down among the broken rocks with a rapidity and force which showed what must be its fury when swollen by a storm among the mountains, here breaking into wreaths of rippling foam where some unseen ledge chafed its current, there roaring and surging white as December's snow among the great round-headed rocks, and there again wheeling in sullen eddies, dark and deceitful, round and round some deep rock-rimmed basin.

Here and there, indeed, it spread out into wide, shallow, rippling rapids, filling the whole bottom of the ravine from side to side, but more generally it did not occupy above a fourth part of the space below, leaving sometimes on this margin, sometimes on that broad pebbly banks, or slaty ledges, affording an easy footing and a clear path to the angler in its troubled waters.

After a rapid glance over the well-known scene, Jasper plunged into the coppice, and following a faint track worn by the feet of the wild-deer in the first instance, and widened by his own bolder tread, soon reached the bottom of the chasm, though not until he had flushed from the dense oak covert two noble black cocks with their superb forked tails, and glossy purple-lustered plumage, which soared away, crowing their bold defiance, over the heathery moorlands.

Once at the water's edge, the young man's tackle was speedily made ready, and in a few minutes his long line went whistling through the air, as he wielded the powerful two-handed rod, as easily as if it had been a stripling's reed, and the large gaudy peacock-fly alighted on the wheeling eddies, at the tail of a long arrowy shoot, as gently as if it had settled from too long a flight. Delicately, deftly, it was made to dance and skim the clear, brown surface, until it had crossed the pool and neared the hither bank; then again, obedient to the pliant wrist, it arose on glittering wing, circled half around the angler's head, and was sent fifteen yards aloof, straight as a wild bee's flight, into a little mimic whirlpool, scarce larger than the hat of the skilful fisherman, which spun round and round just to leeward of a gray ledge of limestone. Scarce had it reached its mark before the water broke all around it, and the gay deceit vanished, the heavy swirl of the surface, as the break was closing, indicating the great size of the fish which had risen. Just as the swirl was subsiding, and the forked tail of the monarch of the stream was half seen as he descended, that indescribable but well-known turn of the angler's wrist, fixed the barbed hook, and taught the scaly victim the nature of the prey he had gorged so heedlessly.

With a wild bound he threw himself three feet out of the water, showing his silver sides, with the sea-lice yet clinging to his scales, a fresh sea-run fish of fifteen, ay, eighteen pounds, and perhaps over.

On his broad back he strikes the water, but not as he meant the tightened line; for as he leaped the practised hand had lowered the rod's tip, that it fell in a loose bight below him. Again! again! again! and yet a fourth time he bounded into the air with desperate and vigorous *soubresaults,* like an unbroken steed that would dismount his rider, lashing the eddies of the dark stream into bright bubbling streaks, and making the heart of his captor beat high with anticipation of the desperate struggle that should follow, before the monster should lie panting and exhausted on the yellow sand or moist greensward.

Away! with the rush of an eagle through the air, he is gone like an arrow down the rapids — how the reel rings, and the line whistles from the swift working wheel; he is too swift, too headstrong to be checked as yet; tenfold the strength of that slender tackle might not control him in his first fiery rush.

But Jasper, although young in years, was old in the art, and skilful as the craftiest of the gentle craftsmen. He gives him the butt of his rod steadily, trying the strength of his tackle with a delicate and gentle finger, giving him line at every rush, yet firmly, cautiously, feeling his mouth all the while, and moderating his speed even while he yields to his fury.

Meanwhile, with the eye of intuition, and the nerve of iron, he bounds along the difficult shore, he leaps from rock to rock, alighting on their slippery tops with the firm agility of the rope-dancer, he splashes knee-deep through the slippery shallows, keeping his line ever taut, inclining his rod over his shoulder, bearing on his fish ever with a killing pull, steering him clear of every rock or stump against which he would fain smash the tackle, and landing him at length in a fine open roomy pool, at the foot of a long stretch of white and foamy rapids, down which he has just piloted him with the eye of faith, and the foot of instinct.

And now the great Salmon has turned sulky; like a piece of lead he has sunk to the bottom of the deep black pool, and lies on the gravel bottom in the sullenness of despair.

Jasper stooped, gathered up in his left hand a heavy

pebble, and pitched it into the pool, as nearly as he could guess to the whereabout of his game — another — and another! Aha! that last has roused him. Again he throws himself clear out of water, and again foiled in his attempt to smash the tackle, dashes away down stream impetuous.

But his strength is departing — the vigor of his rush is broken. The angler gives him the butt abundantly, strains on him with a heavier pull, yet ever yields a little as he exerts his failing powers; see, his broad, silver side has thrice turned up, even to the surface, and though each time he has recovered himself, each time it has been with a heavier and more sickly motion.

Brave fellow! his last race is run, his last spring sprung — no more shall he disport himself in the bright reaches of the Tamar; no more shall the Naiads wreathe his clear silver scales with river-greens and flowery rushes.

The cruel gaff is in his side — his cold blood stains the eddies for a moment — he flaps out his death-pang on the hard limestone.

"Who-whoop! a nineteen-pounder!"

Meantime the morning had worn onward, and ere the great fish was brought to the basket, the sun had soared clear above the mist-wreaths, and had risen so high into the summer heaven that his slant rays poured down into the gorge of the stream, and lighted up the clear depths with a lustre so transparent that every pebble at the bottom might have been discerned, with the large fish here and there floating mid-depth, with their heads upstream, their gills working with a quick motion, and their broad tails vibrating at short intervals slowly but powerfully, as they lay motionless in opposition to the very strongest of the swift current.

The breeze had died away, there was no curl upon the water, and the heat was oppressive.

Under such circumstances, to whip the stream was little better than mere loss of time, yet as he hurried with a fleet foot down the gorge, perhaps with some ulterior object, beyond the mere love of sport, Jasper at times cast his fly across the stream, and drew it neatly, and, as he thought, irresistibly, right over the recusant fish; but though once or twice a large lazy Salmon would sail up slowly from the depths, and almost touch the fly with his nose, he either sunk down slowly in disgust, without breaking the water, or flapped his broad tail over the shining fraud as if to mark his contempt.

It had now got to be near noon, for, in the ardor of his success, the angler had forgotten all about his intended breakfast; and, his first fish captured, had contented himself with a slender meal furnished from out his fishing-basket and his leathern bottle.

Jasper had traversed by this time some ten miles in length, following the sinuosities of the stream, and had reached a favorite pool at the head of a long, straight, narrow trench, cut by the waters themselves in the course of time, through the hard schistous rock which walls the torrent on each hand, not leaving the slightest ledge or margin between the rapids and the precipice.

Through this wild gorge of some fifty yards in length, the river shoots like an arrow over a steep inclined plane of limestone rock, the surface of which is polished by the action of the water, till it is as slippery as ice, and at the extremity leaps down a sheer descent of some twelve feet into a large, wide basin, surrounded by softly swelling banks of greensward, and a fair amphitheatre of woodland.

At the upper end this pool is so deep as to be vulgarly deemed unfathomable; below, however, it expands yet wider into a shallow rippling ford, where it is crossed by the highroad, down stream of which again there is another long, sharp rapid, and another fall, over the last steps of the hills; after which the nature of the stream becomes changed, and it murmurs gently onward through a green pastoral country, unrippled and uninterrupted.

Just in the inner angle of the high-road, on the right hand of the stream, there stood an old-fashioned, low-browed, thatch-covered stone cottage, with a rude portico of rustic woodwork overrun with jasmine and virgin-bower, and a pretty flower-garden sloping down in successive terraces to the edge of the basin. Beside this, there was no other house in sight, unless it were part of the roof of a mill which stood in the low ground on the brink of the second fall, surrounded with a mass of willows. But the tall steeple of a country church, raising itself heavenward above the brow of the hill, seemed to show that, although concealed by the undulations of the ground, a village was hard at hand.

The morning had changed a second time, a hazy film had crept up to the zenith, and the sun was now covered with a pale golden veil, and a slight current of air down the gorge ruffled the water.

It was a capital pool, famous for being the temporary haunt of the very finest fish, which were wont to lie there awhile, as if to recruit themselves after the exertions of leaping the two falls and stemming the double rapid, before attempting to ascend the stream farther.

Few, however, even of the best and boldest fishermen, cared to wet a line in its waters, in consequence of the supposed impossibility of following a heavy fish through the gorge below, or checking him at the brink of the fall. It is true, that throughout the length of the pass, the current was broken by bare, slippery rocks peering above the waters, at intervals, which might be cleared by an active cragsman; and it had been in fact reconnoitred by Jasper and others in cool blood, but the result of the examination was that it was deemed impassable.

Thinking, however, little of striking a large fish, and perhaps desiring to waste a little time before scaling the banks and emerging on the high-road, Jasper threw a favorite fly of peacock's herl and gold tinsel lightly across the water; and, almost before he had time to think, had hooked a monstrous fish, which, at the very first leap, he set down as weighing at least thirty pounds.

Thereupon followed a splendid display of piscatory skill. Well knowing that his fish must be lost if he once should succeed in getting his head down the rapid, Jasper exerted every nerve, and exhausted every art to humor, to meet, to restrain, to check him. Four times the fish rushed for the pass, and four times Jasper met him so stoutly with the butt, trying his tackle to the very utmost, that he succeeded in forcing him from the perilous spot. Round and round the pool he had piloted him, and had taken post at length, hoping that the worst was already over, close to the opening of the rocky chasm.

And now perhaps waxing too confident, he checked his fish too sharply. Stung into fury, the monster sprang five times in succession into the air, lashing the water with his angry tail, and then rushed like an arrow down the chasm.

He was gone — but Jasper's blood was up, and thinking of nothing but his sport, he dashed forward, and embarked, with a fearless foot, into the terrible descent.

Leap after leap he took with beautiful precision, alighting firm and erect on the centre of each slippery block, and bounding thence to the next with unerring instinct, guiding his fish the while with consummate skill through the intricacies of the pass.

There were now but three more leaps to be taken before he would reach the flat table-rock above the fall, which once attained, he would have firm foot-hold and a fair field; already he rejoiced, triumphant in the success of his bold attainment, and confident in victory, when a shrill female shriek reached his ears from the pretty flower-garden; caught by the sound, he diverted his eyes, just as he leaped, toward the place whence it came; his foot slipped, and the next instant he was flat on his back in the swift stream, where it shot the most furiously over the glassy rock. He struggled manfully, but in vain. The smooth, slippery surface afforded no purchase to his gripping fingers, no hold to his laboring feet. One fearful, agonizing conflict with the wild waters, and he was swept helplessly over the edge of the fall, his head, as he glanced down foot foremost, striking the rocky brink with fearful violence.

He was plunged into the deep pool, and whirled round and round by the dark eddies long before he rose, but still, though stunned and half-disabled, he strove terribly to support himself, but it was all in vain.

Again he sunk and rose once more, and as he rose that wild shriek again reached his ears, and his last glance fell upon a female form wringing her hands in despair on the bank, and a young man rushing down in wild haste from the cottage on the hill.

He felt that aid was at hand, and struck out again for life — for dear life!

But the water seemed to fail beneath him.

A slight flash sprang across his eyes, his brain reeled, and all was blackness.

He sunk to the bottom, spurned it with his feet, and rose once more, but not to the surface.

His quivering blue hands emerged alone above the relentless waters, grasped for a little moment at empty space, and then disappeared.

— from *Fish and Fishing* (1849)

Fly-Fishing Alone

Thaddeus Norris

With many persons fishing is a mere recreation, a pleasant way of killing time. To the true angler, however, the sensation it produces is a deep unspoken joy, born of a longing for that which is quiet and peaceful, and fostered by an inbred love of communing with nature, as he walks through grassy meads, or listens to the music of the mountain torrent. This is why he loves occasionally — whatever may be his social propensity in-doors — to shun the habitations and usual haunts of men, and wander alone by the stream, casting his flies over its bright waters: or in his lone canoe to skim the unruffled surface of the inland lake, where no sound comes to his ear but the wild, flute-like cry of the loon, and where no human form is seen but his own, mirrored in the glassy water.

No wonder, then, that the fly-fisher loves at times to take a day all by himself; for his very loneliness begets a comfortable feeling of independence and leisure, and a quiet assurance of resources within himself to meet all difficulties that may arise.

As he takes a near cut to the stream, along some blind road or cattle-path, he hears the wood-robin with its "to-whé," calling to its mate in the thicket, where itself was fledged the summer before. When he stops to rest at the "wind clearing," he recalls the traditionary stories told by the old lumbermen, of the Indians who occupied the country when their grandfathers moved out to the "back settlements," and, as he ruminates on the extinction, or silent removal of these children of the forest, he may think of the simple eloquent words of the chief to his companions, the last he uttered: "I will die, and you will go home to your people, and, as you go along, you will see the flowers, and hear the birds sing; but Pushmuttaha will see them and hear them no more; and when you come to your people they will say, 'Where is Pushmuttaha?' and you will say, 'He is dead': then will your words come upon them *like the falling of the great oak in the stillness of the woods."*

As he resumes his walk and crosses the little brook that "goes singing by," he remembers what he has read of the Turks, who built their bowers by the falling water, that they might be lulled by its music, as they smoked and dreamed of Paradise. But when the hoarse roar of the creek, where it surges against the base of the crag it has washed for ages,

strikes his ear, or he hears it brawling over the big stones, his step quickens, and his pulse beats louder — he is no true angler if it does not — and he is not content until he gets a glimpse of its bright rushing waters at the foot of the hill.

Come forth, my little rod — "a better never did itself support upon" *an angler's arm,* — and let us rig up here on this pebbly shore! The rings are in a line, and now with this bit of waxed silk we take a few hitches backward and forward over the little wire loops which point in opposite directions at the ends of the ferules, to keep the joints from coming apart; for it would be no joke to throw the upper part of the rod out of the butt ferule, and have it sailing down some strong rift. The reel is on *underneath,* and not on top, as those Bass-fishers have it, who are always talking of Fire Island, Newport, and Narragansett Bay.

What shall my whip be? The water is full, I'll try a red hackle, its tail tipped with gold tinsel; for my dropper, I'll put on a good-sized coachman with lead-colored wings, and as soon as I get a few handsful of grass, to throw in the bottom of my creel, I'll button on my landing-net and cross over, with the help of this stick of drift-wood, for it is pretty strong wading just here. Do you see that rift, and the flat rock at the lower end of it which just comes above the surface of the water, and divides the stream as it rushes into the pool below? There's fishing in rift and pool both; so I'll begin at the top of the rift, if I can get through these alders. Go in, my little rod, point foremost; I would not break that tip at this time to save the hair on my head; — hold! that twig has caught my dropper — easy, now, — all clear — through the bushes at last.

When I was here last July, and fished the pool below, there was no rift above, the water hardly came above my ankles; now it is knee-deep; if there was less it would be better for the pool; but it makes two casts now, where there was only one last summer, and I have no doubt there is a pretty fellow by the margin of the strong water, on this side of the rock — an easy cast, too, — just about eight yards from the end of my tip. Not there — a little nearer the rock. What a swirl! He did not show more than his back; but he has my hackle. I had to strike him, too, for he took it under water like a bait — they will do so when the stream is full. Get out of that current, my hearty, and don't be flouncing on top, but keep underneath, and deport yourself like an honest, fair fighter! There you are, now in slack water; you can't last long, tugging at this rate; so come along, to my landing-net; it's no use shaking your head at me! What a shame to thrust my thumb under that rosy gill! but there is no help for it, for you might give me the slip as I take the hook out of your mouth, and thrust you, tail-foremost, into the hole of my creel. You are my first fish, and you know you are my *luck;* so I would not lose you even if you were a little fellow of seven inches, instead of a good half-pound. I imbibed that superstition, not to throw away my first fish, when I was a boy, and have never got rid of it. Now, tumble about as much as you please; you have the whole basket to yourself.

Another cast — there ought to be more fish there. He rose short, — a little longer line — three feet more will do it — exactly so. Gently, my nine-incher! Take the spring of the rod for a minute or so — here you are! Once more, now. How the "young 'un" jumps! I'll throw it to him until he learns to catch; there, he has it. No use reeling in a chap of your size, but come along, hand-over-hand; I'll release you. Go, now, and don't rise at a fly again until you are over nine inches.

Not a fly on the water! So I have nothing to imitate, even if imitation were necessary. Take care! that loose stone almost threw me. I'll work my way across the current, and get under the lee of that boulder, and try each side of the rift where it runs into the pool below the flat rock. Not a fish in the slack water on this side; they are looking for grub and larvæ in the rift. Now, how would you like my coach-man, by way of a changing of diet? There's a chance for you — try it. Bosh! he missed it; but he is not pricked. Once more. Oh, ho! is it there you are, my beauty? Don't tear that dropper. Hold him tight, O'Shaughnessy; you are the greatest hook ever invented. How he runs the line out, and plays off into the swift water! It would be rash to check him now; but I'll give him a few feet, and edge him over to the side of the rift where there is slack water. That's better; now tug away, while I recover some of my line. You are off into the current again, are you? but not so wicked. The click on this reel is too weak, by half — he gives in now, and is com-ing along, like an amiable, docile fish, as he is. Whiz! why, what's the matter, now? Has "the devil kicked him on end?" as my friend with the "tarry breeks" has it. He has taken but two or three yards of line, though. How he hugs the bottom, and keeps the main channel! Well, he can't last much longer. Here he comes now, with a heavy drag, and a distressing strain on my middle joint; and now I see him dimly, as I get him into the eddy; but there's something tugging at the tail-fly. Yes, I have a brace of them, and that accounts for the last dash, and the stubborn groping for the bottom. What a clever way of trolling! to get an obliging Trout to take your dropper, and go sailing around with four feet of gut, and a handsome stretcher at the end of it, setting all the fish in the pool crazy, until some unlucky fellow hooks himself in the side of his mouth. How shall I get the pair into my basket? There is no way but reeling close up, and getting the lower one into my net first, and then with another dip to secure the fish on the dropper; but it must be done gently. So — well done; three-quarters of a pound to be credited to the dropper, and a half-pound to the stretcher — total, one pound and a quarter. That will do for the present. So I'll sit down on that flat rock and light my dudeen, and try the remainder of the water presently. I'll not compromise for less than four half-pound fish before I leave the pool.

These are *some* of the incidents that the lone fly-fisher experiences on a favorable day, and the dreams and antici-pations he has indulged in through the long gloomy winter are in part realized. "Real joy," some one has said, is "a serious thing," and the solitary angler proves it conclusively to himself. He is not troubled that some ardent young brother of the rod may fish ahead of him, and disturb the water without availing himself of all the chances; or that a more discreet companion may pass by some of the pools and rifts without bestowing the attention on them they de-serve; but in perfect quietude, and confidence in his ability to meet every contingency that may occur, he patiently and leisurely tries all the places that offer fair. What if he does get hung up in a projecting branch of some old elm, that leans over the water? he does not swear and jerk his line away, and leave his flies dangling there — it is a difficulty that will bring into play his ingenuity, and perhaps his dex-terity in climbing, and he sets about recovering his flies with the same patient steadiness of purpose that Cæsar did in building his bridge, or that possessed Bonaparte in crossing the Alps, and feels as much satisfaction as either of those great generals, in accomplishing his ends.

If he takes "an extraordinary risk" as underwriters call it, in casting under boughs that hang within a few feet of the water, on the opposite side of some unwadeable rift or pool, and his stretcher should fasten itself in a tough twig, or his dropper grasp the stem of an obstinate leaf, he does not give it up in despair, or, consoling himself with the idea that he has plenty of flies and leaders in his book, pull away and leave his pet spinner and some favorite hackle to hang there as a memento of his temerity in casting so near the bushes. Far from it; he draws sufficient line off his reel and through the rings to give slack enough to lay his rod down, marking well where his flies have caught, and finds some place above or below where he can cross; then by twisting with a forked stick, or drawing in the limb with a hooked one, he releases his leader, and throws it clear off into the water, that he may regain it when he returns to his rod, and reels in his line; or he cuts it off and lays it carefully in his fly-book, and then recrosses the river. A fig for clearing-ring and rod-scythe and all such cockney contrivances, he never cumbers his pockets with them. Suppose he does break his rod — he sits patiently down and splices it. If the fracture is a compound one, and it would shorten the piece too much to splice it, he resorts to a sailor's device, and *fishes the stick,* by bind-ing a couple of flat pieces of hard wood on each side.

Captain Marryat, in one of his books, says, a man's whole lifetime is spent in getting into scrapes and getting out of them. This is very much the case with the fly-fisher, and he should always curb any feeling of haste or undue excite-ment, remembering at such times, that if he loses his temper he is apt to lose his fish, and sometimes his tackle also.

My neighbor asked me once if Trout-fishing was not a very unhealthy amusement — he thought a man must fre-quently have damp feet. Well, it is, I answered; but if he gets wet up to his middle at the outset, and has reasonable luck, there is no healthier recreation. — But I have sat here long enough. I'll fill my pipe again and try the head of that swift water — If this confounded war lasts a year longer

"Lynchburg" will go up to three dollars a pound, but it will be cheap then compared with those soaked and drugged segars that are imposed upon us for the "Simon-Pure," under so many captivating names. At all events *this* is what it professes to be, good homely tobac — Whe-ee-euh! What a dash! and how strong and steady he pulls; some old fellow "with moss on his back," from under that log, no doubt of it. Is it line you want? — take it, eight — ten — fifteen feet — but no more if you please. How he keeps the middle of the rift! Don't tell me about the "grace of the curve," and all that sort of thing; if the bend of this rod isn't the line of beauty I never saw it before, except of course in the outline of a woman's drapery. Speaking of lines, I'll get a little of this in as I lead the fellow down stream, even at the risk of disturbing the swim below. It is the best plan with a large fish; I have Sir Humphry Davy's authority for it, although I believe with Fisher, of the *Angler's Souvenir,* that he was more of a philosopher than an angler. Talk of "dressing for dinner," when the fish are rising! Steady and slow, my boy, you are giving in at last — two pounds and a half or not an ounce! now I see you "as through a glass, darkly" — a little nearer, my beauty — Bah! what a fool I am! here a fish of a half-pound has hooked himself amidship, and of course offering five times the resistance he would if fairly hooked in the mouth, and no damage to his breathing apparatus while fighting, either; for he keeps his wind all the while. If he had been regularly harnessed, he could not have pulled with more advantage to himself and greater danger to my tackle in this rough water. I thought I had been deceived in this way often enough to know when a fish was hooked foul.

Now I call it strong wading coming down through that dark ravine; I must take a rest and put on a fresh dropper. And so my friend asked me if it was not very lonesome, fishing by myself. Why these little people of the woods are much better company than folks who continually bore you with the weather, and the state of their stomachs or livers, and what they ate for breakfast, or the price of gold, or the stock-market, when you have forgotten whether you have a liver or not, and don't care the toss of a penny what the price of gold is; or whether "Reading" is up or down. Lonesome! — It was only just now the red squirrel came down the limb of that birch, whisking his bushy tail, and chattering almost in my face. The mink, as he snuffed the fish-tainted air from my old creel, came out from his hole amongst the rocks and ran along within a few feet of me. Did he take my old coat to be a part of this rock, covered with lichens and gray mosses? I recollect once in the dim twilight of evening, a doe with her fawns came down to the stream to drink; I had the wind of her, and could see into her great motherly eyes as she raised her head. A moment since the noisy kingfisher poised himself on the dead branch of the hemlock, over my left shoulder, as if he would peep into the hole of my fish-basket. The little warbler sang in the alders close by my old felt hat, as if he would burst his swelling throat with his loud glad song. Did either of them know that I am of a race whose first impulse is to throw a stone or shoot a gun at them? And the sparrow-hawk on that leafless spray extending over the water, sitting there as grave and dignified as a bank president when you ask him for a discount; is he aware that I can tap him on the head with the tip of my rod? — These are some of the simple incidents on the stream, which afterwards awaken memories,

"That like voices from afar off
Call to us to pause and listen,
Speak in tones so plain and childlike,
Scarcely can the ear distinguish
Whether they are sung or spoken."

But I must start for the open water below — What a glorious haze there is just now, and how demurely the world's great eye peeps through it! Trout are not very shy though, before the middle of May, even when the sun is bright. I have sometimes taken my best fish at high noon, at this season of the year. — I am as hungry as a horsefly, though it is only "a wee short hour ayout the twal." So I'll unsling my creel by that big sycamore, and build my fire in the hollow of it. If I burn it down, there will be no action for trespass in a wooded country like this.

What boys are those crossing the foot-log? I'll press them into my service for awhile, and make them bring wood for my fire. I know them now; the larger one has cause to remember me "with tears of gratitude," for I bestowed on him last summer a score of old flies, a used-up leader, and a limp old rod. He offered me the liberal sum of two shillings for the very implement I have in my hand now; and to buy three flies from me *at four cents apiece,* — Halloo, Paul! what have you done with the rod I gave you — caught many Trout with it this season? Come over the creek, you and your brother, and get me some dry wood, and gather a handful or two of the furze from that old birch to light it with. I'll give you a pair of flies — real gay ones.

Dining *alone* may be counted almost the only drawback to one's taking a day to himself, and you are glad of any stray native who is attracted by the smoke of your fire. Your whiskey is beyond a per-adventure, better than he has in his cupboard at home; he is invariably out of tobacco — a chew or a pipeful, and a swig at your flask will make him communicative. If he has not already dined, he will readily accept a roasted Trout and a piece of bread and butter, and while eating will post you as to all the Trout-streams within ten miles. It is, therefore, a matter of policy to cultivate the good feeling of the natives, the boys especially, as stones are of very convenient size along the creek to throw at a surly fisherman. A few of "Conroy's journal-flies," which have occupied the back leaves of your fly-book for long years, are profitable things to invest in this way, for three boys out of four you meet with, will ask you to sell them "a pair of fly-hooks," which of course results in your giving them a brace or so that are a little the worse for wear, or too gay for your own use.

If the fly-fisher, though, would have "society where none intrudes," or society that *won't* intrude, let him take a lad of ten or twelve along to carry his dinner, and to relieve him after the roast, by transferring part of the contents of his creel to the empty dinner-basket. The garrulity and queer questions of a country boy of this age are amusing, when you are disposed to talk. Any person who has sojourned at my friend Jim Henry's and had his good-natured untiring boy Luther for his *gilly,* will acknowledge the advantage of such a "tail," even if it has not as many joints as a Highland laird's.

If there *is* an objection to a Trout-roast, it is that a man eats too much, and feels lazy after dinner. But what of that? it is a luxurious indolence, without care for the morrow — Care! why, he left that at home when he bought his railroad ticket, and shook off the dust of the city from his hobnailed boots.

What pretty bright Trout there are in this bold rocky creek! it would be called a river in England, and so it is. We Americans have an ugly way of calling every stream not a hundred yards wide, a creek. It is all well enough when the name is applied to some still, sedgy water, which loses half of its depth, and three-fourths of its width, at low tide, and is bank-full on the flood. But speckled fellows like these don't live there. De Kay must have received some inspiration at a Trout-roast, when he gave them the specific name of "Fontinalis," and they are truly the Salmon of the fountain; for a stream like this and its little tributaries, whose fountains are everywhere amongst these rugged hills, are their proper home. What an ignorant fellow Poietes was to ask Halieus if the red spots on a Trout were not "marks of disease — a hectic kind of beauty?" Any boy along the creek knows better. And what a pedantic old theorist Sir Humphry was, to tell him that the absence of these spots was a sign of high condition. Well, it may be in England, for the river Trout there are a different species from ours. But I'll bet my old rod against a bob-fly that there is twice as much pluck and dash in our little fellows with the "hectic" spots. I don't wonder that Trout like these so inspired Mr. Roosevelt, who wrote the *Game Fish of the North,* when, with his fancy in high feather, he mounted his Pegasus and went off. — "How splendid is the sport to deftly throw the long line and small fly, with the pliant single-handed rod, and with eye and nerve on the strain, to watch the loveliest darling of the wave, the spotted naiad, dart from her mossy bed, leap high into the air, carrying the strange deception in her mouth, and, turning in her flight, plunge back to her crystal home."

Julius Caesar! what "high-flying" Trout this gentleman must have met with in his time. Now, I never saw a Trout "dart from her mossy bed," because I never found Trout to lie on a bed of that sort; nor "leap high into the air, and turning in her flight plunge back," as a fish-hawk does. In fact, I may safely say I never saw a Trout *soar* more than eight or ten inches above its "crystal home." I honor "Barnwell" for the Anglomania which has seized him — he has been inoculated with a good scab, and the virus has penetrated his system: but I can't help being reminded by his description, of the eloquence of a member of a country debating society in Kentucky, who commenced — "Happiness, Mr. President, is like a crow situated on some far-distant mountain, which the eager sportsman endeavors in vain to no purpose to reproach." And concluded — "The poor man, Mr. President, reclines beneath the shade of some wide-spreading and umbrageous tree, and calling his wife and the rest of his little children around him bids their thoughts inspire to scenes beyond the skies. He views Neptune, Plato, Venus, and Jupiter, the Lost Pleiades, the Auroly Bolyallis, and other fixed stars, which it was the lot of the immoral Newton first to depreciate and then to deplore."

But a gray-headed man who cannot tie a decent knot in his casting-line without the aid of his spectacles, should forget such nonsense. There is one consolation, however, that this "decay of natur," which brings with it the necessity for glasses in seeing small objects within arm's length, gives in like ratio, the power of seeing one's flies at a distance on the water; there was old Uncle Peter Stewart who could knock a pheasant's head off at fifty yards with his rifle, and

see a gnat across the Beaverkill, when he was past sixty.

Here is the sun shining as bright now as if he had not blinked at noon, and such weather, not too hot and not too cold; I must acknowledge, though, my teeth *did* chatter this morning when I waded across at the ford.

> "Sweet day, so cool, so calm, so bright,
> The bridal of the earth and sky;
> The dew shall weep thy fall to night,
> For thou must die."

I'll start in here, for it appears there is always luck in the pool or rift under the lee of the smoke where one cooks his Trout. It is strange, too, for it seems natural that the smoke would drive the flies away, and as a consequence the fish get out of the notion of rising. But no matter, here goes. Just as I supposed, and a brace of them at the first cast. Come ashore on the sloping gravel, my lively little fellows, — eight and nine inches — the very size for the pan; but who wants to eat fried Trout after cooking them under the ashes or on a forked stick?

There are no good fish here; the water is not much more than knee-deep, and they have no harbor amongst those small pebble-stones. I have thrown in a dozen little fellows within the last ten minutes. I'll go to the tail of that strong rift below the saw-mill. The last time I fished it was when that lean hungry-looking Scotchman came over here from Jim Henry's; he had been sneaking through the bushes and poaching all the little brooks around, where the fish had run up to spawn, with his confounded worm-bait. This stream was low then and the fish shy; I had approached the end of the rift carefully and was trying to raise them at long cast in the deep water, when he — without even saying "by your leave" — waded in within a few yards of where they were rising, and splashed his buckshot sinker and wad of worms right amongst them. I said nothing, and he did not appear to think that interfering with my sport so rudely was any breach of good manners, or of the rules of fair fishing. A Scotchman, to catch Trout with a *worm!* Poor fellow! his piscatory education must have been neglected, or he belonged to that school who brag *only* on numbers. I know a party of that sort who come up here every summer from Easton and bring a *sauer-kraut stanner* to pack their Trout in, and salt down all they take without eating one, until they get home. They catch all they can and keep *all* they catch, great and small. Bah! a poor little *salted* Trout — it tastes more like a piece of "yaller soap" than fish. Such fishermen are but one remove from the bark-peelers I found snaring and netting Trout in the still water below here, last August. I can just see their shanty from here. "Instruments of cruelty are in their habitations. O my soul, come not thou into their secret; unto their assembly, mine honor, be not thou united!"

There is the sawyer's dog; if he comes much nearer I'll psychologize him with one of these "dunnicks"! But he turns tail as soon as I stoop to pick one up. Now for it — just at the end of the swift water — ah! my beauty — fifteen inches, — try it again — I can't raise him. This won't do. Am I cold, or am I nervous, that I should shake like a palsied old man because I missed that fish? Fie on you, Mr. Nestor, you who have run the rapids at the "Rough Waters" on the Nipissiguit, in a birch canoe, with a Salmon at the end of sixty yards of line, and your pipe in your mouth; I thought you had gotten past a weakness of this kind. But it will only make bad worse and convince that Trout of the cheat to throw over him again; so I must leave him now, and get back to the log on that sunny bank and compose myself with a few whiffs, while I change my flies. It will be just fifteen minutes until I knock the ashes out of my pipe; by that time my vaulting friend will likely forget the counterfeit I tried to impose on him, if I offer him something else.

Now Dick gave me this for a meerschaum, and I have no doubt Mr. Doll sold it for one in good faith; but it is a very "pale complected" pipe for one of that family. I have smoked it steadily for a year, and there is only the slightest possible tinge of orange about the root of the stem. It is hardly as dark as this ginger hackle in my hat-band. However, it is light, and carries a big charge for a pipe of its size, and the shortness of the stem brings the smoke so comfortably under the nose — a great desideratum in the open air. The pipe must have been instituted expressly for the fisherman; it is company when he is lonesome, and never talks whens he wants to be quiet; it concentrates his ideas and assists his judgment when he discusses any important matter with himself, such as the selection of a killing stretcher. No wonder the Indians smoked at their council-fires; and, as for the nerves, I'll put it against Mrs. Winslow's soothing syrup. What a pity it is that infants are not taught to smoke! What shall my stretcher be ? that fish refused Hofland's Fancy; now let me try one of my own fancy. Here is something a great deal prettier; a purple body in place of a snuff-brown, and light wings from a lead-colored pigeon instead of a sober woodcock feather. What a pretty fly — half sad, half gay in its attire, like an interesting young widow, when she decides on shedding her weeds, and "begins to take notice." I'll change my dropper also — here it is; body of copper-colored peacock hurl, wings of the feather of an old brown hen, mottled with yellow specks. What a plain homely look it has! it reminds me of "the Girl with the Calico Dress." You are not as showy, my dear miss, as the charming little widow, but certain individuals of my aquaintance are quite conscious of your worth. Let me see which of you will prove most attractive to my speckled friend. So here goes — two to one on the widow — lost, by jingo! He looked at her and sailed slowly away. Has he ever heard of the warning that the sage Mr. Weller gave his son "Samivel"? Perhaps, then, he will take a notion to care! Ah ha! my boy, you would be indiscreet, after all, and the widow has victimized you. Now she'll lead you a dance! Don't be travelling off with her as if you were on your wedding tour, for I know you would like to get rid of her already; but there is no divorce beneath the water, — you are mine, says she, "until death us do part!"

There you are, now! the three-minutes' fight has completely taken the wind out of you. That's the last flap of your tail; the widow has killed you "as dead as a mackerel." Acting the gay Lothario, were you? I know some scaly old fellows who play the same game ashore, stealthily patronizing Mrs. Allen, subsidizing the tailor, bootmaker, dentist, and barber, and slyly endeavoring to take off a discount of twenty-five per cent from old Father Time's bill. But that won't do, for folks of any discernment know at a glance those spavined, short-winded, shaky old fellows, who trot themselves out, as if they were done-up for the horse-market. Lie there, my Turveydrop, until I move down a little, and try under the bushes, on the opposite side.

With this length of line I can just come close enough to the alders to miss them. Dance lightly, O my brown girl, and

follow in her wake, dear widow, as I draw you hitherward. Ah ha! and so it is; there is one dashing fellow who sees charms in your homely dress. How he vaults! — nine rails, and a top rail! Did you ever know Turner Ashby? Not Beau Turner — I mean Black Turner. Did he ever straddle a bit of horse-flesh with more mettle? None of your Conestogas. There he goes again! How long have you belonged to the circus? But he can't run all day at that gait; he begins to flag, at last, and here he is now, coming in on the "quarter stretch." There you are at last — died as game as a Dominica chicken. Once more, now. I knew it. — And again.

Three times my brace of beauties have come tripping home across the deep whirling rapid, and three bright Trout lie on the gravel behind me. I begin at last to long for the sound of some friendly voice, and the sight of a good-humored face. I must keep my appointment with Walter at the foot-bridge; so I am off. Some of the "Houseless" don't like this solitary sport. I know one of them who would as soon be guilty of drinking alone; but *he* is not a contemplative angler, and has never realized how hungry some folks get through the winter for a little fishing. May-be he has never read what William Howitt says, in his *Rural Life in England,* about fishing alone. It will come home to every quiet fly-fisher. See what an unveiling of the heart it is, when the angler is alone with God and Nature.

"People that have not been inoculated with the true spirit may wonder at the infatuation of anglers — but true anglers leave them very contentedly to their wondering, and follow their diversions with a keen delight. Many old men there are of this class that have in them a world of science — not science of the book, or of regular tuition, but the science of actual experience. Science that lives, and will die with them; except it be dropped out piecemeal, and with the gravity becoming its importance, to some young neophyte who has won their good graces by his devotion to their beloved craft. All the mysteries of times and seasons, of baits, flies of every shape and hue; worms, gentles, beetles, composition, or substances found by proof to possess singular charms. These are a possession which they hold with pride, and do not hold in vain. After a close day in the shop or factory, what a luxury is a fine summer evening to one of these men, following some rapid stream, or seated on a green bank, deep in grass and flowers, pulling out the spotted Trout, or resolutely but subtilely bringing some huge Pike or fair Grayling from its lurking place beneath the broad stump and spreading boughs of the alder. Or a day, a summer's day, to such a man, by the Dove or the Wye, amid the pleasant Derbyshire hills; by Yorkshire or Northumbrian stream; by Trent or Tweed; or the banks of Yarrow; by Teith or Leven, with the glorious hills and heaths of Scotland around him. Why, such a day to such a man, has in it a life and spirit of enjoyment to which the feelings of cities and palaces are dim. The heart of such a man — the power and passion of deep felicity that come breathing from mountains and moorlands; from clouds that sail above, and storms blustering and growling in the wind; from all the mighty magnificence, the solitude and antiquity of Nature upon him — Ebenezer Elliott only can unfold. The weight of the poor man's life — the cares of poverty — the striving of huge cities, visit him as he sits by the beautiful stream — beautiful as a dream of eternity, and translucent as the everlasting canopy of heaven above him; — they come, but he casts them off for the time, with the power of one who feels himself strong in the kindered spirit of all things around; strong in the knowledge that he is a man; an immortal — a child and pupil in the world-school of the Almighty. For that day he is more than a king — he has the heart of humanity, and the faith and spirit of a saint. It is not the rod and line that floats before him — it is not the flowing water, or the captured prey, that he perceives in those moments of admission to the heart of nature, so much as the law of the testimony of love and goodness written on everything around him with the pencil of Divine beauty. He is no longer the wearied and oppressed — the trodden and despised — walking in threadbare garments amid men, who scarcely deign to look upon him as a brother man — but he is reassured and recognized to himself in his own soul, as one of those puzzling, aspiring, and mysterious existences for whom all this splendid world was built, and for whom eternity opens its expecting gates. These are magnificent speculations for a poor, angling carpenter or weaver; but Ebenezer Elliott can tell us that they are his legitimate thoughts, when he can break for an instant the bonds of his toiling age, and escape to the open fields. Let us leave him dipping his line in the waters of refreshing thought."

Thus writes William Howitt. But there is the foot-bridge, and here are my little friends, the Sand-pipers. How often the fly-fisher sees them running along the pebbly margin of the Trout stream (as Wilson truly says), "continually nodding their heads"; sometimes starting with their peculiar short shrill note, from their nests in the wave-washed tufts of long grass, flapping along the creek sideways, as if wounded in leg or wing, to decoy the fancied destroyer from the nest of downy little snipelings. And there, where the waters of the noisy rapid find rest in the broad shallow below, is one perched on a big gray boulder, as gray as herself. How lonely she seems there, like the last of her race, were it not that her constant mate is on the strand below, busily engaged picking up larvæ and seedling mussels for its little ones in the nest up the creek.

— from *The American Angler's Book* (1864)

Salmon Lake

Benedict Henry Revoil

I am aware that I am now taking an oft-trod road. Thanks to steam, the Hudson is now a high road which no man who has ever travelled in the Northern United States can have avoided. Who can tell how many pages have been written about or sketches made of its banks? And yet, in these days of locomotion, where will you find a corner which has not been exhausted by our modern scribes with their books of travel and cheap lithographs, even down to the painters of panoramas, whose merits ought to be measured by the square yard? And yet, in spite of all that my readers may have read or seen, the painter and the poet have yet to be found, and the pen and pencil yet to be discovered, that can do justice to the magnificent beauties displayed by the hand of the Almighty on the banks of this noble river. When you are embarked upon the Hudson some fine morning in spring, New York Bay is a splendid introduction to the sublime natural poem whose pages are shortly to be displayed before the eyes of the delighted traveller. To the right, is the picturesque and confused mass which a great city always offers to the eye at a distance, and across the forest of innumerable masts which borders the quays to the left, the pleasant quarter of Hoboken stands in relief against the New Jersey Hills; behind, and in the half-distance are the Battery, Long Island, the Narrows, and a vast plain of water, covered with sails just bellying to the breeze, and all this, when bathed in the calm blue atmosphere of morning, makes up a scene of incomparable beauty. The right bank of the river soon comes forward, and we enter the course of the Hudson, properly so called. On one side is the wall of perpendicular rocks known as the Palisades, and on the other the imperial city of former days, succeeded by a continuous line of cottages and country-houses. Never was contrast more complete; on the one side Nature in her wild simplicity, and on the other the small and comparatively contemptible creations of our civilisation. The steamer, however, carries you at the rate of twenty miles an hour, and you arrive at the extremity of the Palisades. The river widens, and cultivated agricultural land takes the place of the gardens. Villages are grouped upon the banks, and take the place of the country-houses. A few more revolutions of the paddle, and the first undulations which announce the Highlands are visible on the horizon.

From that moment, and for about fifty miles farther on, there is a panorama upon which nature seems to have lavished all that she has in the way of magnificence and variety. The river passes through a chain of mountains whose tops vary in height from little hills to summits of fifteen hundred feet high. These hills border the scene like frames of verdure around landscapes, and occasionally allow a peep at some charming little scene where there is a miniature valley, with pleasant little houses sprinkled here and there with the first buddings of a modern hamlet. Sometimes the perpendicular rocks embank the very brink of the river, and sometimes the chain seems to melt away into the horizon, forming a vast amphitheatre, the furthest boundary of which approaches again, as if to repose by an almost imperceptible inclination in the bed of the river. Here and there soars a lofty peak, clothed with trees, whose top is lost in the clouds. In the middle of the gorge which nature has hollowed out through these undulations, flows the Hudson, describing a thousand windings and presenting pictures infinite in number and variety. Sometimes it opens a straight vista of five or six miles in length, and then it deviates by a graceful curve, whilst further on there is an unexpected angle or elbow. This last variety (which is by no means common in the course of great rivers) occurs here with extraordinary frequency, and produces the most picturesque effects. In certain spots, — at Caldwell, for example, — a promontory seems literally to bar the passage across, and it is only at the moment when this is rounded that the river reveals its course and opens a new horizon.

After quitting the highlands, a blue line denotes another chain of mountains towards the west, a chain more imposing than that which has just been quitted. These are the Catskill Mountains, whose summits attain a height of four thousand feet; but unfortunately for the curious they remain always in the background, and only approach the river to retreat immediately into the distance. A volume would be required to give the reader even the faintest idea of the picture which I have audaciously attempted to paint. How can I convey a tithe of those thousand details which excite the admiration every moment? How paint the streamlet which flows capriciously in a microscopic cascade down the face of the rock, and falls like a silver thread into the thick mossy carpet which lines the bank? How shall I describe the innumerable bays which are formed by the banks of the river where it receives its affluents, and the eyots which lie in the middle of its course? How enumerate, without making my description as monotonous as an itinerary, the towns, villages, and houses which arise out of the banks, as it were, at every turn of the paddle, sometimes upon the summit of a hill, but most frequently on the side of some gentle slope.

When the Catskill Mountains disappear on the horizon, a new phase appears in the physiognomy of Nature. The hills grow less in height and the woods disappear, giving place to fields in full cultivation. The farm and the manufactory have taken the place of the country-house and the fashionable hotel. In fact, we are entering at full speed an agricultural country, the peaceful and laughing features of which accompany the traveller up to Albany. He quitted New York when the sun had scarcely topped the horizon, and has arrived at his destination when the day is sinking into the west.

It was after a journey of this kind that I was seated one evening in the piazza of the hotel at Albany, and was thinking of returning to New York (for I had transacted all my business), when two blacks came up, carrying in a large hamper with two handles an enormous salmon, which seemed to weigh from sixty to seventy pounds.

"What a monster!" I cried. "I never saw such a large one."

"Wall, but Frenchmen don't see everything in creation," cried some one by way of answer, and on turning round indignantly at this somewhat impertinent observation, I saw that it proceeded from an individual who was sitting, or, to be more accurate, lying down in a rocking-chair, whittling a piece of wood with a large bowie-knife. Directly I turned my eyes on this individual, I recognised an old sporting-friend, Horace Mead, of Philadelphia, whose name has been already mentioned in my volume on "Sport in North America."

"Can I believe my eyes, old friend? Is it really you?"

"Myself, and no one else, I guess. I didn't know you at first 'till I head your voice," replied Mead, seizing me by the hands in true American style and nearly wrenching the wrists out of their sockets. "And what are you doing in Albany?"

"I came to report the opening of the Legislature. I've done my work and can now enjoy a week's holiday."

"So much the better! In that case you can come on with me this evening to my shooting-box in the Highlands."

"I certainly can't refuse, if you'll promise me plenty of sport."

"Fishing's the great sport now, and you shall have plenty of that. So finish what you have to do here, and meet me at the bar of the hotel about five o'clock."

At the stipulated time, I found Mead at his post, inbibing a sherry-cobler with great gusto, whilst a similar concoction was awaiting me. "Suck up that," cried he, "and off we go." In a couple of minutes, we had mounted the omnibus for the streamer, and in a short time were descending the Hudson towards Stony Point. At two in the morning, the warning was given by the ringing of a bell, and in a loud, intelligible voice that could be heard all through the steamer: "Passengers for Stony Point on deck!"

It was a pitch-dark night, but thanks to the light on board and the torches of the ferrymen at Stony Point, we landed without any mishap.

"We must put up at the Eagle Tavern until morning," said Mead. "The roads between here and my crib are not good enough to venture on at night. Come on, old friend; follow me."

He led the way forthwith to a very comfortable hotel, where there was accommodation for man and beast, and the landlord received us very cordially, for Mead was one of his best customers. I found the sheet of my bed very white and well aired, and the bed itself soft and comfortable, and soon fell so sound asleep that, at five in the morning, when my friend came to my bedside, he had to give me a good shaking to rouse me from the state of beatitude in which I was plunged.

"Up with you, lazybones," cried he; "I give you ten minutes to dress in."

When I am travelling I never allow any one to tell me twice of laziness, so I jumped up, washed and dressed hastily, and in five minutes was at the door of the tavern taking my place by Mead's side in his waggon, to which was harnessed a capital trotter, with a foot as sure as a mule of the Alps or Pyrenees.

Mead beguiled the drive with many a story of his adventures, and the time seemed short enough when, on turning the corner of a gorge, he exclaimed: "Here we are, my boy; there's the crib behind the little hill."

As he said this, we turned the corner, crossed a wooden bridge which spanned the ravine, and found ourselves opposite a gate or barrier which separated the road from a small plantation of choice trees and shrubs. The barrier was open, for the master of Woodcock House was expected, and we drove along a well-kept carriage drive, bordered by a slope that was literally covered with junipers, chestnuts, and clumps of rhododendrons, kalmias, and azaleas, growing out of the fissures of the rocks in the most luxuriant fashion. Presently we heard the sound of a waterfall, and crossed another bridge made of the rough trunks of trees thrown across a very clear and rapid stream. On the other side of the stream was a green meadow, at further end of which was an elegant cottage, built of wood, with a slate roof. The walls of this abode were clothed with creepers of various kinds, lianas, ivy, clematis, cobeas, and roses full of sweet-smelling bloom, covering all but the windows.

"What say you to this, my friend?" quoth Mead. "This is my country box; the only one I have. Do you like it?"

"Impossible to do otherwise."

"That's well. Hallo, there! Mary!"

In answer to the summons a pleasant-looking old woman appeared at the door of the cottage, followed by a black, who took the horse's head, and we jumped out of the waggon.

"This is an old friend, Mary," said Mead, "and I recommend him to your care; and these, my boy, are my excellent housekeeper Mary, and my faithful Tingo, who's as cute as he's black."

Thus saying, Mead led the way into the parlour of the cottage, a little snuggery of some sixteen square yards, with a table in the middle, and a large fire-place in the Tudor style. Against the wall, opposite the fire-place, was an oak sideboard, with bright pewter dishes, glasses, plates, and two flower vases filled with magnolias, verbenas, and water-lilies. Three engravings, representing hunting subjects, and simply framed, hung against the walls, and, above the mantel-piece, two stag's horns turned upside down, supported four guns in excellent condition. In one of the corners of the room were ranged fishing apparatus of all kinds, and a casting-net quite dry and in a perfect state of repair.

Mary served us an excellent meal, consisting of delicious salmon, trout, roasted woodcocks, &c., followed by a glorious plum-pudding, and washed down with a bottle of claret, that would not have disgraced a first-rate Paris restaurant.

In the evening, Mead told me that next day would be spent at his salmon lake.

"You'll see such fishing," said he, "as you'll remember to your dying day. I must tell you that I'm a kind of fish-merchant, and deal with New York, Albany, and even Boston. My fishery is a very good one, and clears me a good thousand pounds sterling per annum. That's why I bought Woodcock House. It was shockingly out of repair when I first came to live in it; but I've a good nose, and pretty soon reckoned up the possibilities."

Mead then explained to me the nature of his business in detail. He bred and collected salmon and salmon trout, just as others breed horses and rabbits. He had contracts with some of the principal hotels in New York, and some of the larger fishmongers in different parts of the country. His lakes, ponds, and rivers were managed according to a regular plan. Among other advantages, he had but few neighbours, and his property was in the midst of the Catskill Mountains.

Next day he had to supply a certain number of salmon for New York, and to make up the order great activity would be necessary. For the past few days his men had been busily engaged in driving the fish into a certain corner of the lake. The foreman fisherman came that evening to make his report, which was to the effect that the fish were literally swarming in Mount-top Lake; and next morning Mead and myself were there by sunrise. It was a lovely sight. Before us lay the beautiful lake, the extent of which was about a league square. The lake was fed by innumerable streams flowing from the summits of the Catskills, and the overflow was passed through a canal along the valleys until it fell into the Hudson. It was by this watery way that the salmon regained the upper waters from the sea, as far as Cedar Lake, where they found plenty of food, and bred in the most astonishing manner. There were salmon in these waters that weighed up to sixty pounds avoirdupois.

"Now, boys," cried Mead, as soon as we arrived at the fishery, where his men were all waiting for him, "we must have a good haul this morning. I've got to send sixty fish to New York and Philadelphia this evening. Is all ready?"

"Yes, sir," replied the foreman; "and we're quite ready to begin as soon as you give the word."

"In with you, then," cried Mead.

There was a large boat, with an immense seine net leaded and corked. One end was fastened to the shore, and the boat pushed off whilst the foreman payed out the net, and the boat was rowed as quietly as possible in a semicircle until we gained the shore again. As soon as this manœuvre was complete, the boat went outside the semicircle, and eight men began hauling in the net, whilst those in the boat beat the water with oars and boathooks to keep the fish inside the seine. In a very short time the men hauling on the shore felt sufficient resistance to assume then that the draught would be a good one, and in a short time, as the net was drawn upon the shallows, we could perceive those movements which betoken the presence of the fish. In a few minutes, the net was drawn up, and we extracted from its meshes fourteen salmon of various sizes (the weight varying from five-and-twenty to forty pounds), forty-five salmon-trout, with perch, carp, and eels. All that were adjudged to be unsaleable were thrown back into the water, and the remainder were packed up with fresh weed in baskets and carried to the fishery, where they were stored in a cool cellar which had been excavated in the rock. The net was then cast again, and the operation repeated four times in the course of the day, and when night came, my friend, instead of sixty salmon, had sixty-seven to send to his correspondents. A three-horsed waggon conveyed these the same night to Stony Point, where they would meet the steamer to take them to New York and elsewhere. That evening, as we supped gaily in the pretty little parlour of Mead's shooting-box, he promised me some good sport on the morrow after woodcock, and sure enough we bagged nine-and-twenty, with the aid of two fine pointers. That evening we had a torch-light fishing for salmon.

"Take good care," cried Mead to the harpooner, as we got into the boat, "and let's have no mistakes." Thus exhorted, the man never missed his aim once. He stood at the brow of the boat, armed with a three-pronged harpoon, to the handle of which a strong line was fastened by a ring welded to the haft. As we gained the middle of the lake, the foreman lit a torch, and the light was suddenly cast upon the water, so that we could see clearly for about a dozen yards ahead of the boat. A moment afterwards, Mead pointed to a black spot which had risen to the surface a short distance from us.

"A salmon!" he whispered in my ear.

The harpooner had also seen the fish, and brandishing his weapon with a sure arm, he struck the fish so deeply that it was impossible for it to get loose. At the same instant the line began to uncoil with extraordinary rapidity; but before it was all payed out it stopped: the fish was dead. The harpooner and his two mates then hauled in the line, coiling it as they pulled it in, and presently the fish was brought to the surface of the water, and so into the boat. It was a splendid salmon, weighing about forty pounds, and in very fine order. Three times did the harpooner throw his weapon, and landed a fish every time. After this we had seen enough, and went home.

It were needless to recount all the pleasure I experienced whilst enjoying the hospitalities of my old friend of the prairies; but my readers will easily understand that I quitted Woodcock House with regret, and that I am always delighted at receiving a letter from my friend, in memory of past times.

— from *Shooting and Fishing in the Rivers, Prairies, and Backwoods of North America* (1865)

A Maumee Sturgeon

Samuel E. Edwards

Who has not ventured forth on a beautiful summer afternoon, with a kind, warm-hearted friend by his side, and with measured line dropped his baited hook beneath the rippling surface of the shining waters, and then glided smoothly along over the languid water, quite oblivious of time or space, while his fair companion beguiled the hours into minutes, and miles into narrow spaces, until there was a certain feeling of quiet satisfaction, equivalent to — don't care whether fish bite or not — when suddenly the silken thread of conversation is broken by a gentle twitching of the line, and the devoted listener is roused to something like a sense of the painful duty before him — painful, did I say? — yes, painful. Painful because the poor fish's lacerated gill must be separated from the cruel hook? oh, no, not that; but painful because a mind lost to everything but the communion of a kindred spirit must thus focibly and suddenly be brought back to the wakeful and real in life, while it would much rather repose in dreamlike rhapsodies under the soothing influences of quiet, sparkling waters, and still more sparkling wit. But the hook must be drawn to the surface, and there comes up with it a beautiful sunfish. Oh, how delicious that will be fried in sweet butter, and shared with a friend for supper. But the little creature makes many remonstrances against such a course. He writhes his little body into many distorted shapes, and the sympathetic friend by your side pleads so eloquently for the life of the little sufferer that you begin to feel how cruel it would be to kill it, and the hook is much more tenderly removed than perhaps the same hook had been on former occasions, and the little fish, after being admired for a moment, is thrown again into the water, instead of the empty trough that you expected to see by this time well filled. The line is wound up, and the fishing abandoned for the afternoon, and the fisherman relapses again into the before-described state of luxurious repose, while the lazy breeze idly wafts them back to the little port from whence they glided.

Now it is not such a fishing excursion as this that I am going to describe. Indeed, I do not expect it to resemble it in the smallest particular. I have only drawn this opposite sketch, thinking some might have met the former in their own experience, and when compared with some more recent experience, found the contrast pleasant.

I am now going to make just as sudden a transition from the fanciful and false, to the commonplace and true, as the young lover makes when he exchanges the golden hours and honied words of courtship for the leaden years and tart words of dull, prosaic life.

I was living in Hancock Co., Ohio, when I heard of the mammoth fisheries of the Maumee. Now fishing possessed a charm for me second to nothing but hunting, and as it was not the season for hunting, I thought I would fill up the interval of time by fishing. At that age I was rather ambitious, and quite fond of leading the van whenever associated with company in any business. At this time I was quite successful in raising a crew, and started for the "big fisheries," about fifty miles distant. Among the number who accompanied me, was my brother. . . . He had been to the fisheries the previous summer, and so entertained us *en route,* by stories of the size and number of the fish, particularly the sturgeon, until my mind was so engrossed with thoughts of sturgeon that I was ready for battle as soon as one presented itself to my sight.

We had no sooner landed than a large one came popping its head out of the water close to the place where I was standing. I caught a spear which luckily lay on the bank, and started for the fish. The owner of the valuable article saw the trick and hallooed at me to bring back his spear. I told him if I broke it I was able to pay for it. He replied that he did not want the pay, he wanted the spear, which was much more valuable to him at that time and in that place than the money it cost; but I was far out in the water, and did not need the admonition; but my brother explained the case to him, telling him there was no danger of me, I was half fish myself, and if I could not bring it to shore I would go down stream along with it. There were about fifty men on the bank watching the exploit, and what man is not willing to make some ventures where there are others standing by to applaud his heroism? I felt at that time that I could have been a second Napoleon, had the same opportunities for daring bravery presented themselves, and the same number of anxious beholders stood by to watch the result. I fastened a loop of the cord that was attached to the spear around my left hand, and with the instrument of death firmly clenched in my right, I made a bold start toward the young leviathan. Now

I suppose I need not tell the dweller in the Maumee Valley, that the sturgeon is the most powerful fish found in the fresh water. Though very lazy and languid in its movements, it is, when attacked, found to possess immense strength. The water in which I approached him was about two feet deep, and the bottom was of smooth, solid rock. But a few rods further down the stream there was a sudden jog in the limestone rock, and the water was six or eight feet deep, and the current just above very rapid. I knew that my chances of success lay in immediate action, and accordingly I plied the spear. It penetrated the tough hide, and entered the flesh just below the gills. The moment the spear struck him, he made one powerful plunge into the water, carrying the spear quite out of my reach; and I soon discovered that he was not only carrying the spear, but by means of the cord attached to my left hand, I too was following at quite a rapid rate. This unintentional drift down stream gave me no small anxiety as to the result; and after following my captor several rods, I determined to reverse the motion. I had now the disadvantage of heavy clothing, swift current, and a powerful, refractory force, from which I could not get free if I would. But in time of danger my strength never forsook me, and at this time my efforts were equal to the task. I at length swam safely to the shore, the subjugated sturgeon following me at a rapid rate. My friends congratulated me upon having accomplished a very daring feat. We drew the fish ashore, and he measured nine feet in length.

— from *The Ohio Hunter* (1866)

An Exploring Expedition

W. C. Prime

There is a lake over the mountains, some forty miles from the Rookery, which I had long desired to see; but I could never persuade a friend to go with me on an exploring expedition. A recent extension of the railway had made it somewhat more accessible, if I was to give credit to the information given me by a baggage-master, who assured me that the railroad crossed an old wood-road which led in three or four miles to the lake.

There is, I think, a love of novelty in all anglers. We prefer to fish new waters when we can, and it is sometimes pleasanter to explore, even without success, than to take fish in familiar places. New and fine scenery is always worth finding. But I could not beat these ideas practically into the brain of either Steenburger or Doctor Johnston, and I resolved therefore on a solitary expedition to the lake.

I had not then, what I now possess, and strongly recommend to roving anglers, a patent India-rubber raft, made in two cylinders, with a light frame to sit on. This boat or raft, packing in a small compass when not "blown up," weighs less than fifty pounds, and can be carried on a man's shoulders to any lake or pond. I have frequently used it on water never before fished, and to reach which it was necessary to climb hills so steep and so covered with alternate rock and under-brush that two men would have found it quite impossible to carry up safely any boat, however light. An axe and auger wherewith to build a raft were therefore essentials to my equipment, and these, with some hard bread and sandwiches, and one heavy and one light fly-rod, made up the sum total of my luggage.

Taking the forenoon accommodation train up the road, I went forward to find my old informant, the baggage-master, or, if not him, some other one who could supplement my scanty knowledge of the locality I was seeking.

Luckily there was a man who said he knew all about it, and, after riding forty miles or so, the conductor stopped his train at a road-crossing in the woods, I tumbled out, and civilization at once departed from me, drawn by the power of steam.

It had been a sudden idea, and the realization was somewhat discouraging. Alone in the woods, with sundry traps in the way of luggage, and with no other guide than the words of the confident individual I had met on the cars, who said that the lake lay at the foot of a hill to which he pointed across the forest, I set out, and after a half-mile tramp came on the traces of a clearing, and, soon descending into a hollow, found a saw-mill. Two men who were running it were evidently astonished at the appearance of a traveller, but they very good-naturedly offered advice, to wit, that, if one wanted trout-fishing, he could find it then and there in the mill-dam, but that if he went to the lake he would find no trout, for nobody ever could take trout there except through the ice in the winter.

"What size do they take them then?"

"Oh, sometimes five or six pounds."

This was the same story I had heard at a distance, and it confirmed my hopes. I chatted a while with the sawyers, and tried the contents of their pond. A few casts brought up some small trout, and at length a very decent fish, perhaps a pound in weight, rose to the scarlet ibis. Landing him, and leaving him with the others for the use of the men, who had never before seen fly-fishing, and were astonished at the process, I pushed on in the afternoon toward the unknown lake or pond. The road became less a road and more a path as it ascended hill after hill, winding and pleasant, but always tending upward. At last it opened on a large clearing where stood a ruined log-house, deserted long ago, and a tolerably decent barn, in which there was a small quantity of dry hay. This was an unexpected luxury, for I had calculated on a night in camp. I took possession of the only tenantable end of the log-house, deposited my packages, and resolved to make this my headquarters, since it was evident the lake was distant not over a mile at most. Then taking a light rod I plunged into the forest, and in less than half an hour emerged on the banks of the lake. It lacked an hour of sunset, and there was but little time for the examination of the shores. Boat there was none. The unbroken forest surrounded the sheet of water. There was no time this evening to construct a raft, and if I was to have trout for supper, it must be by casting from the shore, and so I went to work at once.

In visiting a new lake like this, the chances are always against the fisherman. He knows nothing of the special haunts of the trout, and can form no opinion of the shape of the bottom of the pond — an idea of which is generally necessary to guide one in looking for this fish. The safest rule is therefore to seek for the main inlet, and, if the water is here found shoal, to wade out far enough to get a cast over deeper water. Beginning on this rule, I had a long hunt for the inlet, and it was after sunset before I found it. It happened fortunately that there was an accumulation here of old drift-wood, well packed together, which supported me, and I had a good clear back cast. For ten or fifteen minutes it was all vain work. Nothing broke the surface which had life. The gloom began to settle on the lake. It grew cold withal, and the wind was sharp. I frankly confess that by this time I wanted fish because I was hungry. If supper were to be confined to three or four pieces of hard bread, it was not to be regarded with any earnest longings and joyous anticipations. If, on the other hand, I could look to the rich salmon-colored meat of a trout as waiting me in the old log-house, it was something worth thinking about.

And as I thought about it, he rose with a heavy rush, and slashed the tail-fly with his own broad tail and went down again. Cast after cast, and he would not rise again. So I fell back at last on the old white moth, and, taking off all the other flies, cast this alone, in the twilight which was now almost darkness. He came up at it the first cast, and took it, head on, following the fly from behind. It is not often on still water that a trout takes a fly with his mouth before striking it with his tail; but they sometimes do it on a white fly in the evening, and from this fact it seems likely that they regard it as an animal moving in the water and not as a fly at all.

He took it and turned down; then, as he felt the hook, swayed off with a long, steady surge, and circled half around me. Supper was tolerably certain now, and my appetite at once rose. In less than five minutes I had him, a good, solid three-pounder, in the landing-net, and at once struck a bee-line for the log-house in the clearing.

The cabin was nothing to boast of as a shelter. The roof was tight over the end opposite the chimney, but the windows were destitute of glass, and the breeze, which had sprung up freshly before I left the lake, was talking loudly to itself inside of the place as I approached it. There was plenty of wood around the old hut, and in ten minutes I had the chimney blazing at a terrible rate. Fire-light is as much a polisher in-doors as moonlight outside. It smooths down all the roughness of an interior. It reddened the walls of the cabin and covered them with dancing images. I had nothing in the way of eatables except the trout, hard bread, and some salt. The salt was the great article. It was on the faith of that salt that I had ventured on the expedition. With a few pinches of salt and a good rod or gun, one may live luxuriously for a while, if he have luck. Without the salt — only imagine it. You may not think much of it as a thing to possess, but just reverse the picture and imagine fish and game in abundance without it, and you may thereby find in some measure what it is worth.

I recall oftentimes a scene at Wady Haifa where the palms of Ethiopia bear golden fruit, but where salt is worth more than golden dates. There I have bought bushels of luxurious fruit for a single handful of the condensed brine from the far-off sea.

One half of the trout was turning before the blaze, hung on the small end of a birch sapling; the other half was reserved for breakfast, for it was by no means certain that any other food was to be found. A pile of hay from the barn made a soft bed in the sheltered end of the room. While the fire

burned I mused, and before the musings had assumed form the trout was cooked, and then my supper was ready and eaten, the bed looked more and more inviting, and by nine or ten o'clock I was sound asleep in the corner.

Morning found me sleeping. The sun and air were streaming in at the window-frames innocent of sash or glass. But while the question of breakfast was under discussion, a voice came in by the same avenues with the sunshine and wind, singing a cheery song, and I saw the tall form of one of the sawyers of the mill swinging along toward the wood in the direction of the lake. He pulled up at a hail and turned to the cabin.

"Glad to see you lively this morning," he said in a hearty voice. "I thought I'd come over and bring you suthin' to eat; expected to find you in camp, down along the pond." Then, entering the cabin and seeing the half of the last night's trout hanging before the fire — "Well, you seem to ha' taken care of yourself. You don't say you got that feller last night with one of them little poles o' yourn?"

We made a substantial meal together at once, and the best thanks that could be given my friend were visible in the justice done to his corn-bread and hard eggs. He had come three miles across the country on this hospitable errand, and was delighted when I proposed to him to spend the day on the lake, and promised to go home with him in the evening.

The first work was the building of a raft. To the uninitiated it is often a puzzle how rafts are constructed by fishermen in the forests, and possibly there are not many sportsmen who have regarded an axe or an auger as parts of an outfit. The two things are essential to a forest expedition, and in going to fish an unknown sheet of water one might almost as well leave his rod behind him as these tools. There are ways of getting on without the auger, but a raft lashed together with withes is a dangerous craft. I have had such a one part with me in mid-lake, while I swam ashore with my rod in my hand, losing even the fish I had taken. In the present case I had both tools. The construction of the raft was very simple. Two pine-trees supplied six logs, each about a foot in diameter, which were rolled into the water and floated side by side, a few inches apart. Across these, smaller timbers were laid, the axe shaping them down flat where wooden pegs were driven in auger-holes through them into the heavy logs. It was but little over an hour's work to complete it, for the timber was at hand in good size and quantity. Then we covered the raft with balsam boughs, to stand or sit or lie down on, and a couple of long poles finished the furniture of the vessel on which we pushed out at the inlet of the lake. The day was so much more beautiful than the previous one that the lake appeared like a new place, and the trout were rising on the surface here and there in a way which indicated that the warm sunshine had brought out some small flies, invisible to the eye at a distance, but satisfactory as indicating that the fish were on the feed. It was nearly ten o'clock when I began casting. But nothing rose to my flies till I had changed them twice or oftener, and had on at length three small gnats, a dun, a yellow, and a black, and then came the first strike at the yellow, a half-pound fish soon killed. Another at the yellow again, a somewhat larger fish, gave me some slight work, and a third took the yellow once more, and thereupon I changed: the dropper yellow, the tail-fly yellow, and intermediate a small scarlet ibis. The first cast made with this new bank, as some men call the arrangement, cost me the scarlet fly. A large fish took the dropper, and at the same instant another struck the ibis. They headed in opposite directions, and the very stroke of the two parted the slender thread. I landed but one of that cast, and only once after that had two at the same time, and then saved them both.

The sport continued good till about one o'clock, and then ceased. The breeze rippled the water, the flies were increasing in number in the warm sunshine, but feeding time was over and the fish went down. I have seen the same thing often on other waters.

The object of the expedition was accomplished. There were trout in the lake — they would rise to the fly. Over a dozen beautiful large fish, and nearly another dozen which ran below a half pound each, were fair evidence of the contents of this water. Six of the smaller fish had been taken with bait by my friend, the sawyer. He had cut a birch rod, and with hook and line which I supplied, and the fin of a trout for bait, which he kept constantly moving near the bottom of the lake, he had captured a half-dozen fair-sized fish.

So we left the raft to drift toward the leeward side of the lake, and started for the log-house in the clearing; and thence, carrying heavy weight, we trudged over the hills to the home of my friend of the mill.

It is one of the most pleasant incidents, not uncommon either, in the life of a roving angler, to find the hospitality of a warm American country home. There is no other country in the world where such incidents can happen, for nowhere else are there outlying farms and homes in the forest, in which one can meet with that measure of refinement and cultivation which marks American farmers' families. Books, magazines, and newspapers find their way into the remotest settlements, and it is a pleasing fact that newness or freshness in the literature is not an essential to its enjoyment. Life glides on so evenly that there is no thirst for novelty, no excitement which requires peculiar stimulus. It is the custom of many anglers whom I know to gather in the autumn all their old magazines and literature of various kinds, and send it to such distant homes in the forest, where it helps the winter through, and where the giver finds, and is sometimes glad to find it in the spring.

My sawyer friend brought me to such a house. The fire-light was shining from the kitchen hearth through the open door as we approached, and an old woman, with a bright and sunny smile on her face, welcomed her son and his guest on the threshold. The two lived together here, in a snug frame house, low down in the valley, and only a half-mile from the open country where was a small village and a church. "If it were daylight, you could see the church," said the old lady, "but as it is, you can only see the lights in Alice Brand's farm-house."

And later in the evening, after we had dined, or supped, royally, and were sitting before the hearth talking of this, that, and the other thing, the old lady told me a story about Alice Brand's farm-house.

Forty years ago Stephen Brand was a farmer in the valley near the church, well to do in the world, and, as he hoped, with some treasure laid up where it could not corrupt. At all events, Stephen was a light in the church, and had been a judge, or something of the sort, in his county. For a long time the stout old man had served his country, and he was beginning to be weary.

He had one son; but Walter Brand, the child of his old age, was a wanderer, and his wife Alice, the daughter of the clergyman, lived in the old house with Stephen, and cared for him and superintended the domestic duties of the home-farm.

Alice had been a favorite in the village before her marriage, and most persons thought well of the match; but Walter was a restless boy, and although sole heir to his father's wealth, which was not small, and although he had a gentle wife at home that loved him truly and fondly, he yet preferred to rove, and seldom returned to the old place under the elms.

They had one child. He was a boy, and from his birth was so like the old man that you were startled and almost frightened at the strange resemblance. There was an old look on the child's face that grew tenfold older every year that he lived, and when he was seven, you might have taken his countenance for that of a man of seventy. He was hopelessly deformed. This sorrowful truth began to force itself on the mother's mind before he was two years old, and at length there could be no doubt of the fact. Like all deformed children of tender-hearted parents, he was far more dear to his mother on this very account, and she cherished him as a very gem lost out of heaven and found by them. And such he was. There was a depth of quiet beauty in his childish soul that passed all sounding. No one seemed to penetrate its mysteries except the old man, his grandfather, and he would sit for hours looking into the large black eyes of the boy, and apparently gazing into the very soul of his pet. They grew to each other. The old man for his sake came half way back to his childhood and met him — for the boy seemed to be half way to old age, even at six years old. Alice was happy in that growing love, and watched them with eyes full of tears at the thought that ere long the old man must go down to silence, and the boy live on alone.

Sometimes they would walk together, and sit down under a tree on the river bank and talk. No one knew what they talked of in such moments, but doubtless the grandfather had visions of the world he was entering, and communicated them to the boy. And so years travelled along, and they all grew older together, and when once in a while Walter came back, the house was happy.

But a change came. The cheek of Stephen Brand grew paler and paler as he grew more feeble, and he felt that the hour was approaching when he must go away by the dark road; and the boy's life was so knitted to that of his grandfather, that he too seemed visibly to fail from day to day. It was a curious circumstance, and did not fail to attract the attention of the family and the neighborhood, and wise old women prophesied that the boy would not outlive the old man.

And now the two talked constantly and steadily from morning till night and late into the night. Sometimes they were seated by the fire in the old hearth, sometimes in the large chairs facing each other that stood in Stephen's room, and as the spring advanced they sat sometimes under the large elm that was near the well, and oftener still on the river bank by the spring. And their conversation was no secret, but was of the high and blessed promises for the future, of the light that shone all along that otherwise dark sad road they were travelling. Alice wept in secret every day, but never let them see her tears. She went cheerfully about her household work, and in the dull routine of a farmer's life sought to forget the bitterness of the coming separation.

It came at length. One pleasant morning in the summer,

when the birds sang with unusual cheer, and sky and earth seemed to come close together in their affection, the inseparable two walked feebly out together, and down to the old seat on the river bank. Alice was alarmed about them, and followed them herself, but when she saw them seated safely she returned and worked sadly on until noon. But they did not return as usual, and she hastened down the pathway across the field, and sought them by the spring. But they were not there. A wild terror seized on her, and she sank trembling on the seat, beside the old man's hat which lay on it. A brief search revealed the sad story. The boy had sought something in the edge of the water, and in his feebleness had fallen. The old man had tried to rescue him, and perished with him. The two were found together, and together carried to the old farm-house, out of which the light had now forever gone.

"Ah," said the old lady, "I've heard the passing-bell many, many times in the valley, but I never heard it sound so strange as it did that afternoon when it came up the valley and I counted it. It was ever so long before I got to eighty-seven, and then I knew that Stephen Brand was gone, and I was just thinking how lonesome poor little Steve would be, when it struck again. Upon my word, sir, it almost knocked me off my chair; and when I counted fourteen, I just sat here trembling all over, and then I fell to crying like any child."

"Mrs. Brand still lives on the farm, I suppose?"

"Alice, you mean? Oh yes. The death of the two who had been so close to her was a heavy affliction, and she was pretty much broken down; but it brought a blessing that repaid her, for Walter came home at once, and somehow their old love sprang up again quite fresh, and he did not go away, and they settled down into a happy sort of life. They're living in the old house now. It's Alice's, for the old man left it to her and not to Walter. He'd be glad to see you, sir. It isn't often he hears from his old friends in the city. She's my cousin, Alice is. Sam, why don't you walk down to the farm and see Walter? It'll do him good, for he's getting old and growing stiff. Sam, you're not afraid of ghosts?"

"No, no, I thank you. I'm too content with your hospitality to go away from it to-night," I said, in reply to Sam's proffer of an escort for the call. But I noticed that it was the allusion to ghosts that had started him out of his easy seat, and I looked for an explanation.

"It's not strange," said my hostess, "that superstitious people should have made a ghost story out of the curious life and death of the old man and his grandson. But for a man six feet high and well educated as Sam is, I call it absurd."

"Sam believes it?"

"Sam declares he saw them. The people used to say they two haunted the side of the brook. Sam goes fishing for trout sometimes of an evening down the hollow, and he declares he saw them one night, the tall old man and the little boy, moving along in the edge of the bushes and looking and pointing toward the old house. But as to its being ghosts he saw I never believed it, I always thought the ghosts were Tim Stevens and his boy on their way to steal Alice Brand's chickens. She generally misses some about the time the ghosts are around." —from *I Go A-Fishing* (1873)

A Fight with a Trout

Charles Dudley Warner

Trout-fishing in the Adirondacks would be a more attractive pastime than it is, but for the popular notion of its danger. The trout is a retiring and harmless animal, except when he is aroused, and forced into a combat; and then his agility, fierceness, and vindictiveness become apparent. No one who has studied the excellent pictures representing men in an open boat, exposed to the assaults of long, enraged trout flying at them through the open air with open mouth, ever ventures with his rod upon the lonely lakes of the forest without a certain terror, or ever reads of the exploits of daring fishermen without a feeling of admiration for their heroism. Most of their adventures are thrilling, and all of them are, in narration, more or less unjust to the trout: in fact, the object of them seems to be to exhibit, at the expense of the trout the shrewdness, the skill, and the muscular power of the sportsman. My own simple story has few of these recommendations.

We had built our bark camp one summer, and were staying on one of the popular lakes of the Saranac region. It would be a very pretty region if it were not so flat, if the margins of the lakes had not been flooded by dams at the outlets, — which have killed the trees, and left a rim of ghastly dead-wood like the swamps of the under-world picture by Doré's bizarre pencil, — and if the pianos at the hotels were in tune. It would be an excellent sporting-region also (for there is water enough) if the fish commissioners would stock the waters, and if previous hunters had not pulled all the hair and skin off from the deer's tails. Formerly sportsmen had a habit of catching the deer by the tails, and of being dragged in mere wantonness round and round the shores. It is well known, that, if you seize a deer by this "holt," the skin will slip off like the peel from a banana. This reprehensible practice was carried so far, that the traveller is now hourly pained by the sight of peeled-tail deer mournfully sneaking about the wood.

We had been hearing, for weeks, of a small lake in the heart of the virgin forest, some ten miles from our camp, which was alive with trout, unsophisticated, hungry trout: the inlet to it was described as *stiff* with them. In my imagination I saw them lying there in ranks and rows, each a foot long, three tiers deep, a solid mass. The lake had never been visited, except by stray sable-hunters in the winter, and was known as the Unknown Pond. I determined to explore it; fully expecting, however, that it would prove to be a delusion, as such mysterious haunts of the trout usually are. Confiding my purpose to Luke, we secretly made our preparations, and stole away from the shanty one morning at day break. Each of us carried a boat, a pair of blankets, a sack of bread, pork, and maple-sugar; while I had my case of rods, creel, and book of flies, and Luke had an axe and the kitchen utensils. We think nothing of loads of this sort in the woods.

Five miles through a tamarack-swamp brought us to the the inlet of Unknown Pond, upon which we embarked our fleet, and paddled down its vagrant waters. They were at first sluggish, winding among *triste* fir-trees, but gradually developed a strong current. At the end of three miles a loud roar ahead warned us that we were approaching rapids, falls, and cascades. We paused. The danger was unknown. We had our choice of shouldering our loads and making a *détour* through the woods, or of "shooting the rapids." Naturally we chose the more dangerous course. Shooting the rapids has often been described, and I will not repeat the description here. It is needless to say that I drove my frail bark through the boiling rapids, over the successive water-falls, amid rocks and vicious eddies, and landed, half a mile below, with whitened hair and a boat half full of water; and that the guide was upset, and boat, contents, and man were strewn along the shore.

After this common experience we went quickly on our journey, and, a couple of hours before sundown, reached the lake. If I live to my dying-day, I never shall forget its appearance. The lake is almost an exact circle, about a quarter of a mile in diameter. The forest about it was untouched by axe, and unkilled by artificial flooding. The azure water had a perfect setting of evergreens, in which all the shades of the fir, the balsam, the pine, and the spruce, were perfectly blended; and at intervals on the shore in the emerald rim blazed the ruby of the cardinal-flower. It was at once evident that the unruffled waters had never been vexed by the keel of a boat. But what chiefly attracted my attention, and amused me, was the boiling of the water, the bubbling and breaking, as if the lake were a vast kettle, with a fire underneath. A tyro would have been astonished at this common phenomenon; but sportsmen will at once understand me when I say that the water *boiled* with the breaking trout. I studied the surface for some time to see upon what sort of flies they were feeding, in order to suit my cast to their appetites; but they seemed to be at play rather than feeding, leaping high in the air in graceful curves, and tumbling about each other as we see them in the Adirondack pictures.

It is well known that no person who regards his reputation will ever kill a trout with any thing but a fly. It requires some training on the part of the trout to take to this method. The uncultivated, unsophisticated trout in unfrequented waters prefers the bait; and the rural people, whose sole object in going a-fishing appears to be to catch fish, indulge them in their primitive taste for the worm. No sportsman, however, will use anything but a fly, except he happens to be alone.

While Luke launched my boat, and arranged his seat in the stern, I prepared my rod and line. The rod is a bamboo, weighing seven ounces, which has to be spliced with a winding of silk thread every time it is used. This is a tedious process; but, by fastening the joints in this way, a uniform spring is secured in the rod. No one devoted to high art would think of using a socket joint. My line was forty yards of untwisted silk upon a multiplying reel. The "leader" (I am very particular about my leaders) had been made to order from a domestic animal with which I had been acquainted. The fisherman requires as good a catgut as the violinist. The interior of the house-cat, it is well known, is exceedingly sensitive; but it may not be so well known that the reason why some cats leave the room in distress when a piano-forte is played is because the two instruments are not in the same key, and the vibrations of chords of the one are in discord with the catgut of the other. On six feet of this superior article I fixed three artificial flies, — a simple brown hackle, a gray body with scarlet wings, and one of my own invention, which I thought would be new to the most experienced fly-catcher. The trout-fly does not resemble any known species of insect. It is a "conventionalized" creation, as we say of ornamentation. The theory is, that, fly-fishing being a high art, the fly must not be a tame imitation of nature, but an artistic suggestion of it. It requires an artist to construct one; and not every bungler can take a bit of red flannel, a peacock's feather, a flash of tinsel thread, a cock's plume, a section of a hen's wing, and fabricate a tiny object that will not look like any fly, but still will suggest the universal conventional fly.

I took my stand in the centre of the tipsy boat; and Luke shoved off, and slowly paddled towards some lily-pads, while I began casting, unlimbering my tools, as it were. The fish had all disappeared. I got out, perhaps, fifty feet of line, with no response, and gradually increased it to one hundred. It is not difficult to learn to cast; but it is difficult to learn not to snap off the flies at every throw. Of this, however, we will not speak. I continued casting for some moments, until I became satisfied that there had been a miscalculation. Either the trout were too green to know what I was at, or they were dissatisfied with my offers. I reeled in, and changed the flies (that is, the fly that was not snapped off). After studying the color of the sky, of the water, and of the foliage, and the moderated light of the afternoon, I put on a series of beguilers, all of a subdued brilliancy, in harmony with the approach of evening. At the second cast, which was a short one, I saw a splash where the leader fell, and gave an excited jerk. The next instant I perceived the game, and did not need the unfeigned "dam" of Luke to convince me that I had snatched his felt hat from his head, and deposited it among the lilies. Discouraged by this, we whirled about, and paddled over to the inlet, where a little ripple was visible in the tinted light. At the very first cast I saw that the hour had come. Three trout leaped into the air. The danger of this manœuvre all fishermen understand. It is one of the commonest in the woods: three heavy trout taking hold at once, rushing in different directions, smash the tackle into flinders. I evaded this catch, and threw again. I recall the moment. A hermit thrush, on the tip of a balsam, uttered his long, liquid, evening note. Happening to look over my shoulder, I saw the peak of Marcy gleam rosy in the sky (I can't help it that Marcy is fifty miles off, and cannot be seen from this region: these incidental touches are always used). The hundred feet of silk swished through the air, and the tail-fly fell as lightly on the water as a three-cent-piece (which no slamming will give the weight of a ten) drops upon the contribution-plate. Instantly there was a rush, a swirl. I struck, and "Got him, my —!" Never mind what Luke said I got him by. "Out on a fly!" continued that irreverent guide; but I told him to back water, and make for the centre of the lake. The trout, as soon as he felt the prick of the hook, was off like a shot, and took out the whole of the line with a rapidity that made it smoke. "Give him the butt!" shouted Luke. It is the usual remark in such an emergency. I gave him the butt; and, recognizing the fact and my spirit, the trout at once sank to the bottom, and sulked. It is the most dangerous mood of a trout; for you cannot tell what he will do next. We reeled up a little, and waited five minutes for him to reflect. A tightening of the line enraged him, and he soon developed his tactics. Coming to the surface, he made straight for the boat faster than I could reel in, and evidently with hostile intentions. "Look out for him!" cried Luke as he came flying in the air. I evaded him by dropping flat in the bottom of the boat; and, when I picked my traps up, he was spinning across the lake as if he had a new idea: but the line was still fast. He did not run far. I gave him the butt again; a thing he seemed to hate, even as a gift. In a moment the evil-minded fish, lashing the water in his rage, was coming back again, making straight for the boat as before. Luke, who was used to these encounters, having read of them in the writings of travellers he had accompanied, raised his paddle in self-defense. The trout left the water about ten feet from the boat, and came directly at me with fiery eyes, his speckled sides flashing like a meteor. I dodged as he whisked by with a vicious slap of his bifurcated tail, and nearly upset the boat. The line was of course slack; and the danger was that he would entangle it about me, and carry away a leg. This was evidently his game; but I untangled it, and only lost a breast-button or two by the swiftly-moving string. The trout plunged into the water with a hissing sound, and went away again with all the line on the reel. More butt; more indignation on the part of the captive. The contest had now been going on for half an hour, and I was getting exhausted. We had been back and forth across the lake, and round and round the lake. What I feared was, that the trout would start up the inlet, and wreck us in the bushes. But he had a new fancy, and began the execution of a manœuvre which I had never read of. Instead of coming straight towards me, he took a large circle, swimming rapidly, and *gradually contracting his orbit*. I reeled in, and kept my eye on him. Round and round he went, narrowing his circle. I began to suspect the game; which was, to twist my head off. When he had reduced the radius of his circle to about twenty-five feet, he struck a tremendous pace through the water. It would be false modesty in a sportsman to say that I was not equal to the occasion. Instead of turning round with him, as he expected, I stepped to the bow, braced myself, and let the boat swing. Round went the fish, and round we went like a top. I saw a line of Mount Marcys all round the horizon; the rosy tint in the west made a broad band of pink along the sky above the tree-tops; the evening start was a perfect circle of light,

a hoop of gold in the heavens. We whirled and reeled, and reeled and whirled. I was willing to give the malicious beast butt and line, and all, if he would only go the other way for a change.

When I came to myself, Luke was gaffing the trout at the boat-side. After he had got him in, and dressed him, he weighed three-quarters of a pound. Fish always lose by being "got in and dressed." It is best to weigh them while they are in the water. The only really large one I ever caught got away with my leader when I first struck him. He weighed ten pounds.

— from *In the Wilderness* (1878)

On Dry-Cow Fishing as a Fine Art

Rudyard Kipling

It must be clearly understood that I am not at all proud of this performance. In Florida men sometimes hook and land, on rod and tackle a little finer than a steam-crane and chain, a mackerel-like fish called "tarpon," which sometime run to 120 pounds. Those men stuff their captures and exhibit them in glass cases and become puffed up. On the Columbia River sturgeon of 150 pounds weight are taken with the line. When the sturgeon is hooked the line is fixed to the nearest pine tree or steamboat-wharf, and after some hours or days the sturgeon surrenders himself, if the pine or the line do not give way. The owner of the line then states on oath that he has caught a sturgeon, and he, too, becomes proud.

These things are mentioned to show how light a creel will fill the soul of a man with vanity. I am not proud. It is nothing to me that I have hooked and played seven hundred pounds weight of quarry. All my desire is to place the little affair on record before the mists of memory breed the miasma of exaggeration.

The minnow cost eighteenpence. It was a beautiful quill minnow, and the tackle-maker said that it could be thrown as a fly. He guaranteed further in respect to the triangles — it glittered with triangles — that, if necessary, the minnow would hold a horse. A man who speaks too much truth is just as offensive as a man who speaks too little. None the less, owing to the defective condition of the present law of libel, the tackle-maker's name must be withheld.

The minnow and I and a rod went down to a brook to attend to a small jack who lived between two clumps of flags in the most cramped swim that he could select. As a proof that my intentions were strictly honourable, I may mention that I was using a light split-cane rod — very dangerous if the line runs through weeds, but very satisfactory in clean water, inasmuch as it keeps a steady strain on the fish and prevents him from taking liberties. I had an old score against the jack. He owed me two live-bait already, and I had reason to suspect him of coming up-stream and interfering with a little bleak-pool under a horse-bridge which lay entirely beyond his sphere of legitimate influence. Observe, therefore, that my tackle and my motives pointed clearly to jack, and jack alone; though I knew that there were monstrous big perch in the brook.

The minnow was thrown as a fly several times, and, owing to my peculiar, and hitherto unpublished, methods of fly throwing, nearly six pennyworth of the triangles came off, either in my coat-collar, or my thumb, or the back of my hand. Fly fishing is a very gory amusement.

The jack was not interested in the minnow, but towards twilight a boy opened a gate of the field and let in some twenty or thirty cows and half-a-dozen cart-horses, and they were all very much interested. The horses galloped up and down the field and shook the banks, but the cows walked solidly and breathed heavily, as people breathe who appreciate the Fine Arts.

By this time I had given up all hope of catching my jack fairly, but I wanted the live-bait and bleak-account settled before I went away, even if I tore up the bottom of the brook. Just before I had quite made up my mind to borrow a tin of chloride of lime from the farm-house — another triangle had fixed itself in my fingers — I made a cast which for pure skill, exact judgement of distance, and perfect coincidence of hand and eye and brain, would have taken every prize at a bait-casting tournament. That was the first half of the cast. The second was postponed because the quill minnow would not return to its proper place, which was under the lobe of my left ear. It had done thus before, and I supposed it was in collision with a grass tuft, till I turned round and saw a large red and white bald faced cow trying to rub what would be withers in a horse with her nose. She looked at me reproachfully, and her look said as plainly as words: "The season is too far advanced for gadflies. What is this strange disease?"

I replied, "Madam, I must apologize for an unwarrantable liberty on the part of my minnow, but if you will have the goodness to keep still until I can reel in, we will adjust this little difficulty."

I reeled in very swiftly and cautiously, but she would not wait. She put her tail in the air and ran away. It was a purely involuntary motion on my part: I struck. Other anglers may contradict me, but I firmly believe that if a man had foulhooked his best friend through the nose, and that friend ran, the man would strike by instinct. I struck, therefore, and the reel began to sing just as merrily as though I had caught my jack. But had it been a jack, the minnow would have come away. I told the tackle-maker this much afterwards, and he laughed and made allusions to the guarantee about holding a horse.

Because it was a fat innocent she-cow that had done me no harm the minnow held — held like an anchor-fluke in coral moorings — and I was forced to dance up and down an interminable field very largely used by cattle. It was like salmon fishing in a nightmare. I took gigantic strides, and every stride found me up to my knees in marsh. But the cow seemed to skate along the squashy green by the brook, to skim over the miry backwaters, and to float like a mist through the patches of rush that squirted black filth over my face. Sometimes we whirled through a mob of her friends — there were no friends to help me — and they looked scandalized; and sometimes a young and frivolous cart-horse would join in the chase for a few miles, and kick solid pieces of mud into my eyes; and through all the mud, the milky smell of kine, the rush and the smother, I was aware of my own voice crying: "Pussy, pussy, pussy! Pretty pussy! Come along then, puss-cat!" You see it is so hard to speak to a cow properly, and she would not listen — no, she would not listen.

Then she stopped, and the moon got up behind the pollards to tell the cows to lie down; but they were all on their feet, and they came trooping to see. And she said, "I haven't had my supper, and I want to go to bed, and please don't worry me." And I said, "The matter has passed beyond any apology. There are three courses open to you, my dear lady. If you'll have the common sense to walk up to my creel I'll get my knife and you shall have all the minnow. Or, again, if you'll let me move across to your near side, instead of keeping me so coldly on your off side, the thing will come away in one tweak. I can't pull it out over your withers. Better still, go to a post and rub it out, dear. It won't hurt much, but if you think I'm going to lose my rod to please you, you are mistaken." And she said, "I don't understand what you are saying. I am very, very unhappy." And I said, "It's all your fault for trying to fish. Do go to the nearest gate-post, you nice fat thing, and rub it out."

For a moment I fancied she was taking my advice. She ran away and I followed. But all the other cows came with us in a bunch, and I thought of Phaeton trying to drive the Chariot of the Sun, and Texan cowboys killed by stampeding cattle, and *Green Grow the Rushes, O!* and Solomon and Job, and "loosing the bands of Orion," and hooking Behemoth, and Wordsworth who talks about whirling round with stones and rocks and trees, and "Here we go round the Mulberry Bush," and "Pippin Hill," and "Hey Diddle Diddle," and most especially the top joint of my rod. Again she stopped — but nowhere in the neighborhood of my knife — and her sisters stood moonfaced round her. It seemed that she might, now, run towards me, and I looked for a tree, because cows are very different from salmon, who only jump against the line, and never molest the fisherman. What followed was worse than any direct attack. She began to buck-jump, to stand on her head and her tail alternately, to leap into the sky, all four feet together, and to dance on her hind legs. It was so violent and improper, so desperately unladylike, that I was inclined to blush, as one would blush at the sight of a prominent statesman sliding down a fire escape, or a duchess chasing her cook with a skillet. That flopsome *abandon* might go on all night in the lonely meadow among the mists, and if it went on all night — this was pure inspiration — I might be able to worry through the fishing line with my teeth.

Those who desire an entirely new sensation should chew with all their teeth, and against time, through a best waterproofed silk line, one end of which belongs to a mad cow dancing fairy rings in the moonlight; at the same time keeping one eye on the cow and the other on the top joint of a split-cane rod. She buck-jumped and I bit on the slack just in front of the reel; and I am in a position to state that that line was cored with steel wire throughout the particular section which I attacked. This has been formally denied by the tackle-maker, who is not to be believed.

The *wheep* of the broken line running through the rings told me that henceforth the cow and I might be strangers. I had already bidden good-bye to some tooth or teeth; but no price is too great for freedom of the soul.

"Madam," I said, "the minnow and twenty feet of very superior line are your alimony without reservation. For the wrong I have unwittingly done to you I express my sincere regret. At the same time, may I hope that Nature, the kindest of nurses, will in due season ——"

She or one of her companions must have stepped on her spare end of the line in the dark, for she bellowed wildly and ran away, followed by all the cows. I hoped the minnow was disengaged at last; and before I went away looked at my watch, fearing to find it nearly midnight. My last cast for the jack was made at 6.23 p.m. There lacked still three and a-half minutes of the half-hour; and I would have sworn that the moon was paling before the dawn!

"Simminly someone were chasing they cows down to bottom o' Ten Acre," said the farmer that evening. "'Twasn't you, sir?"

"Now under what earthly circumstances do you suppose I should chase your cows? I wasn't fishing for them, was I?"

Then all the farmer's family gave themselves up to jam-smeared laughter for the rest of the evening, because that was a rare and precious jest, and it was repeated for months, and the fame of it spread from that farm to another, and yet another at least three miles away, and it will be used again for the benefit of visitors when the freshets come down in spring.

But to the greater establishment of my honour and glory I submit in print this bald statement of fact, that I may not, through forgetfulness, be tempted later to tell how I hooked a bull on a Marlow Buzz, how he ran up a tree and took to water, and how I played him along the London-road for thirty miles, and gaffed him at Smithfield. Errors of this kind may creep in with the lapse of years, and it is my ambition ever to be a worthy member of that fraternity who pride themselves on never deviating by one hair's breadth from the absolute and literal truth.

— from *The Fishing Gazette* (December, 1890)

A Pickerel Yarn

Fred Mather

Two Pritchard brothers, Tom and Harry, came from England and started to make and repair fishing tackle in Fulton street, New York, so long ago that the nearest date I can fix for it is the one so dear to our childhood: "Once upon a time." They are not recorded in the Chinese "Book of the Lily," which was written at the beginning of all things, and so must have come to New York after that period; but it was very long ago. The little shop upstairs was kept busy by anglers who knew of their skill, and also by some of the large fishing tackle houses, which found it more convenient than to send small jobs by express to their factories; and so the brothers found plenty of work to their hands while they lived.

The little shop was a place where one might drop in at any time and feel sure of meeting some of the old-time anglers of the city, and the talk would run on the nearby trout streams, rods, ferrules, flies, the prospect of a run of weakfish, the tides, the last big catch of sheepshead at the wreck of the Black Warrior, and such other things as are discussed where anglers most do congregate. There is no such place in New York City now, and never will be until an angler's club is formed. I meet anglers occasionally in the different fishing tackle emporiums, but they are there on business and not for social talk, as was the case at Pritchards'. We needed such a place then and we need a club now.

Of Tom Pritchard I knew little; he was the eldest, wore gray muttonchop whiskers and attended to business; therefore, as Dame Juliana Berners says, "I write the less of him." When I first knew Harry, some thirty years ago, he must have been a boy of about fifty years old, as convivial as opportunity offered and always ready to tell a story, the impediment in his speech increasing as he neared the climax, when his jaws would work but refuse to deliver a sound until he pressed his fists into his hips and yelled the finale, and this added point to all his yarns. As he put it: "I can s-s-s-sing and I can w-w-whistle, but I'm a s-s-sinner if I can t-t-talk." Frank Endicott once made Harry this proposition: "If you can't talk, don't try; you're too old to learn new tricks. When you've got a fishing yarn to spin, just sing the introduction and descriptive part, and when you get to the last of it — where we are all willing to strain our credulity to believe you — just 'whistle o'er the lave o' it,' as the Scotch

song goes. This will be a great relief to you, and will leave much veracity to your credit with all of us."

Harry was the man who was fishing for black bass on Greenwood Lake when a drunken "guide" tried to bail out the perforated bait car which hung overboard, as has been related, but he had amplified the story with detail and climax until we enjoyed it as something of which we had never heard. But this is a digression.

"N-now Hi'll tell you a t-t-true s-s-story, an' Hi don't c-care hif you b-b-believe hit or not. You halways puts m-me down for l-l-lyin', hanyway, an' Hi' d-d-do' know has hits hany use to t-t-tell you hanythink m-m-more, you wouldn't b-b-believe me, hanyway."

"Go on, Harry," said Endicott, "we always believe you when we are sure you are telling a truthful yarn, and we, as brothers of the angle, realize the fact that there is an angler's license as well as a poet's. Please unfold this truthful yarn; it will place a great balance to your credit."

"Harry," said I, "the trouble with you is your excessive modesty. You evidently never expected me to believe that you killed a forty-foot shark on a sixteen-ounce rod while fishing for small fish in the waters of India, but your glowing account of your four hours' fight with the monster after it had dragged you from the boat, and how you reeled in an gave line while treading water, bore the stamp of authenticity. Then, too, your reeling the great fish in and getting on its back, drowning it by pulling off your boots and jamming them into two of the gill openings, suffocating the fish with hands and feet in the other gill slits while you awaited death when the shark sank, is in memory as distinct as when you told it. I do not doubt the slightest detail, and have often rejoiced at your opportune rescue by the native fishermen, and your restoration to your regiment in Her Majesty's service. Please don't think that we entertain doubts of the truthfulness of your stories, even if such doubts sometimes cross your own mind."

"T-t-that's good. You think Hi don't halways b-b-b-believe my hown s-s-stories. P'r'aps Hi don't b-believe 'em hev'ry time; hall Hi ask is for you to b-b-believe 'em."

"Let me explain," said I, "the funny man of the press has done much to injure the veracity of the angler. He has gone so far as to brand a palpable lie as a 'fish story,' thereby throwing discredit upon our guild. In his **ignorance** that a whale is not a fish he, in his skepticism, goes back many centuries, but now, Harry, let me go beyond the latter-day reporter, who has exhausted his wit upon the appetite of the goat, the disturbing influence of the mother-in-law, and the wholly fictitious accounts of the wealth of the plumber and the ice-man, into the question of the truthfulness of the fisherman. Is he less given to exaggeration than his brother who handles the gun? Is he more unworthy of belief than men who engage in other forms of sport or of business? I'll answer my own questions by saying that he is not, and in proof of this will point to the fact that I have even believed some of your stories."

"I move the previous question," said Mr. Endicott, "all this talk that Mather has shot off is irrelevant and not at all to the point. If Harry has a story to tell it should take precedence of all. Go on, Harry, and tell your story. I'll agree to believe a third of it and Mr. Scott and Fred will believe the other two-thirds. In that way the whole story will be believed without injuring our capacity for believing any stories that others present may inflict on us. Let her go!"

"Well, this here ain't much of a s-s-story, an' I don't care w-w-whether you b-b-believe or not, cause, it's as true as I sit 'ere on this stool, an' that's no lie. Y' see Hi was afishin' for p-p-pickerel up hon Greenwood Lake, hall by my lonesome, han I was a ketchin' s-s-small ones right fast han a keepin' c-c-count by sayin' that m-m-makes nine han' this un's t-t-ten, in that kind o' way ha 'avin' fun —."

"Hold on, Harry," said Endicott, "we want more detail. How big were these small pickerel, and what bait were you using?"

"Hi was b-b-baitin' with live minners, or k-k-killies has they calls 'em hin the salt-water. Hi hain't got h-h-hany of 'em left to prove they was my b-b-bait, but Hi'll hask you to t-t-take my word for 'em. The p-p-pickerel was a-r-r-r-runnin' hextra small that d-d-day, han' the first s-s-singular thing that struck me was their r-r-regular size, han' I

m-m-measured 'em. Hi'm a s-s-sinner hif they wasn't hall just heleven an' a harf h-h-hinches long to a fraction; and I sez to mys-s-self, sez Hi, this here's hall one s-s-school, hall hout o' one litter, but they're b-b-big henuff to take 'ome,' so Hi fishes on."

"How many did you get on this remarkable day?" asked Mr. Scott.

"Hi'm a c-c-comin' to that hif you'll gi' me a c-c-chance. Y'see, Hi was hout for three days' f-f-fishin', an' Hi wanted to keep my f-f-fish halive till I left for 'ome; so Hi 'ad a fish car halongside, han' the p-p-pickerel were dropped into that as fast as Hi p-p-pulled 'em in. They was a-bitin' f-f-fast, an' about s-s-sundown Hi thought the car must be p-p-putty full, for Hi had counted f-f-forty-three, an' Hi'd quit. One m-m-more took hold, han' has 'e was a-kickin' hon the bottom of the boat Hi takes a look in the c-c-car, han' what do you think Hi s-s-see?"

"Well, Harry," said Endicott, "as I have followed the story, I should say that you must have seen forty-three pickerel in a mass and nothing more, because you have not mentioned taking in snapping turtles and other monsters. What else could you have seen? There's nothing remarkable in your yarn so far, that you should preface it, as you did, with the remark that we might not believe it. As far as I am concerned, I am willing to believe not only the third, to which I agreed, but the whole story as well. What did you see?"

"N-n-n-nothing!"

"But," said Mr. Scott, "you put the fish in the car; where were they?"

"Hin the b-b-boat. There was a slat hoff the b-b-bottom of that c-c-car, han' Hi'd been a-c-c-catchin' the same p-p-pickerel hall day, han' e'_____"

Harry's vocal organs gave out. We gravely shook hands, remarked upon the state of the weather and left him trying to finish the story.

— from *Forest and Stream* (September 4, 1897)

The 'Lunge

Stewart Edward White

Dick and I traveled in a fifteen-foot wooden canoe, with grub, duffel, tent, and Deuce, the black-and-white setter dog. As a consequence we were pretty well down toward the water line, for we had not realized that a wooden canoe would carry so little weight for its length in comparison with a birchbark. A good heavy sea we could ride — with proper management and a little bailing; but sloppy waves kept us busy.

Deuce did not like it at all. He was a dog old in the wisdom of experience. It had taken him just twenty minutes to learn all about canoes. After a single tentative trial he jumped lightly to the very centre of his place, with the lithe caution of a cat. Then if the water happened to be smooth, he would sit gravely on his haunches, or would rest his chin on the gunwale to contemplate the passing landscape. But in rough weather he crouched directly over the keel, his nose between his paws, and tried not to dodge when the cold water dashed in on him. Deuce was a true woodsman in that respect. Discomfort he always bore with equanimity, and he must often have been very cold and very cramped.

For just over a week we had been traveling in open water, and the elements had not been kind to us at all. We had crept up under rock-cliff points; had weathered the rips of white water to shelter on the other side, had struggled across open spaces where each wave was singly a problem to fail in whose solution meant instant swamping; had bailed, and schemed, and figured, and carried, and sworn, and tried again, and succeeded with about two cupfuls to spare, until we as well as Deuce had grown a little tired of it. For the lust of travel was on us.

The lust of travel is a very real disease. It usually takes you when you have made up your mind that there is no hurry. Its predisposing cause is a chart or map, and its main symptom is the feverish delight with which you check off the landmarks of your journey. A fair wind of some force is absolutely fatal. With that at your back you cannot stop. Good fishing, fine scenery, interesting bays, reputed game, even camps where friends might be visited — all pass swiftly astern. Hardly do you pause for lunch at noon. The mad joy of putting country behind you eats all other interests. You recover only when you have come to your journey's end a week too early, and you must then search out new voyages to fill in the time.

All this morning we had been bucking a strong north wind. Fortunately, the shelter of a string of islands had given us smooth water enough, but the heavy gusts sometimes stopped us as effectively as though we had butted solid land. Now about noon we came to the last island, and looked out on a five-mile stretch of tumbling seas. We landed the canoe and mounted a high rock.

"Can't make it like this," said I. "I'll take the outfit over and land it, and come back for you and the dog. Let's see that chart."

We hid behind the rock and spread out the map.

"Four miles," measured Dick. "It's going to be a terror."

We looked at each other vaguely, suddenly tired.

"We can't camp here — at this time of day," objected Dick, to our unspoken thoughts.

And then the map gave him an inspiration. "Here's a little river," ruminated Dick, "that goes to a little lake, and then there's another little river that flows from the lake, and comes out about ten miles above here."

"It's a good thirty miles," I objected.

"What of it? asked Dick, calmly.

So the fever-lust of travel broke. We turned to the right behind the last island, searched out the reed-grown opening to the stream, and paddled serenely and philosophically against the current. Deuce sat up and yawned with a mighty satisfaction.

We had been bending our heads to the demon of wind; our ears had been filled with his shoutings, our eyes blinded with tears, our breath caught away from us, our muscles strung to the fiercest endeavor. Suddenly we found ourselves between the ranks of tall forest trees, bathed in a warm sunlight, gliding like a feather from one grassy bend to another of the laziest little stream that ever hesitated as to which way the grasses of its bed should float. As for the wind, it was lost somewhere away up high, where we could hear it muttering to itself about something.

The woods leaned over the fringe of bushes cool and green and silent. Occasionally through tiny openings we caught instant impressions of straight column-trunks and transparent shadows. Minature grass marshes jutted out from the bends of the little river. We idled along as with a homely rustic companion through the aloofness of patrican multitudes.

Every bend offered us charming surprises. Sometimes a muskrat swam hastily in a pointed furrow of ripple; vanishing wings, barely sensed in the flash, left us staring; stealthy withdrawals of creatures, whose presence we realized only in the fact of those withdrawals, snared our eager interest; porcupines rattled and rustled importantly and regally from the water's edge to the woods; herons, ravens, an occasional duck, croaked away at our approach; thrice we surprised eagles, once a tassel-eared Canada lynx. Or, if all else lacked, we still experienced the little thrill of pleased novelty over the disclosure of a group of silvery birches on a knoll; a magnificent white pine towering over the beech and maple forest; the unexpected aisle of a long, straight stretch of the little river.

Deuce approved thoroughly. He stretched himself and yawned and shook off the water, and glanced at me open-mouthed with doggy good-nature, and set himself to acquiring a conscientious olfactory knowledge of both banks of the river. I do not doubt he knew a great deal more about it than we did. Porcupines aroused his especial enthusiasm. Incidentally, two days later he returned to camp after an expedition of his own, bristling as to the face with that animal's barbed weapons. Thenceforward his interest waned.

We ascended the charming little river two or three miles. At a sharp bend to the east a huge sheet of rock sloped from a round grass knoll sparsely planted with birches directly down into a pool. Two or three tree-trunks jammed directly opposite had formed a sort of half dam under which the water lay dark. A tiny grass meadow forty feet in diameter narrowed the stream to half its width.

We landed. Dick seated himself on the shelving rock. I put my fish-rod together. Deuce disappeared.

Deuce always disappeared whenever we landed. With nose down, hindquarters well tucked under him, ears flying, he quartered the forest at high speed, investigating every nook and cranny of it for the radius of a quarter of a mile. When he had quite satisfied himself that we were safe for the moment, he would return to the fire, where he would lie, six inches of pink tongue vibrating with breathlessness, beautiful in the consciousness of virtue. Dick generally sat on a rock and thought. I generally fished.

After a time Deuce returned. I gave up flies, spoons, phantom minnows, artificial frogs, and cray-fish. As Dick continued to sit on the rock and think, we both joined him. The sun was very warm and grateful, and I am sure we both acquired an added respect for Dick's judgment.

Just when it happened neither of us was afterwards able to decide. Perhaps Deuce knew. But suddenly, as often a figure appears in a cinematograph, the diminutive meadow thirty feet away contained two deer. They stood knee deep in the grass, wagging their little tails in impatience of the flies.

"Look a' there!" stammered Dick aloud.

Deuce sat up on his haunches.

I started for my camera.

The deer did not seem to be in the slightest degree alarmed. They pointed four big ears in our direction, ate a few leisurely mouthfuls of grass, sauntered to the stream for a drink of water, wagged their little tails some more, and quietly faded into the cool shadows of the forest.

An hour later we ran out into reeds, and so to the lake.

It was a pretty lake, forest-girt. Across the distance we made out a moving object which shortly resolved itself into a birch canoe. The canoe proved to contain an Indian, an Indian boy of about ten years, a black dog, and a bundle. When within a few rods of each other we ceased paddling and drifted by with the momentum. The Indian was a fine-looking man of about forty, his hair bound with a red fillet, his feet incased in silk-worked moccasins, but otherwise dressed in white men's garments. He smoked a short pipe, and contemplated us gravely.

"Bo' jou', bo' jou'," we called in the usual double-barreled North Country salutation.

"Bo' jou', bo' jou'," he replied.

"Kée-gons?" we inquired as to the fishing in the lake.

"Ah-hah," he assented.

We drifted by each other without further speech. When the decent distance of etiquette separated us, we resumed our paddles.

I produced a young cable terminated by a tremendous spoon and a solid brass snell as thick as a telegraph wire. We had laid in this formidable implement in hopes of a big muscallunge. It had been trailed for days at a time. We had become used to its vibration, which actually seemed to communicate itself to every fiber of the light canoe. Every once in a while we would stop with a jerk that would nearly snap our heads off. Then we would know we had hooked the American continent. We had become used to that also. It generally happened when we attempted a little burst of speed. So when the canoe brought up so violently that all our tinware rolled on Deuce, Dick was merely disgusted.

"There she goes again," he grumbled. "You've hooked Canada."

Canada held quiescent for about three seconds. Then it started due south.

"Suffering serpents!" shrieked Dick.

"Paddle, you sulphurated idiot!" yelled I.

It was most interesting. All I had to do was to hang on and try to stay in the boat. Dick paddled and fumed and splashed water and got more excited. Canada dragged us bodily backward.

Then Canada changed his mind and started in our direction. I was plenty busy taking in slack, so I did not notice Dick. Dick was absolutely demented. His mind automatically reacted in the direction of paddling. He paddled, blindly, frantically. Canada came surging in, his mouth open, his wicked eyes flaming, a tremendous indistinct body lashing foam. Dick glanced once over his shoulder, and let out a frantic howl.

"You've got the sea serpent!" he shrieked.

I turned to fumble for the pistol. We were headed directly for a log stranded on shore, and about ten feet from it.

"Dick!" I yelled in warning.

He thrust his paddle out forward just in time. The stout maple bent and cracked. The canoe hit with a bump that threw us forward. I returned to the young cable. It came in limp and slack.

We looked at each other sadly.

"No use," sighed Dick at last. "They've never invented the words, and we'd upset if we kicked the dog."

I had the end of the line in my hands.

"Look here!" I cried. That thick brass wire had been as cleanly bitten through as though it had been cut with clippers. "He must have caught sight of you," said I.

Dick lifted up his voice in lamentation. "You had four feet of him out of water," he wailed, "and there was a lot more."

"If you had kept cool," said I, severely, "we shouldn't have lost him. You don't want to get rattled in an emergency. There's no sense in it."

"What were you going to do with that?" asked Dick, pointing to where I had laid the pistol.

"I was going to shoot him in the head," I replied, with dignity. "It's the best way to land them."

Dick laughed disagreeably. I looked down. At my side lay our largest iron spoon.

We skirted the left-hand side of the lake in silence. Far out from shore the water was ruffled where the wind swept down, but with us it was as still and calm as the forest trees that looked over into it. After a time we turned short to the left through a very narrow passage between two marshy shores, and so, after a sharp bend of but a few hundred feet, came into the other river.

This was a wide stream, smoothly hurrying, without rapids or tumult. The forest had drawn to either side to let us pass. Here were the wilder reaches after the intimacies of the little river. Across stretches of marsh we could see an occasional great blue heron standing mid-leg deep. Long strings of ducks struggled quacking from invisible pools. The faint marsh odor saluted our nostrils from the point where the lily-pads flashed broadly, ruffling in the wind. We dropped out the smaller spoon and masterfully landed a five-pound pickerel. Even Deuce brightened. He cared nothing for raw fish, but he knew their possibilities. Towards evening we entered the hilly country, and so at the last turned to the left into a sand cove where grew maples and birches in beautiful park order under a hill. There we pitched camp, and, as the flies slacked, built a friendship-fire about which to foregather when the day was done.

Dick still vocally regretted the muscallunge as the largest fish since Jonah. So I told him of my big bear.

One day, late in the summer, I was engaged in packing some supplies along an old fur trail north of Lake Superior. I had accomplished one back-load, and with empty straps was returning to the cache for another. The trail at one point emerged into and crossed an open park some hundreds of feet in diameter, in which the grass grew to the height of the knee. When I was about halfway across, a black bear arose to his hind legs not ten feet from me and remarked *Woof!* in a loud tone of voice. Now, if a man were to say *woof!* to you unexpectedly, even in the formality of an Italian garden or the accustomedness of a city street, you would be somewhat startled. So I went to camp. There I told them about the bear. I tried to be conservative in my description, because I did not wish to be accused of exaggeration. My impression of the animal was that he and a spruce-tree that grew near enough for ready comparison were approximately of the same stature. We returned to the grass park. After some difficulty we found a clear footprint. It was a little larger than that made by a good-sized coon.

"So, you see," I admonished, didactically, "that 'lunge probably was not quite so large as you thought."

"It may have been a Chinese bear," said Dick, dreamily — "a Chinese lady bear, of high degree."

I gave him up.

—from *The Forest* (1903)

How Salmon-Pools Are Named

Sir Herbert Maxwell

The contemplative man in pursuing his special recreation — angling — must often fall to speculating upon the origin of the names attached to salmon-pools in a river. Often they consist simply of the name of the adjacent land or farm, as the far-famed Birgham Dub on the Tweed, associated for all time with the treaty of Birgham, source of three centuries of war between England and Scotland. Others bear descriptive titles, such as, a mile or so below Birgham, that excellent cast the Kirkend, where the river chafes against the rocks on the English banks which support the west end of Carham church. But who shall unravel the secret hidden in the names of other salmon-pools on Tweed — Bloody Breeks, Flummie, The Webs, Jock Sure, The Hen's Leg, and so on? They are indelible; so long as men shall continue to cast angle in these waters they will continue to use these names and never seek to invent others.

Occasionally, at very long intervals, the need arises for a name to distinguish a new pool from its fellows, and the commonest, because the simplest, expedient is to associate it with the lucky angler who first lands a salmon from its depths. It is a sure road to immortality for that individual, but not an easy one. *Non cuivis contingit* — new salmon-pools resemble the pool of Bethesda in this, that some other fellow generally gets there before you, and that fellow's name will remain a household word for unnumbered centuries. Just opposite Dryburgh Abbey is a cast known as Jockie's Hole; who this particular Jockie was, none now may know or tell; but Jockie's name is as sure of immortality as that of Walter Scott, whose last resting-place is within a couple of hundred yards of Jockie's Hole. Jockie earned fame, perhaps, by one of those flukes which impart so much of its fascination to the angler's craft, and perhaps I may be permitted space to chortle mildly over a happy accident which has lately brought similar distinction upon me.

Well, this narrative, at all events, begins with a blank day. We had fished all one April day — a friend and myself — without stirring anything on two of the best beats of the river. The water was in perfect trim, we knew there were fish in it — at least I felt sure they were there — but the sun blazed fiercely from its rising to its setting, and kept them down. Thinks I to myself these are Norwegian symptoms — a full river and a blazing sun; why don't we adopt Norwegian precautions, fishing early and late, and do our sleeping in the day-time? My friend would not hearken. He vowed the fish had not come up. So next morning I sallied forth alone before 6 A.M. It was the 20th of April (1901), so it was full light, but the sun was still behind the shoulder of Lamarkan. The grass was white and crisp with frost, and the water had fallen a foot in the night.

A couple of hours later, by which time the sun was high in the heavens, I was returning to breakfast with a couple of lovely spring salmon in the bast basket, when my path took me along the verge of a cliff overhanging a rough stream which I had often eyed curiously, thinking it a likely harbour for fish. But at the foot of the cliff the water was thickly overhung with big alders, leafless as yet, but presenting an almost absolute veto to any attempt at fishing the place. No human being, I firmly believed, was ever so foolish as to attempt to put a fly over it; even had he succeeded in doing so it was obvious that he could not hope to secure a fish, supposing one should hook himself, for the trees grew close and bent low over the current, which sweeps deep and strong along the near bank.

However, the devil is always at one's ear to suggest easy roads to ruin, and albeit past experience has made one very shy of listening to his suggestions, on this occasion I lent him a willing ear. It would be a grand thing even to raise a salmon where no man had done the like. As to landing him time enough to think of that later.

Celui qui n'a jamais eu ses moments de folie est moins sage qu'il ne le pense. I felt I was doing a very silly thing. Visions of a good breakfast awaiting me at home presented themselves in glowing colours. The utmost that could result from such a harebrained attempt was to hook a fish and let him break the line, and every angler must answer for himself whether it is better to have hooked and lost than never to have hooked at all. Salmon are probably unanimous against the proposition. But the sun had not yet struck this part of the stream; it looked uncommonly 'fishy.' I descended the cliff and found myself among the alder stems. By clambering about twenty yards upstream I discovered a grassy ledge in the rock face, about six feet by two, opposite which was an opening in the screen of alders some six yards wide. To cast was impossible, but I managed to flop out enough line to let the current do the rest, and the Black Ranger, which had done much good work already that morning, was presently swimming twenty yards below me. Through the network of drooping branches I saw a slight commotion. 'That's him!' quoth I, with better emphasis than syntax, and sure enough a very vigorous fish was fast. Then I realized the full hopelessness of my plight. Behind me was the cliff, a sheer rock forty feet high; to the right and left stood the alders, making movement impossible in all directions save one — namely, into the roaring stream. Meanwhile, the salmon had made free with my predicament, and was careering about in the pool fifty yards below. Twice, thrice, I reeled him up into the strong water, and each time he dashed away down stream. External help was out of the reckoning; the loudest halloo, even if it were heard above the roar of the waters, could only fall on the unsympathetic tympana of curlews and cock grouse; and as for landing that fish unaided, it was not to be done, for I was standing on the only foothold between the top of the cliff and the margin, and that was ten feet above the water. Not a human soul was likely to pass that way till the angler whose beat was there on the morrow. . . . By Jove! To-morrow's Sunday! I was faint with hunger already. I should die of exhaustion before Monday. No, bitter as it was to part with such a pretty fish, there was nothing else for it, and I braced myself for the inevitable.

At least I tried to do so, and utterly failed. Never but once have I had to pull deliberately on a fish till the line broke, and that 'once' has permanently tinged my character with melancholy. There was another way, but it was not a seductive one. This was to try and cross the water, which was of doubtful depth, undoubtedly cold, very strong, and so rough that it seemed improbable a man could keep his feet in such a torrent. The further bank was fairly open; once over there and the fish was mine, if the hook held. To attempt to land a fish on the opposite side of a stream to where he is hooked is sometimes a risky experiment. The strain on the hook is changed to the opposite direction to that in which it was embedded, and often pulls it out. However, by this time the salmon had tired himself, and was lying still in the quieter water below me. I slipped cautiously down the rock into the river, and straddling wide, the best way of resisting a strong current, slowly felt my way into midstream. The water turned out no deeper than waist-high, but it was mighty strong, very cold, and the bottom very rough. I shall not easily forget the sense of triumph with which I stood at last on the far bank. Hitherto the balance of odds had been enormously in favour of the fish; now it was not less so on my side. In a few seconds I had the gaff in him, a pretty twelve-pounder, and then set out on the return journey through the stream to regain the property left on the other bank.

That anonymous pool must henceforth bear a name, and if there be justice in the affairs of men, that should surely be his who killed the first salmon therein. *Sic itur ad astra!*

— from *Memories of the Months* (1903)

Fishing with a Worm

Bliss Perry

Below the lower road the Taylor Brook becomes uncertain water. For half a mile it yields only fingerlings, for no explainable reason; then there are two miles of clean fishing through the deep woods, where the branches are so high that you can cast a fly again if you like, and there are long pools, where now and then a heavy fish will rise; then comes a final half mile through the alders, where you must wade, knee to waist deep, before you come to the bridge and the river. Glorious fishing is sometimes to be had here, especially if you work down the gorge at twilight, casting a white miller until it is too dark to see. But alas, there is a well-worn path along the brook, and often enough there are the very footprints of the fellow ahead of you, signs as disheartening to the fisherman as ever were the footprints on the sand to Robinson Crusoe.

But "between the roads" it is "too much trouble to fish;" and there lies the salvation of the humble fisherman who disdains not to use the crawling worm, nor, for that matter, to crawl himself, if need be, in order to sneak under the boughs of some overhanging cedar that casts a perpetual shadow upon the sleepy brook. Lying here at full length, with no elbow room to manage the rod, you must occasionally even unjoint your tip and fish with that, using but a dozen inches of line, and not letting so much as your eyebrows show above the bank. Is it a becoming attitude for a middle-aged citizen of the world? That depends upon how the fish are biting. Holing a putt looks rather ridiculous also, to the mere observer, but it requires, like brook fishing with a tip only, a very delicate wrist, perfect tactile sense, and a fine disregard of appearances.

There are some fishermen who always fish as if they were being photographed. The Taylor Brook "between the roads" is not for them. To fish it at all is back-breaking, trouser-tearing work; to see it thoroughly fished is to learn new lessons in the art of angling.

To watch R., for example, steadily filling his six-pound creel from that unlikely stream is like watching Sargent paint a portrait. R. weighs two hundred and ten. Twenty years ago he was a famous amateur pitcher, and among his present avocations are violin playing, which is good for the wrist, taxidermy, which is good for the eye, and shooting woodcock, which before the days of the new Nature Study used to be thought good for the whole man. R. began as a fly-fisherman, but by dint of passing his summers near brooks where fly-fishing is impossible, he has become a stout-hearted apologist for the worm. His apparatus is most singular. It consists of a very long, cheap rod, stout enough to smash through bushes, and with the stiffest tip obtainable. The lower end of the butt, below the reel, fits into the socket of a huge extra butt of bamboo, which R. carries unconcernedly. To reach a distant hole, or to fish the lower end of a ripple, R. simply locks his reel, slips on the extra butt, and there is a fourteen-foot rod ready for action. He fishes with a line unbelievably short, and a Kendal hook far too big; and when a trout jumps for that hook, R. wastes no time in maneuvering for position. The unlucky fish is simply "derricked" to borrow a word from Theodore, most saturnine and profane of Moosehead guides.

"Shall I play him awhile?" shouted an excited sportsman to Theodore, after hooking his first big trout.

"— no!" growled Theodore in disgust. "Just derrick him right into the canoe!" An heroic method, surely; though it once cost me the best squaretail I ever hooked, for Theodore had forgotten the landing net, and the gut broke in his fingers as he tried to swing the fish abroad. But with these lively quarterpounders of the Taylor Brook, derricking is a safer procedure. Indeed, I have sat dejectedly on the far end of a log, after fishing the hole under it in vain, and seen the mighty R. wade downstream close behind me, adjust that comical extra butt, and jerk a couple of half-pound trout from under the very log on which I was sitting. His device on this occasion, as I well remember, was to pass his hook but once through the middle of a big worm, let the worm sink to the bottom and crawl along it at his leisure. The trout could not resist.

Once, and once only, have I come near equaling R.'s record, and the way he beat me then is the justification for a whole philosophy of worm-fishing. We were on this very Taylor Brook, and at five in the afternoon both baskets were two thirds full. By count I had just one more fish than he. It was raining hard.

"You fish down through the alders," said R. magnanimously. "I'll cut across and wait for you at the sawmill. I don't want to get any wetter, on account of my rheumatism."

This was rather barefaced kindness — for whose rheumatism was ever the worse for another hour's fishing? But I weakly accepted it. I coveted three or four good trout to top off with — that was all. So I tied on a couple of flies and began to fish the alders, wading waist-deep in the rapidly rising water, down the long green tunnel under the curving boughs. The brook fairly smoked with the rain, by this time, but when did one fail to get at least three or four trout out of his best half mile of the lower brook? Yet I had no luck. I tried one fly after another, and then, as a forlorn hope — though it sometimes has a magic of its own — I combined a brown hackle for the tail fly with a twisting worm on the dropper. Not a rise!

I thought of R. sitting patiently in the sawmill, and I fished more conscientiously than ever.

Venture as warily, use the same skill,
Do your best, whether winning or losing it,
If you choose to play! — is my principle.

Even those lines, which by some subtle telepathy of the trout brook murmur themselves over and over to me in the waning hours of an unlucky day, brought now no consolation. There was simply not one fish to be had, to any fly in the book, out of that long, drenching, darkening tunnel. At last I climbed out of the brook, by the bridge. R. was sitting on the fence, his neck and ears carefully turtled under his coat collar, the smoke rising and the rain dripping from the inverted bowl of his pipe. He did not seem to be worrying about his rheumatism.

"What luck?" he asked.

"None at all," I answered morosely. "Sorry to keep you waiting."

"That's all right," remarked R. "What do you think I've been doing? I've been fishing out of the sawmill window just to kill time. There was a patch of floating sawdust there, — kind of unlikely place for trout, anyway, — but I thought I'd put on a worm and let him crawl around a little." He opened his creel as he spoke.

"But I didn't look for a pair of 'em," he added. And there, on top of his smaller fish, were as pretty a pair of three-quarter-pound brook trout as were ever basketed.

"I'm afraid you got pretty wet," said R. kindly.

"I don't mind that," I replied. And I didn't. What I minded was the thought of an hour's vain wading in that roaring stream, whipping it with fly after fly, while R., the foreordained fisherman, was sitting comfortably in a sawmill, and derricking that pair of three-quarter-pounds in through the window! I had ventured more warily than he, and used, if not the same skill, at least the best skill at my command. My conscience was clear, but so was his; and he had had the drier skin and the greater magnanimity and the biggest fish besides. There is much to be said, in a world like ours, for taking the world as you find it and for fishing with a worm.

— from *The Atlantic Monthly* (May, 1904)

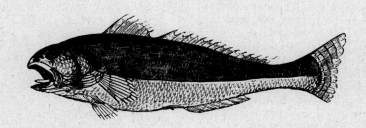

Specifications: Rods

Fresh Water Spinning Rods

Model No.: PG30L
Length: 6½', 7'
No. Pieces: 2
No. Guides: 5 ceramic
Tip Top: Ceramic
Rec. Lure Wt.: ⅛-½ oz.
Action: Light
Handle: Double locking ring reel seat — anodized aluminum with textured walnut inlay, coated cork grips and bright aluminum appointments.

Model No.: PG30M. Same as Model PG30L except:
Rec. Lure Wt.: ¼-¾ oz.
Action: Medium

Model No.: PG32. Same as Model PG30L except:
Rec. Lure Wt.: ⅛-¾ oz.
Action: Medium-light

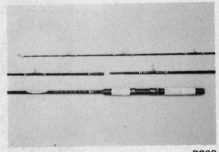

PC30

Model No.: PC30
Length: 6½', 7'
No. Pieces: 2
No. Guides: 5 chrome-plated stainless steel
Tip Top: Carboloy
Rec. Lure Wt.: ⅛-⅝ oz.
Action: Medium-light
Handle: Double locking ring anodized aluminum reel seat with specie cork grips.

Model No.: PC31. Same as Model PC30 except:
Length: 7'
Rec. Lure Wt.: ¼-¾ oz.
Action: Medium

Model No.: PC33. Same as Model PC30 except:
Length: 6'10"
Rec. Lure Wt.: ¼-1 oz.
Action: Medium-heavy

Model No.: T30
Length: 6½', 7', 7½'
No. Pieces: 2
No. Guides: 5 chrome-plated stainless steel
Tip Top: Carboloy
Rec. Lure Wt.: 3/16-⅝ oz.
Action: Medium
Handle: Double locking ring anodized aluminum reel seat with specie cork grips.

Model No.: T32. Same as Model T30 except:
Length: 6½', 7'
Rec. Lure Wt.: ⅛-½ oz.
Action: Medium-light

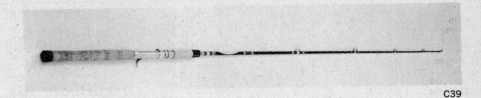

C39

Model No.: T36. Same as Model T30 except:
Length: 5'10"
No. Pieces: 1
No. Guides: 4 chrome-plated stainless steel
Rec. Lure Wt.: ¼-1 oz.
Action: Medium-heavy

Model No.: T37. Same as Model T30 except:
Length: 6'3"
Rec. Lure Wt.: ¼-1 oz.
Action: Medium-heavy

Model No.: C30
Length: 6½', 7'
No. Pieces: 2
No. Guides: 4 chrome-plated stainless steel
Tip Top: Chrome-plated stainless steel
Rec. Lure Wt.: 3/16-½ oz.
Action: Medium-light
Handle: Red anodized aluminum reel seat with tapered specie cork grips.

Model No.: C32. Same as Model C30 except:
Length: 6', 6½', 7'
Rec. Lure Wt.: ⅛-½ oz.

Model No.: C33. Same as Model C30 except:
Length: 8'6"
No. Guides: 6
Rec. Lure Wt.: 1/16-¼ oz.
Action: Light

Model No.: C39. Same as Model C30 except:
Length: 5'10"
No. Pieces: 1
Rec. Lure Wt.: ½-1¼ oz.
Action: Heavy
Handle: Chrome double locking triggered reel seat with specie cork grips.

Model No.: F30
Length: 6½', 7'
No. Pieces: 2
No. Guides: 4 chrome-plated stainless steel
Tip Top: Chrome-plated steel
Rec. Lure Wt.: ⅛-½ oz.
Action: Medium-light
Handle: Black anodized aluminum reel seat with specie cork grips.

Model No.: F33. Same as Model F30 except:
Length: 8'
No. Guides: 5
Rec. Lure Wt.: 1/16-¼ oz.
Action: Light

Model No.: B30
Length: 6½', 7'
No. Pieces: 2
No. Guides: 4 chrome-plated stainless steel
Tip Top: Chrome-plated steel
Rec. Lure Wt.: ⅛-⅜ oz.
Action: Light
Handle: Gold and brown anodized aluminum reel seat with specie cork grips.

Ultralight & Powerlite Spinning Rods

Model No.: PG20
Length: 5½'
No. Pieces: 2
No. Guides: 4 chrome-plated stainless steel
Tip Top: Carboloy
Rec. Lure Wt.: 1/16-⅜ oz.
Action: Ultralight
Handle: Double locking ring anodized aluminum reel seat with textured walnut inlay, coated cork grips and bright aluminum appointments for perfect blending of foregrips and rod blanks.

Model No.: PG26. Same as Model PG20 except:
Length: 5'9"
Rec. Lure Wt.: ⅛-¾ oz.
Action: Powerlite

Model No.: PC20
Length: 5½'
No. Pieces: 2
No. Guides: 4 chrome-plated stainless steel
Tip Top: Carboloy
Rec. Lure Wt.: 1/16-⅜ oz.
Action: Ultralight
Handle: Double locking ring, anodized aluminum reel seat with specie cork grips.

Model No.: PC26. Same as Model PC20 except:
Length: 5'9"
Rec. Lure Wt.: ⅛-¾ oz.
Action: Powerlite

Model No.: T21
Length: 5', 5½'
No. Pieces: 2
No. Guides: 4 chrome-plated stainless steel
Tip Top: Carboloy
Rec. Lure Wt.: 1/16-¼ oz.
Action: Ultralight
Handle: Double locking ring, anodized aluminum reel seat with unique designed specie cork grips.

Model No.: C21
Length: 5', 5½'
No. Pieces: 2
No. Guides: 5' rods: 3; 5½' rods: 4; chrome-plated stainless steel
Tip Top: Chrome-plated stainless steel
Rec. Lure Wt.: 1/16-¼ oz.
Action: Ultralight
Handle: Red anodized aluminum reel seat with specie cork grips.

Model No.: C25. Same as Model C21 except:
Length: 5'3"
No. Pieces: 1
No. Guides: 4
Rec. Lure Wt.: ¼-⅝ oz.
Action: Medium-light

Berkley (cont'd.)

Model No.: C26. Same as Model C21 except:
Length: 5'9"
No. Guides: 4
Rec. Lure Wt.: ⅛-¾ oz.
Action: Light

Model No.: F21
Length: 5', 5½'
No. Pieces: 2
No. Guides: 3 chrome-plated stainless steel
Tip Top: Chrome-plated steel
Rec. Lure Wt.: ¹⁄₁₆-¼ oz.
Action: Ultralight
Handle: Black anodized aluminum reel seat with unique designed specie cork grips.

Model No.: B21
Length: 5½'
No. Pieces: 2
No. Guides: 3 chrome-plated stainless steel
Tip Top: Chrome-plated steel
Rec. Lure Wt.: ¹⁄₁₆-¼ oz.
Action: Ultralight
Handle: Gold and brown anodized aluminum reel seat with unique designed specie cork grips.

Spin-Casting Rods

Model No.: PG10L
Length: 6', 6½'
No. Pieces: 2
No. Guides: 5 carboloy
Tip Top: Carboloy
Rec. Lure Wt.: ⅛-½ oz.
Action: Light
Handle: Live action nylon/fiberglass handle. Metal horizontal locking device coated cork grip. Bright aluminum appointments for perfect blending of foregrips and rod blanks textured woodgrain foregrip.

Model No.: PG10M. Same as Model PG10L except:
Rec. Lure Wt.: ¼-¾ oz.
Action: Medium

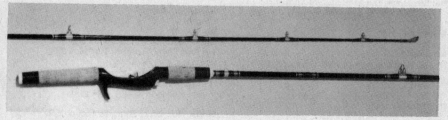

C10

Model No.: C10
Length: 6', 6½'
No. Pieces: 2
No. Guides: 4 chrome-plated stainless steel
Tip Top: Chrome-plated stainless steel
Rec. Lure Wt.: ¹⁄₁₆-½ oz.
Action: Medium-light
Handle: Live action nylon/fiberglass handle with horizontal lockup device specie cork front and rear grips.

Model No.: PC10
Length: 6', 6½'
No. Pieces: 2
No. Guides: 5 chrome-plated stainless steel

Tip Top: Carboloy
Rec. Lure Wt.: ⅛-⅝ oz.
Action: Medium-light
Handle: Live action nylon/fiberglass handle metal horizontal lockup device specie cork grips.

Model No.: T10
Length: 6', 6½'
No. Pieces: 2
No. Guides: 4 chrome-plated stainless steel
Tip Top: Carboloy
Rec. Lure Wt.: ⅛-⅝ oz.
Action: Medium-light
Handle: Live action nylon/fiberglass handle metal horizontal lockup device specie cork front and rear grips.

Model No.: F10
Length: 6', 6½'
No. Pieces: 2
No. Guides: 4 chrome-plated stainless steel
Tip Top: Chrome-plated steel
Rec. Lure Wt.: ⅛-½ oz.
Action: Medium-light
Handle: Live action nylon/fiberglass handle with horizontal lockup device specie cork grips.

Model No.: B10
Length: 6', 6½'
No. Pieces: 2
No. Guides: 4 chrome-plated stainless steel
Tip Top: Chrome-plated steel
Rec. Lure Wt.: ⅛-⅜ oz.
Action: Light
Handle: Live action nylon/fiberglass handle with horizontal lockup device specie cork grips.

Bait-Casting Rods

Model No.: PC16M
Length: 5½', 6'
No. Pieces: 1
No. Guides: 6 ceramic

Tip Top: Ceramic
Rec. Lure Wt.: ¼-¾ oz.
Action: Medium
Handle: Detachable bait-casting handle with specie cork grips.

Model No.: PCML. Same as Model PC16M except:
Length: 5'2"
No. Guides: 5
Rec. Lure Wt.: ³⁄₁₆-⅝ oz.
Action: Medium-light

Model No.: PC16MH. Same as Model PC16M except:
Rec. Lure Wt.: ¼-1 oz.

Action: Medium-heavy

Model No.: PC16H. Same as Model PC16M except:
Length: 5½'
Rec. Lure Wt.: ⅜-1¼ oz.
Action: Heavy

Model No.: PC160
Length: 4'2"
No. Pieces: 1
No. Guides: 6 ceramic
Tip Top: Ceramic
Rec. Lure Wt.: ³⁄₁₆-⅝ oz.
Action: Medium-light
Handle: No handle

Model No.: PC161. Same as Model PC160 except:
Length: 4½', 5'
Rec. Lure Wt.: ¼-¾ oz.
Action: Medium

Model No.: PC163. Same as Model PC160 except:
Length: 4½', 5'
Rec. Lure Wt.: ¼-1 oz.
Action: Medium-heavy

Model No.: T15
Length: 5½'
No. Pieces: 1
No. Guides: 5 chrome-plated stainless steel
Tip Top: Chrome-plated stainless steel
Rec. Lure Wt.: ¼-¾ oz.
Action: Medium
Handle: Detachable handle—T15-5½' only. Live action nylon/fiberglass handle, metal horizontal lockup device.

Model No.: T18. Same as Model T15 except:
Action: Heavy

Model No.: C12
Length: 5½'
No. Pieces: 1
No. Guides: 5 chrome-plated stainless steel
Tip Top: Chrome-plated stainless steel
Rec. Lure Wt.: ³⁄₁₆-⅝ oz.
Action: Medium-light
Handle: Detachable bait-casting handle with specie cork grips.

Model No.: C15. Same as Model C12 except:
Action: Medium

Model No.: C16. Same as Model C12 except:
Action: Medium-heavy

Model No.: B14
Length: 5'
No. Pieces: 1
No. Guides: 4 chrome-plated stainless steel
Tip Top: Chrome-plated steel
Rec. Lure Wt.: ½-1¼ oz.
Action: Heavy
Handle: Live action nylon/fiberglass handle with metal horizontal lockup device and specie cork grips.

Model No.: B15. Same as Model B14 except:
Length: 5½'
Rec. Lure Wt.: ¼-¾ oz.
Action: Medium

Model No.: B16. Same as Model B14 except:
Length: 5½', 6'
Rec. Lure Wt.: ⅜-1 oz.
Action: Medium-heavy

Fly Rods

Model No.: PG40
Length: 6'3", 7', 7½', 8', 8½'
No. Pieces: 2
No. Guides: 6'3" rods: 5; 7', 7½', 8' rods: 6;
8½' rods: 7; all stainless steel snake
guides and one carboloy stripper guide
Tip Top: Chrome-plated stainless steel
Rec. Line: 6'3" rods: 4
7' rods: 5
7½' rods: 6
8' rods: 7
8½' rods: 8
Handle: Double locking anodized aluminum
fixed reel seat with textured walnut inlay,
coated cork grip and bright aluminum
appointments for perfect blending of
foregrips and rod blanks.

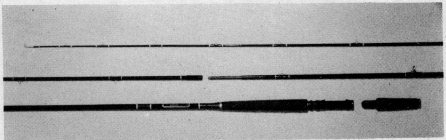

PG45

Model No.: PG45
Length: 9'3"
No. Pieces: 2
No. Guides: 9 stainless steel snake guides
and 1 carboloy stripper guide
Tip Top: Chrome-plated stainless steel
Rec. Line: 9
Handle: Double locking anodized aluminum
fixed reel seat with coated cork grip and
bright aluminum appointments.
Detachable butt grip.

Model No.: PC40
Length: 8', 8½'
No. Pieces: 2
No. Guides: 8' rods: 6; 8½' rods: 7; all
stainless steel snake guides and one
chrome-plated stainless steel stripper
guide
Tip Top: Chrome-plated stainless steel
Rec. Line: 8' rods: 7
8½': 8
Handle: Double locking ring with fixed
anodized aluminum reel seat and specie
cork foregrip.

Model No.: T40
Length: 8', 8½'
No. Pieces: 2
No. Guides: 5 stainless steel snake guides
and 1 chrome-plated steel stripper guide
Tip Top: Chrome-plated stainless steel
Rec. Line: 8' rods: 7
8½' rods: 8

Handle: Double locking ring, anodized
aluminum fixed reel seat with specie
cork foregrip.

Model No.: C40
Length: 7½', 8', 8½'
No. Pieces: 2
No. Guides: 5 stainless steel snake guides
and 1 chrome-plated stainless steel
stripper guide
Tip Top: Chrome-plated stainless steel
Rec. Line: 7' rods: 5
7½' rods: 6
8' rods: 7
8½' rods: 8
Handle: Red anodized fixed aluminum reel
seat with specie cork foregrip.

Model No.: F40
Length: 7', 7½', 8', 8½'
No. Pieces: 2
No. Guides: 5 stainless steel guides and
1 chrome-plated stainless steel stripper
guide
Tip Top: Chrome-plated stainless steel
Rec. Line: 7' rods: 5
7½' rods: 6
8' rods: 7
8½' rods: 8
Handle: Black anodized aluminum fixed
reel seat with specie cork foregrip.

Model No.: B40
Length: 8', 8½'
No. Pieces: 2
No. Guides: 4 stainless steel snake guides
and 1 chrome-plated stainless steel
stripper guide
Tip Top: Chrome-plated stainless steel
Rec: Line: 8' rods: 7
8½' rods: 8
Handle: Gold and brown anodized aluminum
fixed reel seat with specie cork foregrip.

Salt Water Spinning Rods

Model No.: T62
Length: 6½', 7'
No. Pieces: 2
No. Guides: 4 chrome-plated stainless steel
Tip Top: Chrome-plated stainless steel
Rec. Lure Wt.: ⅜-¾ oz.
Action: Medium
Handle: Chrome reel seat with double
locking rings and specie cork grips.

Model No.: T63. Same as Model T62 except:
Length: 7'

No. Pieces: 1
Rec. Lure Wt.: ½-1 oz.
Action: Medium fast taper

Model No.: T65. Same as Model T62 except:
Length: 7'
No. Guides: 7
Rec. Lure Wt.: ¾-1½ oz.
Action: Medium fast taper

Model No.: T66. Same as Model T62 except:
Rec. Lure Wt.: ½-1 oz.
Action: Medium fast taper

Model No.: T90. Same as Model T62 except:
Length: 6½', 7', 8', 9', 10½', 12'
No. Guides: 6½', 7' rods: 4
8', 9', 10½' rods: 5
12' rods: 6
Rec. Lure Wt.: 6½' rods: 1½-2½ oz.
7', 9' rods: 2-3 oz.
8' rods: 1-2½ oz.
10½' rods: 2½-4 oz.
12' rods: 3-4½ oz.
Action: Medium fast taper

Model No.: T95. Same as Model T62 except:
Length: 7½', 8½'
No. Guides: 7½' rods: 5
8½' rods: 6
Rec. Lure Wt.: 7½' rods: 1-2 oz.
8½' rods: 1½-2½ oz.
Action: Medium fast taper
Handle: Chrome reel seat with double locking
rings and specie cork grips.

Model No.: T98. Same as Model T62 except:
Length: 9', 10', 11½'
No. Guides: 9', 10' rods: 5
11½' rods: 6
Rec. Lure Wt.: 9' rods: 4-5 oz.
10' rods: 5-6 oz.
11' rods: 6-8 oz.
Action: Heavy
Handle: Chrome double locking reel seat
with specie cork grips—split handle with
decorative wraps.

Model No.: B60
Length: 6½', 7'
No. Pieces: 1
No. Guides: 4 chrome-plated stainless steel
Tip Top: Chrome-plated stainless steel
Rec. Lure Wt.: ⅜-¾ oz.
Action: Medium
Handle: Gold and brown anodized locking
reel seat with specie cork grips.

Model No.: B62. Same as Model B60 except:
No. Pieces: 2

Model No.: B63. Same as Model B60 except:
Length: 7'
No. Pieces: 2
Rec. Lure Wt.: ½-1 oz.

Model No.: B90. Same as Model B60 except:
Length: 7', 8', 8½', 9', 10½'
No. Pieces: 2
No. Guides: 8', 8½', 9', 10½' rods: 5
Rec. Lure Wt.: 7' rods: 2-3 oz.
8' rods: 1-2½ oz.
8½' rods: 1½-3 oz.
9' rods: 2-3 oz.
10½' rods: 2½-4 oz.
Action: Medium fast taper

Boat Rods

Model No.: T70
Length: 6½', 7'
No. Pieces: 1
No. Guides: 3 chrome-plated stainless steel
Tip Top: Chrome-plated stainless steel
Action: Medium
Handle: Detachable woodgrain boat handle with double locking ring chrome reel seat and specie cork foregrip.

Model No.: T72. Same as Model T70 except:
Length: 7', 7½'
No. Pieces: 2
No. Guides: 5
Action: Medium-light
Handle: Chrome reel seat with double locking rings and specie cork grips.

Model No.: T73. Same as Model T70 except:
Length: 5½'
Handle: Woodgrain boat handle with chrome reel seat, double locking rings and specie cork foregrip.

Model No.: T103. Same as Model T70 except:
Length: 6'4"
No. Guides: 7
Handle: Chrome reel seat with double locking rings and specie cork grips.

Model No.: T106. Same as Model T70 except:
Length: 6'4"
No. Guides: 7
Tip Top: Carboloy
Handle: Synthetic grip with heavy duty Varmac chrome double locking reel seat.

Model No.: T107. Same as Model T70 except:
Length: 7'3"
No. Guides: 7
Tip Top: Carboloy
Action: Heavy
Handle: Synthetic grip with heavy duty Varmac chrome double locking reel seat.

Model No.: T108. Same as Model T70 except:
Length: 6'11"
Tip Top: Carboloy
Action: Medium-heavy
Handle: Synthetic grip with heavy duty Varmac chrome double locking reel seat.

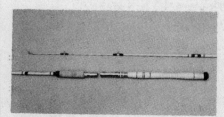

Model No.: B70
Length: 6½', 7', 8', 8½'
No. Pieces: 1
No. Guides: 6', 6½' rods: 3; 7', 8', 8½': 4; all chrome-plated stainless steel.
Tip Top: Chrome-plated stainless steel
Action: 6', 6½', 8', 8½': medium; 7' rods: medium-heavy
Handle: Detachable woodgrain boat handle with double locking ring chrome reel seat and specie cork foregrip.

Model No.: B70RT. Same as Model B70 except:
Length: 6', 6½', 7'
No. Guides: 6', 6½' rods: 3; 7' rods: 4; stainless steel
Tip Top: Roller
Action: 6', 6½' rods: medium; 7' rods; medium-heavy

Model No.: B74. Same as Model B70 except:
Length: 6½'
Action: Medium-light

Model No.: B75. Same as Model B70 except:
Length: 7½'
No. Pieces: 2
No. Guides: 4
Handle: Woodgrain boat handle with double locking ring chrome reel seat and specie cork foregrip.

Model No.: B72. Same as Model B70 except:
Length: 5½', 6'
Handle: Gold and brown anodized aluminum reel seat with specie cork grips.

Boat Spinning Rods

Model No.: T104
Length: 6'7"
No. Pieces: 1
No. Guides: 6 chrome-plated stainless steel
Tip Top: Chrome-plated stainless steel
Action: Medium
Handle: Chrome reel seat with double locking rings and specie cork grips.

Model No.: B71
Length: 7'
No. Pieces: 1
No. Guides: 3 chrome-plated stainless steel
Tip Top: Chrome-plated stainless steel
Action: Medium-heavy
Handle: Detachable woodgrain boat handle with double locking ring chrome reel seat and specie cork foregrip.

Model No.: B73. Same as Model B71 except:
Length: 6', 7'
No. Guides: 6' rods: 4
7' rods: 5
Action: Medium
Handle: Gold and brown anodized aluminum reel seat with specie cork grips.

Regulation IGFA Class Rods

Model No.: RT6
Length: Standard
No. Pieces: 1
No. Guides: 4 chrome-plated stainless steel and 1 roller
Tip Top: Roller
Action: 20 lb. trolling
Handle: Cross slotted Varmac gimbal handle with locking heavy-chromed brass Varmac reel seat and extra long specie cork foregrip.

Model No.: RT9. Same as Model RT6 except:
Action: 30 lb. trolling

Model No.: RT15. Same as Model RT6 except:
Action: 30 lb. trolling

Model No.: RT24
Action: 80 lb. trolling

Model No.: RL30
Length: Standard
No. Pieces: 1
No. Guides: 5 roller
Tip Top: Roller
Action: 30 lb. trolling
Handle: Cross slotted Varmac gimbal handle with locking heavy-chromed brass Varmac reel seat and extra long specie cork foregrip.

Model No.: RL50. Same as Model RL30 except:
Action: 50 lb. trolling

Model No.: RL80. Same as Model RL 30 except:
Action: 80 lb. trolling

Mooching Rods

Model No.: T92
Length: 8½'
No. Pieces: 2
No. Guides: 5 chrome-plated stainless steel
Tip Top: Chrome-plated stainless steel
Action: Medium-mooching
Handle: Anodized aluminum double locking ring reel seat with specie cork grips.

Model No.: T97. Same as Model T92 except:
No. Guides: 5 chrome-plated steel
Action: Salmon/steelhead

Model No.: B91
Length: 8½'
No. Pieces: 2
No. Guides: 4 chrome-plated stainless steel
Tip Top: Chrome-plated stainless steel
Action: Medium-mooching
Handle: Anodized gold and brown aluminum reel seat with specie cork grips.

Popping Rods

Model: T50
Length: 7'
No. Pieces: 1
No. Guides: 3 chrome-plated stainless
Tip Top: Carboloy
Rec. Lure Wt.: ½-1 oz.
Action: Medium
Handle: Chrome trigger reel seat with double locking rings and specie cork grips.

Model No.: B50
Length: 7'
No. Pieces: 1
No. Guides: 4 chrome-plated stainless steel
Tip Tip: Chrome-plated stainless steel
Rec. Lure Wt.: ½-1 oz.
Action: Medium
Handle: Chrome trigger reel seat with double locking rings and specie cork grips.

Trolling Rods

Model No.: B55
Length: 7'
No. Pieces: 2
No. Guides: 4 chrome-plated stainless steel
Tip Top: Chrome-plated stainless steel

Rec. Lure Wt.: 3/16-3/8 oz.
Action: Medium-light
Handle: Anodized gold and brown aluminum reel seat and specie cork grips.

Steelhead Rods

Model No.: PG91
Length: 7'9", 8'3" casting
No. Pieces: 2
No. Guides: 7'9" rods: 6; 8'3" rods: 7; all chrome-plated stainless steel
Tip Top: Carboloy
Rec. Lure Wt.: 3/8-3/4 oz.
Action: Steelhead
Handle: Double locking ring, anodized aluminum reel seat with specie cork grips and bright aluminum appointments for perfect blending of foregrips and rod blanks.

Model No.: PG92. Same as Model PG91 except:
Length: 8' casting
No. Guides: 7 ceramic
Tip Top: Ceramic

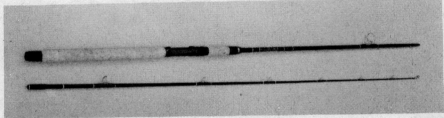

Model No.: PG94. Same as Model PG91 except:
Length: 7'9", 8'3" spinning
No. Guides: 7'9" rods: 7
          8'3" rods: 8

Model No.: T94
Length: 8', 8½'
No. Pieces: 2
No. Guides: 5 chrome-plated stainless steel
Tip Top: Chrome-plated stainless steel
Rec. Lure Wt.: 3/8-3/4 oz.
Action: Steelhead
Handle: Double locking rings, anodized aluminum reel seat with specie cork grips.

Model No.: C94
Length: 8'
No. Pieces: 2
No. Guides: 5 chrome-plated stainless steel
Tip Top: Chrome-plated stainless steel
Rec. Lure Wt.: 3/8-3/4 oz.
Action: Steelhead
Handle: Red anodized aluminum reel seat with specie cork grips

Model No.: B94
Length: 8'
No. Pieces: 2
No. Guides: 5 chrome-plated stainless steel
Tip Top: Chrome-plated stainless steel
Rec. Lure Wt.: 3/8-3/4 oz.
Action: Steelhead
Handle: Gold and brown anodized aluminum reel seat with specie cork grips.

Biscayne

Spinning Rod

Model No.: 2003 series—graphite
Length: 5'8", 6'6", 7'
No. Pieces: 2
No. Guides: 5'8", 6'6": 5; 7': 6; all Fuji speed guides

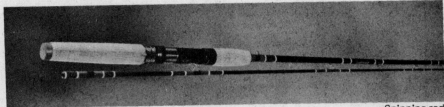

Tip Top: Fuji speed tip top
Action: 5'8": ultra light
      6'6": light
      7' : medium

PG94

Handle: Cal-Air reel seats, cork grips, Pflueger non-skid butt cap. Wrappings are black, yellow and red.

Bait-Casting Rod

Model No.: 2002 series—graphite
Length: 6'
No. Pieces: 2
No. Guides: 7 Fuji speed guides
Tip Top: Fuji speed tip top
Action: Light; medium; heavy
Handle: Extended Fuji offset casting handle. Wrappings are black, yellow and red.

Regulation IGFA Class Rods

Model No.: 2001 series—graphite
Length: 6'8"
No. Pieces: 2
No. Guides: 5 roller (heavy duty AFTCO on 50 lb.; aluminum on 80 lb.)
Tip Top: AFTCO roller
Action: 12 lb. graphite ultra light or light; 20 lb.; 30 lb.; 50 lb.; 80 lb. trolling
Handle: Straight aluminum black butts. Rod butts are hard coat, black nonscratch tubular aluminum. Foregrips are black flock with the front portion wrapped over. Wrappings are black, yellow and red. Curved aluminum butts are available on the 50 lb. and 80 lb. machined reel seat.

Browning

Spinning Rods

Model No.: 332904
Length: 4'6"
No. Pieces: 1
No. Guides: 3 chrome-plated stainless steel
Tip Top: Chrome-plated stainless steel

Spinning rod

Rec. Lure Wt.: 1/16-3/16 oz.
Action: Ultra-light
Handle: Overall 8"; all cork with tapered spin rings reel seat.

Model No.: 332955. Same as Model 332904 except:
Length: 5'6"
No. Pieces: 2
No. Guides: 5
Rec. Lure Wt.: 1/12-1/4 oz.

Model No.: 332905
Length: 6'
No. Pieces: 2
No. Guides: 5 chrome-plated stainless steel
Tip Top: Carboloy
Rec. Lure Wt.: 1/8-3/8 oz.
Action: Light
Handle: Overall 9½"; all cork with tapered spin rings reel seat.

Model No.: 332906. Same as Model 332905 except:
Handle: Overall 12⅞"; fixed reel seat.

Model No.: 332910
Length: 6'
No. Pieces: 2
No. Guides: 5 chrome-plated stainless steel
Tip Top: Carboloy
Rec. Lure Wt.: 1/2-1 1/4 oz.
Action: Heavy freshwater; light saltwater
Handle: Overall 12¾"; fixed reel seat.

Model No.: 332914
Length: 6'6"
No. Pieces: 5
No. Guides: 5 chrome-plated stainless steel
Tip Top: Carboloy
Rec. Lure Wt.: 1/8-3/8 oz.
Action: Light
Handle: Overall 9½"; all cork with tapered spin rings reel seat.

Model No.: 332915
Length: 6'6"
No. Pieces: 2
No. Guides: 5 chrome-plated stainless steel
Tip Top: Carboloy
Rec. Lure Wt.: 3/16-3/4 oz.
Action: Casts a wide range from a delicate minnow to a 5/8 ounce bass plug
Handle: Overall 12¾"; fixed reel seat.

Browning (cont'd.)

Model No.: 332970
Length: 7'
No Pieces: 2
No Guides: 5 chrome-plated stainless steel
Tip Top: Carboloy
Rec. Lure Wt.: ¼-¾ oz.
Action: Medium (for bass, pike, muskies and coho)
Handle: Overall 16"; fixed reel seat.

Model No.: 332971
Length: 7'
No: Pieces: 5 (including handle)
No. Guides: 6 (foul-proof for either spinning or fly line)
Tip Top: Carboloy
Rec. Lure Wt.: ⅛-⅜ oz.
Action: Accommodates either spinning or fly reels
Handle: Overall 13¼"; fixed reel seat.

Bait-Casting Rods

Model No.: 312900
Length: 5'6"
No. Pieces: 1
No. Guides: 5 carboloy
Tip Top: Carboloy
Rec. Lure Wt.: ⅝-1 oz.
Action: Husky (for bass and musky)
Handle: Detachable.

Model No.: 412900. Same as Model 312900 except:
No. Guides: 5 ceramic
Tip Top: Ceramic

Model No.: 312903
Length: 5'6"
No. Pieces: 1
No. Guides: 5 carboloy
Tip Top: Carboloy
Rec. Lure Wt.: ⅜-⅝ oz.
Action: For bass
Handle: Detachable.

Model No.: 412903. Same as Model 312903 except:
No. Guides: 5 ceramic
Tip Top: Ceramic

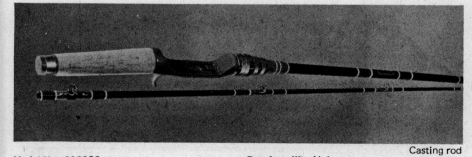

Model No.: 312906
Length: 6'
No. Pieces: 1
No. Guides: 6 carboloy
Tip Top: Carboloy
Rec. Lure Wt.: ⅝-1 oz.
Action: Suited to handle spinners, spoons, poppers and other lures
Handle: Detachable.

Model No.: 412906. Same as Model 312906 except:
No. Guides: 6 ceramic
Tip Top: Ceramic

Model No.: 312910
Length: 6'
No. Pieces: 2 (3 with detachable handle)
No. Guides: 6 carboloy
Tip Top: Carboloy
Rec. Lure Wt.: ¼-⅝ oz.
Action: Light
Handle: Detachable.

Model No.: 412910. Same as Model 312910 except:
No. Guides: 6 ceramic
Tip Top: Ceramic

Model No.: 312920
Length: 6'
No. Pieces: 2 (3 with detachable handle)
No. Guides: 6 carboloy
Tip Top: Carboloy
Rec. Lure Wt.: ⅜-1 oz.
Action: Light
Handle: Detachable.

Model No.: 412920. Same as Model 312920 except:
No. Guides: 6 ceramic
Tip Top: Ceramic

Model No.: 312930
Length: 6'6"
No. Pieces: 2 (3 with detachable handle)
No. Guides: 6 carboloy
Tip Top: Carboloy
Rec. Lure Wt.: ¼-1 oz.
Action: Suited for drifting or bottom fishing live bait
Handle: Detachable.

Fly Rods

Model No.: 322960
Length: 6'

No. Pieces: 2
No. Guides: 1 stripping; 5 snake; all deep chromed stainless steel
Tip Top: Chrome-plated stainless steel

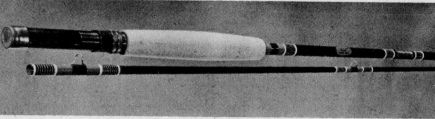

Fly rod

Rec. Line: 5 wt.
Handle: Overall 9¾"; hand shaped grip of 6X super specie cork. Reel seats are bronze anodized. Reel is secured by a contoured hood plus double lock nuts.

Model No.: 322970. Same as Model 322960 except:
Length: 7'
Rec. Line: 6 wt.

Model No.: 322980. Same as Model 322960 except:
Length: 8'
No. Guides: 6 snake
Rec. Line: 6, 7 wt.
Handle: Overall 10¾".

Model No.: 322985. Same as model 322960 except:
Length: 8'6"
No. Guides: 6 snake
Rec. Line: 6, 7 wt.
Handle: Overall 10¾".

Model No.: 322986. Same as Model 322960 except:
Length: 8'6"
No. Guides: 6 snake
Rec. Line: 8, 9 wt.
Handle: Overall 10¾".

Model No.: 322990. Same as Model 322960 except:
Length: 9'
No. Guides: 6 snake
Rec. Line: 8 wt.
Handle: Overall 10¾".

Model No.: 322991. Same as Model 322960 except:
Length: 9'
No. Guides: 6 snake
Rec. Line: 9, 10 wt.
Handle: Overall 10¾"; 6" gaspe butt available.

Salt Water and Heavy Fresh Water Rods

Model No.: 142960 (Spinning)
Length: 7'1½"
No. Pieces: 1
No. Guides: 6 spinning, hard chromed stainless steel
Tip Top: Carboloy
Rec. Lure Wt.: ⅜-2 oz.
Action: Saltwater lightweight

Casting rod

Handle: Overall 22"; 6X super specie cork; fixed bronze anodized alloy reel seat with machined double screw locks.

Model No.: 142961. Same as Model 142960 except:
No. Pieces: 2

Model No.: 142967. Same as Model 142960 except:
Length: 7'6"
Rec. Lure Wt.: ⅝-4 oz.
Action: Surf and jetty casting
Handle: Overall 24¾".

Model No.: 142968. Same as Model 142960 except:
Length: 7'6"
No. Pieces: 2
Rec. Lure Wt.: ⅝-4 oz.
Action: Surf and jetty casting
Handle: Overall 24¾".

Model No.: 142970. Same as Model 142960 except:
Length: 8'¾"
No. Guides: 7 spinning
Rec. Lure Wt.: ⅞-5 oz.
Action: Distance casting
Handle: Overall 24¾".

Model No.: 142971. Same as Model 142960 except:
Length: 8'¾"
No. Pieces: 2
No. Guides: 7 spinning
Rec. Lure Wt.: ⅞-5 oz.
Action: Distance casting
Handle: Overall 24¾".

Model No.: 142985 (Casting)
Length: 8'7"
No. Pieces: 1
No. Guides: 7 casting, chromed brass
Tip Top: Carboloy
Rec. Lure Wt.: 3-8 oz.
Action: Heavy jigging
Handle: Overall 28"; 6X super specie cork; fixed alloy reel seat with machined double screw locks.

Model No.: 172900 (Spin-Cast)
Length: 5'6½"
No. Pieces: 1
No. Guides: 5 spin cast, hard chromed stainless steel
Tip Top: Carboloy
Rec. Lure Wt.: ¾-2 oz.
Action: Jigging and trolling
Handle: Overall 17"; 6X super specie cork; fixed bronze anodized alloy reel seat with machined double screw locks.

Model No.: 172905. Same as Model 172900 except:
Length: 6'6"
No. Guides: 6 spin-cast
Rec. Lure Wt.: ⅝-2 oz.
Action: Popping rod for saltwater
Handle: Overall 17¾".

Model No.: 172906 (Spinning)
Length: 6'6"
No. Pieces: 1
No. Guides: 6 spinning, hard chromed stainless steel

Tip Top: Carboloy
Rec. Lure Wt.: ⅝-2 oz.
Action: For both boat and jetty saltwater
Handle: Overall 17¾"; 6X super specie cork; fixed bronze anodized alloy reel seat with machined double screw locks.

Model No.: 172970 (Casting)
Length: 7'
No. Pieces: 1
No. Guides: 5 casting, chromed brass
Tip Top: Carboloy
Rec. Lure Wt.: ⅝-4 oz.
Action: Popping and trolling
Handle: Overall 17¾"; 6X super specie cork; fixed bronze anodized alloy reel seat with machined double screw locks.

Model No.: 172971 (Trolling)
Length: 7'
No. Pieces: 2
No. Guides: 5 carboloy
Tip Top: Carboloy
Rec. Lure Wt.: ⅞-5 oz.
Action: Light saltwater
Handle: Overall 19"; 6X super specie cork; fixed bronze anodized alloy reel seat with machined double screw locks.

River and Surf Rods

Model No.: 342908
Length: 8'
No. Pieces: 2
No. Guides: 6 spinning, polished hard-chromed, stainless steel
Tip Top: Carboloy
Rec. Lure Wt.: ⅝-2½ oz.
Action: For steelhead and salmon casting on big rivers
Handle: Overall 24"; 6X specie cork; anodized reel seat with double screw locks.

Model No.: 342918. Same as Model 342908 except:
No. Guides: 6 spincast, chromed stainless steel

Model No.: 342909. Same as Model 342908 except:
Length: 9'
Rec. Lure Wt.: ¾-3 oz.
Handle: Overall 24¾".

Model No.: 342919. Same as Model 342908 except:
Length: 9'
No. Guides: 6 spincast, chromed stainless steel
Rec. Lure Wt.: ¾-3 oz.
Handle: Overall 24¾".

Model No.: 342911
Length: 11'
No. Pieces: 2
No. Guides: 7 spinning, polished hard-chromed, stainless steel

Tip Top: Carboloy
Rec. Lure Wt.: 2-7 oz.
Action: Heavy surf
Handle: Overall 28½"; hypalon; anodized reel seat with double screw locks.

Regulation IGFA Class Rods

Model No.: 162920
Length: 6'8"
No. Pieces: 2
No. Guides: 6 AFTCO roller
Tip Top: AFTCO roller
Action: 12 lb. trolling
Handle: Overall 26⅝"; polished rosewood; chromed double lock reel seat and chromed two-way gimbal nock.

Model No.: 162930. Same as Model 162920 except:
Action: 20 lb. trolling

Model No.: 152910. Same as Model 162920 except:
Action: 30 lb. trolling
Handle: Overall 29½".

Model No.: 152915. Same as Model 162920 except:
No. Guides: 5 AFTCO roller
Action: 50 lb. trolling
Handle: Overall 30½".

Lew Childre and Sons

Spinning Rods

Model No.: IL-16HSL
Length: 6'
No. Pieces: 1
No. Guides: 5 Fuji speed guides
Tip Top: Fuji speed tip top
Rec. Lure Wt.: ⅛-½ oz.
Action: Extra light
Handle: Spinning, light.

Model No.: 1-16HSL. Same as Model 1L-16HSL except:
Rec. Lure Wt.: ⅜-⅝ oz.
Action: Light

Model No.: 4-16HSML. Same as model 1L-16HSL except:
Rec. Lure Wt.: ⅜-1 oz.
Action: Medium
Handle: Spinning, medium-light.

Model No.: 1L-26HSL
Length: 6', 6'6"

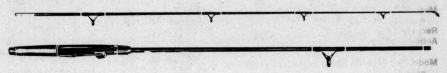

1L-26HSL

No. Pieces: 2
No. Guides: 5 Fuji speed guides
Tip Top: Fuji tip top
Rec. Lure Wt.: ⅛-⅜ oz.
Action: Extra light

Handle: 6' rod: spinning, light
6'6" spinning, medium-light.

Model No.: 1-26HSL, 1-27HSML. Same as
model 1L-26HSL except:
Length: 6', 6'6", 7'
Rec. Lure Wt.: ⅜-⅝ oz.
Action: Light
Handle: 6' rod: spinning, light
6'6", 7' rod: spinning, medium-light.

Model No.: 4-266HSML. Same as Model
1L-26HSL except:
Length: 6'6"
Rec. Lure Wt.: ⅜-1 oz.
Action: Medium
Handle: Spinning, medium-light.

Model No.: EIL-286S
Length: 8'6"
No. Pieces: 2
No. Guides: 5 Fuji speed guides
Tip Top: Fuji speed tip top
Rec. Lure Wt.: Salmon eggs; live bait
Action: Extra light
Handle: Blank through handle construction.

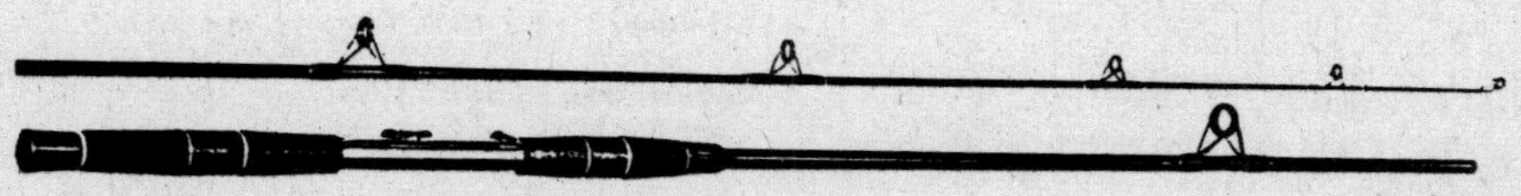

No. Guides: 6 Fuji speed rings
Tip Top: Fuji tip top
Rec. Lure Wt.: ⅜-⅝ oz.
Action: Light
Handle: Offset.

Model No.: I-156HO. Same as Model I-152HO
except:
Length: 5'6"

Model No.: 4-156HO. Same as Model
I-152HO except:
Length: 5'6"
Action: Medium

Model No.: I-159HO
Length: 5'9"
No. Pieces: 1
No. Guides: 6 Fuji speed rings
Tip Top: Fuji tip top
Rec. Lure Wt.: ⅜-⅝ oz.
Action: Light
Handle: Offset.

Model No.: 6-158HO
Length: 5'8"

Model No.: I-159SO. Same as Model I-156SO
except:
Length: 5'9".

Model No.: 4-156SO. Same as Model
I-156SO except:
Length: 5'6"
Rec. Lure Wt.: ⅜-1 oz.
Action: Medium

Model No.: 6-158SO. Same as Model
I-156SO except:
Length: 5'8"
Rec. Lure Wt.: ½-1¼ oz.
Action: Heavy

Spinning Rods

Model No.: IL-16SSL
Length: 6'
No. Pieces: 1
No. Guides: 5 slip-on hard rings
Tip Top: Stainless steel
Rec. Lure Wt.: ⅛-½ oz.
Action: Extra light
Handle: Spinning ultra-light; spinning,
light; spinning medium-light.

Model No.: I-16SSL. Same as Model
IL-16SSL except:
Rec. Lure Wt.: ⅜-⅝ oz.
Action: Light

Model No.: 4-16SSML. Same as Model
IL-16SSL except:
Length: 6'6"
No. Pieces: 2
Rec. Lure Wt.: ⅜-1 oz.
Action: Medium

Model No.: IL-26SSL
Length: 6'
No. Pieces: 2
No. Guides: 5 slip-on hard rings
Tip Top: Stainless steel
Rec. Lure Wt.: ⅛-½ oz.
Action: Extra Light
Handle: Spinning ultra-light; spinning, light;
spinning medium-light.

Model No.: I-26SSL. Same as Model
IL-26SSL except:
Rec. Lure Wt.: ⅜-⅝ oz.
Action: Light

Model No.: IL-266SSML
Length: 6'6"
No. Pieces: 2
No. Guides: 5 slip-on hard rings
Tip Top: Stainless steel
Rec. Lure Wt.: ⅛-½ oz.
Action: Extra Light
Handle: Spinning ultra-light; spinning, light;
spinning medium-light.

Model No.: I-266SSML. Same as Model
IL-266SSML except:
Rec. Lure Wt.: ⅜-⅝ oz.
Action: Light

Model No.: 4-266SSML. Same as Model
IL-266SSML except:
Rec. Lure Wt.: ⅜-1 oz.
Action: Medium

EI-279S

Model No.: EI-279S. Same as Model EIL-286S
except:
Length: 7'9"
Rec. Lure Wt.: Lightweight lures; live bait
Action: Light

Model No.: E6-279S. Same as Model
EIL-286S except:
Length: 7'9"
Rec. Lure Wt.: Heavy lures and leads
Action: Heavy

Bait-Casting Rods

Model No.: IL-16HO
Length: 6'
No. Pieces: 1
No. Guides: 6 Fuji speed rings
Tip Top: Fuji tip top
Rec. Lure Wt.: ⅛-½ oz.
Action: Extra light
Handle: Offset.

Model No.: I-16HO. Same as Model IL-16HO
except:
Rec. Lure Wt.: ⅜-⅝ oz.
Action: Light

Model No.: 4-16HO. Same as Model IL-16HO
except:
Rec. Lure Wt.: ⅜-1 oz.
Action: Medium

Model No.: 6-16HO. Same as Model IL-16HO
except:
Rec. Lure Wt.: ½-1¼ oz.
Action: Heavy

Model No.: I-152HO
Length: 5'2"
No. Pieces: 1

No. Pieces: 1
No. Guides: 6 Fuji speed rings
Tip Top: Fuji tip top
Rec. Lure Wt.: ⅜-⅝ oz.
Action: Heavy
Handle: Offset.

Model No.: IL-16SO
Length: 6'
No. Pieces: 1
No. Guides: 6 slip-on hard rings
Tip Top: Stainless steel
Rec. Lure Wt.: ⅛-½ oz.
Action: Extra Light
Handle: #0 offset; #02HC two-handed
offset; black bass.

Model No.: I-16SO. Same as Model IL-16SO
except:
Rec. Lure Wt.: ⅜-⅝ oz.
Action: Light

Model No.: 4-16SO. Same as Model IL-16SO
except:
Rec. Lure Wt.: ⅜-1 oz.
Action: Medium

Model No.: 6-16SO. Same as Model IL-16SO
except:
Rec. Lure Wt.: ½-1¼ oz.
Action: Heavy

Model No.: I-156SO
Length: 5'6"
No. Pieces: 1
No. Guides: 6 slip-on hard rings
Tip Top: Stainless steel
Rec. Lure Wt.: ⅜-⅝ oz.
Action: Light
Handle: #0 offset; #02HC two-handed
offset; black bass.

Model No.: I-27SSML
Length: 7'
No. Pieces: 2
No. Guides: 5 slip-on hard rings
Tip Top: Stainless steel
Rec. Lure Wt.: ⅜-⅝ oz.
Action: Light
Handle: Spinning ultra-light; spinning, light; spinning medium-light.

Continental Arms

Fly Rods

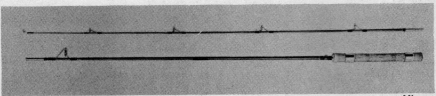

Micron

Model No.: Micron
Length: 5½', 7½'
No. Pieces: 2
No. Guides: 4 carboloy snake guides and 1 carboloy stripper guide
Tip Top: Carboloy
Rec. Line: 1-6 wt.
Handle: One piece specie cork with tapered slide rings and hook keeper.

Daiwa

Fresh Water Spinning Rods

Model No.: 2019
Length: 5'
No. Pieces: 1
No. Guides: 5 chrome-plated stainless steel
Tip Top: Stainless steel
Rec. Lure Wt.: Not specified
Action: Ultra Light
Handle: Specie cork grip with anodized aluminum reel seat.

Model No.: 2210. Same as Model 2019 except:
Length: 5½'
No. Pieces: 2
Action: Light

Model No.: 2212
Length: 6½'
No. Pieces: 2
Action: Medium

Model No.: 4312
Length: 6½'
No. Pieces: 2
No. Guides: 5 chrome-plated stainless steel
Tip Top: Stainless steel
Rec. Lure Wt.: Not specified
Action: Medium
Handle: Specie cork grip with fixed anodized aluminum reel seat.

Model No.: 4313. Same as Model 4312 except:
Length: 7'

Model No.: 4312D. Same as Model 4312 except:
No. Guides: 5 dialoy
Tip Top: Dialoy

Model No.: 4313D. Same as Model 4312 except:
Length: 7'
No. Guides: 5 dialay
Tip Top: Dialay

Model No.: 312
Length: 6½', 7'
No. Pieces: 2

No Guides: 5 chrome-plated stainless steel
Tip Top: Stainless steel
Rec. Lure Wt.: Not specified
Action: Medium-light
Handle: Specie cork grip with fixed anodized aluminum reel seat.

Model No.: 3019D
Length: 5'
No. Pieces: 2
No. Guides: 5 chrome-plated stainless steel
Tip Top: Stainless steel
Rec. Lure Wt.: Not specified
Action: Ultra-light
Handle: Specie cork grip with fixed anodized aluminum reel seat; duck butt handle.

Model No.: 3012
Length: 6½', 7'
No. Pieces: 2
No. Guides: 5 chrome-plated stainless steel
Tip Top: Stainless steel
Rec. Lure Wt.: Not specified
Action: Medium-light
Handle: Specie cork grip with fixed anodized aluminum reel seat.

Model No.: 1010
Length: 5½', 6'
No. Pieces: 2
Tip Top: Stainless steel
No. Guides: 5
Rec. Lure Wt.: Not specified
Action: Medium
Handle: Specie cork grip with fixed anodized aluminum reel seat.

Model No.: 8019
Length: 5'
No. Pieces: 2
No. Guides: 5 chrome-plated stainless steel
Tip Top: Dialoy
Rec. Lure Wt.: Not specified
Action: Ultra-light
Handle: Specie cork grip with fixed anodized aluminum reel seat with double locking nut.

Model No.: 8012. Same as Model 8019 except:

Length: 6½', 7'
Action: Medium-light

Model No.: 8025. Same as Model 8019 except:
Length: 8', 9'
Action: Medium

Spin — Casting Rods

Model No.: 2231
Length: 6'
No. Pieces: 2
No. Guides: 5 chrome-plated stainless steel
Tip Top: Stainless steel
Rec. Lure Wt.: Not specified
Action: Medium-light
Handle: Specie cork grip with fixed anodized aluminum reel seat.

Model No.: 3031
Length: 6', 6½'
No. Pieces: 2
No. Guides: 5 chrome-plated stainless steel
Tip Top: Stainless steel
Rec. Lure Wt.: Not specified
Action: Medium-light
Handle: Specie cork grip.

Model No.: 1030
Length: 5½'
No. Pieces: 2
No. Guides: 5 chrome-plated stainless steel
Tip Top: Stainless steel
Rec. Lure Wt.: Not specified
Action: Medium
Handle: Specie cork grip.

Fly Rods

Model No.: 3044
Length: 7½'
No. Pieces: 2
No. Guides: 6 snake guides with stainless steel stripping guide
Tip Top: Chrome
Rec. Line: 7
Handle: Specie cork grip with fixed anodized aluminum reel seat.

Model No.: 3045. Same as Model 3044 except:
Length: 8' 8½'
Rec. Line: 8

Model No.: 3047. Same as Model 3044 except:
Length: 9'
Rec. Line: 9

Salt Water Spinning Rods

Model No.: 324
Length: 7½', 8', 9'
No. Pieces: 2
No. Guides: 5 chrome-plated stainless steel
Tip Top: Chrome-plated stainless steel
Rec. Lure Wt.: Not specified
Action: Medium
Handle: Specie cork grip with double locking chrome-plated reel seat.

Model No.: 3100
Length: 8', 8½'
No. Pieces: 2

No. Guides: 6 chrome-plated stainless steel
Tip Top: Chrome-plated stainless steel
Rec. Lure Wt.: Not specified
Action: Light
Handle: Specie cork grips with chrome-plated double locking reel seat.

Model No.: 8100D. Same as Model 3100 except:
No. Guides: 6 dialoy

Model No.: 3024
Length: 7½', 8', 9'
No. Pieces: 2
No. Guides: 5 chrome-plated stainless steel
Tip Top: Chrome-plated
Rec. Lure Wt.: Not specified
Action: Medium-light
Handle: Specie cork grip with double locking brass chrome-plated reel seat.

Model No.: 3027. Same as Model 3024 except:
Length: 9', 10'
Action: Medium

Fresh and Salt Water Spinning Rods

Model No.: 4423
Length: 7'
No. Pieces: 1
No. Guides: 5 chrome-plated stainless steel
Tip Top: Chrome-plated stainless steel
Rec. Lure Wt.: Not specified
Action: Medium-heavy
Handle: Specie cork grip with double locking brass chrome-plated reel seat.

Model No.: 4324. Same as Model 4423 except:
Length: 7½', 8', 9'
No. Pieces: 2

Model No.: 4329. Same as Model 4423 except:
Length: 10'
No. Pieces: 2
Action: Medium

Salt Water Rod

Model No.: 621
Length: 11', 13', 15'
No Pieces: 3 (except 15' rod: 4)
No. Guides: Not specified; chrome-plated stainless steel
Tip Top: Chrome-plated stainless steel
Rec. Lure Wt.: Not specified
Action: Medium-heavy
Handle: Double locking brass chrome reel seat.

Boat Rods

Model No.: 3722
Length: 6¾', 7¼', 7¾'
No. Pieces: 1
No. Guides: 5
Tip Top: Not specified
Rec. Lure Wt.: Not specified
Action: Heavy
Handle: Specie cork with fixed reel seat.

Model No.: 3722C. Same as Model 3722 except:
No. Guides: 5 conventional

Model No.: 3471D
Length: 6', 6½'
No. Pieces: 1
No. Guides: Not specified; all conventional dialoy guides
Tip Top: Not specified
Rec. Lure Wt.: Not specified
Action: Fast taper heavy
Handle: Not specified.

Model No.: 3471RT. Same as Model 3471D except:
Tip Top: Roller

Model No.: 3275
Length: 8', 9'
No. Pieces: 2
No. Guides: Not specified
Tip Top: Not specified
Rec. Lure Wt.: Not specified
Action: Medium-light

Regulation IGFA Class Rods

Model No.: 8083-20
Length: 6'8"
No. Pieces: 2
No. Guides: 3 roller
Tip Top: Roller
Action: 20 lb. trolling
Handle: Not specified.

Model No.: 8083-30. Same as Model 8083-20 except:
Action: 30 lb. trolling

Model No.: 8083-50. Same as Model 8083-20 except:
Action: 50 lb. trolling

Model No.: 8083-80. Same as Model 8083-20 except:
Action: 80 lb. trolling

Model No.: 8083-130. Same as Model 8083-20 except:
Action: 130 lb. trolling

Model No.: 8083-U. Same as Model 8083-20 except:
Action: Unlimited class

Popping Rod

Model No.: 363
Length: 7'
No. Pieces: 1
No. Guides: 5
Tip Top: Not specified
Rec. Lure Wt.: Not specified
Action: Medium
Handle: Cork grip with fixed reel seat.

Bait-Casting Rods

Model No.: 331
Length: 6'
No. Pieces: 2
No. Guides: Not specified; chrome-plated stainless steel spinning guides
Tip Top: Chrome-plated stainless steel
Rec. Lure Wt.: Not specified

Action: Medium-light
Handle: Specie cork grip with positive locking spin-casting handle.

Model No.: 340. Same as Model 331 except:
Length: 5½'
No. Pieces: 1
Action: Worm rod

Model No.: 80831
Length: 6'
No. Pieces: 2
No. Guides: 5 chrome-plated stainless steel spinning guides
Tip Top: Dialoy
Rec. Lure Wt.: Not specified
Action: Light
Handle: Specie cork grip with positive locking spin-casting handle.

Model No.: 4331
Length: 6', 6½', 7'
No. Pieces: 2
No. Guides: 5 chrome-plated stainless steel
Tip Top: Chrome-plated stainless steel
Rec. Lure Wt.: Bait and jig casting
Action: Fast taper medium-heavy
Handle: Positive locking with specie cork grip.

Model No.: 4430
Length: 5', 5½', 6'
No. Pieces: 1
No. Guides: 5 dialoy
Tip Top: Dialoy
Rec. Lure Wt.: Worm and jigging
Action: Fast taper heavy
Handle: Positive locking with specie cork grip.

Eagle Claw

Spinning Rods

Model No.: MB865
Length: 7'
No. Pieces: 2
No. Guides: 6 chromed
Tip Top: Chromed
Rec. Lure Wt.: Not specified
Action: Parabolic
Handle: Cork with fixed reel seat.

Model No.: MB865M. Same as Model MB865 except:
Action: Modified impact

Model No.: MB965F
Length: 6½', 7', 8', 8½'
No. Pieces: 2
No. Guides: 6 chromed carbon steel
Tip Top: Chromed carbon steel
Rec. Lure Wt.: Not specified
Action: Medium parabolic
Handle: Cork with fixed anodized aluminum reel seat.

Model No.: MB965FM. Same as Model MB965F except:
Length: 6½', 7'
Action: Modified impact action

Model No.: MBFLX. Same as Model MB965F except:

Length: 6½′, 7′
Action: Heavier action
Handle: Lighter reel seat.

Model No.: MJCF
Length: 6½′, 7′
No. Pieces: 2
No. Guides: 6 chromed stainless steel
Tip Top: Chromed stainless steel
Rec. Lure Wt.: Not specified
Action: Parabolic
Handle: Not specified.

Model No.: MJCF
Length: 8′
No. Pieces: 2
No. Guides: 6 chromed stainless steel
Tip Top: Chromed stainless steel
Rec. Lure Wt.: Heavy lures and bait
Action: Heavy
Handle: Not specified.

Model No.: MJCFM. Same as Model MJCF
except:
Length: 6½′, 7′
Action: Modified impact action

Model No.: M4465F
Length: 6½′, 7′
No. Pieces: 2
No. Guides: 6 hard chromed stainless steel
Tip Top: Tungsten carbide
Rec. Lure Wt.: Not specified
Action: Impact
Handle: Cork with fixed anodized aluminum reel seat and double locking rings.

Model No.: MSDS
Length: 6½′, 7′
No. Pieces: 2
No. Guides: 6 tungsten carbide
Tip Top: Tungsten carbide
Rec. Lure Wt.: Not specified
Action: Modified impact
Handle: Cork with fixed anodized aluminum reel seat and double locking rings.

Model No.: MA2L
Length: 6½′, 7′
No. Pieces: 2
No. Guides: 6 hard chromed stainless steel
Tip Top: Tungsten carbide
Rec. Lure Wt.: Not specified
Action: Impact
Handle: Cork with fixed anodized aluminum reel seat.

Model No.: MLWL
Length: 5′, 5½′, 6′, 6½′
No. Pieces: 2
No. Guides: 6 chromed stainless steel
Tip Top: Chromed stainless steel
Rec. Lure Wt.: Not specified
Action: Light parabolic
Handle: Cork with fixed anodized aluminum reel seat and double locking rings.

Model No.: LWLX. Same as Model MLWL
except:
Length: 4½′, 5′, 5½′
No. Pieces: 1

Model No.: MLW
Length: 5′, 6′, 6½′
No. Pieces: 2
No. Guides: 4 chromed stainless steel

Tip Top: Chromed stainless steel
Rec. Lure Wt.: Not specified
Action: Light parabolic
Handle: Specie cork reel seat with sliding rings.

Model No.: LWLW
Length: 5′, 5′4″, 5′8″
No. Pieces: 2
No. Guides: 5 chromed stainless steel
Tip Top: Chromed stainless steel
Rec. Lure Wt.: Plastic worm
Action: Pro-action
Handle: Cork with fixed anodized aluminum reel seat and double locking rings.

Model No.: MPLL
Length: 7′
No. Pieces: 2
No. Guides: 7 hard chromed stainless steel
Tip Top: Chromed stainless steel
Rec. Lure Wt.: Eggs, grubs and other light baits
Action: Fly rod action
Handle: Cork with anodized aluminum reel seat and chromed hood and sleeve.

Model No.: MPLS
Length: 7½′, 8′, 8½′, 9′
No. Pieces: 1
No. Guides: 5 hard chromed stainless steel
Tip Top: Chromed stainless steel
Rec. Lure Wt.: 7½′ rods: bait or trolling with light lures; 8′ rods: light lead or weighted flies; 8½′ rods: ⅜ oz.; 9′ rods:
Action: Light
Handle: Cork with fixed reel seat.

Model No. MPLX
Length: 6½′, 7′
No. Pieces: 1
No. Guides: 5 hard chromed stainless steel
Tip Top: Chromed stainless steel
Rec. Lure Wt.: Not specified
Action: Worm rod
Handle: Cork with fixed reel seat.

Model No.: MPLMC. Same as Model MPLX
except:
Length: 10′
Action: Mooching rod

Model No.: MPLFX. Same as Model MPLX
except:
Length: 8′3″, 9′
Action: Spinning steelhead; salmon

Model No.: MBNWS
Length: 8′, 8½′
No. Pieces: 1
No. Guides: 5 chromed stainless steel
Tip Top: Chromed stainless steel
Rec. Lure Wt.: Not specified
Action: Heavy
Handle: Cork with fixed reel seat.

Model No.: MB877. Same as Model MBNWS
except:
Length: 7′7″
Handle: Lighter weight reel seat.

Model No.: M8480
Length: 8′, 8½′
No. Pieces: 1
No. Guides: 5 hard chromed stainless steel
Tip Top: Chromed stainless steel

Rec. Lure Wt.: Not specified
Action: Impact, heavy duty
Handle: Cork with fixed anodized aluminum reel seat and double locking rings.

Model No.: M60DLS. Same as Model M8480 except:
Length: 8½′
Action: Full parabolic

Model No.: MB9SH
Length: 9′
No. Pieces: 1
No. Guides: 5 hard chromed stainless steel
Tip Top: Chromed
Rec. Lure Wt.: Not specified
Action: Heavy, salt water
Handle: Cork with fixed anodized aluminum reel seat and double locking rings.

Model No.: MSEA. Same as Model MB9SH
except:
Length: 7½′, 8′
Action: Light, salt water

Model No.: JRM
Length: 7′3″
No. Pieces: 2
No. Guides: 6 chrome stainless steel guides
Tip Top: Chrome stainless steel
Rec. Lure Wt.: Not specified
Action: Heavy
Handle: Detachable specie cork with chromed reel seat.

Model No.: MOS
Length: 6½′, 7′, 7½′, 8′, 8½′, 9′
No. Pieces: 2
No. Guides: 7 hard chromed stainless steel
Tip Top: Chromed stainless steel
Rec. Lure Wt.: Not specified
Action: Ocean (for fishing Coho and Chinook Salmon)
Handle: Cork with fixed reel seat.

Model No.: MOSS
Length: 10′
No. Pieces: 2
No. Guides: 7 hard chromed stainless steel
Tip Top: Chromed stainless steel
Rec. Lure Wt.: Not specified
Action: Ocean surf
Handle: Cork with fixed reel seat.

Model No.: OSX. Same as Model MOSS
except:
Length: 6½′, 7′, 7½′, 8′
No. Pieces: 1

Model No. 8770SP
Length: 7′
No. Pieces: 1
No. Guides: 5 hard chromed stainless steel (extra heavy duty)
Tip Top: Stainless steel
Rec. Lure Wt.: Not specified
Action: All-purpose
Handle: Cork with fixed reel seat.

Model No.: M4TMS
Length: 6½′
No. Pieces: 4 (breaks down to 24″ overall)
No. Guides: 5 hard chromed stainless steel
Tip Top: Chromed stainless steel
Rec. Lure Wt.: Not specified
Action: All-purpose

Handle: Cork with anodized aluminum reel seat and screw locking rings.

Model No.: M4TMH. Same as Model M4TMS except:
Length: 7½'
Action: Heavy

Model No.: M4TMSW. Same as Model M4TMS except:
Action: Heavy worm rod

Model No.: M4FRS. Same as Model M4TMS except:
Action: Medium parabolic

Model No.: M4LWL
Length: 5', 5½', 6'
No. Pieces: 4
No. Guides: 5 chromed stainless steel
Tip Top: Chromed stainless steel
Rec. Lure Wt.: Not specified
Action: Light
Handle: Cork with fixed anodized aluminum reel seat.

Model No.: M6TMS
Length: 6'9"
No. Pieces: 6
No. Guides: 5 stainless steel guides
Tip Top: Chromed
Rec. Lure Wt.: Not specified
Action: Light
Handle: Cork with fixed anodized aluminum reel seat.

Model No.: LWLFD
Length: 6½'
No. Pieces: 1
No. Guides: 4 foul-proof
Tip Top: Tungsten carbide
Rec. Lure Wt.: Worm
Action: Light
Handle: Specie cork with fixed anodized reel seat.

Model No.: MPLSX
Length: 7½'
No. Pieces: 2
No. Guides: 5 hard chromed stainless steel
Tip Top: Chromed stainless steel
Rec. Lure Wt.: Worm
Action: Light
Handle: Cork with fixed anodized aluminum reel seat, chromed hood and sleeve.

Model No.: MB960FML
Length: 6', 6½', 7'
No. Pieces: 2
No. Guides: 6 chromed carbon steel
Tip Top: Chromed carbon steel
Rec. Lure Wt.: Not specified
Action: Medium parabolic
Handle: Cork with fixed anodized aluminum reel seat.

Model No.: M5565
Length: 6½'
No. Pieces: 2
No. Guides: 6 hard chromed stainless steel
Tip Top: Tungsten carbide
Rec. Lure Wt.: Worm
Action: Impact
Handle: Cork with fixed anodized aluminum reel seat and double locking rings.

Model No.: SWBC
Length: 8', 9'
No. Pieces: 1
No. Guides: 5 hard chromed stainless steel (extra heavy duty)
Tip Top: Chromed stainless steel
Rec. Lure Wt.: Not specified
Action: Ocean surf
Handle: Cork with fixed chromed reel seat.

Model No.: MSTS
Length: 6', 6½', 7'
No. Pieces: 2
No. Guides: 7 hard chromed stainless steel (extra heavy duty)
Tip Top: Chromed stainless steel
Rec. Lure Wt.: Not specified
Action: All-purpose
Handle: Cork with fixed chrome reel seat.

Model No.: CPLW
Length: 5'4", 5'8"
No. Pieces: 1
No. Guides: 5 ceramic
Tip Top: Ceramic
Rec. Lure Wt.: Not specified
Action: Ultra light
Handle: Cork with fixed reel seat.

Model No.: PLW. Same as Model CPLW except:
No. Guides: 5 carbide
Tip Top: Carbide

Model No.: CPWDS
Length: 6½'
No. Pieces: 1
No. Guides: 5 ceramic
Tip Top: Ceramic
Rec. Lure Wt.: Not specified
Action: Not specified
Handle: Detachable; cork with fixed reel seat.

Model No.: PWDS. Same as Model CPWDS except:
No. Guides: 5 carbide
Tip Top: Carbide

Model No.: MCPWS
Length: 6½', 7'
No. Pieces: 2
No. Guides: 5 ceramic
Tip Top: Ceramic
Rec. Lure Wt.: Not specified
Action: Not specified
Handle: Specie cork pistol grip; handle is fitted with 26/64 female ferrule; also comes with a 26/64 male ferrule for attaching to rod blade.

Model No.: MPWS. Same as Model MCPWS except:
No. Guides: 5 carbide
Tip Top: Carbide

Model No.: MTM
Length: 6½', 7'
No. Pieces: 2
No. Guides: 5
Tip Top: Not specified
Rec. Lure Wt.: Plastic worm
Action: Not specified
Handle: Cork with fixed reel seat.

Model No.: MTM
Length: 6½', 7'

No. Pieces: 2
No. Guides: 5 hard chromed stainless steel
Tip Top: Chromed stainless steel
Rec. Lure Wt.: Plastic worm
Action: Not specified
Handle: Cork with fixed anodized aluminum reel seat and chromed hood and sleeve.

Model No.: PLW
Length: 5', 5'4", 5'8"
No. Pieces: 1
No. Guides: 5 tungsten carbide
Tip Top: Tungsten carbide
Rec. Lure Wt.: Worm
Action: Pro-action worm rod
Handle: Cork with fixed anodized aluminum reel seat and double locking rings.

Model No.: MPWS
Length: 6½', 7'
No. Pieces: 2
No. Guides: 5 tungsten carbide
Tip Top: Tungsten carbide
Rec. Lure Wt.: Worm
Action: Pro-action worm rod
Handle: Cork with fixed anodized aluminum reel seat and double locking rings.

Spin-Casting Rods

Model No.: MB1360
Length: 6', 6½'
No. Pieces: 2
No. Guides: 6 chrome-plated
Tip Top: Chrome-plated
Rec. Lure Wt.: Not specified
Action: Parabolic
Handle: Cork with baked enamel die-cast aluminum reel seat.

Model No.: MB1360M. Same as Model MB1360 except:
Action: Modified impact

Model No.: B1350W
Length: 5', 5½', 6', 6½'
No. Pieces: 1
No. Guides: 6 chrome-plated
Tip-Top: Chrome-plated
Rec. Lure Wt.: Not specified
Action: Pro-action
Handle: Cork with fixed baked enamel die-cast aluminum reel seat.

Model No.: MB1360X. Same as Model B1350W except:
Length: 6'
No. Pieces: 2

Model No.: MB2370
Length: 7'
No. Pieces: 2
No. Guides: 6 chromed carbon steel
Tip Top: Chromed carbon steel
Rec. Lure Wt.: Not specified
Action: Parabolic
Handle: Cork with fixed baked enamel die cast aluminum reel seat.

Model No.: MB2360. Same as Model MB2370 except:
Length: 6', 6½'
Action: Modified impact action

Model No.: MGCJM
Length: 6', 6½'

No. Pieces: 2
No. Guides: 6 chromed stainless steel
Tip Top: Chromed stainless steel
Rec. Lure Wt.: Not specified
Action: Modified impact
Handle: Cork with baked enamel die-cast aluminum reel seat.

Model No.: MDRC
Length: 6', 6½', 7'
No. Pieces: 2
No Guides: 6 hard chromed stainless steel
Tip Top: Tungsten carbide
Rec. Lure Wt.: Not specified
Action: Impact
Handle: Cork with baked die-cast aluminum reel seat.

Model No.: DHC
Length: 5', 5½', 6'
No. Pieces: 1
No. Guides: 6 hard chromed stainless steel
Tip Top: Chromed stainless steel
Rec. Lure Wt.: Not specified
Action: Pro-action
Handle: Cork with baked enamel die-cast aluminum reel seat.

Model No.: DHCC. Same as Model DHC except:
Handle: Ferruled detachable comfort grip.

Model No.: MDHC
Length: 5½', 6', 6½'
No. Pieces: 2
No. Guides: 6
Tip Top: Not specified
Rec. Lure Wt.: Not specified
Action: Not specified
Handle: Cork with fixed reel seat.

Model No.: MSDC
Length: 5½', 6', 6½'
No. Pieces: 2
No. Guides: 6 tungsten carbide
Tip Top: Tungsten carbide
Rec. Lure Wt.: Not specified
Action: Impact action
Handle: Cork with fixed baked enamel die cast aluminum reel seat.

Model No.: SDC
Length: 5', 5½', 6'
No. Pieces: 1
No. Guides: 6 tungsten carbide
Tip Top: Tungsten carbide
Rec. Lure Wt.: Not specified
Action: Pro-action
Handle: Cork with detachable baked enamel die-cast aluminum reel seat.

Model No.: SDCC. Same as Model SDC except:
Length: 5½', 6'
Handle: Ferruled detachable comfort grip.

Model No.: M2RC
Length: 6', 6½', 7'
No. Pieces: 2
No. Guides: 6 hard chromed stainless steel
Tip Top: Tungsten carbide
Rec. Lure Wt.: Not specified
Action: Impact
Handle: Cork with baked die-cast aluminum reel seat.

Model No.: 2RCH
Length: 5½', 6', 6½'
No. Pieces: 1
No. Guides: 6
Tip Top: Not specified
Rec. Lure Wt.: Not specified
Action: Worm
Handle: Detachable.

Model No.: 2RCHC. Same as Model 2RCH except:
Length: 5½', 6'
Handle: Ferruled detachable comfort grip.

Model No.: MLWC
Length: 6', 6½'
No. Pieces: 2
No. Guides: 6 chromed stainless steel
Tip Top: Chromed stainless steel
Rec. Lure Wt.: Not specified
Action: Light parabolic
Handle: Cork with baked enamel die-cast aluminum reel seat.

Model No.: MDWM
Length: 7'8"
No. Pieces: 2
No. Guides: Not specified; hard chromed stainless steel
Tip Top: Chromed stainless steel
Rec. Lure Wt.: Not specified
Action: Light
Handle: Cork with baked enamel die-cast aluminum reel seat.

Model No.: MDW. Same as Model MDWM except:
Length: 6'
Action: Worm and muskie

Model No.: DWX. Same as Model MDWM except:
Length: 6'
No. Pieces: 1
Action: Heavy
Handle: Detachable ferruled.

Model No.: M4TMC
Length: 6½'
No. Pieces: 4
No. Guides: 5 hard chromed stainless steel
Tip Top: Chromed stainless steel
Rec. Lure Wt.: Not specified
Action: All-purpose
Handle: Cork with baked enamel die-cast aluminum reel seat.

Model No.: M4TMCH. Same as Model M4TMC except:
Rec. Lure Wt.: Up to 1 oz.
Action: Medium

Model No.: M4TMCW. Same as Model M4TMC except:
Action: Heavy worm

Model No.: M6TMC
Length: 6½'
No. Pieces: 6
No. Guides: 5 stainless steel
Tip Top: Chromed stainless steel
Rec. Lure Wt.: Not specified
Action: All-purpose
Handle: Cork with baked enamel die-cast aluminum reel seat.

Model No.: MB1355M
Length: Not specified
No. Pieces: 2
No. Guides: 4 chrome-plated
Tip Top: Chrome-plated
Rec. Lure Wt.: Not specified
Action: Modified impact
Handle: Cork with baked enamel die-cast aluminum reel seat.

Model No.: CDHC5
Length: 5', 5½', 6'
No. Pieces: 1
No. Guides: 5 ceramic
Tip Top: Ceramic
Rec. Lure Wt.: Not specified
Action: Not specified
Handle: Detachable with fixed reel seat.

Model No.: LWLWC
Length: 5'4"
No. Pieces: 1
No. Guides: 4 chromed stainless steel
Tip Top: Chromed stainless steel
Rec. Lure Wt.: Not specified
Action: Light
Handle: Cork with fixed reel seat.

Model No.: LWLWD. Same as Model LWLWC except:
Length: 6½'
Handle: Detachable ferruled handle.

Casting Rods

Model No.: MOSC
Length: 8½', 9'
No. Pieces: 2
No. Guides: 7 hard-chromed stainless steel casting
Tip Top: Braced
Rec. Lure Wt.: Not specified
Action: Coho/Chinook
Handle: Brass chrome-plated reel seat with double locking rings.

Model No.: MPLC
Length: 8', 8½'
No. Pieces: 2
No. Guides: Not specified; hard-chromed stainless steel casting
Tip Top: Braced chromed stainless steel
Rec. Lure Wt.: Not specified
Action: Heavy
Handle: Anodized aluminum reel seat, extra length specie cork grip.

Salt Water Casting Rods

Model No.: MA9SH
Length: 9'
No. Pieces: 2
No. Guides: Not specified; hard-chromed stainless steel casting
Tip Top: Braced
Rec. Lure Wt.: Not specified
Action: Heavy
Handle: Fixed anodized aluminum reel seat with double locking rings.

Model No.: M8480R. Same as Model MA9SH except:
Length: 8'
Action: Impact

Boat Casting Rod

Model No.: MDF
Length: 8½'
No. Pieces: 2
No. Guides: Not specified; hard-chromed stainless steel
Tip Top: Braced
Rec. Lure Wt.: Not specified
Action: Heavy
Handle: Fixed anodized aluminum reel seat with double locking rings.

Mooching Rod

Model No.: MPLMC
Length: 10'
No. Pieces: 2
No. Guides: Not specified; hard-chromed stainless steel
Tip Top: Braced
Rec. Lure Wt.: Not specified
Action: Heavy
Handle: Anodized aluminum reel seat with double locking rings.

Popping Rods

Model No.: M8770-ST
Length: 7'
No. Pieces: 2
No. Guides: 7 hard-chromed stainless steel
Tip Top: Hard-chromed stainless steel
Rec. Lure Wt.: Not specified
Action: Not specified
Handle: Chromed reel seat.

Model No.: M8770-J. Same as Model M8770-ST except:
Handle: Chromed reel seat with finger trigger.

Model No.: 8765
Length: 6½'
No. Pieces: 2
No. Guides: Not specified; hard-chromed stainless steel extra heavy duty spinning
Tip Top: Braced hard-chromed
Rec. Lure Wt.: Not specified
Action: Not specified
Handle: Chromed reel seat with finger trigger.

Model No. AFS. Same as Model 8765 except:
Length: 7'

Model No.: 8770. Same as Model 8765 except:
Length: 7'

Model No.: CAFS7
Length: 7'
No. Pieces: 2
No. Guides: 4 ceramic
Tip Top: Ceramic
Rec. Lure Wt.: Not specified
Action: Not specified
Handle: Chromed reel seat with finger trigger.

Trolling Rods

Model No.: MTR
Length: 6½', 7', 7½', 8'
No. Pieces: 2
No. Guides: 5 chrome-plated stainless steel
Tip Top: Chrome-plated stainless steel
Rec. Lure Wt.: Not specified
Action: Light
Handle: Hardwood handle with cork foregrip.

Model No.: MTRL. Same as Model MTR except:
Tip Top: Light sensitive tip for fresh water

Model No.: MPLT
Length: 8'
No. Pieces: 2
No. Guides: 6 hard-chromed stainless steel
Rec. Lure Wt.: Not specified
Action: Light
Handle: Hardwood with cork foregrip and anodized reel seat.

Model No.: MBNWT
Length: 7'4"
No. Pieces: 2
No. Guides: 4 chromed stainless steel
Tip Top: Chromed stainless steel
Rec. Lure Wt.: Not specified
Action: Heavy
Handle: Chromed reel seat with finger trigger, hardwood rear grip, and cork foregrip.

Model No.: M8485TR
Length: 8½'
No. Pieces: 2
No. Guides: 6 hard-chromed stainless steel casting
Tip Top: Braced
Rec. Lure Wt.: Not specified
Action: Heavy
Handle: Anodized aluminum double locking rings, hardwood handle, and cork foregrip.

Model No.: GTRT
Length: 7½'
No. Pieces: 2
No. Guides: 3 chromed stainless steel casting
Tip Top: Steel roller
Rec. Lure Wt.: Not specified
Action: Ocean trolling
Handle: Detachable hardwood handle with cork foregrip and rubber butt cap.

Steelhead

Model No.: M8485
Length: 8½'
No. Pieces: 2
No. Guides: Not specified; hard-chromed stainless steel
Tip Top: Braced
Rec. Lure Wt.: Not specified
Action: Steelhead
Handle: Fixed anodized aluminum reel seat with double locking rings.

Worm Rods

Model No.: CPWR
Length: 5½', 6', 6½'
No. Pieces: 2
No. Guides: 5 ceramic
Tip Top: Ceramic
Rec. Lure Wt.: Not specified
Action: Worm
Handle: Spin cast comfort grip, detachable handle.

Model No.: PWR. Same as Model CPWR except:
No. Guides: 5 carbide
Tip Top: Carbide

Fly Rods

Model No.: MLWFF5, MLWFF5½
Length: 5', 5½'
No. Pieces: 2
No. Guides: 5 stainless steel snake guides plus one chromed stainless steel stripper guide
Tip Top: Chromed
Rec. Line: Not specified
Handle: Anodized reel seat of lightweight aluminum.

Model No.: M4LWFF
Length: 6½'
No. Pieces: 4
No. Guides: Not specified; stainless steel snake guides plus one chromed stripper guide
Tip Top: Chromed
Rec. Line: 6 wt.
Handle: Anodized aluminum reel seat.

Model No.: M4TMF
Length: 7½'
No. Pieces: 4
No. Guides: 5 stainless steel snake guides plus one chromed stripper guide
Tip Top: Chromed
Rec. Line: 7 wt.
Handle: Granger nickel silver reel seat, specie cork grip.

Model No.: M6TMF
Length: 6'9"
No. Pieces: 6
No. Guides: 5 stainless steel snake guides plus one chromed stripper guide
Tip Top: Chromed
Rec. Line: 7 wt.
Handle: Anodized reel seat of light aluminum.

Model No.: M4FRF
Length: 7½'
No. Pieces: 4
No. Guides: 5 stainless steel snake guides plus one chromed stripper guide
Tip Top: Chromed
Rec. Line: 7 wt.
Handle: Anodized screw lock reel seat, specie cork grip.

Model No.: M8599
Length: 9'
No. Pieces: 2
No. Guides: 7 stainless steel and one chromed stripper guide
Tip Top: Hand chrome-plated
Rec. Line: 10 wt.
Handle: Anodized aluminum reel seat, specie cork grip.

Model No.: MPFLS-9
Length: 9'
No. Pieces: 2
No. Guides: 6 chromed stainless steel spinning guides
Tip Top: Chromed
Rec. Line: 10 wt.
Handle: Special extension butt, anodized aluminum reel seat, specie cork grip.

Model No.: MLWFF
Length: 6', 6½', 7'
No. Pieces: 2
No. Guides: 5 stainless steel snake guides plus one chromed stainless steel stripper
Tip Top: Chromed
Rec. Line: 6 wt.
Handle: Anodized reel seats of lightweight aluminum.

Model No.: M2A
Length: 7½', 8', 8½', 9'
No. Pieces: 2
No. Guides: Not specified; gold finished stainless steel plus one hard-chromed stripper
Tip Top: Hard-chromed
Rec. Line: 7'—6 wt., 7½', 8', 8½'—7 wt., 9'—9 wt.
Handle: Anodized aluminum reel seat.

Model No.: MB8A
Length: 7', 7½', 8', 8½', 9'
No. Pieces: 2
No. Guides: Chromed stripper guide
Tip Top: Not specified
Rec. Line: 7'—6 wt., 7'6"—7 wt., 8' and 8'6"—7 wt., 9'—9 wt.
Handle: Aluminum reel seat, specie cork grip.

Model No.: M3A
Length: 7½', 8', 8½', 9'
No. Pieces: 2
No. Guides: 6 stainless steel snake guides plus one chromed stripper guide
Tip Top: Chromed
Rec. Line: 7½', 8', 8½'—7 wt., 9'—9 wt.
Handle: Specie cork grip.

Model No.: M4A
Length: 8', 8½'
No. Pieces: 2
No. Guides: 7 chromed stainless steel
Tip Top: Chromed stainless steel
Rec. Line: 7 wt.
Handle: Anodized reel seat of lightweight aluminum.

Model No.: MB2580
Length: 8'
No. Pieces: Not specified
No. Guides: Not specified; chromed stainless steel stripper
Tip Top: Chromed
Rec. Line: 7 wt.
Handle: Anodized aluminum reel seat.

Model No.: MB2585. Same as Model MB2580 except:
Length: 8½'

Spin/Fly Rods

Model No.: M4TMU
Length: 7½'
No. Pieces: 4
No. Guides: 6 stainless steel
Tip Top: Chromed stainless steel
Action: Medium parabolic
Rec. Line: 7 wt.
Rec. Lure Wt.: Not specified
Handle: Reversible handle with screw lock anodized aluminum reel seat, specie cork grip.

Model No.: M4TMUL. Same as Model M4TMU except:
Length: 6½'
Rec. Lure Wt.: Up to ¼ oz.

Model No.: M4FRU
Length: 7½'
No. Pieces: 4
No. Guides: 6 stainless steel
Tip Top: Chromed stainless steel
Rec. Line: 7 wt.
Handle: Screw lock anodized aluminum reversible reel seat, specie cork grip.

Model No.: M4PLP
Length: 7½'
No. Pieces: 4
No. Guides: 5 stainless steel snake guides plus one spinning butt stripper
Tip Top: Chromed stainless steel
Rec. Line: Not specified
Handle: Anodized aluminum reel seat and gold-plated sliding rings on cork foregrip.

Model No.: M6TMU
Length: 6'9"
No. Pieces: 6
No. Guides: 5 stainless steel
Tip Top: Chromed stainless steel
Rec. Line: Not specified
Handle: Screw lock anodized aluminum reversible reel seat, specie cork grip.

All-Purpose Travel Rod

Model No.: VM8TM—sets up as 5 different rods
Length: 6'9"
No. Pieces: 8
No. Guides: Not specified; chromed stainless steel
Tip Top: Chromed stainless steel
Rec. Lure Wt.: Not specified
Action: Not specified
Handle: Reversible with specie cork grips.

Red Snapper Rod

Model No.: RS-6
Length: 6'
No. Pieces: 1
No. Guides: 7 chromed stainless steel casting
Tip Top: Braced chromed
Rec. Lure Wt.: Not specified
Action: Heavy
Handle: Brass chrome-plated reel seat with double locking rings, extra long specie cork grip.

Fenwick

Spinning Rods

Model No.: 945
Length: 4½'
No. Pieces: 1
No. Guides: Not specified; ceramic
Tip Top: Ceramic
Rec. Lure Wt.: ⅛-½ oz.
Action: Heavy
Handle: Double locking aluminum reel seat, cork grip.

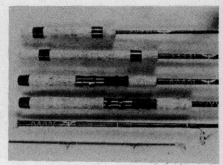

Spinning rods

Model No.: 953
Length: 5'3"
No. Pieces: 1
No. Guides: Not specified; ceramic
Tip Top: Ceramic
Rec. Lure Wt.: ⅛-⅝ oz.
Action: Heavy
Handle: Double locking aluminum reel seat, cork grip.

Model No.: G-953-graphite. Same as Model 953.

Model No.: 960
Length: 6'
No. Pieces: 1
No. Guides: Not specified; ceramic
Tip Top: Ceramic
Rec. Lure Wt.: ½-1 oz.
Action: Heavy
Handle: Double locking aluminum reel seat, cork grip.

Model No.: 965
Length: 6½'
No. Pieces: 1
No. Guides: Not specified; ceramic
Tip Top: Ceramic
Rec. Lure Wt.: ½-1 oz.
Action: Heavy
Handle: Double locking aluminum reel seat, cork grip.

Model No.: 970
Length: 7'
No. Pieces: 1
No. Guides: Not specified; ceramic
Tip Top: Ceramic
Rec. Lure Wt.: ½-1 oz.
Action: Heavy
Handle: Double locking aluminum reel seat, cork grip.

Model No.: PLS605
Length: 6'
No. Pieces: 2
No. Guides: Not specified; ceramic
Tip Top: Ceramic
Rec. Lure Wt.: ¼-½ oz.
Action: Medium
Handle: Double locking aluminum reel seat, cork grip.

Model No.: PLS61
Length: 6'
No. Pieces: 2
No. Guides: Not specified; hard-chrome spin guides

Tip Top: Carbide
Rec. Lure Wt.: ⅜-⅝ oz.
Action: Medium
Handle: Double locking aluminum reel seat, cork grip.

Model No.: PLS615. Same as Model PLS61 except:
No. Guides: Not specified; ceramic
Tip Top: Ceramic

Model No.: PLS65
Length: 6½'
No. Pieces: 2
No. Guides: Not specified; hard-chrome spin guides
Tip Top: Carbide
Rec. Lure Wt.: ¼-⅝ oz.
Action: Medium
Handle: Double locking aluminum reel seat, cork grip.

Model No.: PLS65S. Same as Model PLS65 except:
No. Guides: Not specified; ceramic
Tip Top: Ceramic

Model No.: PLS66
Length: 6½'
No. Pieces: 2
No. Guides: Not specified; ceramic
Tip Top: Ceramic
Rec. Lure Wt.: ½-1 oz.
Action: Heavy
Handle: Double locking aluminum reel seat, cork grip.

Model No.: PLS70
Length: 7'
No. Pieces: 2
No. Guides: Not specified; hard-chrome spin guides
Tip Top: Carbide
Rec. Lure Wt.: ¼-⅝ oz.
Action: Medium
Handle: Double locking aluminum reel seat, cork grip.

Model No.: PLS70S. Same as Model PLS70 except:
No. Guides: Not specified; ceramic
Tip Top: Ceramic

Model No.: PLS70-4. Same as Model PLS70 except:
No. Pieces: 4
Rec. Lure Wt.: ⅛-⅝ oz.

Model No.: PLS72
Length: 7'
No. Pieces: 2
No. Guides: Not specified; ceramic
Tip Top: Ceramic
Rec. Lure Wt.: ½-1 oz.
Action: Heavy
Handle: Double locking aluminum reel seat, cork grip.

Model No.: PLS75
Length: 7½'
No. Pieces: 2
No. Guides: Not specified; hard-chrome braced spinning guides
Tip Top: Carbide
Rec. Lure Wt.: ¼-⅝ oz.
Action: Light
Handle: Double locking aluminum or chrome-plated brass reel seat, cork grip with butt cap and winding check.

Model No.: FS79. Same as Model PLS75 except:
Length: 7'9"

Model No.: FS83. Same as Model PLS75 except:
Length: 8'3"

Model No.: FS50
Length: 5'
No. Pieces: 2
No. Guides: Not specified; chrome-plated stainless steel
Tip Top: Carbide
Rec. Lure Wt.: ¹⁄₁₆-¼ oz.

Spinning rods

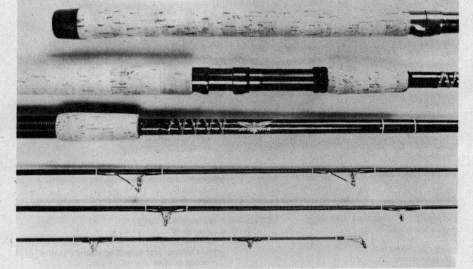

Action: Ultra-light
Handle: Cork grip with sliding rings.

Model No.: FS55
Length: 5½'
No. Pieces: 2
No. Guides: Not specified; chrome-plated stainless steel
Tip Top: Carbide
Rec. Lure Wt.: ¹⁄₁₆-¼ oz.
Action: Ultra-light
Handle: Cork grip with sliding rings.

Model No.: FS60
Length: 6'
No. Pieces: 2
No. Guides: Not specified; chrome-plated stainless steel
Tip Top: Carbide
Rec. Lure Wt.: ¹⁄₁₆-¼ oz.
Action: Ultra-light
Handle: Cork grip with sliding rings.

Model No.: FS61. Same as Model FS60 except:
Handle: Double locking aluminum reel seat, cork grip.

Model No.: FS64
Length: 6½'
No. Pieces: Not specified
No. Guides: Not specified; chrome-plated stainless steel
Tip Top: Carbide
Rec. Lure Wt.: ⅛-⅜ oz.
Action: Ultra-light
Handle: Cork grip with sliding rings.

Model No.: FS65
Length: 6½'
No. Pieces: Not specified
No. Guides: Not specified; chrome-plated stainless steel
Tip Top: Carbide
Rec. Lure Wt.: ¼-½ oz.
Action: Light
Handle: Fixed double locking reel seat, cork grip.

Model No.: FS65-4. Same as Model FS65 except:
No. Pieces: 4
Rec. Lure Wt.: ⅛-⅜ oz.

Model No.: FS70
Length: 7'
No. Pieces: Not specified
No. Guides: Not specified; chrome-plated stainless steel
Tip Top: Carbide
Rec. Lure Wt.: ¼-½ oz.
Action: Light
Handle: Double locking aluminum reel seat, cork grip.

Model No.: FS70-4. Same as Model FS70 except:
No. Pieces: 4
Rec. Lure Wt.: ⅛-½ oz.

Model No.: FS75
Length: 7½'
No. Pieces: Not specified
No. Guides: Not specified; chrome-plated stainless steel

Tip Top: Carbide
Rec. Lure Wt.: ¼ - ½ oz.
Action: Light
Handle: Double locking aluminum reel seat, cork grip.

Model No.: FS80
Length: 8'
No. Pieces: 2
No. Guides: Not specified; hard-chrome braced spinning guides
Tip Top: Carbide
Rec. Lure Wt.: ⅜-1 oz.
Action: Medium-light
Handle: Double locking aluminum or chrome-plated brass reel seat, cork grip with butt cap and winding check.

Model No.: FS85. Same as Model FS80 except:
Length: 8½'

Model No.: FS90. Same as Model FS80 except:
Length: 9'

Model No.: FS86
Length: 8½'
No. Pieces: 2
No. Guides: Not specified; hard-chrome braced spinning guides
Tip Top: Carbide
Rec. Lure Wt.: ⅝-1½ oz.
Action: Medium
Handle: Double locking aluminum or chrome-plated brass reel seat, cork grip with butt cap and winding check.

Model No.: FS88. Same as Model FS86

Model No.: GFS70-graphite
Length: 7'
No. Pieces: Not specified
No. Guides: Not specified; chrome-plated stainless steel
Tip Top: Carbide
Rec. Lure Wt.: ¼-½ oz.
Action: Light
Handle: Double locking aluminum reel seat, cork grip.

Model No.: GFS83-graphite
Length: 8'3"
No. Pieces: 2
No. Guides: Not specified; hard-chrome braced spinning guides
Tip Top: Carbide
Rec. Lure Wt.: ¼-⅝ oz.
Action: Light
Handle: Not specified.

Model No.: FS67-4
Length: 5'9"
No. Pieces: 4
No. Guides: Not specified; chrome-plated stainless steel
Tip Top: Carbide
Rec. Lure Wt.: ⅟₁₆-⅜ oz.
Action: Ultra-light
Handle: Cork grip with aluminum sliding rings.

Model No.: 140
Length: 4½'
No. Pieces: 1

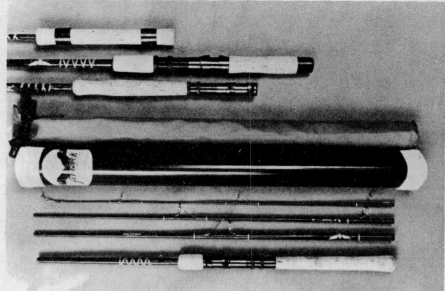

Voyageur rods

No. Guides: Not specified; chrome-plated stainless steel
Tip Top: Carbide
Rec. Lure Wt.: ⅟₁₆-¼ oz.
Action: Ultra-light
Handle: Cork grip with sliding rings.

Model No.: G145-graphite
Length: 4½'
No. Pieces: 1
No. Guides: Not specified; chrome-plated stainless steel
Tip Top: Carbide
Rec. Lure Wt.: ⅟₁₆-¼ oz.
Action: Ultra-light
Handle: Cork grip with sliding rings.

Salt Water Spinning Rods

Model No.: PS90
Length: 9'
No. Pieces: Not specified
No. Guides: Not specified; hard-chrome braced
Tip Top: Carbide
Rec. Lure Wt.: 1-4 oz.
Action: Heavy
Handle: Double locking reel seat, cork grip.

Model No.: PS105. Same as Model PS90 except:
Length: 10½'
Rec. Lure Wt.: 3-6 oz.

Model No.: PS100. Same as Model PS90 except:
Length: 10'
Rec. Lure Wt.: 4-10 oz.

Model No.: PS120. Same as Model PS90 except:
Length: 12'
Rec. Lure Wt.: 3-6 oz.

Model No.: PB73
Length: 7'3"

No. Pieces: Not specified
No. Guides: Not specified; hard-chrome braced
Tip Top: Carbide
Rec. Lure Wt.: ½-1½ oz.
Action: Fast
Handle: Heavy duty reel seat, cork grip.

Spin-Casting Rods

Model No.: FC60
Length: 6'
No. Pieces: 2
No. Guides: Not specified; ceramic
Rec. Lure Wt.: ¼-⅝ oz.
Action: Light
Handle: Hypalon foregrips with rear cork grips and heavy duty tempered aluminum notched butt ferrules. Detachable soft plastic butt cap.

Model No.: FC65. Same as Model FC60 except:
Length: 6½'
Rec. Lure Wt.: ⅜-⅝ oz.

Model No.: GFC554-graphite. Same as Model FC60 except:
Length: 5½'
No. Pieces: 1
Rec. Lure Wt.: ⅜-¾ oz.
Action: Medium

Model No.: 1060. Same as Model FC60 except:
No. Pieces: 1

Model No.: 1155. Same as Model FC60 except:
Length: 5½'
No. Pieces: 1
Rec. Lure Wt.: ⅜-¾ oz.
Action: Medium

Model No.: 1160. Same as Model FC60 except:

No. Pieces: 1
Rec. Lure Wt.: ⅜-¾ oz.
Action: Medium

Bait-Casting Rods

Model No.: PLC60
Length: 6'
No. Pieces: 2
No. Guides: Not specified; ceramic
Tip Top: Ceramic
Rec. Lurt Wt.: ½-1 oz.
Action: Power
Handle: Hypalon foregrips with rear corkgrips and heavy duty tempered aluminum notched butt ferrules. Detachable soft plastic butt cap.

Model No.: 1255. Same as Model PLC60 except:
Length: 5½'
No. Pieces: 1
No. Guides: Not specified; carbide
Tip Top: Carbide

Model No.: 1260. Same as Model PLC60 except:
No. Pieces: 1
No. Guides: Not specified; carbide
Tip Top: Carbide

Model No.: 1450. Same as Model PLC60 except:
Length: 5'
No. Pieces: 1

Model No.: 1455. Same as Model PLC60 except:
Length: 5½'
No. Pieces: 1

Model No.: 1460. Same as Model PLC60 except:
No. Pieces: 1

Model No.: GFC555-graphite. Same as Model PLC60 except:
Length: 5½'
No. Pieces: 1

Model No.: GFC605-graphite. Same as Model PLC60 except:
No. Pieces: 1

Model No.: 1457
Length: 5½'
No. Pieces: 1
No. Guides: Not specified; ceramic
Tip Top: Ceramic
Rec. Lure Wt.: ⅝-1⅝ oz.
Action: Fast tip; extra power
Handle: Hypalon foregrip with cork rear grips and heavy duty notched tempered aluminum butt ferrules. Detachable soft plastic butt cap.

Model No.: GFC557. Same as Model 1457 except graphite

Model No.: 1465
Length: 6½'
No. Pieces: 1
No. Guides: Not specified; ceramic
Tip Top: Ceramic
Rec. Lure Wt.: ½-1 oz.
Action: Extra power
Handle: Hypalon foregrips with cork rear grips and heavy duty notched tempered aluminum butt ferrules. Detachable soft plastic butt cap.

Model No.: 1256. Same as Model 1465 except:
Length: 5½'
No. Guides: Not specified; carbide
Tip Top: Carbide
Rec. Lure Wt.: ⅝-1¼ oz.

Model No.: 1261. Same as Model 1465 except:
No. Guides: Not specified; carbide
Tip Top: Carbide
Rec. Lure Wt.: ⅝-1¼ oz.

Model No.: 1456. Same as Model 1465 except:
Length: 5½'
Rec. Lure Wt.: ⅝-1¼ oz.

Saltwater rods

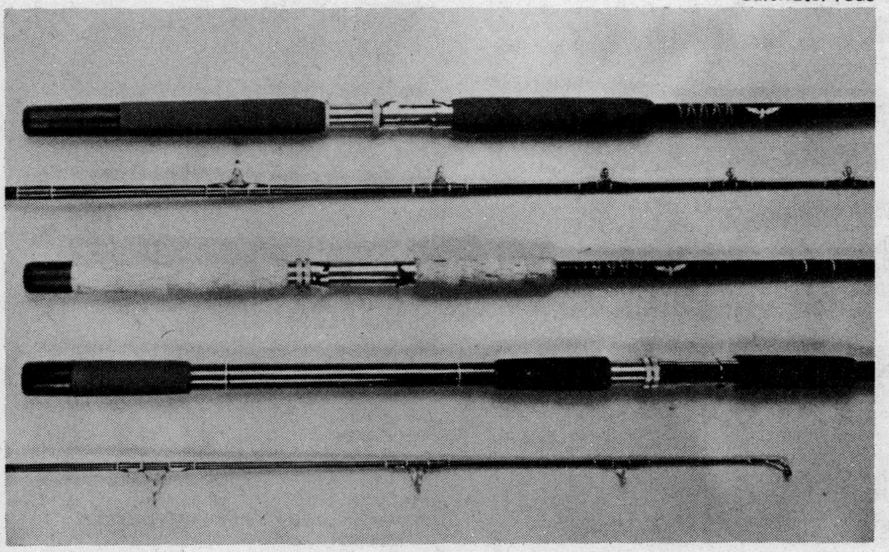

Model No.: 1461. Same as Model 1465 except:
Rec. Lure Wt.: ⅝-1¼ oz.

Model No.: GFC556-graphite. Same as Model 1465 except:
Length: 5½'
Rec. Lure Wt.: ⅝-1¼ oz.

Model No.: FS110
Length: 9'
No. Pieces: 2
No. Guides: Not specified; hard-chrome braced spinning guides
Tip Top: Carbide
Rec. Lure Wt.: ⅜-¾ oz.
Action: Casting rod
Handle: Double locking aluminum or chrome-plated brass reel seats, cork grip with butt cap and winding check.

Salt Water Bait-Casting Rods

Model No.: PLB70C
Length: 7'
No. Pieces: 2
No. Guides: Not specified; hard-chrome braced spin guides
Tip Top: Carbide
Rec. Lure Wt.: Trolling
Action: Medium
Handle: Double locking reel seats, cork grips.

Model No.: PLB76. Same as Model PLB70C except:
Length: 7½'
Rec. Lure Wt.: ½-¾ oz.

Model No.: PLB79. Same as Model PLB70C except:
Length: 7'9"
Rec. Lure Wt.: ⅝-1½ oz.

Model No.: PLB83. Same as Model PLB70C except:
Length: 8'3"
Rec. Lure Wt.: ¾-2 oz.

Model No.: PLB90. Same as Model PLB70C except:
Length: 9'
Rec. Lure Wt.: 1-3 oz.

Steelhead-Casting Rods

Model No.: FS79C
Length: 7'9"
No. Pieces: 2
No. Guides: Not specified; ceramic
Tip Top: Ceramic
Rec. Lure Wt.: ¼-⅝ oz.
Action: Steelhead
Handle: Double locking aluminum or chrome-plated brass reel seat, cork grip with butt cap and winding check.

Model No.: FS80C. Same as Model FS79C except:
Length: 8'
Rec. Lure Wt.: ⅜-1 oz.

Model No.: FS83C. Same as Model FS79C except:
Length: 8'3"

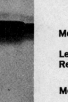

Model No.: FS85C. Same as Model FS79C
except:
Length: 8½'
Rec. Lure Wt.: ⅜-1 oz.

Model No.: GFS83C-graphite. Same as
Model FS79C except:
Length: 8'3"

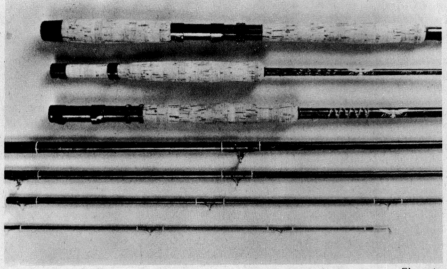

Fly rods

Fly Rods

Model No.: FF535
Length: 5'3"
No. Pieces: 2
No. Guides: Chrome-plated
Tip Top: Chrome-plated
Rec. Line: 5 wt.
Handle: Cork grip.

Model No.: FF605. Same as Model FF535
except:
Length: 6'

Model No.: FF705. Same as Model FF535
except:
Length: 7'

Model No.: FF706. Same as Model FF535
except:
Length: 7'
Rec. Line: 6 wt.

Model No.: FF755. Same as Model FF535
except:
Length: 7½'

Model No.: GFF755. Same as Model FF755
except graphite

Model No.: FF756. Same as Model FF535
except:
Length: 7½'
Rec. Line: 6 wt.

Model No.: FF756-4. Same as Model FF756
except:

No. Pieces: 4
Handle: Shaped cork with lightweight
aluminum reel seat, single lock nut,
hook keeper.

Model No.: FF805. Same as Model FF535
except:
Length: 8'

Model No.: FF806. Same as Model FF535
except:
Length: 8'
Rec. Line: 6 wt.

Model No.: FF806-4. Same as Model FF806
except:
No. Pieces: 4
Handle: Shaped cork with lightweight
aluminum reel seat, single lock nut, hook
keeper.

Model No.: GFF806-graphite. Same as Model
FF535 except:
Length: 8'
Rec. Line: 6 wt.

Model No.: FF807. Same as Model FF535
except:
Length: 8'
Rec. Line: 7 wt.

Model No.: FF855. Same as Model FF535
except:
Length: 8½'

Model No.: FF856. Same as Model FF535
except:
Length: 8½'
Rec. Line: 6 wt.

Model No.: FF856-5. Same as Model FF856
except:
No. Pieces: 5
Handle: Shaped cork with lightweight
aluminum reel seat, single lock nut,
hook keeper.

Model No.: GFF856-graphite. Same as
Model FF535 except:
Length: 8½'
Rec. Line: 6 wt.

Model No.: FF857. Same as Model FF535
except:
Length: 8½'
Rec. Line: 7 wt.

Model No.: FF858. Same as Model FF535
except:
Length: 8½'
Rec. Line: 8 wt.

Model No.: FF858-6. Same as Model FF858
except:
No. Pieces: 6
Handle: Shaped cork with lightweight
aluminum reel seat, single lock nut,
hook keeper.

Model No.: GFF858-graphite. Same as Model
FF535 except:
Length: 8½'
Rec. Line: 8 wt.

Model No.: FF908. Same as Model FF535
except:
Length: 9'
Rec. Line: 8 wt.

Model No.: GFF908-graphite. Same as
Model FF535 except:
Length: 9'
Rec. Line: 8 wt.

Model No.: FF909. Same as Model FF535
except:
Length: 9'
Rec. Line: 9 wt.
Handle: Cork grip with 6" detachable
fighting butt.

Model No.: FF9010. Same as Model FF535
except:
Length: 9'
Rec. Line: 10 wt.
Handle: Cork grip with 6" detachable
fighting butt.

Model No.: GFF9010-graphite. Same as
Model FF535 except:
Length 9'
Rec. Line: 10 wt.
Handle: Cork grip with 6" detachable
fighting butt.

Model No.: FF9310. Same as Model FF535
except:
Length: 9'3"
Rec. Line: 10 wt.
Handle: Cork grip with 6" detachable
fighting butt.

Model No.: GFF704-graphite
Length: 7'
No. Pieces: 2
No. Guides: Chrome-plated
Tip Top: Chrome-plated
Rec. Line: 4 wt.
Handle: Shaped cork with lightweight
aluminum reel seat.

Saltwater Fly Rods

Model No.: FF9012
Length: 9'
No. Pieces: 2
No. Guides: Not specified; chrome-plated
Tip Top: Chrome-plated
Rec. Line: 12 wt.
Handle: Cork grip with permanently attached 2" fighting butt.

Model No.: GFF9012. Same as Model FF9012 except graphite

Model No.: FF9311
Length: 9'3"
No. Pieces: 2
No. Guides: Not specified; chrome-plated
Tip Top: Chrome-plated
Rec. Line: 11 wt.
Handle: Cork grip with 6" detachable fighting butt.

Mooching Rods

Model No.: FS88C
Length: 8½'
No. Pieces: 2
No. Guides: Not specified; ceramic
Tip Top: Ceramic
Rec. Lure Wt.: ⅝-1½ oz.
Action: Heavy
Handle: Chrome-plated double locking brass reel seat, cork grip.

Model No.: FS89C. Same as Model FS88C except:
Length: 8'10"
Rec. Lure Wt.: 1-2½ oz.

Popping, Musky and Deep Jigging Rods

Model No.: 762
Length: 6'
No. Pieces: 1
No. Guides: Not specified; ceramic
Tip Top: Ceramic
Rec. Lure Wt.: ½-1½ oz.
Action: Heavy
Handle: Double locking chrome-plated reel seat, cork grip.

Model No.: 770
Length: 7'
No. Pieces: 1
No. Guides: Not specified; chrome-plated stainless steel
Tip Top: Ceramic
Rec. Lure Wt.: ½-1 oz.
Action: Heavy
Handle: Double locking chrome-plated reel seat, cork grip.

Model No.: 771
Length: 7'
No. Pieces: 1
No. Guides: Not specified; ceramic
Tip Top: Ceramic
Rec. Lure Wt.: ¾-3 oz.
Action: Heavy
Handle: Double locking chrome-plated reel seat, cork grip.

Model No.: 772
Length: 7'

No. Pieces: 1
No. Guides: Not specified; ceramic
Tip Top: Ceramic
Rec. Lure Wt.: 1-5 oz.
Action: Heavy
Handle: Double locking chrome-plated reel seat, cork grip.

Model No.: PLP56
Length: 5½'
No. Pieces: 2
No. Guides: Not specified; ceramic
Tip Top: Ceramic
Rec. Lure Wt.: 1-3 oz.
Acton: Heavy
Handle: Double locking chrome-plated reel seat, cork grip.

Model No.: PLP62
Length: 6'2"
No. Pieces: 2
No. Guides: Not specified; ceramic
Tip Top: Ceramic
Rec. Lure Wt.: ½-1½ oz.
Action: Heavy
Handle: Double locking chrome-plated reel seat, cork grip.

Model No.: PLP65
Length: 6½'
No. Pieces: 2
No. Guides: Not specified; ceramic
Tip Top: Ceramic
Rec. Lure Wt.: ½-1 oz.
Action: Heavy
Handle: Double locking chrome-plated reel seat, cork grip.

Model No.: PLP71
Length: 7'
No. Pieces: 2
No. Guides: Not specified; ceramic
Tip Top: Ceramic
Rec. Lure Wt.: ½-1 oz.
Action: Heavy
Handle: Double locking chrome-plated reel seat, cork grip.

Trolling Rods

Model No.: 610 (Deluxe)
Length: 6'9"
No. Pieces: 2
No. Guides: 5 Aftco roller
Tip Top: Aftco roller
Rec. Lure Wt.: Not specified
Action: Trolling rod
Line Class: 12 lb.
Handle: Hypalon covered stainless steel with gimbal nock.

Model No.: 620. Same as Model 610 except:
Line Class: 20 lb.

Model No.: 630. Same as Model 610 except:
Line Class: 30 lb.

Model No.: 640. Same as Model 610 except:
Line Class: 50 lb.

Model No.: 660. Same as Model 610 except:
Length: 7'1"
No. Guides: 5 Mildrum double roller
Tip Top: Mildrum double roller
Line Class: 80 lb.

Model No.: 670. Same as Model 610 except:
Length: 7'1"
No. Guides: 5 Mildrum double roller
Tip Top: Mildrum double roller
Line Class: 130 lb.

Model No.: 611 (Standard)
Length: 6'9"
No. Pieces: 1
No. Guides: Not specified; carbide
Tip Top: Roller
Rec. Lure Wt.: Not specified
Action: Trolling rod
Line Class: 12 lb.
Handle: Hypalon covered stainless steel with gimbal nock.

Model No.: 621. Same as Model 611 except:
Line Class: 20 lb.

Model No.: 631. Same as Model 611 except:
Line Class: 30 lb.

Model No.: 641. Same as Model 611 except:
Line Class: 50 lb.

Model No.: 831. Same as Model 611 except:
Line Class: 30 lb.
Handle: Handle does not detach.

Model No.: 522 (Boat)
Length: 7'6"
No. Pieces: 2
No. Guides: Not specified; carbide
Tip Top: Roller
Rec. Lure Wt.: Not specified
Action: Trolling rod
Line Class: 18-25 lb.
Handle: Hypalon with rubber butt cap and chrome-plated double locking reel seat.

Model No.: 532. Same as Model 522 except:
Line Class: 25-40 lb.

Model No.: 663 (Offshore)
Length: 7'1"
No. Pieces: 2
No. Guides: Not specified; Mildrum braced tuna intermediate guides plus one Mildrum double roller lead guide
Tip Top: Mildrum double roller
Rec. Lure Wt.: Not specified
Action: Trolling rod
Line Class: 80 lb.
Handle: Hypalon covered stainless steel with gimbal nock and double locking reel seat.

Model No.: 673. Same as Model 663 except:
Line Class: 130 lb.

Fly/Spin Combo Rods

Model No.: SF74-4
Length: 7'
No. Pieces: 4
No. Guides: Not specified; chrome-plated
Tip Top: Chrome-plated
Rec. Line: 6 wt.
Handle: Cork grip.

Model No.: SF75-5. Same as Model SF74-4 except:
Length: 7½'
No. Pieces: 5

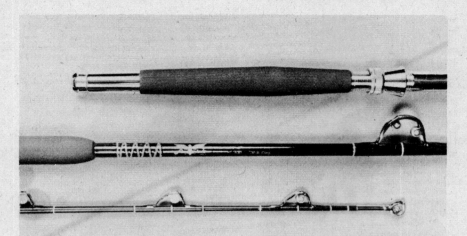

Big game offshore trolling rods

Combo Trolling/Jig Rod

Model No.: PT809
Length: 6'8"
No. Pieces: 1
No. Guides: 6 braced conventional guides
Tip Top: Roller tip
Rec. Lure Wt.: 2-10 oz.
Action: Heavy
Handle; Double locking reel seat, cork grip.

Live Bait and Jig Rods

Model No.: PB60C
Length: 6'
No. Pieces: 1
No. Guides: Not specified; braced
Tip Top: Carbide
Rec. Lure Wt.: ½-1½ oz.
Action: Fast power
Handle: Double locking reel seat, cork grip.

Model No.: JB65C. Same as Model PB60C
 except:
Length: 6½'
Rec. Lure Wt.: ½-2 oz.

Model No.: JB70C. Same as Model PB60C
 except:
Length: 7'
Rec. Lure Wt.: ¾-4 oz.

Model No.: PB78C. Same as Model PB60C
 except:
Length: 7'8"
Rec. Lure Wt.: ¾-2 oz.

Model No.: PJ83C. Same as Model PB60C
 except:
Length: 8'3"
Rec. Lure Wt.: 1½-8 oz.

Garcia

Spinning Rods

Model No.: B551 (Brown Series)
Length: 7'5"
No. Pieces: 2

No. Guides: 7 hard-chromed guides plus one
 braced stripping guide
Tip Top: Tungsten carbide
Rec. Lure Wt.: ⅜-3 oz.
Action: Light-medium; ultra-fast taper
Handle: Not specified.

Model No.: B552. Same as Model B551
 except:
Length: 7½'
Rec. Lure Wt.: ⅝-4 oz.

Model No.: B546
Length: 6½'
No. Pieces: 4
No. Guides: 4 chrome-plated
Tip Top: Chrome-plated
Rec. Lure Wt.: ¼-½ oz.
Action: Light
Handle: Not specified.

Freshwater Spinning Rods

Model No.: 2110 (Deluxe Series)
Length: 6½'
No. Pieces: 2
No. Guides: 5 genuine agate
Tip Top: Genuine agate
Rec. Lure Wt.: ¼-½ oz.
Action: Light
Handle: Not specified.

Model No.: 2111 (Deluxe Series)
Length: 7'
No. Pieces: 2
No. Guides: 5 genuine agate
Tip Top: Genuine agate
Rec. Lure Wt.: ¼-⅝ oz.
Action: Medium
Handle: Not specified.

Model No.: 2112 (Deluxe Series)
Length: 6'
No. Pieces: 1
No. Guides: 5 genuine agate
Tip Top: Genuine agate
Rec. Lure Wt.: ⅝-1¼ oz.
Action: Heavy; fast taper
Handle: Not specified.

Model No.: B112. Same as Model 2112
 except:
No. Guides: Not specified; carbide

Model No.: B122 (Deluxe Series)
Length: 6½'
No. Pieces: 2
No. Guides: 5 carbide
Tip Top: Carbide
Rec. Lure Wt.: ⅜-¾ oz.
Action: Medium
Handle: Not specified.

Model No.: B123. Same as Model B122
 except:
Length: 7'
Rec. Lure Wt.: ⅜-1 oz.

Model No.: 2121 (Deluxe Series)
Length: 5'
No. Pieces: 2
No. Guides: 4 hard-chromed stainless steel
 guides plus one braced stripper
Tip Top: Hard-chromed stainless steel
Rec. Lure Wt.: 1⁄16-¼ oz.
Action: Ultra-light
Handle: Not specified.

Model No.: 2132 (Deluxe Series)
Length: 5½'
No. Pieces: 2
No. Guides: 4 hard-chromed stainless steel
 guides plus one braced stripper
Tip Top: Hard-chromed stainless steel
Rec. Lure Wt.: ⅛-½ oz.
Action: Light; fast taper
Handle: Not specified.

Model No.: 2134 (Deluxe Series)
Length: 6'
No. Pieces: 2
No. Guides: 4 hard-chromed stainless steel
 guides plus one braced stripper
Tip Top: Hard-chromed stainless steel
Rec. Lure Wt.: ¼-⅝ oz.
Action: Light; fast taper
Handle: Not specified.

Model No.: 2133. Same as Model 2134
 except:
Length: 7'
No. Guides: 5
Rec. Lure Wt.: ¼-½ oz.

Model No.: 2135. Same as Model 2134
 except:
Length: 6½'
No. Guides: 5
Rec. Lure Wt.: ¼-½ oz.

Model No.: 2140 (Deluxe Series)
Length: 6'
No. Pieces: 1
No. Guides: 7 hard-chromed stainless steel
 plus one braced stripper
Tip Top: Tungsten carbide
Rec. Lure Wt.: ⅜-1 oz.
Action: Medium; ultra-fast taper
Handle: Not specified.

Model No.: B501 (Brown Series)
Length: 5½'
No. Pieces: 2
No. Guides: 4 hard-chromed stainless steel
Tip Top: Hard-chromed stainless steel
Rec. Lure Wt.: ⅛-½ oz.
Action: Light; fast taper
Handle: Not specified.

Model No.: 2500. Same as Model B501
except:
Length: 5'
Rec. Lure Wt.: 1/16-1/4 oz.
Action: Ultra-light

Model No.: 2503. Same as Model B501
except:
Length: 6'
No. Pieces: 2
Rec. Lure Wt.: 1/16-1/4 oz.
Action: Ultra-light

Model No.: B503 (Brown Series)
Length: 5'
No. Pieces: 2
No. Guides: 4 hard-chromed stainless steel
Tip Top: Carbide
Rec. Lure Wt.: 3/8-5/8 oz.
Action: Medium; fast taper
Handle: Not specified.

Model No.: 2505 (Brown Series)
Length: 6½'
No. Pieces: 2
No. Guides: 4 hard-chromed stainless steel
Tip Top: Hard-chromed stainless steel
Rec. Lure Wt.: 1/4-1/2 oz.
Action: Light
Handle: Not specified.

Model No.: B508. Same as Model 2505
except:
No. Guides: 5 carbide
Tip Top: Carbide
Action: Light; fast taper

Model No.: 2502. Same as Model 2505
except:
Length: 6'
Rec. Lure Wt.: 1/4-5/8 oz.
Action: Light; fast taper

Model No.: 2507. Same as Model 2505
except:
Length: 7'
No. Guides: 5

Model No.: 2508. Same as Model 2505
except:
No. Guides: 5
Action: Light; fast taper

Model No.: 2510. Same as Model 2505
except:
Length: 7'
Rec. Lure Wt.: 1/4-5/8 oz.
Action: Light; fast taper

Model No.: 2512 (Brown Series)
Length: 6½'
No. Pieces: 2
No. Guides: 5 hard-chromed stainless steel
Tip Top: Hard-chromed stainless steel
Rec. Lure Wt.: 3/8-3/4 oz.
Action: Medium
Handle: Not specified.

Model No.: 2513. Same as Model 2512
except:
Length: 7'
Rec. Lure Wt.: 3/8-1 oz.

Model No.: B512. Same as Model 2512
except:
No. Guides: Not specified; carbide
Tip Top: Carbide

Model No.: 2601 (Blue Series)
Length: 5'
No. Pieces: 2
No. Guides: 4 hard-chromed
Tip Top: Hard-chromed
Rec. Lure Wt.: 1/16-1/4 oz.
Action: Ultra-light
Handle: Cork handle with sliding rings.

Model No.: B601. Same as Model 2601
except:
Length: 5½'
Handle: Fixed reel seat.

Model No.: 2604 (Blue Series)
Length: 6½'
No. Pieces: 2
No. Guides: 4 hard-chromed
Tip Top: Hard-chromed
Rec. Lure Wt.: 1/4-1/2 oz.
Action: Light
Handle: Not specified.

Model No.: 2605 (Blue Series)
Length: 7'
No. Pieces: 2
No. Guides: 4 hard-chromed
Tip Top: Hard-chromed
Rec. Lure Wt.: 1/4-1/2 oz.
Action: Light
Handle: Not specified.

Model No.: 2606 (Blue Series)
Length: 7'
No. Pieces: 2
No. Guides: 4 hard-chromed stainless steel
Tip Top: Hard-chromed stainless steel
Rec. Lure Wt.: 3/8-3/4 oz.
Action: Medium
Handle: Not specified.

Model No.: 2609 (Blue Series)
Length: 6½'
No. Pieces: 2
No. Guides: 4 hard-chromed
Tip Top: Hard-chromed
Rec. Lure Wt.: 1/4-5/8 oz.
Action: Light; fast taper
Handle: Not specified.

Model No.: 2610 (Blue Series)
Length: 7'
No. Pieces: 2
No. Guides: 4 hard-chromed
Tip Top: Hard-chromed
Rec. Lure Wt.: 1/4-1/2 oz.
Action: Light; fast taper
Handle: Not specified.

Model No.: 8201 (Avocado Series)
Length: 5½'
No. Pieces: 2
No. Guides: 4 hard-chromed stainless steel
Tip Top: Hard-chromed stainless steel
Rec. Lure Wt.: 1/8-1/2 oz.
Action: Light; fast taper
Handle: Not specified.

Model No.: 8208 (Avocado Series)
Length: 6½'
No. Pieces: 2
No. Guides: 5 hard-chromed stainless steel
Tip Top: Hard-chromed stainless steel
Rec. Lure Wt.: 1/4-1/2 oz.
Action: Light; fast taper
Handle: Not specified.

Model No.: 8210 (Avocado Series)
Length: 7'
No. Pieces: 2
No. Guides: 5 hard-chromed stainless steel
Tip Top: Hard-chromed stainless steel
Rec. Lure Wt.: 1/4-1/2 oz.
Action: Light; fast taper
Handle: Not specified.

Model No.: 8212 (Avocado Series)
Length: 6½'
No. Pieces: 2
No. Guides: 5 hard-chromed stainless steel
Tip-Top: Hard-chromed stainless steel
Rec. Lure Wt.: 3/8-3/4 oz.
Action: Medium
Handle: Not specified.

Saltwater Spinning Rods

Model No.: 2154 (Deluxe Series)
Length: 10'
No. Pieces: 2
No. Guides: 7 hard-chromed stainless steel
Tip Top: Tungsten carbide
Rec. Lure Wt.: 1-4½ oz.
Action: Medium; fast taper
Handle: Not specified.

Model No.: 2553 (Brown Series)
Length: 9½'
No. Pieces: 2
No. Guides: 6 hard-chromed guides plus
one braced stripping guide
Tip Top: Tungsten carbide
Rec. Lure Wt.: 1-4½ oz.
Action: Medium; fast taper
Handle: Not specified.

Model No.: 2554. Same as Model 2553
except:
Length: 10'
No. Guides: 7

Model No.: 2571. Same as Model 2553
except:
Length: 9'
No. Guides: 7
Rec. Lure Wt.: 1-4 oz.

Model No.: 2573. Same as Model 2553
except:
Length: 11'4"
No. Guides: 8
Rec. Lure Wt.: 2-5 oz.
Action: Heavy

Model No.: 2653 (Blue Series)
Length: 7'4"
No. Pieces: 1
No. Guides: 4 hard-chromed stainless steel
Tip Top: Hard-chromed stainless steel
Rec. Lure Wt.: Not specified
Action: Medium
Handle: Detachable hardwood handle,
chrome-plated reel seat, neoprene foregrip.

Model No.: 2654 (Blue Series)
Length: 10'
No. Pieces: 2
No. Guides: 6 hard-chromed stainless steel
Tip Top: Hard-chromed stainless steel
Rec. Lure Wt.: 1-4½ oz.
Action: Medium; fast taper
Handle: Not specified.

Model No.: 8255 (Avocado Series)
Length: 7½'
No. Pieces: 2
No. Guides: 6 varmac hard-chromed stainless steel guides plus one braced stripper
Tip Top: Hard-chromed stainless steel
Rec. Lure Wt.: ⅝-4 oz.
Action: Light-medium; fast taper
Handle: Not specified.

Model No.: 8271 (Avocado Series)
Length: 9'
No. Pieces: 2
No. Guides: 6 hard-chromed varmac guides plus one braced stripping guide
Tip Top: Hard-chromed stainless steel
Rec. Lure Wt.: 1-4 oz.
Action: Medium; fast taper
Handle: Not specified.

Steelhead and Saltwater Spinning Rods

Model No.: 2506 (Brown Series)
Length: 7'
No. Pieces: 2
No. Guides: 5 hard-chromed guides plus one braced stripping guide
Tip Top: Tungsten carbide
Rec. Lure Wt.: ⅝-1 oz.
Action: Fast taper; light for saltwater, medium-heavy for freshwater
Handle: Not specified.

Model No.: 2509 (Brown Series)
Length: 7'
No. Pieces: 1
No. Guides: 7 hard-chromed guides plus one braced stripping guide
Tip Top: Tungsten carbide
Rec. Lure Wt.: ½-1½ oz.
Action: Light; fast taper
Handle: Not specified.

Model No.: 2551 (Brown Series)
Length: 8'
No. Pieces: 2
No. Guides: 5 hard-chromed guides plus one braced stripping guide
Tip Top: Tungsten carbide
Rec. Lure Wt.: ⅝-2½ oz.
Action: Medium; fast taper
Handle: Not specified.

Model No.: 2552. Same as Model 2551 except:
Length: 8½'

Model No.: 2650 (Blue Series)
Length: 8'
No. Pieces: 2
No. Guides: 5 hard-chromed stainless steel
Tip Top: Hard-chromed stainless steel
Rec. Lure Wt.: ⅝-1¼ oz.
Action: Light
Handle: Not specified.

Model No.: 2651 (Blue Series)
Length: 8½'
No. Pieces: 2
No. Guides: 5 hard-chromed stainless steel
Tip Top: Hard-chromed stainless steel
Rec. Lure Wt.: ⅝-1½ oz.
Action: Light-medium
Handle: Not specified.

Model No.: 2652 (Blue Series)
Length: 9'
No. Pieces: 2
No. Guides: 5 hard-chromed stainless steel
Tip Top: Hard-chromed stainless steel
Rec. Lure Wt.: 1-3 oz.
Action: Medium
Handle: Not specified.

Model No.: 2655 (Blue Series)
Length: 9½'
No. Pieces: 2
No. Guides: 6 hard-chromed stainless steel
Tip Top: Hard-chromed stainless steel
Rec. Lure Wt.: 1-3 oz.
Action: Medium
Handle: Not specified.

Model No.: 8206 (Avocado Series)
Length: 7'
No. Pieces: 2
No. Guides: 5 hard-chromed stainless steel guides plus one braced stripper
Tip Top: Hard-chromed stainless steel
Rec. Lure Wt.: ⅝-1 oz.
Action: Fast taper; light for saltwater, medium-heavy for freshwater
Handle: Not specified.

Model No.: 8252 (Avocado Series)
Length: 8½'
No. Pieces: 2
No. Guides: 5 varmac hard-chromed stainless steel guides plus one braced stripper
Tip Top: Hard-chromed stainless steel
Rec. Lure Wt.: ⅝-2½ oz.
Action: Medium; fast taper
Handle: Not specified.

Model No.: 8267 (Avocado Series)
Length: 8'
No. Pieces: 2
No. Guides: 5 hard-chromed stainless steel guides plus one braced stripper
Tip Top: Hard-chromed stainless steel
Rec. Lure Wt.: ⅝-1¼ oz.
Action: Light-medium
Handle: Not specified.

Model No.: 8268 (Avocado Series)
Length: 8½'
No. Pieces: 2
No. Guides: 5 hard-chromed stainless steel guides plus one braced stripper
Tip Top: Hard-chromed stainless steel
Rec. Lure Wt.: ⅝-1½ oz.
Action: Light-medium
Handle: Not specified.

Baitcasting Rod

Model No.: B520 (Brown Series)
Length: 5½'
No. Pieces: 2
No. Guides: 4 hard-chromed stainless steel
Tip Top: Tungsten carbide
Rec. Lure Wt.: 1¾-6 oz.
Action: Very heavy; musky taper
Handle: Two-handed.

Spincasting and Baitcasting Rods

Model No.: 2212 (Deluxe Series)
Length: 5½'
No. Pieces: 1
No. Guides: 6 hard-chromed stainless steel guides plus one braced stripper

Tip Top: Tungsten carbide
Rec. Lure Wt.: ½-1 oz.
Action: Medium-soft
Handle: Not specified.

Model No.: 2213. Same as Model 2212 except:
Rec. Lure Wt.: ⅝-1¼ oz.
Action: Medium-stiff

Model No.: 2214. Same as Model 2212 except:
Length: 6'
Rec. Lure Wt.: ⅜-1 oz.
Action: Medium

Model No.: 2218
Length: 6½'
No. Pieces: 2
No. Guides: 5 hard-chromed stainless steel guides plus one braced stripper
Tip Top: Tungsten carbide
Rec. Lure Wt.: ⅜-⅝ oz.
Action: Medium; fast taper
Handle: Not specified.

Model No.: 2229 (Deluxe Series)
Length: 5½'
No. Pieces: 1
No. Guides: 6 carbide
Tip Top: Carbide
Rec. Lure Wt.: ⅜-¾ oz.
Action: Medium; fast taper
Handle: Not specified.

Model No.: 2521 (Brown Series)
Length: 6'
No. Pieces: 2
No. Guides: 4 hard-chromed stainless steel
Tip Top: Hard-chromed stainless steel
Rec. Lure Wt.: ½-¾ oz.
Action: Medium
Handle: Not specified.

Model No.: 2522
Length: 6½'
No. Pieces: 2
No. Guides: 5 hard-chromed stainless steel
Tip Top: Hard-chromed stainless steel
Rec. Lure Wt.: ¼-⅝ oz.
Action: Light
Handle: Not specified.

Model No.: 2524 (Brown Series)
Length: 6'
No. Pieces: 1
No. Guides: 5 hard-chromed stainless steel
Tip Top: Hard-chromed stainless steel
Rec. Lure Wt.: ¼-⅝ oz.
Action: Light; fast taper
Handle: Not specified.

Model No.: 2526 (Brown Series)
Length: 6½'
No. Pieces: 2
No. Guides: 5 hard-chromed stainless steel
Tip Top: Hard-chromed stainless steel
Rec. Lure Wt.: ⅜-⅝ oz.
Action: Medium; fast taper
Handle: Not specified.

Model No.: 2525. Same as Model 2526 except:
Length: 7'
Rec. Lure Wt.: ⅜-¾ oz.
Handle: Two-hand handle.

Model No.: 2528. Same as Model 2526
except:
Length: 6'
Rec. Lure Wt.: ⅜-¾ oz.

Model No.: 2621 (Blue Series)
Length: 6½'
No. Pieces: 2
No. Guides: 5 hard-chromed
Tip Top: Hard-chromed
Rec. Lure Wt.: ¼-⅝ oz.
Action: Light
Handle: Not specified.

Model No.: 2622 (Blue Series)
Length: 6'
No. Pieces: 2
No. Guides: 4 hard-chromed
Tip Top: Hard-chromed
Rec. Lure Wt.: ¼-½ oz.
Action: Light
Handle: Not specified.

Model No.: 2629 (Blue Series)
Length: 5'8"
No. Pieces: 1
No. Guides: 4 hard-chromed
Tip Top: Hard-chromed
Rec. Lure Wt.: ¼-⅝ oz.
Action: Medium; fast taper
Handle: Not specified.

Model No.: 2628 (Blue Series)
Length: 6'
No. Pieces: 2
No. Guides: 4 hard-chromed
Tip Top: Hard-chromed
Rec. Lure Wt.: ¼-⅝ oz.
Action: Light; fast taper
Handle: Not specified.

Model No.: 8226 (Avocado Series)
Length: 6½'
No. Pieces: 2
No. Guides: 5 hard-chromed stainless steel
Tip Top: Hard-chromed stainless steel
Rec. Lure Wt.: ⅜-⅝ oz.
Action; Medium; fast taper
Handle: Not specified.

Model No.: 8228 (Avocado Series)
Length: 6'
No. Pieces: 2
No. Guides: 5 hard-chromed stainless steel
Tip Top: Hard-chromed stainless steel
Rec. Lure Wt.: ⅜-¾ oz.
Action: Medium; fast taper
Handle: Not specified.

Saltwater Rods

Model No.: B571 (Brown Series)
Length: 7'
No. Pieces: 1
No. Guides: 6 hard-chromed varmac guides plus one braced stripper
Tip Top: Hard-chromed varmac
Rec. Lure Wt.: ¾-1½ oz.
Action: Light
Handle: Brass reel seat with two locking rings, neoprene handle and foregrip.

Model No.: B572 (Brown Series)
Length: 6'10"
No. Pieces: 2
No. Guides: 6 hard-chromed stainless steel plus one braced stripper

Tip Top: Hard-chromed stainless steel
Rec. Lure Wt.: 1-2½ oz.
Action: Medium; fast taper
Handle: Brass reel seat with two locking rings, neoprene handle and foregrip.

Model No.: B573 (Brown Series)
Length: 6'4"
No. Pieces: 1
No. Guides: 5 hard-chromed stainless steel guides plus one braced stripper
Tip Top: Hard-chromed stainless steel
Rec. Lure Wt.: 1-2½ oz.
Action; Medium; fast taper
Handle: Brass reel seat with two locking rings, neoprene handle and foregrip.

Model No.: B574. Same as Model B573
except:
Length: 6'10"
No. Guides: 6 hard-chromed
Rec. Lure Wt.: 1-3 oz.

Model No.: B575 (Brown Series)
Length: 7'
No. Pieces: 1
No. Guides: 6 hard-chromed plus one braced stripper
Tip Top: Hard-chromed
Rec. Lure Wt.: 1½-4 oz.
Action: Medium; fast taper
Handle: Brass reel seat with two locking rings, neoprene handle and foregrip.

Model No.: B576 (Brown Series)
Length: 8'
No. Pieces: 1
No. Guides: 7 hard-chromed varmac stainless steel guides plus one braced stripper
Tip Top: Hard-chromed varmac stainless steel
Rec. Lure Wt.: 1½-4 oz.
Action: Medium; fast taper
Handle: Brass reel seat with two locking rings, neoprene handle and foregrip.

Boat Rods

Model No.: 2531 (Brown Series)
Length: 7'
No. Pieces: 1
No. Guides: 4 hard-chromed stainless steel
Tip Top: Tungsten carbide
Rec. Lure Wt.: 3-5 oz.
Action: Heavy; fast taper
Handle: Neoprene foregrips, detachable hardwood butt.

Model No: 2559 (Brown Series)
Length: 7'8"
No. Pieces: 1
No. Guides: 4 hard-chromed guides plus one braced stripping guide
Tip Top: Tungsten carbide
Rec. Lure Wt.: 1-4 oz.
Action: Medium
Handle: Detachable hardwood butt, neoprene foregrip.

Model No.: 2662 (Blue Series)
Length: 6½'
No. Pieces: 1
No. Guides: 4 hard-chromed carbon steel
Tip Top: Hard-chromed carbon steel
Rec. Lure Wt.: Not specified
Action: Heavy

Handle: Detachable wood handle, neoprene foregrip, heavily-chromed, front locking reel seat.

Model No.: 2663 (Blue Series)
Length: 7'
No. Pieces: 1
No. Guides: 4 hard-chromed carbon steel
Tip Top: Hard-chromed carbon steel
Rec. Lure Wt.: 1¼-3 oz.
Action: Medium
Handle: Detachable wood handle, neoprene foregrip, front locking reel seat.

Model No.: 2565 (Brown Series)
Length: 6'8"
No. Pieces: 1
No. Guides: 6 tungsten carbide
Tip Top: Tungsten carbide
Rec. Lure Wt.: Not specified
Action: Not specified
Handle: Neoprene foregrip, detachable hardwood butt. Gimbal shape handle with rubber butt cap.

Model No.: 2668 (Blue Series)
Length: 6½'
No. Pieces: 1
No. Guides: 4 bridged hard-chromed stainless steel
Tip Top: Roller
Rec. Lure Wt.: Not specified
Action: Heavy
Handle: Detachable hardwood butt with gimbal taper.

Model No.: 2877 (Black Series)
Length: 5½'
No. Pieces: 1
No. Guides: 3 hard-chromed stainless steel spinning
Tip Top: Hard-chromed stainless steel
Rec. Lure Wt.: 1¾-3½ oz.
Action: Light-medium
Handle: Detachable butt.

Model No.: 2891 (Black Series)
Length: 5½'
No. Pieces: 1
No. Guides: 3 hard-chromed carbon steel conventional
Tip Top: Hard-chromed carbon steel
Rec. Lure Wt.: 2½-4 oz.
Action: Light
Handle: Detachable butt.

Model No.: 8293 (Avocado Series)
Length: 6½'
No. Pieces: 1
No. Guides: 4 hard-chromed stainless steel
Tip Top: Hard-chromed stainless steel
Rec. Lure Wt.: 1¾-3½ oz.
Action: Medium
Handle: Detachable hardwood butt.

Model No.: 8294 (Avocado Series)
Length: 6½'
No. Pieces: 1
No. Guides: 4 hard-chromed
Tip Top: Hard-chromed
Rec. Lure Wt.: 1¾-3½ oz.
Action: Light-medium
Handle: Detachable butt.

Model No.: 8297 (Avocado Series)
Length: 6½'

No. Pieces: 1
No. Guides: 4 hard-chromed
Tip Top: Hard-chromed
Rec. Lure Wt.: 2½-5 oz.
Action: Medium
Handle: Detachable butt.

Boat and Trolling Rods

Model No.: 2878 (Black Series)
Length: 6'
No. Pieces: 1
No. Guides: 4 hard-chromed carbon steel
Tip Top: Hard-chromed carbon steel
Rec. Lure Wt.: Not specified
Action: Heavy
Handle: Glass shaft continuing through cork butt.

Model No.: 2879 (Black Series)
Length: 6½'
No. Pieces: 1
No. Guides: 4 hard-chromed carbon steel
Tip Top: Roller
Rec. Lure Wt.: Not specified
Action: Heavy
Handle: Shaft continuing through hardwood butt.

Model No.: 2889 (Black Series)
Length: 6'5"
No. Pieces: 1
No. Guides: 4 hard-chromed stainless steel roller
Tip Top: Hard-chromed stainless steel roller
Rec. Lure Wt.: Not specified
Action: Heavy
Handle: Detachable butt.

Model No.: 2892 (Black Series)
Length: 6½'
No. Pieces: 1
No. Guides: 4 hard-chromed carbon steel
Tip Top: Hard-chromed carbon steel
Rec. Lure Wt.: 1-2½ oz.
Action: Light
Handle: Detachable butt.

Model No.: 2893 (Black Series)
Length: 6½'
No. Pieces: 1
No. Guides: 4 hard-chromed carbon steel
Tip Top: Hard-chromed carbon steel
Rec. Lure Wt.: 1-3 oz.
Action: Light
Handle: Trigger reel seat, detachable butt.

Model No.: 2894 (Black Series)
Length: 6½'
No. Pieces: 1
No. Guides: 4 hard-chromed carbon steel
Tip Top: Hard-chromed carbon steel
Rec. Lure Wt.: 1¾-3½ oz.
Action: Light-medium
Handle: Detachable butt.

Model No.: 2897 (Black Series)
Length: 6½'
No. Pieces: 1
No. Guides: 4 hard-chromed carbon steel
Tip Top: Hard-chromed carbon steel
Rec. Lure Wt.: 2½-5 oz.
Action: Medium
Handle: Detachable butt.

Model No.: 2898 (Black Series)
Length: 6'5"
No. Pieces: 1
No. Guides: 4 hard-chromed carbon steel
Tip Top: Hard-chromed carbon steel
Rec. Lure Wt.: Not specified
Action: Heavy
Handle: Detachable butt.

Model No. 2899 (Black Series)
Length: 6'5"
No. Pieces: 1
No. Guides: 4 hard-chromed carbon steel
Tip Top: Roller
Rec. Lure Wt.: Not specified
Action: Heavy
Handle: Detachable butt.

Saltwater Trolling Rods

Model No.: B570 (Brown Series)
Length: 7'
No. Pieces: 1
No. Guides: 5 varmac hard-chromed stainless steel
Tip Top: Aftco roller
Rec. Lure Wt.: Not specified
Action: Heavy
Handle: Brass reel seat with two locking rings, neoprene handle and foregrip. Double-slotted gimbal nock and removable rubber butt cap.

Model No.: B591 (Big Game Series)
Length: Not specified
No. Pieces: 1
No. Guides: 4 varmac hard-chromed stainless steel ring guides plus one Aftco double roller stripper guide
Tip Top: Aftco roller
Rec. Lure Wt.: Not specified
Action: 6 thread; 20 lb. class
Handle: Chrome-plated screw locking reel seat with double locking rings. Specie cork foregrip and a detachable hardwood butt, heavily chromed cross-slotted gimbal nock.

Model No.: B592 (Big Game Series)
Length: Not specified
No. Pieces: 1
No. Guides: 4 varmac hard-chromed stainless steel ring guides plus one Aftco double roller stripper guide
Tip Top: Aftco roller
Rec. Lure Wt.: Not specified
Action: 9 thread; 30 lb. class
Handle: Chrome-plated screw locking reel seat with double locking rings. Specie cork foregrip and a detachable hardwood butt, heavily chromed cross-slotted gimbal nock.

Model No.: B593 (Big Game Series)
Length: Not specified
No. Pieces: 1
No. Guides: 4 varmac hard-chromed stainless steel ring guides plus one Aftco double roller stripper guide
Tip Top: Aftco roller
Rec. Lure Wt.: Not specified
Action: 15 thread; 80 lb. class
Handle: Chrome-plated screw locking reel seat with double locking rings. Specie

cork foregrip and a detachable hardwood butt, heavily chromed cross-slotted gimbal nock.

Model No.: B594 (Big Game Series)
Length: Not specified
No. Pieces: 1
No. Guides: 4 varmac hard-chromed stainless steel ring guides plus one Aftco double roller stripper guide
Tip Top: Aftco roller
Rec. Lure Wt.: Not specified
Action: 24 thread; 80 lb. class
Handle: Machined chrome-plated screw locking reel seat with double locking rings. Specie cork foregrip and a detachable hardwood butt, heavily chromed cross-slotted gimbal nock.

Model No.: 2595 (Big Game Series)
Length: Not specified
No. Pieces: 1
No. Guides: 4 varmac hard-chromed stainless steel ring guides plus one Aftco double roller stripper guide
Tip Top: Mildrum double roller
Rec. Lure Wt.: Not specified
Action: 39 thread; 130 lb. class
Handle: Machined chrome-plated screw locking reel seat with double locking rings. Specie cork foregrip and a detachable hardwood butt, heavily chromed cross-slotted gimbal nock.

Spinning and Trolling Rod

Model No.: 2888 (Black Series)
Length: 7½'
No. Pieces: 1
No. Guides: 4 hard-chromed stainless steel
Tip Top: Hard-chromed stainless steel
Rec. Lure Wt.: 1-3 oz.
Action: Medium
Handle: Detachable butt.

Worm Rods

Model No.: 2154 (Brown Series)
Length: 5½'
No. Pieces: 1
No. Guides: 5 hard-chromed stainless steel
Tip Top: Hard-chromed stainless steel
Rec. Lure Wt.: ⅜-1 oz.
Action: Heavy
Handle: Not specified.

Model No.: B514. Same as Model 2514 except:
No. Guides: Not specified; carbide
Tip Top: Carbide

Model No.: 2516 (Brown Series)
Length: 6'
No. Pieces: 1
No. Guides: 6 hard-chromed stainless steel guides plus one braced stripper
Tip Top: Hard-chromed stainless steel
Rec. Lure Wt.: ⅜-¾ oz.
Action: Medium; fast taper
Handle: Not specified.

Model No.: 2529. Same as Model 2516 except:
Length: 5'8"
No. Guides: 4

Model No.: B529. Same as Model 2529 except:
Length: 5'8"
No. Pieces: 2
No. Guides: 4

Model No.: 8225 (Avocado Series)
Length: 5'
No. Pieces: 1
No. Guides: 5 hard-chromed stainless steel guides plus one braced stripper
Tip Top: Hard-chromed stainless steel
Rec. Lure Wt.: ½-1 oz.
Action: Medium-stiff
Handle: Not specified.

Model No.: 8229 (Avocado Series)
Length: 5'8"
No. Pieces: 1
No. Guides: 4 hard-chromed stainless steel
Tip Top: Hard-chromed stainless steel
Rec. Lure Wt.: ⅜-¾ oz.
Action: Medium; fast taper
Handle: Not specified.

Model No.: 8314 (Ambassadeur Series)
Length: 4½'
No. Pieces: 1
No. Guides: 4 tungsten carbide
Tip Top: Tungsten carbide
Rec. Lure Wt.: ½-1 oz.
Action: Medium-stiff
Handle: Not specified.

Model No.: 8315 (Ambassadeur Series)
Length: 5'
No. Pieces: 1
No. Guides: 5 tungsten carbide
Tip Top: Tungsten carbide
Rec. Lure Wt.: ½-1 oz.
Action: Medium-stiff
Handle: Not specified.

Model No.: 8316 (Ambassadeur Series)
Length: 5½'
No. Pieces: 2
No. Guides: 6 tungsten carbide
Tip Top: Tungsten carbide
Rec. Lure Wt.: ½-1 oz.
Action: Medium-soft
Handle: Cushion-foam foregrip.

Model No.: 8317 (Ambassadeur Series)
Length: 5½'
No. Pieces: 1
No. Guides: 6 tungsten carbide
Tip Top: Tungsten carbide
Rec. Lure Wt.: ⅝-1¼ oz.
Action: Medium-light
Handle: Not specified.

Model No.: 8318 (Ambassadeur Series)
Length: 5½'
No. Pieces: 1
No. Guides: 6 tungsten carbide

Tip Top: Tungsten carbide
Rec. Lure Wt.: ⅝-1¼ oz.
Action: Medium-stiff
Handle: Not specified.

Model No.: 8319 (Ambassadeur Series)
Length: 6'
No. Pieces: 1
No. Guides: 6 tungsten carbide
Tip Top: Tungsten carbide
Rec. Lure Wt.: ½-1 oz.
Action: Medium-soft
Handle: Not specified.

Model No.: 8321 (Ambassadeur Series)
Length: 6'
No. Pieces: 1
No. Guides: 6 tungsten carbide
Tip Top: Tungsten carbide
Rec. Lure Wt.: ⅝-1¼ oz.
Action: Medium-light
Handle: Not specified.

Model No.: 8322 (Ambassadeur Series)
Length: 6'
No. Pieces: 1
No. Guides: 6 tungsten carbide guides
Tip Top: Tungsten carbide
Rec. Lure Wt.: ⅜-1 oz.
Action: Medium
Handle: Not specified.

Model No.: 8324 (Ambassadeur Series)
Length: 6½'
No. Pieces: 2
No. Guides: 6 tungsten carbide
Tip Top: Tungsten carbide
Rec. Lure Wt.: ½-1 oz.
Action: Medium-soft
Handle: Not specified.

Model No.: 8326 (Ambassadeur Series)
Length: 6'
No. Pieces: 2
No. Guides: 6 tungsten carbide
Tip Top: Tungsten carbide
Rec. Lure Wt.: ⅝-1¼ oz.
Action: Medium-light
Handle: Cushion-foam foregrip.

Worm Spinning Rods

Model No.: 2511 (Brown Series)
Length: 6'
No. Pieces: 1
No. Guides: 6 hard-chromed stainless steel guides plus one braced stripping guide
Tip Top: Tungsten carbide
Rec. Lure Wt.: ⅜-¾ oz.
Action: Medium
Handle: Not specified.

Model No.: B511. Same as Model 2511 except:
No. Guides: Tungsten carbide

Model No.: B517. Same as Model 2511 except:
Length: 5½'
No. Guides: 5

Model No.: 8216 (Avocado Series)
Length: 6'

No. Pieces: 1
No. Guides: 6 hard-chromed stainless steel guides plus one braced stripper
Tip Top: Hard-chromed stainless steel
Rec. Lure Wt.: ⅜-¾ oz.
Action: Medium; fast taper
Handle: Not specified.

Model No.: 8217 (Avocado Series)
Length: 5½'
No. Pieces: 2
No. Guides: 5 hard-chromed stainless steel guides plus one braced stripper
Tip Top: Hard-chromed stainless steel
Rec. Lure Wt.: ⅜-¾ oz.
Action: Medium; fast taper
Handle: Not specified.

Worm Musky Rod

Model No.: 8220 (Avocado Series)
Length: 5½'
No. Pieces: 1
No. Guides: 4 hard-chromed
Tip Top: Hard-chromed stainless steel
Rec. Lure Wt.: 1¾-6 oz.
Action: Very heavy
Handle: Not specified.

Fly Rods

Model No.: 2060 (Long Flex/Long Lift Charles Ritz)
Length: 6½'
No. Pieces: 2
No. Guides: 7 chromed stainless steel snake guides plus hard-chromed stainless steel stripper guide
Tip Top: Hard-chromed stainless steel
Rec. Line: 6, 7
Handle: Fitted with Cal Air machined reel seat.

Model No.: 2061 (Long Flex/Long Lift Charles Ritz)
Length: 7'1"
No. Pieces: 2
No. Guides: 8 chromed stainless steel snake guides plus hard-chromed stainless steel stripper guide
Tip Top: Hard-chromed stainless steel
Rec. Line: 6, 7
Handle: Fitted with Cal Air machined reel seat.

Model No.: 2062 (Long Flex/Long Lift Charles Ritz)
Length: 7'10"
No. Pieces: 2
No. Guides: 7 chromed stainless steel snake guides plus one hard-chromed stainless steel stripper guide
Tip Top: Hard-chromed stainless steel
Rec. Line: 6, 7
Handle: Fitted with Cal Air machined reel seat.

Model No.: 2063 (Long Flex/Long Lift Charles Ritz)
Length: 8'2"
No. Pieces: 2

No. Guides: 9 chromed stainless steel guides plus one hard-chromed stainless steel stripper guide
Tip Top: Hard-chromed stainless steel
Rec. Line: 6, 7
Handle: Fitted with Cal Air machined reel seat.

Model No.: 2064 (Long Flex/Long Lift Charles Ritz)
Length: 8'5"
No. Pieces: 2
No. Guides: 10 chromed stainless steel snake guides plus one hard-chromed stainless steel stripper guide
Tip Top: Hard-chromed stainless steel
Rec. Line: 8, 9
Handle: Fitted with Cal Air machined reel seat.

Model No.: 2402 (Deluxe Series)—dry fly action
Length: 7'
No. Pieces: 2
No. Guides: 5 stainless steel snake guides plus one genuine agate stripping guide
Tip Top: Stainless steel
Rec. Line: 6 wt.
Handle: Not specified.

Model No.: 2404. Same as Model 2402 except:
Length: 8'

Model No.: 2405. Same as Model 2402 except:
Length: 8½'
No. Guides: 6
Rec. Line: 7 wt.

Model No.: 2536 (Brown Series)
Length: 7'10"
No. Pieces: 2
No. Guides: 5 stainless steel snake guides plus one stainless steel stripping guide
Tip Top: Hard-chromed
Rec. Line: 7 wt.
Handle: Not specified.

Model No.: 2537. Same as Model 2536 except:
Length: 8½'
No. Guides: 6 snake guides
Rec. Line: 9 wt.

Model No.: 2636 (Blue Series)
Length: 7'3"
No. Pieces: 2
No. Guides: 5 stainless steel snake guides plus one hard-chromed stripping guide
Tip Top: Hard-chromed
Rec. Line: 6 wt.
Handle: Not specified.

Model No.: 2637 (Blue Series)
Length: 8'
No. Pieces: 2
No. Guides: 4 stainless steel snake guides plus one hard-chromed stripping guide
Tip Top: Hard-chromed
Rec. Line: 6 wt.
Handle: Not specified.

Model No.: 2638 (Blue Series)
Length: 8½'
No. Pieces: 2

No. Guides: 5 stainless steel snake guides plus one hard-chromed stripping guide
Tip Top: Hard-chromed
Rec. Line: 7 wt.
Handle: Not specified.

Model No.: 2639 (Blue Series)
Length: 9'
No. Pieces: 2
No. Guides: 6 stainless steel snake guides plus one hard-chromed stripping guide
Tip Top: Hard-chromed
Rec. Line: 8
Handle: Not specified.

Model No.: 8237 (Avocado Series)
Length: 8'
No. Pieces: 2
No. Guides: 5 stainless steel snake guides plus one hard-chromed stripping guide
Tip Top: Hard-chromed
Rec. Line: 6 wt.
Handle: Not specified.

Model No.: B547—dry-fly action
Length: 7½'
No. Pieces: 5
No. Guides: 4 stainless steel snake guides plus one chrome-plated carbon steel stripper guide
Tip Top: Hard-chromed stainless steel
Rec. Line: 9
Handle: Not specified.

Model No.: B548 light spinning or dry-fly action
Length: 6'8"
No. Pieces: 5
No. Guides: 6 Allan Spiralite guides
Tip Top: Hard-chromed stainless steel
Rec. Line: 6 (as a spinning rod uses ¼-½ oz. lures)
Handle: Reversible.

Saltwater Fly Rods

Model No.: 2065 (Long Flex/ Long Lift Charles Ritz)
Length: 8'5"
No. Pieces: 2
No. Guides: 10 heavy-gauge chromed stainless steel snake guides plus one hard-chromed stainless steel stripper guide
Tip Top: Hard-chromed stainless steel
Rec. Line: 9, 10
Handle: Two-inch and four-inch extension butts for two-handed casting. Fitted with Cal Air machined reel seats.

Model No.: 2066 (Long-Flex/Long Lift Charles Ritz)
Length: 8'10"
No. Pieces: 2
No. Guides: 11 heavy-gauge chromed stainless steel snake guides plus one hard-chromed stainless steel stripper guide
Rec. Line: 10, 11
Handle: Four-inch and nineteen-inch extension butts for two-handed casting. Fitted with Cal Air machined reel seat.

Coho Rod

Model No.: 2656 (Blue Series)
Length: 7'9"
No. Pieces: 2

No. Guides: 5 hard-chromed stainless steel
Tip Top: Hard-chromed stainless steel
Rec. Lure Wt.: 1-3 oz.
Action: Medium
Handle: Not specified.

Popping Rods

Model No.: 2531 (Brown Series)
Length: 6'9"
No. Pieces: 1
No. Guides: 4 hard-chromed stainless steel
Tip Top: Tungsten carbide
Rec. Lure Wt.: ½-¾ oz.
Action: Light; fast taper
Handle: Detachable butt, neoprene foregrip.

Model No.: 2533. Same as Model 2531 except:
Length: 7'
No. Guides: 5

Model No.: 2887 (Black Series)
Length: 7'
No. Pieces: 1
No. Guides: 5 hard-chromed carbon steel
Tip Top: Hard-chromed carbon steel
Rec. Lure Wt.: ½-1½ oz.
Action: Light
Handle: Detachable butt, trigger reel seat.

Model No.: 8333 (Ambassadeur Series)
Length: 7'
No. Pieces: 1
No. Guides: 5 tungsten carbide
Tip Top: Tungsten carbide
Rec. Lure Wt.: ½-¾ oz.
Action: Light; fast taper
Handle: Not specified.

Gladding

Spinning Rods

Model No.: 1-246-050 (Classic IV Series)
Length: 5'
No. Pieces: Not specified
No. Guides: 4 stainless steel
Tip Top: Carboloy
Rec. Lure Wt.: Not specified
Action: Ultra-light
Handle: Die-cast aluminum offset handle, rubber-protected, epoxy-coated aluminum butt cap and forecap. Specie cork grip with anodized aluminum fixed reel seat with "duoloc" reel hoods.

Model No.: 1-204-260
Length: 6'
No. Pieces: 2
No. Guides: 3 chromed
Tip Top: Chromed
Rec. Lure Wt.: Not specified
Action: Spinning rod
Handle: Specie cork fore and rear grips, aluminum reel seat with sliding hood and locking ring.

Model No.: 1-212-260
Length: 6'
No. Pieces: 2
No. Guides: 3 chrome-plated
Tip Top: Chrome-plated
Rec. Lure Wt.: Not specified
Action: Medium

Handle: Man-size handle with cork fore and rear grips, fixed reel seat, locking ring hoods of ABS.

1-220-266

Model No.: 1-220-266
Length: 6½'
No. Pieces: 2
No. Guides: 3 chrome
Tip Top: Chrome
Rec. Lure Wt.: Not specified
Action: Spinning rod
Handle: Specie cork fore and rear grips, anodized aluminum fixed reel seat with sliding hood and locking ring.

Model No.: 1-223-380
Length: 8'
No. Pieces: 2
No. Guides: 4 stainless steel
Tip Top: Stainless steel
Rec. Lure Wt.: Not specified
Action: Medium
Handle: Full-size cork grips, chrome-on-brass reel seat.

Model No.: 1-223-310. Same as Model 1-223-380 except:
Length: 10'
No. Guides: Not specified; stainless steel

Model No.: 1-223-390. Same as Model 1-223-380 except:
Length: 9'
No. Guides: Not specified; stainless steel

Model No.: 1-223-466 (Stripper Special)
Length: 6½'
No. Pieces: 2
No. Guides: 4 stainless steel
Tip Top: Stainless steel
Rec. Lure Wt.: Not specified
Action: Spinning rod
Handle: Not specified.

Model No.: 1-223-460. Same as Model 1-233-466 except:
Length: 6'

Model No.: 1-224-868 (All Carbide Guide Series)
Length: 6'8"
No. Pieces: 2
No. Guides: 4 carbide
Tip Top: Carbide
Rec. Lure Wt.: Not specified
Action: Medium
Handle: Specie cork fore and rear grips, non-rusting anodized aluminum handle with fixed reel seat.

Model No.: 1-228-266 (White Knight Series)
Length: 6½'
No. Pieces: 2
No. Guides: 4 chrome-plated
Tip Top: Chrome-plated
Rec. Lure Wt.: Not specified
Action: Medium
Handle: Cork grips, anodized aluminum reel seat.

Model No.: 1-228-270. Same as Model 1-228-266 except:
Length: 7'

Model No.: 1-230-150 (Forester Series)
Length: 5'
No. Pieces: 2
No. Guides: 4 hard-chromed "V" frame
Tip Top: Not specified
Rec. Lure Wt.: Not specified
Action: Light
Handle: Cork fore and rear grips, anodized locking reel seat.

Model No.: 1-230-266 (Forester Series)
Length: 6½'
No. Pieces: 2
No. Guides: 4 hard-chromed "V" frame
Tip Top: Not specified
Rec. Lure Wt.: Not specified
Action: Medium
Handle: Full-size handle with cork rear and fore grips, anodized locking reel seat.

Model No.: 1-232-050 (Outdoorsman Series)
Length: 5'
No. Pieces: 2
No. Guides: 4 hard chrome-plated
Tip Top: Hard chrome-plated
Rec. Lure Wt.: Not specified
Action: Ultra-light
Handle: Cork rear and fore grips, anodized aluminum fixed reel seat, spinning handle with locking ring.

Model No.: 1-232-056. Same as Model 1-232-050 except:
Length: 5½'

1-232-266

Model No.: 1-232-266 (Outdoorsman Series)
Length: 6½'
No. Pieces: 2
No. Guides: Not specified; hard-chrome
Tip Top: Hard-chrome
Rec. Lure Wt.: Not specified
Action: Fast taper
Handle: Metal casting handle with drive reel lock, anodized aluminum fixed seat, spinning handle with locking ring.

Model No.: 1-232-270. Same as Model 1-232-266 except:
Length: 7'

Model No.: 1-232-970. Same as Model 1-232-266 except:
Length: 7'
No. Guides: 4 hard-chrome
Action: Power-flex

Model No.: 1-233-470 (Outdoorsman Saltwater Rod Series)

Length: 7'
No. Pieces: 2
No. Guides: 4
Tip Top: Not specified
Rec. Lure Wt.: Not specified
Action: Medium
Handle: Handle has heavy-chromed brass reel seat with double-locking rings, extra-long cork fore and rear grips with rubber butt cap.

Model No.: 1-233-410. Same as Model 1-233-470 except:
Length: 10'

Model No.: 1-233-480. Same as Model 1-233-470 except:
Length: 8'

Model No.: 1-233-490. Same as Model 1-233-470 except:
Length: 9'

Model No.: 1-233-870. Same as Model 1-233-470 except:
Action: Fast taper

Model No.: 1-233-876. Same as Model 1-233-470 except:
Length: 7½'
Action: Fast taper

Model No.: 1-233-880. Same as Model 1-233-470 except:
Length: 8'
Action: Fast taper

Model No.: 1-233-890. Same as Model 1-233-470 except:
Length: 9'
Action: Fast taper

Model No.: 1-236-866 (Classic I Series)
Length: 6½'
No. Pieces: 2
No. Guides: 5 stainless steel
Tip Top: Carbide
Rec. Lure Wt.: Not specified
Action: Vari-flex
Handle: Full cork grips, anodized fixed reel seat with locking ring, aluminum casting handle with epoxy finish. Rubber-protected metal butt cap and forecap.

Model No.: 1-236-870. Same as Model 1-236-866 except:
Length: 7'

Model No.: 1-236-970. Same as Model 1-236-866 except:
Length: 7'
Action: Power-flex

Model No.: 1-242-050 (Classic III Series)
Length: 5'
No. Pieces: 2
No. Guides: 4 carbide
Tip Top: Carbide

Rec. Lure Wt.: Not specified
Action: Ultra-light
Handle: Not specified

Model No.: 1-242-866. Same as Model
1-242-050 except:
Length: 6½'
No. Guides: 5 carbide
Action: Vari-flex

Model No.: 1-242-870. Same as Model
1-242-050 except:
Length: 7'
No. Guides: Not specified; carbide
Action: Vari-flex

Model No.: 1-242-970. Same as Model
1-242-050 except:
Length: 7'
No. Guides: Not specified; carbide
Action: Power-flex

Model No.: 1-246-266 (Classic IV Series)
Length: 6½'
No. Pieces: Not specified
No. Guides: 5 stainless steel
Tip Top: Carboloy
Rec. Lure Wt.: Not specified
Action: Uni-flex
Handle: Die-cast aluminum offset handle,
rubber-protected, epoxy-coated aluminum
butt cap and forecap. Specie cork grip
with anodized aluminum fixed reel seat
with "duoloc" reel hoods.

Model No.: 1-246-270. Same as Model
1-246-266 except:
Length: 7'

Model No.: 1-332-966 (Bassin' Man Series)
Length: 6½'
No. Pieces: 1
No. Guides: 5 stainless steel
Tip Top: Stainless steel
Rec. Lure Wt.: Not specified
Action: Medium-heavy
Handle: Handle has specie cork fore and rear
grips, anodized aluminum fixed reel seat.

Model No.: 1-334-050
Length: 5'
No. Pieces: 1
No. Guides: 2 chrome
Tip Top: Chrome
Rec. Lure Wt.: Not specified
Action: Ultra-light
Handle: Specie cork fore and rear grips,
anodized fixed reel seat with sliding hood
and locking ring.

Model No.: 1-632-266 (Outdoorsman
Spinning Pack Rod
Length: 6½'
No. Pieces: 6

No. Guides: 5 hard chrome-plated
Tip Top: Hard chrome-plated
Rec. Lure Wt.: Not specified
Action: Medium-light
Handle: Fixed anodized reel seat, cork grips.

Saltwater Spinning Rods

Model No.: 1-229-370 (White Knight Series)

1-242-870

Length: 7'
No. of Pieces: 2
No. Guides: 4 stainless steel flex
Tip Top: Stainless
Rec. Lure Wt.: Not specified
Action: Medium
Handle: Saltwater size cork grips, corrosion-
resistant reel seat.

Model No.: 1-229-376. Same as Model
1-229-370 except:
Length: 7½'

Model No.: 1-229-380. Same as Model
1-229-370 except:
Length: 8'

Model No.: 1-229-386. Same as Model
1-229-370 except:
Length: 8½'

Model No.: 1-229-390. Same as Model
1-229-370 except:
Length: 9'
No. Guides: 5

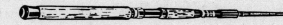

Model No.: 1-243-870 (Classic III Series)
Length: 7'
No. Pieces: 2
No. Guides: 6 stainless steel
Tip Top: Carbide
Rec. Lure Wt.: Not specified
Action: Fast taper

1-334-050

Handle: Specie cork fore-grip, oversize rear
grip with rubber butt cap. Heavy chromed
brass reel seat with double-locking rings.

Model No.: 1-243-860. Same as Model
1-243-870 except:
Length: 7½'
No. Guides: Not specified; stainless steel

Model No.: 1-243-880. Same as Model
1-243-870 except:
Length: 8'
No. Guides: Not specified; stainless steel

Model No.: 1-243-890. Same as Model
1-243-870 except:
Length: 9'
No. Guides: Not specified; stainless steel

Casting Rods

Model No.: 1-004-250
Length: 5'
No. Pieces: 1
No. Guides: 2 chromed
Tip Top: Chromed
Rec. Lure Wt.: Not specified
Action: Not specified
Handle: Die-cast aluminum handle, specie
cork grip, positive-locking reel fastener.

Spin Cast Rods

Model No.: 1-104-256
Length: 5½'
No. Pieces: 2
No. Guides: 2 chromed
Tip Top: Chromed
Rec. Lure Wt.: Not specified
Action: Not specified
Handle: Die-cast aluminum handle, specie
cork grip, positive-locking reel fastener.

Model No.: 1-130-260 (Forester Series)
Length: 6'
No. Pieces: 2
No. Guides: 4 hard-chromed "V" frame
Tip Top: Not specified
Rec. Lure Wt.: Not specified
Action: Medium
Handle: Genuine cork grip, simplified reel
seat fastener.

Model No.: 1-132-260 (Outdoorsman Series)
Length: 6'

1-243-880

No. Pieces: 2
No. Guides: 5 hard chrome-plated
Tip Top: Hard chrome-plated
Rec. Lure Wt.: Not specified
Action: Medium
Handle: Cork fore and rear grips, spiral drive
reel seat fastener, metal casting handle
with spiral drive reel lock, anodized
aluminum fixed seat spinning handle with
locking ring.

Model No.: 1-132-266. Same as Model
1-132-260 except:
Length: 6½'

Model No.: 1-136-860 (Classic I Series)
Length: 6'
No. Pieces: 2
No. Guides: 4 stainless steel guides
Tip Top: Carbide
Rec. Lure Wt.: Not specified
Action: Vari-flex
Handle: Rubber-protected metal butt cap
and forecap, epoxy finished. Contoured
specie cork grips. Die-cast aluminum
casting handles with epoxy finish,
aluminum fixed seat spinning handle with
locking ring.

Model No.: 1-136-460. Same as Model 1-136-860 except:
Action: Power-flex

Model No.: 1-136-866. Same as Model 1-136-860 except:
Length: 6½'

Model No.: 1-142-860
Length: 6'
No. Pieces: 2
No. Guides: 5 Carbide
Tip Top: Carbide
Rec. Lure Wt.: Not specified
Action: Vari-flex
Handle: Super strength handle.

Model No.: 1-142-460. Same as Model 1-142-860 except:
Action: Power-flex

Model No.: 1-142-866. Same as Model 1-142-860 except:
Length: 6½'

Model No.: 1-146-260 (Classic IV Series)
Length: 6'
No. Pieces: Not specified
No. Guides: 5 stainless steel
Tip Top: Carboloy
Rec. Lure Wt.: Not specified
Action: Uniflex flex
Handle: Die-cast aluminum offset handle, rubber-protected, epoxy-coated aluminum butt cap and forecap. Specie cork grips with anodized aluminum fixed reel seat with "duoloc" reel hoods.

Model No.: 1-146-266. Same as Model 1-146-260 except:
Length: 6½'

Model No.: 1-632-256 (Outdoorsman Spin Cast Pack Rod)
Length: 5½'
No. Pieces: 5
No. Guides: 3 hard chrome-plated
Tip Top: Hard chrome-plated
Rec. Lure Wt.: Not specified
Action: Medium-light
Handle: Cast aluminum offset handle, spiral-drive reel seat fastener, cork grips.

Freshwater Spin Cast Rods

Model No.: 1-120-260
Length: 6'
No. Pieces: 2
No. Guides: 3 chrome
Tip Top: Chrome
Rec. Lure Wt.: Not specified
Action: Not specified
Handle: Die-cast aluminum handle, specie cork grip, positive-locking reel seat.

Model No.: 1-124-860 (All Carbide Guide Series)
Length: 6'
No. Pieces: 2
No. Guides: 4 carbide
Tip Top: Carbide
Rec. Lure Wt.: Not specified
Action: Medium
Handle: Specie cork fore and rear grips, non-rusting die cast aluminum handle with chip-resistant finish.

Fresh Water Spin Cast Rod

Model No.: 1-128-260 (White Knight Series)
Length: 6'
No. Pieces: 2
No. Guides: 4 chrome-plated
Tip Top: Chrome-plated

1-142-866

Rec. Lure Wt.: Not specified
Action: Medium
Handle: Die-cast handle, genuine cork grips, high-strength metal reel seats.

Bait-Casting Rods

Model No.: 1-032-461 (Bassin' Man Series)
Length: 6'
No. Pieces: 1
No. Guides: 5 stainless steel
Tip Top: Stainless steel
Rec. Lure Wt.: Not specified
Action: Medium
Handle: Die-cast aluminum offset handle coated with chip resistant epoxy, contour fitting pistol grip of non-slip material.

Model No.: 1-032-561. Same as Model 1-032-461 except:
Action: Medium-heavy

Model No.: 1-042-461 (Bassin' Man Series)
Length: 6'
No. Pieces: 1
No. Guides: 5 speed guides
Tip Top: Not specified
Rec. Lure Wt.: Not specified
Action: Medium
Handle: Die-cast aluminum offset handle coated with epoxy, contoured rear pistol grip of non-slip material. Cork fore grip and positive-locking reel seat fastener.

1-120-260

Model No.: 1-042-561. Same as Model 1-042-461 except:
Action: Medium-heavy

Model No.: 1-060-557 (Bassin' Man Series)
Length: 5½'
No. Pieces: 1
No. Guides: 6 speed guides
Tip Top: Not specified

Rec. Lure Wt.: Not specified
Action: Medium-heavy
Handle: Die-cast aluminum with epoxy coating, specie cork fore grip, contoured pistol rear grip of non-slip material. Reel seat fastener locks swiftly and securely.

Model No.: 1-060-561. Same as Model 1-060-557 except:
Length: 6'
Action: Medium-heavy

Casting/Spin Cast Rods

Model No.: 1-036-460 (Classic I Series)
Length: 6'
No. Pieces: 1
No. Guides: 4 stainless steel
Tip Top: Carbide
Rec. Lure Wt.: Not specified
Action: Power-flex
Handle: Super-strength detachable handle with self-aligning fore-grip chuck, tapered cork rear grip, spiral drive reel seat fastener. Die cast aluminum casting handles with epoxy finish, aluminum fixed seat spinning handle with locking ring.

Model No.: 1-042-356 (Classic III Series)
Length: 5½'
No. Pieces: 1
No. Guides: 4 carbide
Tip Top: Carbide
Rec. Lure Wt.: Not specified
Action: Uni-flex
Handle: Detachable handle with self-aligning fore-grip chuck, specie cork grip, spiral-drive reel seat fastener.

Model No.: 1-042-460. Same as Model 1-042-356 except:
Length: 6'
Action: Power-flex

Model No.: 1-112-260
Length: 6'
No. Pieces: 2
No. Guides: 3 hard chrome-plated
Tip Top: Hard chrome-plated
Rec. Lure Wt.: Not specified
Action: Medium
Handle: Super strength die cast metal handle with cork grip, simplified reel fastener.

Spin Cast Wormin' Rods

Model No.: 1-024-456 (All Carbide Guide Series)
Length: 5½'
No. Pieces: 1
No. Guides: 4 carbide
Tip Top: Carbide
Rec. Lure Wt.: Large lures, plastic worms, live bait
Action: Bass/worm
Handle: Non-rusting die cast aluminum handle, specie cork fore and rear grips.

Model No.: 1-024-460. Same as Model 1-024-456 except:
Length: 6'

Surf Casting Rod

Model No.: 1-033-692 (Outdoorsman Saltwater Rod Series)
Length: 9½'
No. Pieces: 2
No. Guides: 3 stainless steel saltwater casting rings
Tip Top: Not specified
Rec. Lure Wt.: Not specified
Action: Heavy
Handle: Double locking chromed brass reel seat, 4½' cork fore grip, detachable wood rear grip, cushioned butt cap.

Boat Rods

Model No.: 1-503-356
Length: 5½'
No. Pieces: 1
No. Guides: 2
Tip Top: Not specified
Rec. Lure Wt.: Not specified
Action: Medium-light
Handle: Detachable wood butt, chrome-on-brass reel seat, cork forward grip.

Model No.: 1-509-660 (Forester Series)
Length: 6'
No. Pieces: 1
No. Guides: 3
Tip Top: Roller
Rec. Lure Wt.: Not specified
Action: Not specified
Handle: Extra-heavy solid fiberglass shaft runs all the way through the handle. Chromed brass reel seats with double-locking rings.

Model No.: 1-609-660. Same as Model 1-509-660 except:
No. Guides: 2 plus roller guide

Model No.: 1-609-661. Same as Model 1-509-660 except:
No. Guides: All roller

Model No.: 1-511-250
Length: 5'
No. Pieces: 1
No. Guides: 3 stainless steel saltwater
Tip Top: Stainless steel
Rec. Lure Wt.: Not specified
Action: Light
Handle: Chromed brass double-locking reel seat.

Model No.: 1-511-256. Same as Model 1-511-250 except:
Length: 5½'

Model No.: 1-511-359. Same as Model 1-511-250 except:
Length: 5'10"
Action: Medium

Model No.: 1-511-370. Same as Model 1-511-250 except:
Length: 7'
No. Guides: 4 stainless steel
Action: Medium

Model No.: 1-511-560. Same as Model 1-511-250 except:
Length: 6'
Action: Heavy

Model No.: 1-511-660 (Forester Series)
Length: 6'
No. Pieces: 1
No. Guides: 2 stainless steel heavy-duty salt water

1-503-356

Tip Top: Stainless steel
Rec. Lure Wt.: Not specified
Action: Extra-heavy
Handle: Extra-sturdy handle has fiberglass shaft extending from wood rear grip to butt.

Model No.: 1-011-660. Same as Model 1-511-660 except:
Tip Top: Roller

IGFA Class Boat Rods

Model No.: 1-609-305 (Forester Series)
Length: Not specified
No. Pieces: 1
No. Guides: 3 stainless steel guides plus one roller butt guide
Tip Top: Roller
Rec. Lure Wt.: Not specified
Action: 30-50 lb.
Handle: Detachable handle has loc-top, chromed brass gimbal butt, double-locking reel seat, hardwood handle, cork fore grip.

Model No.: 1-611-203 (Forester Series)
Length: Not specified
No. Pieces: 1
No. Guides: AFTCO roller
Tip Top: Not specified
Rec. Lure Wt.: Not specified
Action: 20-30 lb.
Handle: Not specified.

Model No.: 1-611-305. Same as Model 1-611-203 except:
Action: 30-50 lb.

Model No.: 1-611-508. Same as Model 1-611-203 except:
Action: 50-80 lb.

1-511-359

Boat Spinning Rods

Model No.: 1-811-366 (Forester Series)
Length: 6½'

No. Pieces: 1
No. Guides: 4 stainless steel "V" frame
Tip Top: Stainless
Rec. Lure Wt.: Not specified
Action: Medium
Handle: Not specified.

Model No.: 1-811-370. Same as Model 1-811-366 except:
Length: 7'

Model No.: 1-833-276
Length: 7½'
No. Pieces: 1
No. Guides: 4 stainless steel guides plus one 40mm "V" frame stripper guide
Tip Top: Not specified
Rec. Lure Wt.: Not specified
Action: Fast tip
Handle: Heavy-chromed brass reel seat, cork fore grip, detachable wood rear grip.

Boating and Trolling Rods

Model No.: 1-533-366 (Outdoorsman Saltwater Rod Series)
Length: 6½'
No. Pieces: 1
No. Guides: 4 hard chrome-plated
Tip Top: Hard chrome-plated
Rec. Lure Wt.: Not specified
Action: Medium-heavy
Handle: Heavy-chromed brass reel seat, detachable wood rear grip, 4½" cork fore grip.

Model No.: 1-803-366
Length: 6½'
No. Pieces: 1
No. Guides: 3 stainless steel
Tip Top: Stainless steel
Rec. Lure Wt.: Not specified
Action: Not specified
Handle: Detachable wood butt, chrome-on-brass reel seat.

IGFA Saltwater Trolling Rods

Model No.: 1-667-300
Length: 7'
No. Pieces: 1
No. Guides: 4 stainless steel
Tip Top: Roller
Rec. Lure Wt.: Not specified
Action: 30 lb. light
Handle: Hardwood handles, "Nuevo" fore grip, brass reel seat, trolling butts.

Model No.: 1-667-400. Same as Model 1-667-300 except:
Action: 40 lb. medium

Model No.: 1-667-500. Same as Model 1-667-300 except:
Action: 50 lbs. medium-heavy

Model No.: 1-667-600. Same as Model 1-667-300 except:
Action: 60 lb. heavy

Model No.: 1-965-200
Length: 7'1"
No. Pieces: 1
No. Guides: 5 "AFTCO" roller
Tip Top: Roller

Rec. Lure Wt.: Not specified
Action: 20 lb. light
Handle: "Nuevo" fore grips, detachable hardwood handles, brass chromed reel seats.

Model No.: 1-965-000. Same as Model 1-965-200 except:
Action: Unlimited lb. heavy

Model No.: 1-965-130. Same as Model 1-965-200 except:
Action: 130 lb. heavy

Model No.: 1-965-300. Same as Model 1-965-200 except:
Action: 30 lb.

Model No.: 1-965-500. Same as Model 1-965-200 except:
Action: 50 lb. medium

Model No.: 1-965-800. Same as Model 1-965-200 except:
Action: 80 lb. heavy

Model No.: 1-967-200 Royal II (Royal Custom Series)
Length: 6'9"
No. Pieces: 1
No. Guides: 7 hard-chromed stainless steel saltwater
Tip Top: Roller
Rec. Lure Wt.: Not specified
Action: 20 lb.
Handle: "Nuevo" fore grip, hardwood handles, locktop chrome reel seats, chrome gimbal knocks.

Model No.: 1-967-300 Royal III. Same as Model 1-967-200 except:
No. Guides: 6 "AFTCO" roller
Action: 30 lb.

Model No.: 1-967-000 Royal VII. Same as Model 1-967-200 except:
No. Guides: 5 mildrum roller
Action: Unlimited

Model No.: 1-967-130 Royal VI. Same as Model 1-967-200 except:
No. Guides: 5 mildrum roller
Action: 130 lb.

Model No.: 1-967-500 Royal IV. Same as Model 1-967-200 except:
No. Guides: 6 "AFTCO" roller
Action: 50 lb.

Model No.: 1-967-800 Royal V. Same as Model 1-967-200 except:
No. Guides: 5 "AFTCO" roller
Action: 80 lb.

Trolling, Boat and Pier Rods

Model No.: 1-665-259
Length: 5'10"
No. Pieces: 1
No. Guides: 3 stainless steel
Tip Top: Carboloy
Rec. Lure Wt.: Not specified
Action: 20 lb. light
Handle: "Nuevo" fore grip, detachable boat butt with brass chrome reel seat.

Model No.: 1-665-363. Same as Model 1-665-259 except:
Length: 5'10"
Action: 40 lb. medium

Model No.: 1-665-376. Same as Model 1-665-259 except:
Length: 7'6"
Action: 25 lb. medium

Model No.: 1-665-380. Same as Model 1-665-259 except:
Length: 8'
Action: 30 lb. medium

Fly Rods

Model No.: 1-412-270
Length: 7'
No. Pieces: 2
No. Guides: 3 snake guides plus one hard chrome-plated stripper guide
Tip Top: Not specified
Rec. Line: 6 wt.
Handle: Not specified.

Model No.: 1-420-280
Length: 8'
No. Pieces: 2
No. Guides: 3 snake guides plus one hard chrome-plated stripper guide
Tip Top: Hard chrome-plated
Rec. Line: 7 wt.
Handle: Half-wells specie cork grip, anodized adjustable reel seat for either single action or automatic fly reel.

Model No.: 1-428-280 (White Knight Series) Medium Action
Length: 8'
No. Pieces: 2
No. Guides: 3 snake guides plus one hard chrome-plated stripper guide
Tip Top: Hard chrome-plated
Rec. Line: 7 wt.
Handle: Genuine cork grip, ABS reel seats.

Model No.: 1-428-286. Same as Model 1-428-280 except:
Length: 8½'

Model No.: 1-432-270 (Outdoorsman Series)
Length: 7'
No. Pieces: 2
No. Guides: 5 snake guides plus one hard chrome-plated stripper guide
Tip Top: Hard chrome-plated
Rec. Line: 5 wt.
Handle: Specie cork grip handle, anodized aluminum locking reel seat and anodized aluminum fixed spinning handle with locking ring.

Model No.: 1-432-280. Same as Model 1-432-270 except:
Length: 8'
Rec. Line: 7 wt.

Model No.: 1-432-286. Same as Model 1-432-270 except:
Length: 8½'
Rec. Line: 8 wt.

Model No.: 1-436-280 (Classic I Series)
Length: 8'
No. Pieces: 2
No. Guides: 5 snakes guides plus one stripper guide
Tip Top: Carbide
Rec. Line: 7 wt.
Handle: Tapered cork grip handle, two-tone anodized reel seat with locking ring. Die-cast aluminum casting handle with epoxy finish. Rubber-protected metal butt cap

1-412-270

and forecap, epoxy finish.

Model No.: 1-436-286. Same as Model 1-436-280 except:
Length: 8½'
Rec. Line: 8 wt.

Model No.: 1-442-280 (Classic III Series)
Length: 8'
No. Pieces: 2
No. Guides: 6 stainless steel snake guides plus one carbide stripper guide
Tip Top: Not specified
Rec. Line: 7 wt.
Handle: Handle has "duo-loc" anodized reel seat.

Model No.: 1-442-286. Same as Model 1-442-280 except:
Length: 8½'
Rec. Line: 8 wt.

Model No.: 1-446-270 (Classic IV Series)
Length: 7'
No. Pieces: Not specified
No. Guides: 6 stainless steel snake guides plus one stripper guide
Tip Top: Stainless steel
Rec. Line: 6 wt.
Handle: Die-cast aluminum offset handle, rubber-protected, epoxy-coated aluminum butt cap and forecap. Specie cork grip

1-432-270

with anodized aluminum fixed reel with "duoloc" reel hoods.

Model No.: 1-446-276. Same as Model 1-446-270 except:
Length: 7½'
No. Guides: 7 stainless steel snake guides plus one stripper guide

Model No.: 1-446-280. Same as Model 1-446-270 except:
Length: 8'
No. Guides: 7 stainless steel snake guides plus one stripper guide
Rec. Line: 7 wt.

1-446-286

Model No.: 1-446-286. Same as Model 1-446-270 except:
Length: 8½'
No. Guides: 7 stainless steel snake guides plus one stripper guide
Rec. Line: 7 wt.

Model No.: 1-446-393. Same as Model 1-446-270 except:
Length: 9'3"
No. Guides: 7 stainless steel snake guides plus two stripper guides
Rec. Line: 7 wt.

Model No.: 1-632-270 (Outdoorsman Pack Fly Rod)
Length: 7'
No. Pieces: 6
No. Guides: 4 stainless steel snake guides plus one stripper guide
Tip Top: Not specified
Rec. Line: 7 wt.
Handle: Anodized locking reel seat.

Saltwater Spinning & Surf Rods

Model No.: 1-265-311
Length: 11'
No. Pieces: 2
No. Guides: 6 stainless steel
Tip Top: Carboloy
Rec. Lure Wt.: Not specified
Action: Medium; straight taper
Handle: "Nuevo" grips.

Model No.: 1-267-380
Length: 8'
No. Pieces: 2
No. Guides: 5 stainless steel
Tip Top: Carboloy
Rec. Lure Wt.: Not specified
Action: Medium; multiple taper
Handle: "Nuevo" grips.

Model No.: 1-267-310. Same as Model 1-267-380 except:
Length: 10'

Model No.: 1-267-390. Same as Model 1-267-380 except:
Length: 9'

Model No.: 1-267-410. Same as Model 1-267-380 except:
Length: 10'
Action: Heavy

Model No.: 1-267-412. Same as Model 1-267-380 except:
Length: 12'
Action: Heavy

Model No.: 1-267-415. Same as Model 1-267-380 except:
Length: 15'
Action: Heavy

Model No.: 1-267-490. Same as Model 1-267-380 except:
Action: Heavy

Popping Rod

Model No.: 1-033-270 (Outdoorsman Saltwater Rod Series)
Length: 7'
No. Pieces: 1
No. Guides: 4 stainless steel
Tip Top: Stainless steel
Rec. Lure Wt.: Not specified
Action: Popping
Handle: Straight handle has chromed brass reel seat with barrel trigger and double lock, cork fore and rear grips.

Salmon & Steelhead Rods

Model No.: 1-065-290
Length: 9'
No. Pieces: 2
No. Guides: 6 stainless steel
Tip Top: Carboloy
Rec. Lure Wt.: Not specified
Action: Light; straight taper
Handle: Extra-length two-handed specie cork grips, chrome on brass reel seats with double-locking rings.

Model No.: 1-065-390. Same as Model 1-065-290 except:
Action: Medium

Model No.: 1-667-280
Length: 8'
No. Pieces: 2
No. Guides: 5 stainless steel saltwater spinning guides
Tip Top: Carboloy
Rec. Lure Wt.: Not specified
Action: Light; multiple taper
Handle: Extra-length two-handed specie cork grips, anodized reel seats with double-locking rings

Model No.: 1-067-286. Same as Model 1-667-280 except:
Length: 8'6"

Model No.: 1-067-390. Same as Model 1-667-280 except:
Length: 9'
No. Guides: 6 conventional saltwater
Action: Medium
Handle: Chromed double-locking reel seat.

Model No.: 1-667-286. Same as Model 1-667-280 except:
Length: 8'6"

Magnum Bass Rods

Model No.: 1-046-556 (Classic IV Series)
Length: 5½'

No. Pieces: Not specified
No. Guides: 5 stainless steel
Tip Top: Carbide
Rec. Lure Wt.: Not specified
Action: Not specified
Handle: Extra-strength handle, comfortable rubber butt cap, rugged screw-locking device.

Model No.: 1-046-560. Same as Model 1-046-556 except:
Length: 6'

Hardy Bros.

Fly Rods

Model No.: Palakona Super Light Cane
Length: 6', 6'8", 7'2"
No. Pieces: 2
No. Guides: Not specified; agatipe
Tip Top: Stainless steel
Rec. Line: 5 wt.
Handle: Shaped solid cork, skeletal reel seat and sliding ring, capped butt.

Model No.: Same as Palakona Super Light Cane except:
Length: 7'6"
Rec. Line: 6 wt.

Fly rod

Model No.: Palakona Medium Action Cane
Length: 8', 8½', 8'9"
No. Pieces: 2
No. Guides: 2; agatipe
Tip Top: Stainless steel
Rec. Line: 7, 8 wt.
Handle: Solid cork, shaped to hand, fixed screw grip and cork covered housing.

James Heddon's Sons

Spinning Rods

Model No.: 3670 solid
Length: 6'
No. Pieces: 2
No. Guides: 3
Tip Top: Not specified
Rec. Lure Wt.: Not specified
Action: Universal
Handle: Not specified.

Model No.: 4565. Same as Model 3670 except: tubular
Length: 6'9"

Model No.: 3771
Length: 6'
No. Pieces: 2
No. Guides: 2 chromed "V" frame
Tip Top: Chrome
Rec. Lure Wt.: Not specified
Action: Universal
Handle: Natural-tone aluminum fixed reel seat, specie cork fore and rear grips.

4663

Model No.: 4663
Length: 6½'
No. Pieces: 2
No. Guides: 4 chromed "V" frames
Tip Top: Not specified
Rec. Lure Wt.: Not specified
Action: Universal
Handle: Aluminum fixed reel seat, specie cork rear and fore grips.

Model No.: 4665. Same as Model 4663 except:
Length: 7'

Model No.: 7242
Length: 6½'
No. Pieces: 2
No. Guides: 5 hard-chrome
Tip Top: Carboloy
Rec. Lure Wt.: Not specified
Action: Controlled flex
Handle: 14" tapered handle, anodized, rubber tipped butt cap. Tapered "Burnt Cork" grip, foregrip and universal, locking hood reel seat.

Model No.: 7244. Same as Model 7242 except:
Length: 7'

Model No.: 7246
Length: 6'9"
No. Pieces: 2
No. Guides: 5 hard-chrome
Tip Top: Carboloy
Rec. Lure Wt.: Not specified
Action: Vari-Power
Handle: 14" special taper handle, anodized rubber tipped butt caps, tapered "Burnt Cork" grip and foregrip with anodized reel hoods, lock nut seat.

Model No.: 7444
Length: 6'3"
No. Pieces: 2
No. Guides: 5
Tip Top: Not specified
Rec. Lure Wt.: Not specified
Action: Worm rod
Handle: Not specified.

Model No.: 7545 (Walleye Special)
Length: 6'3"
No. Pieces: 2
No. Guides: 5
Tip Top: Not specified
Rec. Lure Wt.: Not specified
Action: Not specified
Handle: Not specified.

Model No.: 7574
Length: 6'9"
No. Pieces: 2
No. Guides: 5 carboloy
Tip Top: Carboloy
Rec. Lure Wt.: ½0-1 oz.

Action: Vari-Power
Handle: Walnut inlay handle, satin anodized fixed reel seat.

Model No.: 7564
Length: 7'
No. Pieces: 2
No. Guides: 5 carboloy
Tip Top: Carboloy
Rec. Lure Wt.: Not specified
Action: Controlled flex
Handle: Walnut inlay handle, satin anodized fixed reel seat.

Model No.: 7642
Length: Not specified
No. Pieces: 2
No. Guides: 5 gold-plated stainless
Tip Top: Carboloy
Rec. Lure Wt.: Not specified
Action: Not specified
Handle: Specie cork handles, foregrips, aluminum reel seats, nylon locks.

7648 — SPINNING, 4-PIECE

7648

Model No.: 7648. Same as Model 7642 except:
No. Pieces: 4

Model No.: 7662
Length: 5'7"
No. Pieces: 1
No. Guides: Not specified; ceramic
Tip Top: Not specified
Rec. Lure Wt.: Not specified
Action: Medium-heavy
Handle: Fixed reel seat.

Model No.: 7663. Same as Model 7662 except:
Length: 6'3"
Action: Worm

Model No.: 7664. Same as Model 7662 except:
Length: 6'6"
Action: Controlled flex

Fresh Water Spinning Rods

Model No.: 716
Length: 6½'
No. Pieces: 2
No. Guides: 5 chromed stainless
Tip Top: Not specified
Rec. Lure Wt.: Not specified
Action: Medium; fast taper
Handle: Chromed reel seat with black locking nuts and hoods.

Model No.: 718. Same as Model 716 except:
Length: 7'

Model No.: 720. Same as Model 716 except:
Ultralight
Length: 5½'

Model No.: 845
Length: 6'
No. Pieces: 2
No. Guides: Not specified; chromed
Tip Top: Chromed
Rec. Lure Wt.: Not specified
Action: ML
Handle: Deluxe mark handles, specie cork grips, anodized reel seats.

Model No.: 846. Same as Model 845 except:
Length: 6'6"
Action: VP

Model No.: 848. Same as Model 845 except:
Length: 7'
Action: VP

Model No.: 7408
Length: 5'3"
No. Pieces: 1
No. Guides: Not specified
Tip Top: Not specified
Rec. Lure Wt.: Not specified
Action: Spinning MH
Handle: Not specified.

Model No.: 7410. Same as Model 7408 except:
Length: 5'7"

Ocean Spinning Rods

Model No.: 2104
Length: 8'
No. Pieces: 2
No. Guides: Not specified; hard-chromed
Tip Top: Stainless steel
Rec. Lure Wt.: Not specified
Action: Not specified
Handle: Extra-long 12½" tapered "Burnt Cork," rubber ball-type butt cap, anodized reel hoods, double lock nuts, seat. 4½" "Burnt Cork" foregrip.

Model No.: 2105. Same as Model 2104 except:
Length: 8½'

Model No.: 2106. Same as Model 2104 except:
Length: 9'
Handle: 14½" tapered "Burnt Cork".

Model No.: 2107. Same as Model 2104 except:
Length: 9½'
Handle: 14½" tapered "Burnt Cork".

Model No.: 2108. Same as Model 2104 except:

James Heddon's Sons (cont'd.)

Length: 10'
Handle: 14½" tapered "Burnt Cork".

Model No.: 8505
Length: 8'
No. Pieces: 2
No. Guides: Not specified; braced
Tip Top: Not specified
Rec. Lure Wt.: Not specified
Action: Medium; fast taper
Handle: Specie cork fore and rear grips, rubber butt caps. Reel seats highly corrosion resistant.

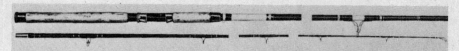

Model No.: 8510. Same as Model 8505
except:
Length: 8½'

Model No.: 8515. Same as Model 8505
except:
Length: 9'

Model No.: 8520. Same as Model 8505
except:
Length: 9½'

Model No.: 8525. Same as Model 8505
except:
Length: 10'
No. Guides: 6

Saltwater Surf Spin Rods

7505

Model No.: 7505
Length: 8'
No. Pieces: 2
No. Guides: Not specified; corrosion resistant
Tip Top: Not specified
Rec. Lure Wt.: Not specified
Action: Not specified
Handle: Specie cork butts and foregrips. Corrosion resistant, reel seats.

Model No.: 7510. Same as Model 7505
except:
Length: 8½'

Model No.: 7515. Same as Model 7505
except:
Length: 9'

Model No.: 7520. Same as Model 7505
except:
Length: 9½'

Model No.: 7525. Same as Model 7505
except:
Length: 10'

Model No.: 7530. Same as Model 7505
except:
Length: 11'

Casting Rods

3335

Model No.: 3335
Length: 5½'
No. Pieces: 1
No. Guides: 3 chromed "V" frame

Tip Top: Chrome
Rec. Lure Wt.: Not specified
Action: Universal
Handle: Detachable offset handle, "speed-grip" reel holder, specie cork grip.

Model No.: 6101
Length: 5½'
No. Pieces: 1
No. Guides: Not specified; ceramic
Tip Top: Not specified
Rec. Lure Wt.: Not specified
Action: Medium
Handle: Standard.

Model No.: 6105. Same as Model 6101
except:
Length: 6'

Model No.: 6110. Same as Model 6101
except:
Handle: Pistol grip.

Model No.: 6115. Same as Model 6101
except:
Action: Medium-heavy
Handle: Pistol grip.

Model No.: 6120. Same as Model 6101
except:
Length: 6'
Action: Medium-heavy
Handle: Pistol grip.

6277 — casting, 5½, 1-piece

6277

Model No.: 6277
Length: 5½'
No. Pieces: 2
No. Guides: 4
Tip Top: Not specified
Rec. Lure Wt.: Not specified

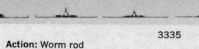

Action: Worm rod
Handle: Not specified.

Model No.: 6322
Length: 5½'
No. Pieces: 2
No. Guides: 5
Tip Top: Not specified
Rec. Lure Wt.: Not specified
Action: Worm rod
Handle: Walnut and tenite inlaid handles.

Freshwater Casting Rods

Model No.: 6270
Length: 5'6"
No. Pieces: 1
No. Guides: Not specified
Tip Top: Not specified
Rec. Lure Wt.: Not specified
Action: Cast MH
Handle: Not specified.

Model No.: 6271. Same as Model 6270
except:
Length: 6'

Model No.: 6272. Same as Model 6270
except:
Length: 5'10"
Action: Cast H

Spin-Casting Rods

Model No.: 3450
Length: 5½'
No. Pieces: 2
No. Guides: 3
Tip Top: Not specified
Rec. Lure Wt.: Not specified
Action: Universal
Handle: Not specified.

Model No.: 4243. Same as Model 3450
except: tubular
Length: 6'3"

Model No.: 3551
Length: 5½'
No. Pieces: 2
No. Guides: 3 chromed "V" frame
Tip Top: Chrome
Rec. Lure Wt.: Not specified
Action: Universal

Handle: Fixed aluminum handle, "speed-grip" reel holders, specie cork grip.

Model No.: 3553. Same as Model 3551
except:
Length: 6'

Model No.: 4443
Length: 6'
No. Pieces: 2
No. Guides: 4 chromed "V" frame
Tip Top: Not specified
Rec. Lure Wt.: Not specified
Action: Universal
Handle: Fixed aluminum handle, "speed-grip" reel holder, specie cork grips.

Model No.: 4446. Same as Model 4443 except:
Length: 6½'

Model No.: 6248
Length: 6'
No. Pieces: 2
No. Guides: 4 hard-chrome
Tip Top: Carboloy
Rec. Lure Wt.: Not specified
Action: Controlled flex
Handle: Aluminum offset handle, anodized rubber tipped butt caps. Tapered "Burnt Cork" grip, self-aligning "Screw-Lok" foregrip with universal, locking hood reel seat.

Model No.: 6244. Same as Model 6248 except:
Action: Vari-Power

Model No.: 6275
Length: 5'8"
No. Pieces: 2
No. Guides: 5
Tip Top: Not specified
Rec. Lure Wt.: Not specified
Action: Worm rod
Handle: Not specified.

Model No.: 6446
Length: Not specified
No. Pieces: 2
No. Guides: 5 gold-plated stainless
Tip Top: Carboloy
Rec. Lure Wt.: Not specified
Action: Not specified
Handle: Specie cork handles, foregrips, aluminum reel seats, nylon locks.

Model No.: 6448. Same as Model 6446 except:
No. Pieces: 4

Model No.: 6575 (Walleye special)
Length: 5'8"
No. Pieces: 2
No. Guides: 5
Tip Top: Not specified
Rec. Lure Wt.: Not specified
Action: Not specified
Handle: Not specified.

Model No.: 6744
Length: 6'
No. Pieces: 2
No. Guides: 5 hard-chrome
Tip Top: Carboloy
Rec. Lure Wt.: Not specified

Action: Vari-Power
Handle: Fixed aluminum offset handle, anodized, rubber tipped butt cap, tapered "Burnt Cork" grip, foregrip with universal, locking hood reel seat.

Fresh Water Spin-Casting Rods

Model No.: 816
Length: 6'
No. Pieces: 2
No. Guides: Not specified; chromed
Tip Top: Chromed
Rec. Lure Wt.: Not specified
Action: VP
Handle: Deluxe mark handles, specie cork grips, anodized reel seats.

Model No.: 818. Same as Model 816 except:
Length: 6'6"

Model: 706
Length: 6'
No. Pieces: 2
No. Guides: 4 chromed stainless
Tip Top: Not specified
Rec. Lure Wt.: Not specified
Action: Medium; fast taper
Handle: Chromed reel seat with black locking nuts and hoods.

Model No.: 708. Same as Model 706 except:
Length: 6½'

Casting/Spin-Casting Rods

6318

Model No.: 6318
Length: 6'
No. Pieces: 2
No. Guides: 4 carboloy
Tip Top: Carboloy
Rec. Lure Wt.: Not specified
Action: Controlled flex
Handle: Walnut inlay handle.

6916

Model No.: 6916. Same as Model 6318 except:
Length: 6½'
No. Pieces: 2

Model No.: 6926. Same as Model 6318 except:
No Pieces: 2
Action: Vari-Power

Model No.: 6743

Length: 6'
No. Pieces: 2
No. Guides: 5 hard-chrome
Tip Top: Carboloy
Rec. Lure Wt.: Not specified
Action: Controlled flex
Handle: Fixed aluminum offset handle, anodized rubber-tipped butt cap. Tapered "Burnt Cork" grip, foregrip and universal, locking hood reel seat.

Model No.: 6746. Same as Model 6743 except:
Length: 6½'

Fly Rods

Model No.: 876
Length: 8'
No. Pieces: 2
No. Guides: Not specified; chromed
Tip Top: Chromed
Rec. Line: Not specified
Handle: Deluxe mark handles, specie cork grips, anodized reel seats.

Model No.: 878. Same as Model 876 except:
Length: 8'6"

Model No.: 4885
Length: 8'
No. Pieces: 2
No. Guides: 5 stainless snake guides with chromed "V" frame stripping guide
Tip Top: Not specified
Rec. Line: Not specified
Handle: Full size handle, bright aluminum reel seat, tapered specie cork grip.

Model No.: 4887. Same as Model 4885 except:
Length: 8½'

Model No.: 8245
Length: 8'
No. Pieces: 2
No. Guides: 5 stainless steel snake guides with hard-chrome stripping guide
Tip Top: Stainless steel
Rec. Line: Not specified
Handle: Custom handle, anodized butt cap, tapered "Burnt Cork" grip. Anodized component, positve locking hood reel seat.

Model No.: 8246. Same as Model 8245 except: Power Plus Action
Length: 8'3"

Model No.: 8247. Same as Model 8245 except:
Length: 8½'

Model No.: 8545
Length: Not specified
No. Pieces: 2
No. Guides: 6 gold-plated stainless with gold-plated stainless stripping guide
Tip Top: Carboloy
Rec. Line: Not specified
Handle: Specie cork handles, foregrips, aluminum reel seats, nylon locks.

Model No.: 8548. Same as Model 8545 except:
No. Pieces: 4

Model No.: 8251 (Mark Wet)
Length: 7'
No. Pieces: 2
No. Guides: Not specified
Tip Top: Not specified
Rec. Line: Not specified
Handle: Imported specie cork handle.

Model No.: 8252. Same as Model 8251 except:
Length: 7½'

Model No.: 8253. Same as Model 8251 except:
Length: 8'

Model No.: 8255. Same as Model 8251 except:
Length: 8½'

Model No.: 8467
Length: 8½'
No. Pieces: 2
No. Guides: 8 stainless and carboloy guides with stripping guide
Tip Top: Stainless and carboloy
Rec. Line: Not specified
Handle: Walnut inlay handle, anodized reel seat.

Model No.: 8651 (Mark Dry)
Length: 7'
No. Pieces: 2
No. Guides: Not specified
Tip Top: Not specified
Rec. Line: Not specified
Handle: Imported specie cork handle.

Model No.: 8652. Sames as Model 8651 except:
Length: 7½'

Model No.: 8653. Sames as Model 8651 except:
Length: 8'

Model No.: 8655. Sames as Model 8651 except:
Length: 8½'

Model No.: 726
Length: 8'
No. Pieces: 2
No. Guides: Not specified

Tip Top: Not specified
Rec. Line: Not specified
Handle: Chromed reel seat with black locking nuts and hoods.

Model No.: 728. Same as Model 726 except:
Length: 8½'

Model No.: 2506
Length: 9'
No. Pieces: 2
No. Guides: 4
Tip Top: Stainless steel
Rec. Line: Not specified
Handle: Extra long handle with "Burnt Cork" grip and 4" foregrip. Rubber bolt-type butt caps and heavy chromed reel hoods, double lock nuts, seat.

Saltwater Boat and Trolling Rods

2401

Model No.: 2401
Length: 6½'
No. Pieces: 1
No. Guides: 6 hard-chrome
Tip Top: Hard-chrome
Rec. Lure Wt.: Not specified
Action: Sturdy
Handle: Heavy duty detachable or one-piece hand finish hickory handle with rubber ball-type butt caps. Heavy chromed reel hoods, double lock nuts, seat and 4" foregrip of "Burnt Cork."

Model No.: 2411. Same as Model 2401 except:
Length: 7'
Action: Standard

Saltwater Mooching Rod

Model No.: 2216
Length: 9'
No. Pieces: 2
No. Guides: 10
Tip Top: Stainless steel
Rec. Lure Wt.: Not specified
Action: Not specified
Handle: Extra-long, fixed seat type handle with 14½" tapered "Burnt Cork" grip and 4½" "Burnt Cork" foregrip. Rubber ball-type butt caps and anodized reel hoods, double lock nuts, seat.

726

Model No.: 7538
Length: 8½'
No. Pieces: 2
No. Guides: Not specified; corrosion resistant

Tip Top: Not specified
Rec. Lure Wt.: Not specified
Action: Fast taper
Handle: Specie cork butts and foregrips. Corrosion resistant, reel seats.

Saltwater Salmon / Steelhead Rods

Model No.: 7540
Length: 8'
No. Pieces: 2
No. Guides: Not specified; corrosion resistant
Tip Top: Not specified
Rec. Lure Wt.: Not specified
Action: Fast taper
Handle: Specie cork butts and foregrips. Corrosion resistant, reel seats.

Model No.: 7542. Same as Model 7540 except:
Length: 8½'

Saltwater Popping Cast Rod

Model No.: 7536
Length: 7'
No. Pieces: 1
No. Guides: Not specified; corrosion resistant
Tip Top: Not specified
Rec. Lure Wt.: Not specified
Action: Fast taper
Handle: Specie cork butts and foregrips, corrosion resistant, reel seats.

Saltwater Popping Spin Rod

Model No.: 7535
Length: 7'
No. Pieces: 1
No. Guides: Not specified; corrosion resistant
Tip Top: Not specified
Rec. Lure Wt.: Not specified
Action: Fast taper
Handle: Specie cork butts and foregrips, corrosion resistant, reel seats.

Boat/Bay/Pier Rods

Model No.: 9050
Length: 5½'
No. Pieces: Not specified
No. Guides: 2 corrosion-resistant chrome
Tip Top: Not specified
Rec. Lure Wt.: Not specified
Action: Not specified
Handle: American hardwood handles. Butt .375

Model No.: 9051. Same as Model 9050 except:
Handle: Butt .450

Model No.: 9052. Same as Model 9050 except:
Length: 6'
Handle: Butt .450

Spinning Rods

Model No.: 1-016 (Midnight Series)
Length: 6'
No. Pieces: 2
No. Guides: 3 chromed steel
Tip Top: Chromed
Rec. Lure Wt.: Not specified
Action: Spinning rod
Handle: Specie cork grips with clear anodized aluminum fixed reel seat.

Model No.: 1-017 (Midnight Series)
Length: Not specified
No. Pieces: Not specified
No. Guides: 3 chromed steel
Tip Top: Chromed
Rec. Lure Wt.: Not specified
Action: Spinning rod
Handle: Clear anodized aluminum fixed reel seat with specie cork grips.

1-027

Model No.: 1-027 (Tuffy Series)
Length: 6½'
No. Pieces: 2
No. Guides: 4 stainless
Tip Top: Stainless
Rec. Lure Wt.: Not specified
Action: Spinning rod
Handle: Anodized aluminum reel seat with specie cork grips.

Model No.: 1-028 (Tuffy Series)
Length: 7'
No. Pieces: 2
No. Guides: 5 stainless
Tip Top: Stainless
Rec. Lure Wt.: Not specified
Action: Spinning rod
Handle: Anodized aluminum reel seat with specie cork grips.

Model No.: 1-125 (Fly Wate Series)
Length: 5½'
No. Pieces: 2
No. Guides: 4 stainless foulproof
Tip Top: Ovallan
Rec. Lure Wt.: Not specified
Action: Spinning rod
Handle: Anodized reel seat with specie cork grip.

1-127

Model No.: 1-127 (Fly Wate Series)
Length: 6½'
No. Pieces: 2
No. Guides: 4 Ovallan stainless wire frame
Tip Top: Ovallan stainless wire frame
Rec. Lure Wt.: Not specified
Action: Spinning rod
Handle: Anodized reel seat with specie cork grip.

Model No.: 1-128. Same as Model 1-127 except:
Length: 7'
No. Guides: 5 Ovallan

1-129

Model No.: 1-129 (Fly Wate Series)
Length: 9'
No. Pieces: 2
No. Guides: 6 stainless wire frame Ovallan
Tip Top: Carboloy
Rec. Lure Wt.: Not specified
Action: Spinning rod
Handle: Chrome-plated brass reel seat.

Model No.: 1-666 (Portage Rod)
Length: 6½'
No. Pieces: 6
No. Guides: 4 stainless steel
Tip Top: Stainless steel
Rec. Lure Wt.: Not specified
Action: Spinning rod
Handle: Not specified.

Model No.: 81-715 (Blue Chip Series)
Length: 5½'
No. Pieces: 2
No. Guides: 4 stainless foulproof
Tip Top: Carboloy
Rec. Lure Wt.: Not specified
Action: Spinning rod
Handle: Specie cork with gold anodized rings.

81-716

Model No.: 81-716. Same as Model 81-715 except:
Length: 6'
No. Guides: 5 stainless foulproof

Model No.: 81-717 (Blue Chip Series)
Length: 6½'
No. Pieces: 2
No. Guides: 5 stainless wire frame plus one carboloy gathering guide
Tip Top: Carboloy
Rec. Lure Wt.: Not specified
Action: Spinning rod
Handle: Brown and gold anodized reel seat with gold double lock rings. Specie cork grips, gold anodized caps.

Model No.: 81-718. Same as Model 81-717 except:
Length: 7'

Model No.: 81-777. Same as Model 81-717 except:
Length: 6½'
No. Pieces: 2
Action: Medium-heavy

Spin Casting Rods

Model No.: 5-001 (Ivory Series)
Length: 5½'
No. Pieces: 2
No. Guides: 3 chromed steel
Tip Top: Chromed
Rec. Lure Wt.: Not specified
Action: Casting
Handle: Specie cork grip and ABS reel seat.

Model No.: 5-011 (Midnight Series)
Length: 5½'
No. Pieces: 2
No. Guides: 3 chromed steel
Tip Top: Chromed
Rec. Lure Wt.: Not specified
Action: Fast tip
Handle: Specie cork grip with cast aluminum reel seat.

Model No.: 5-012 (Midnight Series)
Length: 6'
No. Pieces: 2
No. Guides: 4 chromed steel
Tip Top: Chromed
Rec. Lure Wt.: Not specified
Action: Fast tip
Handle: Cast aluminum reel seat and specie cork grip.

Model No.: 5-036 (Tuffy Series)
Length: 6'
No. Pieces: 2
No. Guides: 3 chromed steel
Tip Top: Chromed
Rec. Lure Wt.: Not specified
Action: Casting
Handle: Cast aluminum handle with specie cork grips.

Model No.: 5-037 (Tuffy Series)
Length: 6½'
No. Pieces: 2
No. Guides: 4 chromed steel
Tip Top: Chromed
Rec. Lure Wt.: Not specified
Action: Casting
Handle: Cast aluminum handle with specie cork grips.

Model No.: 5-135 (Fly Wate Series)
Length: 5½'
No. Pieces: 2
No. Guides: 3 stainless wire frame Ovallan
Tip Top: Ovallan
Rec. Lure Wt.: Not specified

Action: Casting
Handle: Specie cork grip with cast aluminum fast locking reel seat.

Model No.: 5-136. Same as Model 5-135 except:
Length: 6'

5-137

Model No.: 5-137. Same as Model 5-135 except:
Length: 6½'
No. Guides: 4 stainless wire frame Ovallan

Model No.: 5-545 (Ivory Series)
Length: 4½'
No. Pieces: 1
No. Guides: 2 chromed steel
Tip Top: Chromed
Rec. Lure Wt.: Not specified
Action: Casting
Handle: Specie cork grip and ABS reel seat.

Model No.: 5-550 (Ivory Series)
Length: 5'
No. Pieces: 1
No. Guides: 3 chromed steel
Tip Top: Chromed
Rec. Lure Wt.: Not specified
Action: Casting
Handle: Specie cork grip and ABS reel seat.

Model No.: 5-555 (Ivory Series)
Length: 5½'
No. Pieces: 1
No. Guides: 3 chromed steel
Tip Top: Chromed
Rec. Lure Wt.: Not specified
Action: Casting
Handle: Specie cork grip and ABS reel seat.

Model No.: 5-666 (Portage Rods)
Length: 5½'
No. Pieces: 5
No. Guides: 4 chromed steel
Tip Top: Not specified
Rec. Lure Wt.: Not specified
Action: Casting
Handle: Not specified.

Model No.: 85-756 (Blue Chip Series)
Length: 6'
No. Pieces: 2
No. Guides: 4 stainless wire frame plus one carboloy gathering guide
Tip Top: Carboloy
Rec. Lure Wt.: Not specified
Action: Casting
Handle: Specie cork grips. Fast locking cast aluminum reel seat. Gold-plated butt and foregrip caps.

Model No.: 85-757. Same as Model 85-756 except:
Length: 6½'
No. Guides: 5 stainless

Fly Rods

Model No.: 3-015 (Tuffy Series)

Length: 7½'
No. Pieces: 2
No. Guides: 4 snake guides plus one chromed steel stripper
Tip Top: Chromed steel
Rec. Line: 5 wt.
Handle: Specie cork grip with aluminum reel seat.

Model No.: 3-016 (Tuffy Series)
Length: 8'
No. Pieces: 2
No. Guides: 4 snake guides plus one chromed steel stripper
Tip Top: Chromed steel
Rec. Line: 6 wt.
Handle: Specie cork grip with aluminum reel seat.

Model No.: 3-017 (Tuffy Series)
Length: 8½'
No. Pieces: 2
No. Guides: 5 snake guides plus one chromed steel stripper
Tip Top: Chromed steel
Rec. Line: 8 wt.
Handle: Specie cork grip with aluminum reel seat.

Model No.: 3-175 (Fly Wate Series)
Length: 7½'
No. Pieces: 2
No. Guides: 4 stainless snake guides plus one carboloy stripper
Tip Top: Stainless
Rec. Line: 5 wt.
Handle: Anodized reel seat with double lock rings. Specie cork grip.

Model No.: 3-176. Same as Model 3-175 except:
Length: 8'
No. Guides: 5 stainless snake guides plus one carboloy stripper
Rec. Line: 6 wt.

Model No.: 3-177. Same as Model 3-175 except:
Length: 8½'
No. Guides: 6 stainless snake guides plus one carboloy stripper
Rec. Line: 8 wt.

Model No.: 3-666 (Portage Rod)
Length: 6½'
No. Pieces: 6
No. Guides: 4
Tip Top: Not specified
Rec. Line: 6, 7 wt.
Handle: Not specified.

Model No.: 73-434 (Bass Pro)
Length: 7'
No. Pieces: 2
No. Guides: 4 chromed stainless plus one carboloy stripper

Tip Top: Stainless
Rec. Line: 8, 9 wt.
Handle: Specie cork grip. Brown and gold anodized reel seat with gold double lock rings.

Saltwater Fly Rod

Model No.: 3-178 (Fly Wate Series)
Length: 9'
No. Pieces: 2
No. Guides: 7 stainless snake guides plus one carboloy stripper
Tip Top: Stainless
Rec. Line: 8¾ wt.
Handle: Chrome-plated brass reel seat with detachable fighting butt.

Fly Casting Fly Rod

Model No.: 83-734 (Blue Chip Series)
Length: 7'
No. Pieces: 2

3-017

No. Guides: 4 stainless guides plus one carboloy stripper
Tip Top: Not specified
Rec. Line: Not specified
Handle: Specie cork and gold anodized lock rings, specie cork grip.

Spin and Fly Rod

Model No.: 31-666 (Portage Rod)
Length: 6½'
No. Pieces: 6
No. Guides: 4 stainless steel
Tip Top: Not specified
Rec. Line: 6, 7 wt.
Handle: Fixed reel seat.

Popping Rod

Model No.: 2-257 (Fly Wate Series)
Length: 7'
No. Pieces: 2
No. Guides: 4 stainless wire frame
Tip Top: Stainless braced
Rec. Lure Wt.: Not specified
Action: Popping rod
Handle: Finger grip chrome-plated brass reel seat, specie cork grips.

Boat-Bay-Pier Rods

Model No.: 6-016 (Tuffy Series)
Length: 6'
No. Pieces: 1
No. Guides: 3 heavy duty chromed
Tip Top: Chromed
Rec. Lure Wt.: Not specified
Action: Boat rod
Handle: Detachable wood handle, specie cork foregrip with chrome-plated brass reel seat.

Model No.: 6-106 (Ivory Series)
Length: 6'
No. Pieces: 1
No. Guides: 3 chrome-plated stainless

Tip Top: Chrome-plated
Rec. Lure Wt.: Not specified
Action: Medium
Handle: Detachable wood handle, chrome-plated brass reel seat with wood foregrip.

Specialty Worm Rods
Spinning Style

71-414

Model No.: 71-414
Length: 5'
No. Pieces: 1
No. Guides: 4 carboloy
Tip Top: Carboloy
Rec. Lure Wt.: Not specified
Action: Worm rod
Handle: Hooded anodized reel seat, double lock rings and specie cork grips.

Model No.: 71-416
Length: 6'
No. Pieces: 1
No. Guides: 4 stainless wire frame guides plus one carboloy gathering guide
Tip Top: Carboloy
Rec. Lure Wt.: Not specified
Action: Worm rod
Handle: Specie cork grips with hooded anodized reel seat and double lock rings.

71-466

Model No.: 71-466
Length: 6'
No. Pieces: 1
No. Guides: 5 carboloy
Tip Top: Carboloy
Rec. Lure Wt.: Not specified
Action: Worm rod
Handle: Specie cork grips with hooded anodized reel seat and double lock rings.

Specialty Worm Rods
Casting Style

Model No.: 74-405
Length: 5'
No. Pieces: 1
No. Guides: 3 stainless wire frame "worm" guides plus one carboloy gathering guide
Top Top: Carboloy
Rec. Lure Wt.: Not specified
Action: Worm rod
Handle: Specie cork grips with speed locking reel seat.

Model No.: 74-406
Length: 5½'
No. Pieces: 1
No. Guides: 4 stainless wire frame "worm" guides plus one carboloy gathering guide
Tip Top: Carboloy
Rec. Lure Wt.: Not specified
Action: Worm rod
Handle: Specie cork grip with speed locking reel seat.

Model No.: 74-446
Length: 5½'
No. Pieces: 1
No. Guides: 5 carboloy

Tip Top: Carboloy
Rec. Lure Wt.: Not specified
Action: Worm rod
Handle: Specie cork grip with speed locking reel seat.

Casting Worm Rods

Model No.: 84-005 (Blue Chip Series)
Length: 5'
No. Pieces: 1
No. Guides: 5 carboloy
Tip Top: Carboloy
Rec. Lure Wt.: Not specified
Action: Worm rod
Handle: Anodized fast-lock reel seat, specie cork grips with gold anodized butt and foregrip caps.

Model No.: 4-145 (Fly Wate Series)
Length: 5½'
No. Pieces: 1
No. Guides: 4 Ovallan stainless
Tip Top: Stainless
Rec. Lure Wt.: Not specified
Action: Heavy
Handle: Fast locking anodized aluminum reel seat, 7" specie cork butt grip with bumper.

Pflueger

Spinning Rods

Model No.: 104SP
Length: 6', 6'6", 7'
No. Pieces: 2
No. Guides: 5 Fuji
Tip Top: Fuji
Rec. Lure Wt.: Not specified
Action: Medium
Handle: Select specie cork rear and foregrip with aluminum reel seat.

202SP

Model No.: 202SP
Length: 5', 5'6", 6'6", 7'
No. Pieces: 2
No. Guides: 5'-4, 5'6"-4, 6'6"-4, 7'-5 Stainless Steel
Tip Top: Carboloy
Rec. Lure Wt.: Not specified
Action: 5'-ultra-light, 5'6"-medium, 6'6"-light, 7'-light
Handle: Aluminum reel seat with specie cork rear and foregrip.

Model No.: 481SP
Length: 6'6"
No. Pieces: 1
No. Guides: 4
Tip Top: Not specified
Rec. Lure Wt.: Not specified
Action: Light
Handle: Aluminum reel seat, cork grip.

Model No.: 501SP
Length: 6'
No. Pieces: 1
No. Guides: 3 chromed stainless steel
Tip Top: Not specified
Rec. Lure Wt.: Not specified
Action: Light
Handle: Specie cork grip with fixed reel seat.

Salt Water Spinning Rods

Model No.: 487SWS
Length: 7'6"
No. Pieces: 2
No. Guides: 5 chromed stainless steel
Tip Top: Supported
Rec. Lure Wt.: Not specified
Action: Heavy
Handle: Corrosion-proof delrin reel seat, cork grip.

Model No.: 101SWSP6-6
Length: 6'6"
No. Pieces: 2
No. Guides: 5 stainless steel
Tip Top: Carboloy
Rec. Lure Wt.: Not specified
Action: Light
Handle: Heavy anodized reel seat, specie cork grip, and rubber butt cap.

Model No.: 101SWSP7-6. Same as Model 101SWSP6-6 except:
Length: 7'6"
No. Guides: 6 stainless steel
Action: Medium-heavy fast tip

Spin-Casting Rods

Model No.: 104PB
Length: 6', 6'6"
No. Pieces: 2
No. Guides: 5 Fuji hard-speed ring
Tip Top: Fuji hard-speed
Rec. Lure Wt.: Not specified
Action: Medium
Handle: Cork foregrip and reargrip.

Model No.: 202PB
Length: 6', 6'6"
No. Pieces: 2

No. Guides: 4 stainless steel
Tip Top: Carboloy
Rec. Lure Wt.: Not specified
Action: Light
Handle: Cork foregrip and oversized cork rear grip.

Model No.: 481PB
Length: 6'
No. Pieces: 2
No. Guides: 4
Tip Top: Not specified
Rec. Lure Wt.: Not specified
Action: Medium-light
Handle: Deluxe double offset handle with select specie cork grip.

Model No.: 501PB
Length: 5'6"
No. Pieces: 2

No. Guides: 3 chromed steel
Tip Top: Chromed steel
Rec. Lure Wt.: Not specified
Action: Light
Handle: Aluminum handle with cork grip and screw-lock seat.

Bait-Casting Rods

Model No.: 104BC
Length: 5'6", 6'
No. Pieces: 2
No. Guides: 5 Fuji
Tip Top: Fuji
Rec. Lure Wt.: Not specified
Action: Medium-heavy
Handle: Extra-light pistol grip, detachable.

Model No.: 202BC
Length: 5', 5'6", 6'
No. Pieces: 1
No. Guides: 5', 5'6"-4 stainless steel, 6'-5 stainless steel
Tip Top: Carboloy
Rec. Lure Wt.: Not specified
Action: Heavy
Handle: Cork grip.

Model No.: 451BC
Length: 5'6"
No. Pieces: 2
No. Guides: 3 carbon steel and chromed
Tip Top: Carbon steel and chromed
Rec. Lure Wt.: Not specified
Action: Heavy
Handle: Sliding lock.

Model No.: 201BC6-0
Length: 6'
No. Pieces: 1
No. Guides: 4 stainless steel
Tip Top: Carboloy
Rec. Lure Wt.: Not specified
Action: Medium-fast tip
Handle: Deluxe detachable handle with select specie cork rear grip and locking reel seat.

Fly Rods

Model No.: 104F
Length: 7'6", 8'
No. Pieces: 2
No. Guides: 7 Fuji stripper
Tip Top: Not specified
Rec. Line: 7'6"-6 or 7 wt., 8'-8 or 9 wt.
Handle: Deluxe aluminum reel seat and select specie cork grip.

Model No.: 101F8-0
Length: 8'
No. Pieces: 2
No. Guides: 8 chromed

Tip Top: Not specified
Rec. Line: 8 or 9 wt.
Handle: Aluminum reel seat.

Model No.: 201F7-6
Length: 7'6"
No. Pieces: 2
No. Guides: 6 gold-plated stainless steel
Tip Top: Gold-plated stainless steel
Rec. Line: 6 or 7 wt.
Handle: Reel seat is screw lock type, cork grip.

Model No.: 201F8-6. Same as Model 201F7-6 except:
Length: 8'6"
Rec. Line: 8 or 9 wt.

Phillipson/3M

Fly Rods

Model No.: EF66
Length: 6½'
No. Pieces: 2
No. Guides: Not specified; ceramic
Tip Top: Ceramic
Rec. Line: 4 wt.
Handle: Cork grip.

Model No.: EF70. Same as Model EF66 except:
Length: 7'
Rec. Line: 5 wt.

Model No.: EF76
Length: 7½'
No. Pieces: 2
No. Guides: Not specified; ceramic
Tip Top: Ceramic
Rec. Line: 5 or 6 wt.
Handle: Cork grip.

Model No.: EF80S. Same as Model EF76 except:
Length: 8'
Rec. Line: 9 wt.

Model No.: EF80. Same as Model EF76 except:
Length: 8'
Rec. Line: 6 or 7 wt.

Model No.: EF86. Same as Model EF76 except:
Length: 8½'
Rec. Line: 7 or 8 wt.

Quick

Spinning Rods

Model No.: 6055
Length: 5½'
No. Pieces: 1
No. Guides: Not specified; polygon
Tip Top: Not specified
Rec. Lure Wt.: Not specified
Action: Light
Handle: Neo-grip.

Model No.: 6065
Length: 6½'
No. Pieces: 2
No. Guides: Not specified
Tip Top: Not specified
Rec. Lure Wt.: Not specified
Action: Fast taper
Handle: Neo-grip.

Model No.: 6060. Same as Model 6065 except:
Length: 6'
Action: Medium-heavy

Model No.: 6066. Same as Model 6065 except:
Action: Medium-heavy

Model No.: 6070. Same as Model 6065 except:
Length: 7'

Model No.: 6071. Same as Model 6065 except:
Length: 7'
Action: Medium-heavy

Model No.: UL6056R
Length: 5½'
No. Pieces: 2
No. Guides: Not specified
Tip Top: Not specified
Rec. Lure Wt.: Not specified
Action: Ultra-light
Handle: Cork grip.

Model No.: UL6056. Same as Model UL6056R except:
Length: 6'
Handle: Neo-grip.

Model No.: FS65
Length: 6½'
No. Pieces: 1
No. Guides: Not specified; polygon
Tip Top: Tungsten carbide
Rec. Lure Wt.: Not specified
Action: Powerful
Handle: Not specified.

Model No.: FS70. Same as Model FS65 except:
Length: 7'

Fresh Water Spinning Rods

Model No.: 6065R
Length: 6½'

No. Pieces: 2
No. Guides: Not specified
Tip Top: Not specified
Rec. Lure Wt.: Not specified
Action: Fast taper
Handle: Cork grip.

Model No.: 6070R
Length: 7'
No. Pieces: 2
No. Guides: Not specified
Tip Top: Not specified
Rec. Lure Wt.: Not specified
Action: Fast taper
Handle: Cork grip.

Salt Water Spinning Rods

Model No.: 6077R
Length: 7'
No. Pieces: 2
No. Guides: Not specified
Tip Top: Not specified
Rec. Lure Wt.: Not specified
Action: Light
Handle: Cork grip.

Model No.: 6088R
Length: 8'
No. Pieces: 2
No. Guides: Not specified
Tip Top: Not specified
Rec. Lure Wt.: Not specified
Action: Fast taper
Handle: Not specified.

Model No.: 6090R. Same as Model 6088R
    except:
Length: 9'

Model No.: CS70
Length: 7'
No. Pieces: 1
No. Guides: Not specified; polygon
Tip Top: Tungsten carbide
Rec. Lure Wt.: Not specified
Action: Fast tip
Handle: Not specified.

Bait-Casting Rods

Model No.: CS60
Length: 6'
No. Pieces: 1
No. Guides: Not specified; polygon
Tip Top: Carbide
Rec. Lure Wt.: Not specified
Action: Power
Handle: Cork grip.

Model No.: CS75
Length: 7'
No. Pieces: 1
No. Guides: 7 heavy duty conventional
    guide or 7 Polygon Spinning guides
Tip Top: Tungsten carbide
Rec. Lure Wt.: Not specified
Action: Heavy
Handle: Not specified.

Model No.: FC56
Length: 5½'
No. Pieces: 1
No. Guides: Not specified; carboloy
Tip Top: Carboloy
Rec. Lure Wt.: Not specified

Action: Medium-stiff
Handle: Detachable offset casting, positive
    locking, and self aligning.

Model No.: FC58. Same as Model FC56
    except:
Length: 5'9"

Model No.: FC59. Same as Model FC56
    except:
Length: 5'9"
Action: Medium-light

Model No.: FC60. Same as Model FC56
    except:
Length: 6'
Action: Medium

Fly Rods

Model No.: 6176
Length: 7½'
No. Pieces: 2
No. Guides: Not specified
Tip Top: Not specified
Rec. Line: Light weights
Handle: Not specified.

Model No.: 6180
Length: 8'
No. Pieces: 2
No. Guides: Not specified
Tip Top: Not specified
Rec. Line: Not specified
Handle: Not specified.

Model No.: 6186. Same as Model 6180
    except:
Length: 8½'

Mooching Rods

Model No.: 6086
Length: 8½'
No. Pieces: Not specified
No. Guides: Not specified
Tip Top: Not specified
Rec. Lure Wt.: Not specified
Action: Light
Handle: Not specified.

Steelhead Rods

Model No.: 6080
Length: 8'
No. Pieces: 2
No. Guides: Not specified
Tip Top: Not specified
Rec. Lure Wt.: Not specified
Action: Light
Handle: Neo-grip.

Model No.: 6080R
Length: 8'
No. Pieces: 2
No. Guides: Not specified
Tip Top: Not specified
Rec. Lure Wt.: Not specified

Action: Light
Handle: Cork grip.

Model No.: 6081
Length: 8'
No. Pieces: Not specified
No. Guides: Not specified
Tip Top: Not specified
Rec. Lure Wt.: Not specified
Action: Light
Handle: Not specified.

FC60

Scientific Anglers/3M

Fly Rods

Model No.: System 4
Length: 7'2"
No. Pieces: 2
No. Guides: Not specified; hand chrome-
    plated stainless steel guides plus one
    carboloy stripping guide
Tip Top: Hard chrome-plated stainless steel
Rec. Line: 4 wt.
Handle: Lightweight anodized aluminum
    reel seat, double lock rings, specie cork
    comfort grip.

Model No.: System 5. Same as Model System
    4 except:
Length: 7'7"
Rec. Line: 5 wt.

Model No.: System 6. Same as Model System
    4 except:
Length: 8'1"
Rec. Line: 6 wt.

Model No.: System 7. Same as Model System
    4 except:
Length: 8'5"
Rec. Line: 7 wt.

Model No.: System 8. Same as Model System
    4 except:
Length: 8'8"
Rec. Line: 8 wt.

Model No.: System 9. Same as Model System
    4 except:
Length: 8'11"
Rec. Line: 9 wt.

Model No.: System 10. Same as Model
    System 4 except:
Length: 9'1"
Rec. Line: 10 wt.

Model No.: System 11. Same as Model
    System 4 except:
Length: 9'3"
Rec. Line: 11 wt.

Shakespeare

Spinning Rods

Model No.: 200 series
Length: 6'6", 7'
No. Pieces: 1
No. Guides: Not specified; stainless steel wire frame
Tip Top: Carbide
Rec. Lure Wt.: Not specified
Action: Medium
Handle: Not specified.

Model No.: 200 series
Length: 5'6"
No. Pieces: 1
No. Guides: Not specified; Fuji
Tip Top: Fuji
Rec. Lure Wt.: Not specified
Action: Medium
Handle: Not specified.

Model No.: SP608
Length: 6'6", 7'0"
No. Pieces: 2
No. Guides: 5 gold-plated, stainless steel, wire frame
Tip Top: Carbide, gold-plated, stamped frame
Rec. Lure Wt.: ¼-⅝ oz.
Action: Light
Handle: Cork grip with plastic forecap and butt cap.

Model No.: SP708
Length: 6'6", 7'0"
No. Pieces: 2
No. Guides: 5 carbide ring, wire frame, Mildrum
Tip Top: Carbide ring, wire frame
Rec. Lure Wt.: Not specified
Action: Kwik-taper
Handle: Reel seat—black barrel, natural hoods and two locking rings, specie cork grip with plastic forecap and butt cap.

Bait-Casting Rods

Model No.: BC00H
Length: 5'6", 6'0"
No. Pieces: 1
No. Guides: 5'6"—5, 6'0"—6, stainless stamped frame with carbide ring
Tip Top: Wire frame, Mildrum, carbide ring
Rec. Lure Wt.: Not specified
Action: Heavy
Handle: Double offset, detachable, black anodized collet and Reel-Tyte-Lock, cork grip.

Model No.: BC708MH
Length: 5'6", 6'0"
No. Pieces: 1
No. Guides: 5 Fuji red ceramic
Tip Top: Fuji red ceramic
Rec. Lure Wt.: Not specified
Action: Medium-heavy
Handle: Double offset, detachable, Reel-Tyte Lock, hypalon grip with natural aluminum butt cap.

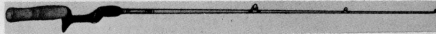

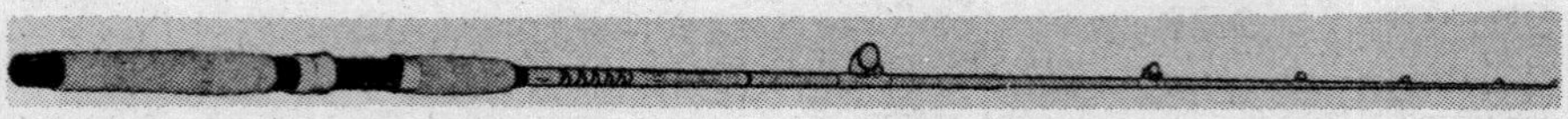

PB-B11

Model No.: PB-B11
Length: 5'6"
No. Pieces: 2
No. Guides: 2 stamped frame, chrome-plated steel
Tip Top: Stamped frame, chrome-plated steel
Rec. Lure Wt.: ¼-½ oz.
Action: Light
Handle: Single offset, non-detachable, clamp and screw for retaining reel, specie cork grip.

Model No.: PB160
Length: 6'0"
No. Pieces: 2
No. Guides: 3 chrome-plated steel, stamped frame
Tip Top: Chrome-plated steel, stamped frame
Rec. Lure Wt.: ⅜-⅝ oz.
Action: Medium
Handle: Double offset non-detachable handle with black butt cap, specie cork grip.

Model No.: PB180
Length: 6'0", 6'6"
No. Pieces: 2
No. Guides: 4 stamped frame, stainless steel
Tip Top: Chrome-plated, stamped frame
Rec. Lure Wt.: ¼-⅝ oz.

SP708

Action: KT
Handle: Non-detachable, double offset, Reel-Tyte-Lock, specie cork grip, black plastic butt cap.

Model No.: PB170. Same as Model PB180 except:
Rec. Lure Wt.: ⅜-⅝ oz.
Action: AT

Model No.: PB408
Length: 6'0", 6'6"
No. Pieces: 2
No. Guides: 4 stamped frame, chrome-plated
Tip Top: Stamped frame, chrome-plated
Rec. Lure Wt.: ¼-⅝ oz.
Action: Standard-taper
Handle: Non-detachable, double offset, Reel-Tyte-Lock, cork grip, black plastic butt cap.

Model No.: PB508
Length: 6'0", 6'6"
No. Pieces: 2
No. Guides: 5 stamped frame, stainless steel, gold-plated
Tip Top: Stamped frame, stainless steel, gold-plated
Rec. Lure Wt.: Not specified
Action: Heavy
Handle: Specie cork grip, black plastic fore cap and butt cap.

Model No.: 200 Series
Length: 5'6", 6'
No. Pieces: 1

No. Guides: Not specified; Fuji
Tip Top: Fuji
Rec. Lure Wt.: Not specified
Action: Not specified
Handle: Cork foregrip.

Fly Rods

Model No.: FY708
Length: 7'6", 8'0", 8'6"
No. Pieces: 2
No. Guides: 7'6"—6, 8'0"—7, 8'6"—7; stainless steel snake guides plus one wire frame stainless stripper guide
Tip Top: Stainless steel
Rec. Line: 7'6"—6 wt., 8'0"—7 wt., 8'6"—8 wt.
Handle: Cork grip, black barrel reel seat with single lock ring.

Model No.: FY708F. Same as Model FY708 except:
Length: 8'0", 8'6"

Model No.: FY940
Length: 8'6", 9'0"
No. Pieces: 2
No. Guides: 1 wire frame, stainless steel stripper guide, 1 wire frame, stainless guide, 6 stainless steel snake guides
Tip Top: Stainless steel
Rec. Line: 11 wt.
Handle: Anodized aluminum reel seat with double locking rings, specie cork grip.

Model No.: 200 series
Length: 8'6"
No. Pieces: Not specified
No. Guides: Not specified; Fuji stripper guide
Tip Top: Not specified
Rec. Line: Not specified
Handle: Specie cork grip.

Model No.: Graflite—carbon filament
Length: 8'
No. Pieces: 1
No. Guides: Not specified
Tip Top: Not specified
Rec. Line: 6 wt.
Handle: Cork grip.

Pushbutton Rod

Model No.: 200 series
Length: 6', 6'6"
No. Pieces: Not specified
No. Guides: Not specified; stainless steel wire frame
Tip Top: Carbide
Rec. Lure Wt.: Not specified
Action: Medium
Handle: Double offset handle.

St. Croix

Spinning Rods

Model No.: 82
Length: 6'6"
No. Pieces: 2

No. Guides: 3 chrome-plated
Tip Top: Chrome-plated
Rec. Lure Wt.: Thru ⅜ oz.
Action: Fast
Handle: Aluminum reel seat.

Model No.: 83UL
Length: 5'6"
No. Pieces: 1
No. Guides: 3 chrome-plated
Tip Top: Chrome-plated
Rec. Lure Wt.: Thru ¼ oz.
Action: Ultra-light
Handle: Aluminum rings, cork grip.

Model No.: 208
Length: 8'
No. Pieces: 2
No. Guides: 5 graduated stainless steel
Tip Top: Stainless steel
Rec. Lure Wt.: Not specified
Action: Extra-fast
Handle: Chrome reel seats with double lock rings, specie cork grip, rubber butt cap.

Model No.: 209. Same as Model 208 except:
Length: 9'

Model No.: 201. Same as Model 208 except:
Length: 10'

Model No.: 507
Length: 7'
No. Pieces: 1
No. Guides: Not specified; double wound stainless steel
Tip Top: Carboloy
Rec. Lure Wt.: Not specified
Action: Spinning
Handle: Double locking ring, chrome reel seat, cork grip.

Model No.: 508. Same as Model 507 except:
Length: 8'

Model No.: 509. Same as Model 507 except:
Length: 9'

Model No.: 510. Same as Model 507 except:
Length: 10'

Model No.: 511. Same as Model 507 except:
Length: 11'
No. Pieces: 2

Model No.: 513. Same as Model 507 except:
Length: 13'
No. Pieces: 2

Model No.: 682
Length: 6'
No. Pieces: 1
No. Guides: 6 Fuji
Tip Top: Fuji
Rec. Lure Wt.: Not specified
Action: Ultra-light
Handle: Specie cork with brown reel seat, gold double locking rings, and gold butt and foregrip caps.

Model No.: 683. Same as Model 682 except:
No. Guides: 6 carboloy
Tip Top: Carboloy

Model No.: 701
Length: 8'
No. Pieces: 2
No. Guides: 5 stainless steel
Tip Top: Not specified
Rec. Lure Wt.: Not specified
Action: Medium
Handle: Chrome-plated brass reel seat with double lock rings, specie cork handle, cork foregrip.

Model No.: 702. Same as Model 701 except:
Length: 8'6"
No. Guides: 6 stainless steel
Tip Top: Stainless steel

Model No.: 703. Same as Model 701 except:
Length: 9'
No. Guides: 6 stainless steel

Model No.: 704
Length: 5'6"
No. Pieces: 1
No. Guides: 7 stainless steel
Tip Top: Stainless steel
Rec. Lure Wt.: Not specified
Action: Medium
Handle: Specie cork handle, chrome-plated brass reel seat with double lock rings, cork foregrip.

Model No.: 705. Same as Model 704 except:
Length: 6'3"

Model No.: 706. Same as Model 704 except:
Length: 7'
No. Pieces: 2

Model No.: 707. Same as Model 704 except:
Length: 8'
No. Pieces: 2

Model No.: 708. Same as Model 704 except:
Length: 7'
Action: Medium-heavy

Model No.: 709. Same as Model 704 except:
Length: 8'
No. Pieces: 2
Action: Medium-heavy

Model No.: 710. Same as Model 704 except:
Length: 11'6"
No. Pieces: 2
No. Guides: 5 stainless steel
Action: Heavy

Model No.: 711. Same as Model 704 except:
Length: 13'
No. Pieces: 2
No. Guides: 6 stainless steel
Action: Heavy

Model No.: 721
Length: 6'6"
No. Pieces: 2
No. Guides: 4 stainless steel
Tip Top: Stainless steel
Rec. Lure Wt.: Not specified
Action: Spinning
Handle: Chrome reel seat.

Model No.: 722. Same as Model 721 except:
Length: 7'

Model No.: 731
Length: 5'6"
No. Pieces: 2
No. Guides: 5 stainless steel
Tip Top: Stainless steel
Rec. Lure Wt.: Not specified
Action: Spinning
Handle: Plain reel seat.

Model No.: 732. Same as Model 731 except:
Length: 6'6"

Model No.: 733. Same as Model 731 except:
Length: 7'

Model No.: 740
Length: 6'6"
No. Pieces: 2
No. Guides: Not specified; stainless steel
Tip Top: Stainless steel
Rec. Lure Wt.: Not specified
Action: Spinning
Handle: Reel seat with double locking ring.

Model No.: 741. Same as Model 740 except:
Length: 7'

Model No.: 747UL. Same as Model 740 except:
Length: 5'6"

Model No.: 742
Length: 8'6"
No. Pieces: 2
No. Guides: Not specified; heavy duty stainless steel
Tip Top: Stainless steel
Rec. Lure Wt.: Not specified
Action: Heavy
Handle: Not specified.

Model No.: 743. Same as Model 742 except:
No. Guides: Not specified; conventional

Model No.: 746
Length: 6'
No. Pieces: 1
No. Guides: 5 Fuji
Tip Top: Fuji
Rec. Lure Wt.: Not specified
Action: Spinning
Handle: Diamond wrap butt.

Model No.: 800
Length: 6'9"
No. Pieces: 2
No. Guides: Not specified
Tip Top: Not specified
Rec. Lure Wt.: Not specified
Action: Not specified
Handle: Cork grip.

Model No.: 800UL
Length: 5'6"
No. Pieces: 2
No. Guides: 3 chrome-plated
Tip Top: Chrome-plated

Rec. Lure Wt.: Thru ¼ oz.
Action: Ultra-light
Handle: Aluminum rings on specie cork grip with black tenite butt and forecaps.

Model No.: 869
Length: 6'9"
No. Pieces: 2
No. Guides: 4 chrome-plated
Tip Top: Chrome-plated
Rec. Lure Wt.: Thru ⅜ oz.
Action: Light
Handle: Brown and gold anodized reel seat, brown tapered tenite fore and butt caps, specie cork grip.

Model No.: 875
Length: 6'6"
No. Pieces: 2
No. Guides: 3 gold-plated
Tip Top: Gold-plated
Rec. Lure Wt.: Not specified
Action: Magna-flex
Handle: Anodized reel seat, specie cork grips, brown tenite butt cap, aluminum winding check.

Model No.: 1073-SM
Length: 7'3"
No. Pieces: 2
No. Guides: 5
Tip Top: Not specified
Rec. Lure Wt.: Not specified
Action: Medium-light
Handle: Chrome-plated brass reel seat with double locking rings, select specie cork handle and foregrip.

Model No.: 1085-SM. Same as Model 1073-SM except:
Length: 8'3"
Action: Medium

Model No.: F1210
Length: 7'
No. Pieces: 1
No. Guides: 4 double wrapped stainless steel
Tip Top: Carboloy
Rec. Lure Wt.: Not specified
Action: Spinning
Handle: Chrome reel seat with double locking rings.

Model No.: F1212. Same as Model F1210 except:
No. Pieces: 2

Model No.: F1214. Same as Model F1210 except:
Length: 8'
No. Guides: 5 stainless steel double wrapped

Model No.: F1216. Same as Model F1210 except:
Length: 7'6"
No. Guides: 5 stainless steel double wrapped

Model No.: F1220. Same as Model F1210 except:
Length: 6'6"

Model No.: F1222. Same as Model F1210 except:
Length: 6'6"
No. Pieces: 2

Model No.: F1226. Same as Model F1210 except:
Length: 8'
No. Pieces: 2
No. Guides: 5 stainless steel guides

Model No.: F1230. Same as Model F1210 except:
Length: 7'6"
No. Pieces: 2

Model No.: F1232. Same as Model F1210

Model No.: F1234. Same as Model F1210 except:
No. Pieces: 2

Model No.: 3000
Length: 6'9"
No. Pieces: 2
No. Guides: 3 stainless steel wire frame guides plus one carboloy stripper guide
Tip Top: Carboloy
Rec. Lure Wt.: Thru ⅜ oz.
Action: Master
Handle: Tapered black tenite fore and butt caps, specie cork grips, and hook keeper.

Model No.: 3001UL
Length: 5'6"
No. Pieces: 2
No. Guides: 4 stainless steel
Tip Top: Stainless steel
Rec. Lure Wt.: Thru ¼ oz.
Action: Ultra-light
Handle: Contoured specie cork handle and foregrip, brown anodized reel seat.

Model No.: 3203
Length: 6'3"
No. Pieces: 2
No. Guides: 3 chrome-plated
Tip Top: Chrome-plated
Rec. Lure Wt.: Not specified
Action: Spinning
Handle: Anodized reel seat, specie cork grips, black tenite butt cap, aluminum winding check.

Model No.: 3275
Length: 6', 6'6"
No. Pieces: 2
No. Guides: 3 chrome-plated
Tip Top: Chrome-plated
Rec. Lure Wt.: Not specified
Action: Spinning
Handle: Anodized reel seat, specie cork grips, black tenite butt cap.

Model No.: 7080-XLF
Length: 5'6", 6'6", 7'
No. Pieces: 2
No. Guides: 5'6"—4 line guides, 6'6"—5 line guides, 7'—5 line guides plus one carboloy stripper guide on all
Tip Top: Carboloy
Rec. Lure Wt.: Thru ⅜ oz.
Action: Light
Handle: Anodized reel seat with double locking rings, select specie cork grips and gold anodized caps, hook keeper.

Model No.: 7080-XXL. Same as Model 7080-XLF except:
Length: 6', 5'
No. Guides: 5'—4 guides, 6'—5 lightweight foulproof guides
Rec. Lure Wt.: Thru ¼ oz.
Handle: Super-select specie cork, crested gold anodized tapered band reel seat.

Model No.: 7080-XLM. Same as Model 7080-XLF except:
Length: 6'9"
No. Guides: 6 carboly
Tip Top: Carboloy
Rec. Lure Wt.: ⅜-¾ oz.
Action: Medium

Model No.: 7081-XXL. Same as Model 7080-XLF except:
Length: 5',
No. Pieces: 1
Handle: Super-select specie cork, crested gold anodized tapered band reel seat.

Model No.: 8000
Length: 6'6", 7'
No. Pieces: 2
No. Guides: 4 stainless steel Ovallan oval
Tip Top: Stainless steel Ovallan
Rec. Lure Wt.: Thru ⅜ oz.
Action: Light
Handle: Anodized brown and silver reel seat, tapered metallic brown tenite fore and butt caps, specie cork grips, hook keeper.

Model No.: 8000M. Same as Model 8000 except:
Length: 6'6"
Rec. Lure Wt.: ⅜-⅝ oz.
Action: Medium

Model No.: 8000UL. Same as Model 8000 except:
Length: 5'6"
Rec. Lure Wt.: Thru ¼ oz.
Action: Ultra-light

Model No.: 8001. Same as Model 8000 except:
Length: 7'
No. Guides: 4 Fuji
Tip Top: Fuji
Rec. Lure Wt.: ⅜ oz.

Model No.: 8011
Length: 6'6"
No. Pieces: 4
No. Guides: 5 Ovallan
Tip Top: Ovallan
Rec. Lure Wt.: Thru ⅜ oz.
Action: Spinning
Handle: Brown and gold reel seat, cork grip, brown tenite fore and butt caps.

Model No.: 8065
Length: 6'6", 7', 7'6"
No. Pieces: Not specified
No. Guides: 6'6", 7'—4 stainless steel guides, 7'6"—5 stainless steel guides plus one carboloy stripper guide on all
Tip Top: Carboloy
Rec. Lure Wt.: ¼-⅝ oz.
Action: Magna-taper
Handle: Anodized reel seat, brown tenite butt cap, specie cork grips, aluminum winding check, and hook keeper.

Model No.: 8100
Length: 6'6"
No. Pieces: Not specified
No. Guides: Not specified; carboloy
Tip Top: Not specified
Rec. Lure Wt.: Thru ⅜ oz.
Action: Light
Handle: Not specified.

Model No.: 8100M
Length: 6'6", 7'
No. Pieces: 2
No. Guides: 6 carboloy
Tip Top: Carboloy
Rec. Lure Wt.: ⅜-⅝ oz.
Action: Medium
Handle: Chrome reel seat with double locking rings, chrome.

Model No.: WSP661
Length: 6'6"
No. Pieces: 2
No. Guides: 4 monoloop
Tip Top: Monoloop
Rec. Lure Wt.: ⅜ oz.
Action: Hercules
Handle: Plain reel seat, cork butt grip.

Model No.: WSP662
Length: 6'6"
No. Pieces: 2
No. Guides: 4 wire frame guides plus one carboloy stripper guide
Tip Top: Carboloy
Rec. Lure Wt.: ⅝ oz.
Action: Magna
Handle: Brown and gold reel seats, specie cork butt grip, copper tenite butt and forecaps.

Model No.: WSP603. Same as Model WSP662 except:
Length: 6'
No. Pieces: 1

Model No.: WSP663
Length: 6'6"
No. Pieces: 2
No. Guides: 6 carboloy
Tip Top: Carboloy
Rec. Lure Wt.: ⅝ oz.
Action: Magna
Handle: Brown and gold double lock ring reel seat, specie cork grip, aluminum butt and forecaps.

Model No.: Colt-5
Length: 6'
No. Pieces: 2
No. Guides: 3 chrome-plated
Tip Top: Chrome-plated
Rec. Lure Wt.: Not specified
Action: Spinning
Handle: Tapered composition cork handle, black plastic butt and forecaps, tapered aluminum ring reel lock.

Salt Water Spinning Rods

Model No.: F-1108
Length: 8'
No. Pieces: 1
No. Guides: Not specified; stainless steel foul proof
Tip Top: Thread wraps
Rec. Lure Wt.: Not specified
Action: Spinning
Handle: Chrome reel seats and double locking rings.

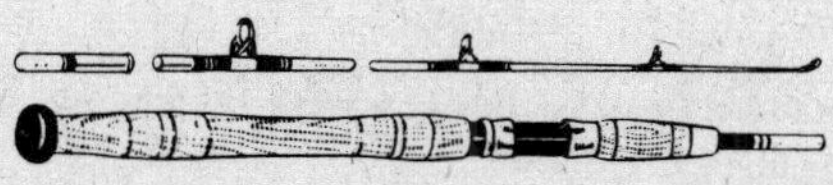

Model No.: F-1110. Same as Model F-1108 except:
Length: 7'
Handle: ⅞" reel seat.

Model No.: F-1112. Same as Model F-1108 except:
Length: 7'
No. Pieces: 2
Handle: ⅞" reel seat.

Model No.: F-1114. Same as Model F-1108.

Model No.: F-1116. Same as Model F-1108 except:
Length: 7'6"

Model No.: F-1120. Same as Model F-1108 except:
Length: 6'6"
Handle: ⅞" reel seat.

Model No.: F-1122. Same as Model F-1108 except:
Length: 6'6"
No. Pieces: 2
Handle: ⅞" reel seat.

Model No.: F-1124. Same as Model F-1108

Model No.: F-1126. Same as Model F-1108 except:
No. Pieces: 2

Model No.: F-1130. Same as Model F-1108 except:
Length: 7'6"
No. Pieces: 2

Model No.: F-1132. Same as Model F-1108 except:
Length: 7'
Handle: ⅞" reel seat.

Model No.: F-1134. Same as Model F-1108 except:
Length: 7'
No. Pieces: 2
Handle: ⅞" reel seat.

Casting Rods

Model No.: 50
Length: 5'6"
No. Pieces: 1
No. Guides: 3 chrome-plated
Tip Top: Chrome-plated

Rec. Lure Wt.: Thru ⅝ oz.
Action: Casting
Handle: Detachable offset aluminum handle, positive locking metal reel lock.

Model No.: 1085
Length: 8'3"
No. Pieces: 2
No. Guides: 5 wire frame
Tip Top: Wire frame
Rec. Lure Wt.: Not specified
Action: Medium
Handle: Chrome-plated brass reel seat with double locking rings, specie cork handle and foregrip, aluminum winding check.

Model No.: 1004. Same as Model 1085 except:
Length: 9'

Model No.: 5100HFT
Length: 5'6"
No. Pieces: Not specified
No. Guides: 3 stainless steel wire frame casting guides plus one carboloy stripper guide
Tip Top: Carboloy
Rec. Lure Wt.: Thru 1 oz.
Action: Medium-heavy
Handle: Detachable handle with chrome-plated chuck nut.

Model No.: 5101HFT. Same as Model 5100HFT except:
Handle: Non-detachable handle with cork foregrip, specie cork grips, black tenite butt cap, chrome-plated brass positive action traveling reel lock.

Model No.: 5400
Length: 6'2"
No. Pieces: 1
No. Guides: 5 carboloy
Tip Top: Carboloy
Rec. Lure Wt.: Thru 1 oz.
Action: Medium-light
Handle: Black epoxy finish offset handle with chrome-plated positive locking reel seat, select specie cork grip, polished chrome butt cap.

Model No.: 7105
Length: 4'6"
No. Pieces: 1
No. Guides: 2 chrome-plated
Tip Top: Chrome-plated
Rec. Lure Wt.: Not specified
Action: Heavy
Handle: Black offset aluminum handle with delrin reel lock, specie cork grip, black tenite butt cap, aluminum winding check.

Model No.: 7107. Same as Model 7105 except:
Length: 5'6"
No. Guides: 3 chrome-plated
Handle: Detachable handle of black epoxy finish aluminum, delrin reel lock, specie cork grip, black tenite butt cap.

Model No.: Colt-1
Length: 5'
No. Pieces: 1
No. Guides: 2 coil
Tip Top: Coil

Rec. Lure Wt.: Not specified
Action: Casting
Handle: Plastic offset handle with screw-type reel lock.

Model No.: Colt-2. Same as Model Colt-1 except:
Handle: Black plastic offset handle, screw-type reel lock, composition cork grip, black tenite butt cap.

Model No.: Colt-3. Same as Model Colt-1 except:
Handle: Burnished offset metal handle, screw-type reel lock, tapered composition cork grip, black tenite butt cap.

Model No.: Colt-4. Same as Model Colt-1 except:
No. Guides: 2 mono/loop
Tip Top: Mono/loop
Handle: Burnished offset metal handle, screw-type reel lock, tapered composition cork grip, black tenite butt cap.

Spin-Casting Rods

Model No.: 52
Length: 6'
No. Pieces: 2
No. Guides: 3 chrome-plated
Tip Top: Chrome-plated
Rec. Lure Wt.: Thru ⅜ oz.
Action: Spinning
Handle: Aluminum with positive locking metal reel lock.

Model No.: 53UL. Same as Model 52 except:
Length: 5'6"
No. Pieces: 1
Action: Ultra-light

Model No.: 146
Length: 4'6", 5', 5'6"
No. Pieces: 1
No. Guides: 3 chrome-plated, 2 on 4'6"
Tip Top: Chrome-plated
Rec. Lure Wt.: Not specified
Action: Casting
Handle: Aluminum offset handle, screw-type reel lock, specie cork grip, black tenite butt cap.

Model No.: 247. Same as Model 146 except:
Length: 5'6"

Model No.: 540
Length: 6', 6'6"
No. Pieces: 2
No. Guides: 3 chrome-plated
Tip Top: Chrome-plated
Rec. Lure Wt.: Thru ⅜ oz.
Action: Spinning
Handle: Black offset aluminum handle, specie cork grips, black tenite butt cap, aluminum winding check.

Model No.: 563
Length: 6'3"
No. Pieces: 2

No. Guides: 4 chrome-plated
Tip Top: Chrome-plated
Rec. Lure Wt.: Thru ⅜ oz.
Action: Light
Handle: Offset handle, locking reel seat, tapered brown tenite fore and butt caps, specie cork grip.

Model No.: 580
Length: 5½'
No. Pieces: 1
No. Guides: 5 Fuji
Tip Top: Fuji
Rec. Lure Wt.: Not specified
Action: Ultra-light
Handle: Deluxe detachable brown handle, all weather pistol grips.

Model No.: 581. Same as Model 580 except:
No. Guides: 5 carboloy
Tip Top: Carboloy

Model No.: 584
Length: 5½'
No. Pieces: 1
No. Guides: 5 Fuji
Tip Top: Fuji
Rec. Lure Wt.: Not specified
Action: Ultra-light
Handle: Deluxe detachable brown handle, all weather pistol grips.

Model No.: 585. Same as Model 584 except:
No. Guides: 5 carboloy
Tip Top: Carboloy

Model No.: 660
Length: 5'6", 6'
No. Pieces: 2
No. Guides: 3 gold-plated
Tip Top: Gold-plated
Rec. Lure Wt.: Not specified
Action: Magna-flex
Handle: Aluminum offset handle with non-corrosive delrin reel lock, specie cork grip, brown tenite butt cap, aluminum winding check.

Model No.: 56. Same as Model 660 except:
Length: 5'6"

Model No.: 720
Length: 6'
No. Pieces: 2
No. Guides: 3 stainless steel
Tip Top: Stainless steel
Rec. Lure Wt.: Not specified
Action: Casting
Handle: Non-detachable reel seat.

Model No.: 730
Length: 6'
No. Pieces: 2
No. Guides: 4 stainless steel
Tip Top: Stainless steel
Rec. Lure Wt.: Not specified
Action: Casting
Handle: Non-detachable handle, plain reel seat.

Model No.: 745
Length: 5'6"
No. Pieces: 1
No. Guides: 5 Fuji
Tip Top: Fuji
Rec. Lure Wt.: Not specified
Action: Casting
Handle: Diamond wrap butt.

Model No.: 2000
Length: 6'6"
No. Pieces: 2
No. Guides: 3 stainless steel wire frame guides plus one carboloy stripper guide
Tip Top: Carboloy
Rec. Lure Wt.: Thru ⅜ oz.
Action: Light
Handle: Offset aluminum handle with fast mounting, firm locking reel lock. Brown tapered tenite fore and butt caps, specie cork grips, and hook keeper.

Model No.: 2104
Length: 5', 5'6"
No. Pieces: 1
No. Guides: 3 chrome-plated
Tip Top: Chrome-plated
Rec. Lure Wt.: Not specified
Action: Casting
Handle: Black aluminum offset detachable handle, positive reel lock, specie cork grip, black tenite butt cap.

Model No.: 2205
Length: 5'6", 6'
No. Pieces: 2
No. Guides: 3 chrome-plated
Tip Top: Chrome-plated
Rec. Lure Wt.: Not specified
Action: Spinning
Handle: Black aluminum offset handle, positive reel lock, specie cork butt and foregrips, black tenite butt cap, aluminum winding check.

Model No.: 5050
Length: 6'
No. Pieces: 2
No. Guides: 4 stainless steel Ovallan
Tip Top: Stainless steel Ovallan
Rec. Lure Wt.: Thru ⅜ oz.
Action: Light
Handle: Brown epoxy finished offset handle with comfort flared finger grip, locking reel seat, tapered metallic brown tenite fore and butt caps, specie cork grips, and hook keeper.

Model No.: 5050M. Same as Model 5050 except:
Length: 6'6"
Rec. Lure Wt.: ⅜-⅝ oz.
Action: Medium

Model No.: 5050UL. Same as Model 5050 except:
Length: 5'6"
No. Guides: 3 stainless steel Ovallan
Rec. Lure Wt.: Thru ¼ oz.
Action: Ultra-light

Model No.: 5065
Length: 6'6"
No. Pieces: 2
No. Guides: 4 stainless steel
Tip Top: Not specified

Rec. Lure Wt.: ¼-⅝ oz.
Action: Magna-taper
Handle: Removable offset handle with chrome-plated permanently locking reel seat, metallic brown tapered tenite butt cap, and specie cork grip.

Model No.: 5150-M
Length: 6'6"
No. Pieces: 2
No. Guides: 6 carboloy
Tip Top: Carboloy
Rec. Lure Wt.: ⅜-⅝ oz.
Action: Medium
Handle: Black epoxy finished offset handle with chrome-plated positive locking reel seat. Chromed fore and butt caps with tenite inserts, select specie cork fore and butt grips and hook keeper.

Model No.: 7050-XL
Length: 6'6"
No. Pieces: 2
No. Guides: 5 line guides plus one carboloy stripper guide
Tip Top: Carboloy
Rec. Lure Wt.: Thru ⅜ oz.
Action: Light
Handle: Select specie cork fore and butt grips, gold anodized caps, quick mounting reel lock of gold-plated brass, adjustable finger grip, and hook keeper.

Model No.: 7050-XLM. Same as Model 7050-XL except:
Length: 6'9"
No. Guides: 6 carboloy
Rec. Lure Wt.: ⅜-¾ oz.

Model No.: 8010
Length: 6'
No. Pieces: 4
No. Guides: 5 Ovallan
Tip Top: Ovallan
Rec. Lure Wt.: Thru ⅜ oz.
Action: Casting
Handle: Brown epoxy finish offset handle with sure locking reel seat, cork butt grip, brown tenite fore and butt caps.

Model No.: WR-1, WR-2, WR-3
Length: 5'9"
No. Pieces: 1
No. Guides: 6 carboloy
Tip Top: Carboloy
Rec. Lure Wt.: Not specified
Action: Casting
Handle: Anodized aluminum cap.

Model No.: Colt-7
Length: 5'6"
No. Pieces: 2
No. Guides: 2 chrome-plated
Tip Top: Chrome-plated
Rec. Lure Wt.: Not specified
Action: Casting
Handle: Black plastic offset handle, tapered composition cork grip, black tenite butt cap.

Model No.: WSC561
Length: 5'6"

No. Pieces: 1
No. Guides: 4 monoloop
Tip Top: Monoloop
Rec. Lure Wt.: ⅜ oz.
Action: Hercules
Handle: Brown epoxy finish handle, cork butt grip, aluminum winding check.

Model No.: WSC602
Length: 6'
No. Pieces: 1
No. Guides: 3 wire frame guides plus one carboloy stripper guide
Tip Top: Carboloy
Rec. Lure Wt.: ⅜ oz.
Action: Impact
Handle: Brown epoxy finish handle with fast lock reel seat, specie cork butt grip, tapered tenite butt and forecaps.

Bait-Casting Rods

Model No.: 1070-LB
Length: 8'6"
No. Pieces: 1
No. Guides: 4 stainless steel
Tip Top: Stainless steel
Rec. Lure Wt.: Not specified
Action: Casting
Handle: Select hardwood detachable handle, brown rubber butt cap, cushionite foregrip, chrome-plated lock type brass reel seat.

Model No.: 1080-LB. Same as Model 1070-LB except:
Length: 9'6"
No. Guides: 5 stainless steel

Boat Rods

Model No.: 7208
Length: 6'6"
No. Pieces: 2
No. Guides: 3 stainless steel
Tip Top: Stainless steel
Rec. Lure Wt.: Not specified
Action: Medium
Handle: Chrome reel seat.

Model No.: 7304
Length: 5'
No. Pieces: 1
No. Guides: 2 chrome-plated
Tip Top: Chrome-plated
Rec. Lure Wt.: Not specified
Action: Light
Handle: Non-detachable wooden handles and foregrips, anodized chrome reel seats, rubber butt cap, metal forecap. Butt diameter—.323.

Model No.: 7305. Same as Model 7304 except:
Handle: Butt diameter—.375

Model No.: 7306
Length: 5'6"
No. Pieces: 1
No. Guides: 2 chrome-plated
Tip Top: Chrome-plated

Rec. Lure Wt.: Not specified
Action: Medium
Handle: Chrome-plated brass reel seats, detachable wood handles and foregrips, metal forecap.

Model No.: 7307. Same as Model 7306 except:
Length: 6', 6'6", 7'
No. Guides: 3 stainless steel
Tip Top: Stainless steel

Model No.: 7307-R. Same as Model 7306 except:
Length: 6'
No. Guides: 3 stainless steel
Tip Top: Roller

Model No.: 7309
Length: 6'6", 7', 7'6"
No. Pieces: 2
No. Guides: 4 stainless steel
Tip Top: Stainless steel
Rec. Lure Wt.: Not specified
Action: Medium-heavy
Handle: Non-detachable handle with chrome-plated brass reel seat, grain wood handles and foregrips, rubber butt caps, metal forecap.

Model No.: 7209. Same as Model 7309 except:
Length: 7', 7'6"
No. Pieces: 1
Handle: Chrome reel seat with detachable handle.

Model No.: 7209-S. Same as Model 7309 except:
Length: 7', 7'6"
No. Pieces: 1
Action: Spin
Handle: Chrome reel seat with detachable handle.

Model No.: 7309-S. Same as Model 7309 except:
Action: Spin

Model No.: 7311
Length: 6'6", 7'
No. Pieces: 2
No. Guides: 3 stainless steel
Tip Top: Stainless steel
Rec. Lure Wt.: Not specified
Action: Heavy
Handle: Chrome-plated brass reel seat, detachable southern ash wooden handle, rubber butt caps, metal forecaps.

Model No.: 7312. Same as Model 7311 except:
Length: 6'6"
No. Guides: 3 stainless steel wire frame
Tip Top: Roller

Model No.: 8110
Length: 6'
No. Pieces: 1
No. Guides: 2 stainless steel
Tip Top: Stainless steel
Rec. Lure Wt.: Not specified
Action: Extra-heavy
Handle: Chrome-plated brass reel seat, southern ash wooden handle and foregrip, rubber butt cap, metal forecap.

Model No.: 8111. Same as Model 8110
  except:
Tip Top: Mildrum roller

Model No.: 8117
Length: 6'6"
No. Pieces: 1
No. Guides: 4 stainless steel wire frame
  salt water
Tip Top: Mildrum roller
Rec. Lure Wt.: Not specified
Action: Medium
Handle: Chrome-plated brass reel seat,
  southern ash handle, bumper type rubber
  butt cap and metal forecap.

Model No.: 8125. Same as Model 8117
  except:
No. Guides: 4 Allan roller

Model No.: 8126. Same as Model 8117
  except:
No. Guides: 4 Fuji

Model No.: 9111
Length: 6'
No. Pieces: 1
No. Guides: 2 stainless steel
Tip Top: Roller
Rec. Lure Wt.: Not specified
Action: Heavy
Handle: Chrome reel seat.

Model No.: 9311. Same as Model 9111
  except:
Length: 6'6", 7'
No. Guides: 3 stainless steel
Handle: Detachable handle, chrome reel seat.

Model No.: 9307
Length: 6'6", 7'
No. Pieces: 1
No. Guides: 3 stainless steel
Tip Top: Stainless steel
Rec. Lure Wt.: Not specified
Action: Medium
Handle: ⅞" chrome reel seat and detachable
  dense wood handle.

Model No.: SG20
Length: 6'9"
No. Pieces: 1
No. Guides: 4 Aftco
Tip Top: Aftco roller
Rec. Lure Wt.: Not specified
Action: Heavy; 20 lb. class
Handle: Cork and rubber foregrip with
  dense wood handle, chrome reel seats,
  double locking ring.

Model No.: SG30. Same as Model SG20
  except:
Action: 30 lb. class

Model No.: SG50. Same as Model SG20
  except:
Action: 50 lb. class

Model No.: SG80. Same as Model SG20
  except:
Action: 80 lb. class

Model No.: B-3661-C
Length: 6'6"
No. Pieces: 1
No. Guides: 3 Allan roller
Tip Top: Mildrum roller
Rec. Lure Wt.: Not specified
Action: Extra-heavy
Handle: Brass and chrome reel seat with
  double locking rings, metal forecap, salt
  water butt cap.

Model No.: B-3662-C. Same as Model
  B-3661-C except:
No. Guides: 3 extra heavy duty stainless
  steel guides plus one Aftco roller stripper
  guide

Model No.: B-3663-C. Same as Model
  B-3661-C except:
No. Guides: 4 Aftco roller

Model No.: B-3664-C. Same as Model
  B-3661-C except:
No. Guides: 4 extra heavy duty stainless
  steel

Model No.: B-3665-C. Same as Model
  B-3661-C except:
No. Guides: 4 extra heavy duty stainless steel
Tip Top: Extra heavy duty stainless steel

Boat Spinning Rod

Model No.: 9209S
Length: 7'
No. Pieces: 2
No. Guides: 4 stainless steel
Tip Top: Stainless steel
Rec. Lure Wt.: Not specified
Action: Medium
Handle: ⅞" black and chrome reel seat,
  non-detachable handle.

Fly Rods

Model No.: 92
Length: 7'6"
No. Pieces: 2
No. Guides: 4 snake
Tip Top: Not specified
Rec. Line: 7 wt.
Handle: Aluminum reel seat.

Model No.: 723
Length: 7'6", 8'3", 8'9"
No. Pieces: 2
No. Guides: 4 snake guides plus one stripper
  guide
Tip Top: Not specified
Rec. Line: Not specified
Handle: Aluminum reel seat.

Model No.: 734
Length: 8'6"
No. Pieces: 2
No. Guides: 6 snake guides plus one stainless
  steel stripper guide
Tip Top: Fly
Rec. Line: Not specified
Handle: ⅞" reel seat.

Model No.: 744
Length: 8'6"
No. Pieces: 2
No. Guides: 7 snake guides plus one stripper
  guide
Tip Top: Not specified
Rec. Line: Not specified
Handle: Not specified.

Model No.: 900
Length: 8'3"
No. Pieces: 2
No. Guides: 4 stainless steel snake guides
  plus one chrome-plated stripper guide
Tip Top: Fly
Rec. Line: 8 wt.
Handle: Cigar shaped specie cork grip,
  aluminum reel seat, aluminum winding
  check.

Model No.: 983
Length: 8'3"
No. Pieces: 2
No. Guides: 5 stainless steel snake guides
  plus one chrome-plated stripper guide
Tip Top: Fly
Rec. Line: 7 wt.
Handle: Anodized brown and gold reel seat,
  cigar shaped specie cork grip.

Model No.: 4000
Length: 8'3"
No. Pieces: 2
No. Guides: 5 stainless steel snake guides
  plus one carboloy stripper guide
Tip Top: Carboloy
Rec. Line: 8 wt.
Handle: Contoured specie cork grip, hook
  keeper.

Model No.: 4001. Same as Model 4000
  except: ferrules.

Model No.: 7090-XL
Length: 8'6"
No. Pieces: 2
No. Guides: 7 snake guides plus one
  carboloy stripper guide
Tip Top: Carboloy
Rec. Line: 8 wt.
Handle: Anodized reel seat with double
  locking rings, contoured handle of select
  specie cork, hook keeper.

Model No.: 7090-XLM. Same as Model
  7090-XL except:
Length: 9'
No. Guides: 8 stainless steel snake guides
  plus one carboloy stripper guide
Tip Top: Stainless steel
Rec. Line: 9-10 wt.

Model No.: 7090-XXL
Length: 6'8"
No. Pieces: 2
No. Guides: 6 stainless steel snake guides
  plus one stripper guide
Tip Top: Stainless steel
Rec. Line: 6 wt.

Handle: Super select specie cork handle, crested tapered band, gold anodized reel seat, and hook keeper.

Model No.: 8012
Length: 7'
No. Pieces: 4
No. Guides: 5 stainless steel snake guides plus one Ovallan stripper guide
Tip Top: Stainless steel
Rec. Line: 7 wt.
Handle: Brown and silver reel seat, aluminum winding check, cork grip.

Model No.: 9000
Length: 8'6", 9'
No. Pieces: Not specified
No. Guides: 5 stainless steel snake guides plus one Ovallan stripper guide
Tip Top: Fly
Rec. Line: 9 wt.
Handle: Anodized brown and silver reel seat, cigar shaped specie cork grip, aluminum winding check, hook keeper.

Model No.: 9065
Length: 8'6"
No. Pieces: Not specified
No. Guides: 8 stainless steel snake guides plus one carboloy stripper guide
Tip Top: Fly
Rec. Line: 9 wt.
Handle: Anodized brown and gold reel seat, contoured specie cork grip, aluminum winding check and hook keeper.

Model No.: 9100
Length: 8'9"
No. Pieces: Not specified
No. Guides: 8 stainless steel snake guides plus one carboloy stripper guide
Tip Top: Fly
Rec. Line: 8 wt.
Handle: Chrome reel seat, select specie contoured grip, hook keeper.

Model No.: Colt-6
Length: 6'6"
No. Pieces: 2
No. Guides: 3 snake guides plus one chrome-plated stripper
Tip Top: Fly
Rec. Line: Not specified
Handle: Tapered composition cork cigar shaped grip, aluminum reel seat, aluminum winding check.

Trolling Rods

Model No.: 1001-NW
Length: 7'6"
No. Pieces: 2
No. Guides: 4 wire frame
Tip Top: Wire frame
Rec. Lure Wt.: Not specified
Action: Trolling
Handle: Chrome reel seat, wooden handle, cushionite foregrip, rubber butt cap.

Model No.: 1001-NWR. Same as Model 1001-NW except:
Tip Top: Roller

Model No.: 1065-RG
Length: 6'6"
No. Pieces: 1
No. Guides: 5 Allan lightweight roller
Tip Top: Roller
Rec. Lure Wt.: Not specified
Action: Trolling
Handle: Chrome reel seat, specie cork handle and foregrip.

Chugging Rods

Model No.: Tom Cat 1
Length: 2'6"
No. Pieces: 1
No. Guides: 1
Tip Top: Not specified
Rec. Lure Wt.: Not specified
Action: Chugging
Handle: Burnished handle with cast on chuck.

Model No.: Tom Cat 2. Same as Model Tom Cat 1 except:
Length: 3'

Model No.: Tom Cat 3. Same as Model Tom Cat 1 except:
Length: 3'6"

Popping Rods

Model No.: 1171-P
Length: 7'
No. Pieces: 1
No. Guides: 4 stainless steel
Tip Top: Stainless steel
Rec. Lure Wt.: Not specified
Action: Popping
Handle: Chrome-plated finger grip reel seat, brown tenite butt cap, specie cork handle.

Model No.: 9109
Length: 6'6"
No. Pieces: 1
No. Guides: 4 chrome-plated
Tip Top: Chrome-plated
Rec. Lure Wt.: Not specified
Action: Popping
Handle: Select hardwood detachable handle, black tenite butt cap, chrome-plated finger grip reel seat, brass/chrome forecap.

Musky Bucktail Rods

Model No.: 1065-M1
Length: 6'6"
No. Pieces: 1
No. Guides: 4 stainless steel wire frame casting guides plus one carboloy stripper guide
Tip Top: Carboloy
Rec. Lure Wt.: Thru 1¼ oz.
Action: Musky bucktail
Handle: Chrome-plated brass reel seat with finger grip, specie cork grips, black tenite butt cap, aluminum winding check.

Model No.: 1065-M2. Same as Model 1065-M1 except:
No. Pieces: 2

Musky Rod

Model No.: 5500
Length: 5'6", 6'6"
No. Pieces: 1
No. Guides: 5'6"-2, 6'6"-4 stainless steel wire frame casting guides plus one carboloy stripper guide
Tip Top: Carboloy
Rec. Lure Wt.: Thru 3 oz.
Action: Heavy
Handle: Chrome-plated brass reel seat with finger grip, specie cork grips, black tenite butt cap, aluminum winding check.

Musky Spinning Rod

Model No.: 1060-S2
Length: 6'
No. Pieces: 2
No. Guides: 4 stainless steel wire frame
Tip Top: Carboloy
Rec. Lure Wt.: Thru 1½ oz.
Action: Firm
Handle: Anodized reel seat, specie cork grips, brown tenite butt and forecaps.

True Temper

Spinning Rods

Model No.: 225T
Length: 6'
No. Pieces: 5
No. Guides: 3 stainless steel
Tip Top: Tungsten carbide
Rec. Lure Wt.: Not specified
Action: Medium-light
Handle: 2 tone anodized aluminum seat.

Model No.: 699
Length: 6¼'
No. Pieces: 2
No. Guides: 3 hard-chromed
Tip Top: Hard-chromed
Rec. Lure Wt.: Not specified
Action: Light tip
Handle: Anodized aluminum seat.

Model No.: 803
Length: 6'4"
No. Pieces: 2
No. Guides: 3 heavy-chromed
Tip Top: Heavy-chromed
Rec. Lure Wt.: ¼-⅝ oz.
Action: Fast tip
Handle: Anodized aluminum seat.

Model No.: 899
Length: 6¼'
No. Pieces: 2
No. Guides: 4 hard-chromed
Tip Top: Hard-chromed
Rec. Lure Wt.: Not specified
Action: Fast tip
Handle: Anodized aluminum seat.

Model No.: 993
Length: 6½'
No. Pieces: 2

No. Guides: 4 heavy-chromed
Tip Top: Heavy-chromed
Rec. Lure Wt.: ¼-⅝ oz.
Action: Fast tip
Handle: Anodized aluminum seat.

Model No.: 994. Same as Model 993 except:
Length: 7'

Length: 6½'
No. Pieces: 2
No. Guides: 4 stainless steel wire frame
Tip Top: Stainless steel
Rec. Lure Wt.: ¼-⅝ oz.
Action: Fast tip
Handle: Anodized aluminum seat and metal protective butt caps with rubber bumper.

Tip Top: Tungsten carbide
Rec. Lure Wt.: ¼-⅝ oz.
Action: Medium; fast tip
Handle: Anodized aluminum seat with double locking rings. Doubly reinforced butt, metal protective butt caps with rubber bumper.

Model No.: 6004 (6000 Holloglass Series)
Length: 7'
No. Pieces: 2
No. Guides: 6 stainless steel wire frame
Tip Top: Tungsten carbide
Rec. Lure Wt.: ¼-⅝ oz.
Action: Medium; fast tip
Handle: Anodized aluminum seat with double locking rings. Doubly reinforced butt, metal protective butt caps with rubber bumper.

Model No.: 63LC
Length: 6½'
No. Pieces: 2
No. Guides: Not specified; stainless steel
Tip Top: Stainless steel
Rec. Lure Wt.: Not specified
Action: Intermediate
Handle: Left hand crank, cork grip.

1000 series

Model No.: 1003
Length: 6½'
No. Pieces: 2
No. Guides: 4 hard-chromed
Tip Top: Hard-chromed
Rec. Lure Wt.: ⅛-⅜ oz.
Action: Fast tip
Handle: Anodized aluminum reel seat.

Model No.: 1003A. Same as Model 1003 except:
Length: 5½'
Action: Ultra fast tip

Model No.: 1004. Same as Model 1003 except:
Length: 7'

Model No.: 1253 (1250 Series)
Length: 6½'
No. Pieces: 2
No. Guides: 4 hard-chromed
Tip Top: Hard-chromed
Rec. Lure Wt.: ¼-⅝ oz.
Action: Fast tip
Handle: Anodized aluminum seat.

Model No.: 1254 (1250 Series)
Length: 7'
No. Pieces: 2
No. Guides: 4 hard-chromed
Tip Top: Hard-chromed
Rec. Lure Wt.: ¼-⅝ oz.
Action: Fast tip
Handle: Anodized aluminum seat.

Model No.: 1256 (1250 Series)
Length: 5½'
No. Pieces: 2
No. Guides: 4 hard-chromed
Tip Top: Hard-chromed
Rec. Lure Wt.: ⅛-¼ oz.
Action: Ultra light
Handle: Anodized aluminum seat.

Model No.: 1503

Model No.: 1504 (1500 Series)
Length: 7'
No. Pieces: 2
No. Guides: 4 stainless steel wire frame
Tip Top: Stainless steel
Rec. Lure Wt.: ¼-⅝ oz.
Action: Fast tip
Handle: Anodized aluminum seat and metal protective butt caps with rubber bumper.

Model No.: 1653 (1650 Series)
Length: 6½'
No. Pieces: 2
No. Guides: 5 stainless steel wire frame
Tip Top: Tungsten carbide
Rec. Lure Wt.: Not specified
Action: Warm
Handle: Anodized aluminum seat with double locking rings. Metal protective butt cap with rubber bumper and doubly reinforced butt.

Model No.: 5707
Length: 5½'
No. Pieces: 2
No. Guides: 3 stainless steel
Tip Top: Not specified
Rec. Lure Wt.: Not specified
Action: Ultralite
Handle: Anodized aluminum seats with cork grip, and double locking rings.

Model No.: 5727
Length: 6'9"
No. Pieces: 2
No. Guides: 4
Tip Top: Not specified
Rec. Lure Wt.: Not specified
Action: Fast tip
Handle: Anodized aluminum seats with cork grip, and double locking rings.

Model No.: 6003 (6000 Holloglass Series)
Length: 6½'
No. Pieces: 2
No. Guides: 6 stainless steel wire frame

Model No.: 63RC. Same as Model 63LC except:
Handle: Popular right hand crank.

Model No.: 633LP
Length: 6'
No. Pieces: 2
No. Guides: Not specified; stainless steel
Tip Top: Stainless steel
Rec. Lure Wt.: Not specified
Action: Fast
Handle: Cork grip.

Model No.: 633RP. Same as Model 633LP except:
Handle: Right hand crank.

Model No.: 5737
Length: 7'
No. Pieces: 2
No. Guides: 4
Tip Top: Not specified
Rec. Lure Wt.: Not specified
Action: Medium
Handle: Anodized aluminum seats with cork grip, and double locking rings.

Salt Water Spinning Rods

Model No.: 8001
Length: 8'
No. Pieces: 2
No. Guides: 6 hard-chromed stainless steel
Tip Top: Not specified
Rec. Lure Wt.: Not specified
Action: Steelhead
Handle: Anodized aluminum seats.

Model No.: 8002. Same as Model 8001 except:
Length: 8½'

Model No.: 8003. Same as Model 8001 except:
No. Guides: 5 hard-chromed stainless steel
Tip Top: Tungsten carbide

Model No.: 8004. Same as Model 8001 except:
Length: 9'
Tip Top: Tungsten carbide

Spin-Casting Rods

Model No.: 200T
Length: 6'
No. Pieces: 5
No. Guides: 3 stainless steel
Tip Top: Tungsten carbide
Rec. Lure Wt.: Not specified
Action: Medium-light
Handle: Cork grip.

Model No.: 696
Length: 5½'
No. Pieces: 1
No. Guides: 4 hard-chromed
Tip Top: Hard-chromed
Rec. Lure Wt.: Not specified
Action: Fast tip
Handle: Positive, screw locking handle with cork forward grip.

Model No.: 697. Same as Model 696 except:
No. Pieces: 2
No. Guides: 3 hard-chromed

Model No.: 698. Same as Model 696 except:
Length: 6'
No. Pieces: 2
No. Guides: 3 hard-chromed

Model No.: 800
Length: 6'
No. Pieces: 1
No. Guides: 4 heavy-chromed
Tip Top: Heavy-chromed
Rec. Lure Wt.: ⅜-¾ oz.
Action: Fast tip
Handle: Positive screw locking, offset handle, cork foregrip.

Model No.: 801. Same as Model 800 except:
Length: 6'4"
No. Pieces: 2
No. Guides: 3 heavy-chromed
Rec. Lure Wt.: ¼-⅝ oz.

Model No.: 896
Length: 5½'
No. Pieces: 1
No. Guides: 4 hard-chromed
Tip Top: Hard-chromed
Rec. Lure Wt.: Not specified
Action: Fast tip
Handle: Deluxe screw locking handle.

Model No.: 897. Same as Model 896 except:
No. Pieces: 2

Model No.: 898. Same as Model 896 except:
Length: 6'
No. Pieces: 2

Model No.: 991
Length: 6'
No. Pieces: 2
No. Guides: 4 heavy-chromed
Tip Top: Heavy-chromed
Rec. Lure Wt.: ⅜-¾ oz.
Action: Fast tip

Handle: Positive screw locking offset handle with cork foregrip.

Model No.: 992. Same as Model 991 except:
Length: 6½'
Rec. Lure Wt.: ¼-⅝ oz.

Model No.: 1001
Length: 6'
No. Pieces: 2
No. Guides: 4 hard-chromed
Tip Top: Hard-chromed
Rec. Lure Wt.: ⅛-⅜ oz.
Action: Fast tip
Handle: Screw locking handle.

Model No.: 1002. Same as Model 1001 except:
Length: 6½'

Model No.: 1251 (1250 Series)
Length: 6'
No. Pieces: 2
No. Guides: 4 hard-chromed
Tip Top: Hard-chromed
Rec. Lure Wt.: ¼-⅝ oz.
Action: Fast tip
Handle: Screw locking handle.

Model No.: 1252 (1250 Series)
Length: 6½'
No. Pieces: 2
No. Guides: 4 hard-chromed
Tip Top: Hard-chromed
Rec. Lure Wt.: ¼-⅝ oz.
Action: Fast tip
Handle: Screw locking handle.

Model No.: 4541A
Length: 3'
No. Pieces: 1
No. Guides: 1 heavy-chromed
Tip Top: Heavy-chromed
Rec. Lure Wt.: Not specified
Action: Fast tip
Handle: Positive screw locking handle, 5" cork grip.

Model No.: 4872. Same as Model 4541 except:
Length: 4½'
No. Guides: 2 heavy-chromed

Model No.: 4873. Same as Model 4541A except:
Length: 5'
No. Guides: 2 heavy-chromed

Model No.: 5717
Length: 6'
No. Pieces: 1
No. Guides: 4 stainless steel
Tip Top: Not specified
Rec. Lure Wt.: Not specified
Action: Heavy duty
Handle: Cork grip.

Model No.: 6000
Length: 5½'
No. Pieces: 1
No. Guides: 6 wire frames
Tip Top: Not specified
Rec. Lure Wt.: ½-1 oz.
Action: Worm

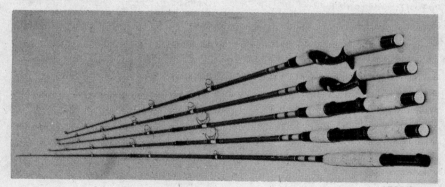

1500 Series

Model No.: 1501 (1500 Series)
Length: 6'
No. Pieces: 2
No. Guides: 4 stainless steel wire frame
Tip Top: Stainless steel
Rec. Lure Wt.: ¼-⅝ oz.
Action: Fast tip
Handle: Front locking handle with metal protective butt caps and rubber bumper.

Model No.: 1502 (1500 Series)
Length: 6½'
No. Pieces: 2
No. Guides: 4 stainless steel wire frame
Tip Top: Stainless steel
Rec. Lure Wt.: ¼-⅝ oz.
Action: Fast tip
Handle: Front locking handle with metal protective butt caps and rubber bumper.

Handle: Metal protective butt caps with rubber bumper, with cork grip.

Model No.: 6002 (6000 Holloglass Series)
Length: 6½'
No. Pieces: 2
No. Guides: 6 tungsten carbide wire frame
Tip Top: Tungsten carbide
Rec. Lure Wt.: ⅛-⅜ oz.
Action: Conventional; fast tip
Handle: Double offset, front locking handle. Metal protective butt caps with rubber bumper, butt doubly reinforced.

Casting Rods

Model No.: 1649 (1650 Series)
Length: 5½'
No. Pieces: 1

No. Guides: 4 stainless steel wire frame
Tip Top: Tungsten carbide
Rec. Lure Wt.: Not specified
Action: Heavy
Handle: Non-detachable handle, metal
protective butt cap with rubber bumper,
doubly reinforced butt.

Bait-Casting Rods

Model No.: 914
Length: 4'
No. Pieces: 1
No. Guides: 2 wire frame stainless steel
Tip Top: Wire frame stainless steel
Rec. Lure Wt.: Not specified
Action: Heavy
Handle: Detachable handle.

Model No.: 915. Same as Model 914 except:
Length: 5'
No. Guides: 3 wire frame stainless steel
Handle: Non-detachable, cork grip.

Model No.: 1250 (1250 Series)
Length: 5½'
No. Pieces: 1
No. Guides: 4 hard-chromed
Tip Top: Hard-chromed
Rec. Lure Wt.: ⅜-¾ oz.
Action: Medium
Handle: Not specified.

Model No.: 1650 (1650 Series)
Length: 5½'
No. Pieces: 1
No. Guides: 5 stainless steel wire frame
Tip Top: Tungsten carbide
Rec. Lure Wt.: Not specified
Action: Worm
Handle: Detachable handle, doubly reinforced
butt, metal protective butt cap with rubber
bumper. Positive screw locking, offset
handle.

Salt Water Casting Rods

Model No.: 8000
Length: 8½'
No. Pieces: 2
No. Guides: 5 hard-chromed stainless steel
Tip Top: Not specified
Rec. Lure Wt.: Not specified
Action: Steelhead
Handle: Anodized aluminum seats.

Model No.: 8005. Same as Model 8000
except:
Length: 7½'
Action: Salmon

Model No.: 8006. Same as Model 8000
except:
Length: 8'
No. Guides: 6 hard-chromed stainless steel
Action: Salmon

Fly Casting Rods

Model No.: 995
Length: 8½'
No. Pieces: 2
No. Guides: 4 heavy-chromed
Tip Top: Heavy-chromed
Rec. Line: 8 wt.
Handle: Anodized aluminum seat.

Model No.: 1005
Length: 8½'
No. Pieces: 2
No. Guides: 5 hard-chromed
Tip Top: Hard-chromed
Rec. Line: 8 wt.
Handle: Anodized aluminum seat.

Model No.: 1255 (1250 Series)
Length: 8½'
No. Pieces: 2
No. Guides: 5 hard-chromed
Tip Top: Hard-chromed
Rec. Line: 7 wt.
Handle: Anodized aluminum seat.

Model No.: 1255A. Same as Model 1255
except:
Length: 8'

Model No.: 1255B. Same as Model 1255
except:
Length: 7½'
Rec. Line: 6 wt.

Model No.: 1255C. Same as Model 1255
except:
Length: 9'

Model No.: 1505 (1500 Series)
Length: 8½'
No. Pieces: 2
No. Guides: 5 stainless steel wire frame
Tip Top: Stainless steel
Rec. Line: 7 wt.
Handle: Anodized aluminum seat and metal
protective butt caps with rubber bumper.

Model No.: 6005 (6000 Holloglass Series)
Length: 8½'
No. Pieces: 2
No. Guides: 9
Tip Top: Not specified
Rec. Line: 9 wt.
Handle: Anodized aluminum seat with double
locking rings. Doubly reinforced butt,
metal protective butt caps with rubber
bumper.

Cast/Spin Casting Rods

Model No.: 510PGH (1650 Series)
Length: 6'
No. Pieces: 1
No. Guides: 5 tungsten carbide
Tip Top: Tungsten carbide
Rec. Lure Wt.: Not specified
Action: Worm
Handle: Detachable handle, doubly reinforced
butt, metal protective butt cap with rubber
bumper. Positive screw locking, offset
handle.

Model No.: 1651 (1650 Series)
Length: 6'
No. Pieces: 1
No. Guides: 5 stainless steel wire frame
Tip Top: Tungsten carbide
Rec. Lure Wt.: Not specified
Action: Worm
Handle: Detachable handle, doubly reinforced
butt, metal protective butt cap with rubber
bumper. Positive screw locking, offset
handle.

Model No.: 6001 (6000 Holloglass Series)
Length: 6'
No. Pieces: 1
No. Guides: 6 tungsten carbide wire frame
Tip Top: Tungsten carbide
Rec. Lure Wt.: ⅝-1¼ oz.
Action: Worm
Handle: Double offset, front locking handle.
Metal protective butt caps with rubber
bumper, butts doubly reinforced.

Casting/Trolling Rods

Model No.: 1652 (1650 Series)
Length: 5'11"
No. Pieces: 2
No. Guides: 4 stainless steel wire frame
Tip Top: Tungsten carbide
Rec. Lure Wt.: Not specified
Action: Heavy
Handle: Detachable handle, doubly reinforced
butt, metal protective butt cap with rubber
bumper. Positive screw locking, offset
handle.

Model No.: 9500
Length: 5'
No. Pieces: 1
No. Guides: 2 wire frame stainless steel
Tip Top: Wire frame stainless steel
Rec. Lure Wt.: Not specified
Action: Light
Handle: Wood grip, chromed brass seat with
double locking rings, detachable.

Model No.: 9505. Same as Model 9500
except:
Length: 5½'
No. Guides: 3 wire frame stainless steel

Model No.: 9510. Same as Model 9500
except:
Length: 5'10"
No. Guides: 3 wire frame stainless steel
Action: Medium

Model No.: 9515. Same as Model 9500
except:
Length: 6'8"
No. Guides: 4 wire frame stainless steel

Model No.: 9520. Same as Model 9500
except:
Length: 5½'
No. Guides: 3 wire frame stainless steel
Action: Heavy

Model No.: 9525. Same as Model 9500
except:
Length: 6'
No. Guides: 3 wire frame stainless steel
Action: Heavy

Model No.: 9530. Same as Model 9500
except:
Length: 6'
No. Guides: 3 wire frame stainless steel
Tip Top: Roller
Action: Heavy roller top

Model No.: 9535. Same as Model 9500
except:
Length: 7'
No. Guides: 4 wire frame stainless steel
Action: Medium

Model No.: 9545
Length: 7½'
No. Pieces: 2
No. Guides: 4 wire frame stainless steel
Tip Top: Wire frame stainless steel
Rec. Lure Wt.: Not specified
Action: Medium-light
Handle: Non-detachable, wood grip, chromed brass seat with double locking rings.

Boat Spinning Rods

Model No.: 9001
Length: 5½'
No. Pieces: 1
No. Guides: 3 stainless steel
Tip Top: Stainless steel
Rec. Lure Wt.: Not specified
Action: Light
Handle: Cork upper grip, wood lower grip, detachable.

Model No.: 9003. Same as Model 9001 except:
Length: 6'5"
Action: Heavy
Handle: Wood upper grip and lower grip, detachable.

Model No.: 9005. Same as Model 9001 except:
Length: 6½'
No. Guides: 4 stainless steel
Action: Medium-light
Handle: Wood upper grip and lower grip, detachable.

Model No.: 9007. Same as Model 9001 except:
Length: 7'
No. Guides: 4 stainless steel
Action: Medium
Handle: Wood upper grip and lower grip, detachable.

Model No.: 9009. Same as Model 9001 except:
Length: 8'
No. Guides: 4 stainless steel
Action: Medium

Salt Water Rods

Model No.: 7776
Length: 6'
No. Pieces: 1
No. Guides: 2 stainless steel
Tip Top: Stainless steel
Rec. Lure Wt.: Not specified
Action: Extra heavy
Handle: Non-detachable wood grip, chromed brass seat with double locking rings.

Model No.: 7777. Same as Model 7776 except:
Tip Top: Roller

Model No.: 7778. Same as Model 7776 except:
Length: 6½'
No. Guides: 3 stainless steel
Tip Top: Roller
Action: Heavy

Model No.: 7779. Same as Model 7776 except:
Length: 7'
No. Guides: 4 stainless steel
Tip Top: Roller

Model No.: 8782
Length: 8'
No. Pieces: 1
No. Guides: 4 stainless steel
Tip Top: Stainless steel
Rec. Lure Wt.: Not specified
Action: Medium
Handle: Chromed brass seat, upper cork grip, detachable.

Model No.: 8777. Same as Model 8782 except:
Length: 6'
No. Guides: 3 stainless steel
Action: Medium-light

Model No.: 8778. Same as Model 8782 except:
Length: 6½'
No. Guides: 3 stainless steel
Action: Light

Model No.: 8780. Same as Model 8782 except:
Length: 7'
No. Guides: 3 stainless steel

Model No.: 8781. Same as Model 8782 except:
Length: 7½'

Popping Rod

Model No.: 8510
Length: 6½'
No. Pieces: 1
No. Guides: 4 stainless steel
Tip Top: Stainless steel
Rec. Lure Wt.: Not specified
Action: Medium
Handle: Chromed brass, finger hook reel seat, white ash handle.

General Purpose Rods

Model No.: 6500
Length: 5'
No. Pieces: 1
No. Guides: 2 stainless steel
Tip Top: Stainless steel
Rec. Lure Wt.: Not specified
Action: Light
Handle: Natural white ash detachable handles and upper grips, chromed brass seats and locking ring.

Model No.: 6505. Same as Model 6500 except:
Length: 5½'

Model No.: 6510. Same as Model 6500 except:
Length: 5'10"
Action: Medium

Model No.: 6515. Same as Model 6500 except:
Length: 6'8"
No. Guides: 3 stainless steel

Model No.: 6520. Same as Model 6500 except:
Length: 5½'
Action: Heavy

Model No.: 6525. Same as Model 6500 except:
Length: 6'
Action: Heavy

Model No.: 6530. Same as Model 6500 except:
Length: 6'
Tip Top: Roller
Action: Heavy roller

Model No.: 6535. Same as Model 6500 except:
Length: 7'
No. Guides: 3 roller
Tip Top: Roller
Action: Medium

Model No.: 6545
Length: 7½'
No. Pieces: 2
No. Guides: 4 stainless steel
Tip Top: Stainless steel
Rec. Lure Wt.: Not specified
Action: Medium-light
Handle: Natural white ash non-detachable handle and upper grip, chromed brass seat and locking ring.

Model No.: 6560
Length: 6'
No. Pieces: 2
No. Guides: 3 stainless steel
Tip Top: Stainless steel
Rec. Lure Wt.: Not specified
Action: Medium-heavy
Handle: Natural white ash non-detachable handle and upper grip, chromed brass seat and locking ring.

Model No.: 6570
Length: 6'
No. Pieces: 1
No. Guides: 3 roller
Tip Top: Roller
Rec. Lure Wt.: Not specified
Action: Heavy all roller
Handle: Natural white ash detachable handle and upper grip, chromed brass seat and locking ring.

Uslan

Spinning Rods

Model No.: 1080GM
Length: 6½'
No. Pieces: 1
No. Guides: 4 stainless steel guides
Tip Top: Stainless steel
Rec. Lure Wt.: Not specified
Action: Not specified
Handle: Black-and-gold anodized locking reel seat, 5" specie cork butt grip, 3" specie cork fore grip.

Model No.: 1085GM. Same as Model 1080GM except:
No. Pieces: 2

Model No.: 1724
Length: 6'
No. Pieces: 1
No. Guides: 4 stainless steel guides
Tip Top: Stainless steel
Rec. Lure Wt.: Not specified
Action: Not specified
Handle: Black-and-gold anodized locking reel seat, 5" specie cork butt, 3½" specie cork fore grip.

Model No.: 2782FT
Length: 6½'
No. Pieces: 2
No. Guides: 5 Stainless steel guides
Tip Top: Stainless steel
Rec. Lure Wt.: Not specified
Action: Light; fast taper
Handle: Black-and-gold anodized locking reel seat, 5" specie cork butt grip, 3½" specie cork fore grip.

Model No.: 1782. Same as Model 2782FT except:
No. Pieces: 1

Model No.: 2783FT
Length: 6½'
No. Pieces: 2
No. Guides: 5 stainless steel guides
Tip Top: Stainless steel
Rec. Lure Wt.: Not specified
Action: Light-medium; fast taper
Handle: Black-and-gold anodized locking reel seat, 5" specie cork butt grip, 3½" specie cork fore grip.

Model No.: 1783FT. Same as Model 2783FT except:
No. Pieces: 1

Model No.: 2783FTSB. Same as Model 2783FT except:
Handle: Shorter butt section.

Model No.: 1082
Length: 6½'
No. Pieces: 2
No. Guides: 5 stainless steel guides
Tip Top: Stainless steel
Rec. Lure Wt.: Not specified
Action: Medium
Handle: Black-and-gold anodized locking reel seat, 5" specie cork butt grip, 3½" specie cork fore grip.

Model No.: 1081. Same as Model 1082 except:
No. Pieces: 1

Model No.: 2787. Same as Model 1082 except:
Action: Heavy

Model No.: 1787. Same as Model 2787 except:
No. Pieces: 1

Model No.: 2847
Length: 7'
No. Pieces: 2
No. Guides: 5 stainless steel guides
Tip Top: Stainless steel
Rec. Lure Wt.: Not specified

Action: Heavy
Handle: Black-and-chrome anodized locking reel seat, 7" specie cork butt grip, 4" specie cork fore grip.

Model No.: 1847. Same as Model 2847 except:
No. Pieces: 1

Model No.: 2844FT. Same as Model 2847 except:
Action: Medium; fast taper

Model No.: 1844FT. Same as Model 2844FT except:
No. Pieces: 1

Model No.: 2906
Length: 7½'
No. Pieces: 2
No. Guides: 5 stainless steel guides
Tip Top: Stainless steel
Rec. Lure Wt.: Not specified
Action: Not specified
Handle: Black-and-chrome anodized locking reel seat, 10" specie cork butt grip, 4" specie cork fore grip.

Model No.: 1906. Same as Model 2906 except:
No. Pieces: 1

Surf Spinning Rods

Model No.: 2964

Length: 8'
No. Pieces: 2
No. Guides: 6 stainless steel guides
Tip Top: Not specified
Rec. Lure Wt.: Not specified
Action: Medium
Handle: 1" black-and-chrome anodized reel seat, 12" specie cork butt grip, 4" specie cork fore grip.

Model No.: 2967
Length: 8'
No. Pieces: 2

No. Guides: 6 stainless steel guides

Tip Top: Not specified
Rec. Lure Wt.: Not specified
Action: Heavy
Handle: 1" black-and-chrome anodized reel seat, 12" specie cork butt grip, 4" specie cork fore grip.

Surf Rod

Model No.: 21206
Length: 10'
No. Pieces: 2
No. Guides: 7 stainless steel spinning guides or heavy chrome-plated ring guides
Tip Top: Not specified
Rec. Lure Wt.: Not specified
Action: Not specified
Handle: 1" varmac reel seat. 8" specie cork butt grip, 4½" specie cork reel-seat grip, 4½" specie cork fore grip.

Spincasting Rods

Model No.: 1684
Length: 6'
No. Pieces: 1
No. Guides: 5 stainless steel guides
Tip Top: Stainless steel
Rec. Lure Wt.: Not specified
Action: Light-medium
Handle: Featherweight offset bait-casting handle and ferrule.

Model No.: 2685. Same as Model 1684 except:

Length: 6½'
No. Pieces: 2
Action: Light-heavy

Model No.: 2624
Length: 5½'
No. Pieces: 2
No. Guides: 4 stainless steel guides
Tip Top: Stainless steel
Rec. Lure Wt.: Not specified
Action: Light-medium
Handle: Featherweight offset bait-casting handle and ferrule.

Bait-Casting Rods

Uslan (cont'd.)

Model No.: 2623
Length: 5½'
No. Pieces: 2
No. Guides: 4 stainless steel guides
Tip Top: Stainless steel
Rec. Lure Wt.: Not specified
Action: Light-medium
Handle: Featherweight offset bait-casting handle and ferrule.

Fly Rods

Model No.: 2724
Length: 6'
No. Pieces: 2
No. Guides: 4 stainless steel snake guides plus one stainless steel chrome-plated stripping guide
Tip Top: Stainless steel chrome-plated
Rec. Line: Not specified
Handle: Black-and-gold anodized deluxe locking-type fly reel seat, 6" specie cork grip.

Model No.: 2784
Length: 6½'
No. Pieces: 2
No. Guides: 5 stainless steel snake guides plus one stainless steel chrome-plated stripping guide
Tip Top: Stainless steel chrome-plated
Rec. Line: Not specified
Handle: Black-and-gold anodized deluxe locking-type fly reel seat, 6" specie cork grip.

Model No.: 2903
Length: 7½'
No. Pieces: 2
No. Guides: 6 stainless steel snake guides plus one stainless steel chrome-plated stripping guide
Tip Top: Stainless steel chrome-plated
Rec. Line: 7 wt.
Handle: Black-and-gold anodized deluxe locking-type fly reel seat, 6" specie cork grip.

Model No.: 2843. Same as Model 2903 except:
Length: 7'

Model No.: 2963
Length: 8'
No. Pieces: 2
No. Guides: 8 stainless steel snake guides plus one stainless steel chrome-plated stripping guide

Tip Top: Stainless steel chrome-plated
Rec. Line: 8 wt.
Handle: Black-and-gold anodized deluxe locking-type fly reel seat, 6" specie cork grip.

Model No.: 21022
Length: 8½'
No. Pieces: 2
No. Guides: 9 stainless steel snake guides plus one stainless steel chrome-plated stripping guide
Tip Top: Stainless steel chrome-plated
Rec. Line: Not specified
Handle: Black-and-gold anodized deluxe locking-type fly reel seat, 6" specie cork grip.

Model No.: 21082
Length: 9'
No. Pieces: 2
No. Guides: 10 stainless steel snake guides plus one stainless steel chrome-plated stripping guide
Tip Top: Stainless steel chrome-plated
Rec. Line: Not specified
Handle: Black-and-gold anodized deluxe locking-type fly reel seat, 6" specie cork grip.

IGFA Regulation Big Game Trolling

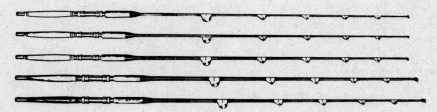

Model No.: RT200
Length: 7'
No. Pieces: Not specified
No. Guides: 5 Aftco roller guides of corrosion-resistant metal
Tip Top: Roller
Rec. Lure Wt.: Not specified
Action: 20 lb. class
Handle: 1" reel seat precision machined, heavy-wall, and chrome-plated. Butt is select clear hickory, assembled with sturdy gimbal and heavily chrome-plated.

Model No.: RT120. Same as Model RT200 except:
Action: 12 lb. class

Model No.: RT300. Same as Model RT200 except:
Action: 30 lb. class

Model No.: RT500. Same as Model RT200 except:
Action: 50 lb. class

Model No.: RT800. Same as Model RT200 except:
Action: 80 lb. class
Handle: Reel seat width is 1⅛".

Model No.: RT1200. Same as Model RT200 except:
Action: 130 lb. class
Handle: Reel seat width is 1⅛".

Popping Rods

Model No.: 2847GP
Length: 7'
No. Pieces: 2
No. Guides: 5 stainless steel guides
Tip Top: Stainless steel
Rec. Lure Wt.: Not specified
Action: Heavy
Handle: Chrome-plated finger-grip reel seat, 10" specie cork butt grip, 3½" specie cork fore grip.

Model No.: 2844FT GP. Same as Model 2847GP except:
Action: Fast taper; medium

Model No.: 2787GP
Length: 6½'
No. Pieces: 2
No. Guides: 5 stainless steel guides
Tip Top: Stainless steel
Rec. Lure Wt.: Not specified
Action: Heavy
Handle: Chrome-plated finger-grip reel seat, 7" specie cork butt grip, 3½" specie cork fore grip.

Model No.: 1787GP. Same as Model 2787GP except:
No. Pieces: 1

Model No.: 2964GP
Length: 8'

No. Pieces: 2
No. Guides: 6 stainless steel guides
Tip Top: Stainless steel
Rec. Lure Wt.: Not specified
Action: Not specified
Handle: Chrome-plated finger-grip reel seat, 12" specie cork butt grip, 4" specie cork fore grip.

Zebco

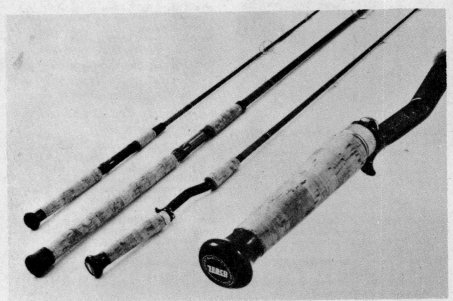

Sundowner

Spinning Rods

Model No.: 7050 (Sundowner rod series)
Length: 5'6"
No. Pieces: 1
No. Guides: Not specified; hard chrome-plated stainless steel
Tip Top: Hard chrome-plated stainless steel
Rec. Lure Wt.: Not specified
Action: Light (for light freshwater)
Handle: Permanent ABS butt caps; flared for greater cushioning.

Model No.: 7400. Same as Model 7050 except:
Length: 6'6"
Action: Medium (for all-around freshwater fishing)

Model No.: 7500. Same as Model 7050 except:
Length: 7'
Action: Medium-heavy (for light saltwater; heavy freshwater)

Model No.: 7550. Same as Model 7050 except:
Length: 7'6"

Action: Medium-heavy (for medium saltwater; heavy freshwater)

Model No.: 7900. Same as model 7050 except:
Length: 9'
Action: Heavy-action surf

Model No.: 7950. Same as Model 7050 except:
Length: 10'
Action: Heavy-action surf

Model No.: 7051. Centennial rod series
Length: 5'6"
No. Pieces: 1
No. Guides: Not specified; hard chrome-plated stainless steel
Tip Top: Hard chrome-plated stainless steel
Rec. Lure Wt.: Not specified
Action: Light (for light freshwater)
Handle: Aluminum, with butt grips and foregrips of specie cork; permanent ABS butt caps.

Model No.: 7101. Same as Model 7051 except:
Length: 6'
Action: Medium (for medium-light freshwater fishing)

Model No.: 7301. Same as Model 7051 except:
Length: 6'6"
Action: Medium (for medium-light freshwater fishing)

Model No.: PS20 (Pro Staff series)
Length: 5'6"
No. Pieces: 1
No. Guides: Not specified; aluminum oxide slipstream guides
Tip Top: Aluminum oxide
Rec. Lure Wt.: Not specified
Action: Light
Handle: Burnt cork; flared butt molded into the rod handle.

Model No.: PS21. Same as Model PS20 except:
Length: 6'6"
Action: Light-medium

Model No.: PS22. Same as Model PS20 except:
Length: 6'6"
Action: Medium

Centennial

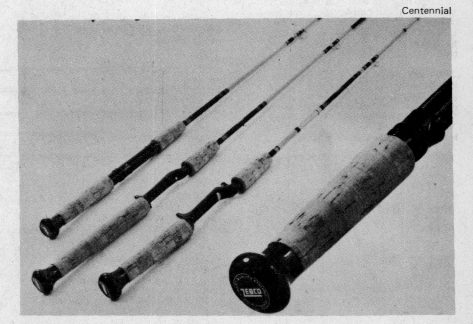

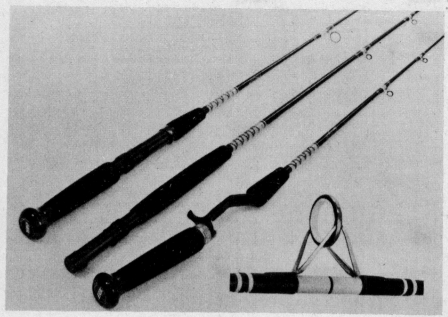

Pro Staff

Tip Top: Hard chrome-plated stainless steel
Rec. Lure Wt.: Not specified
Action: Medium (for medium freshwater fishing)
Handle: Aluminum, with butt.

Model No.: 8406. Same as Model 4060 except:
Length: 5'6"
Action: Heavy (for worm fishing; deep jigging)

Model No.: 8800. Same as Model 4060 except:
Length: 6'
Action: Heavy (for medium-heavy freshwater fishing)

Model No.: 8965. Same as Model 4060 except:
Length: 6'6"
Action: Heavy (for medium saltwater; heavy freshwater fishing)

Model No.: 8570. Same as Model 4060 except:
Length: 7'
Action: Heavy (for heavy freshwater fishing)

Model No.: 6100. Same as Model 4060 except:
Action: Medium (for medium-light freshwater fishing)

Model No.: PS10 (Pro Staff series)
Length: 6'
No. Pieces: 1
No. Guides: Not specified; aluminum oxide slipstream guides
Tip Top: Aluminum oxide
Rec. Lure Wt.: Not specified
Action: Medium
Handle: Burnt cork; flared butt molded into the rod handle.

Model No.: PS12. Same as model PS10 except:
Length: 6'6"
Action: Medium-heavy

Model No.: PS30. Same as Model PS10 except:
Length: 5'
Action: Worm-action

Model No.: PS32. Same as Model PS10 except:
Length: 5'6"
Action: Worm-action

Model No.: PS24. Same as Model PS20 except:
Length: 7'
Action: Medium-heavy

Model No.: PS29. Same as Model PS20 except:
Length: 5'9"
Action: Worm-spin

Spin-Casting Rods

Model No.: 6300. Deluxe, 6200. (Sundowner rod series)
Length: 6'
No. Pieces: 1
No. Guides: Not specified; hard chrome-plated stainless steel
Tip Top: Hard chrome-plated stainless steel
Rec. Lure Wt.: Not specified
Action: Medium (for all freshwater fishing)
Handle: Permanent ABS butt caps; flared for greater cushioning.

Model No.: 8900. Same as Model 6200 except:

Length: 7'
Action: Heavy (for heavy freshwater; light saltwater fishing)

Model No.: 8877. Same as Model 6200 except:
Action: Heavy (for heavy freshwater; medium saltwater fishing)

Model No.: 8816. Same as Model 6200 except:
Length: 5'6"
Action: Heavy (for bass fishing)

Model No.: 8810. Same as Model 6200 except:
Action: Heavy (for bass fishing)

Model No.: 4060 (Centennial rod series)
Length: 5'6"
No. Pieces: 1
No. Guides: Not specified; hard chrome-plated stainless steel

Specifications: Reels

Berkley

Spinning Reels

Model No.: 406
Line Capacity: 150 yds. 8 lb. Trilene XL
Gear Ratio: 3.5 to 1
Weight: 5.5 oz.

Model No.: 412
Line Capacity: 250 yds. 8 lb. Trilene XL
Gear Ratio: 3.3 to 1

Model No.: 420
Line Capacity: 375 yds. 8 lb. Trilene XL
Gear Ratio: 3.2 to 1

Model No.: 420A. Same as Model 420 except:
instant line change adapter
Line Capacity: 100 yd. spools of Trilene XL
(6 lb. on reel, 10 lb. in reserve) and
regular spool wound with 125 yds. 17 lb.
Trilene XL

Model No.: 435
Line Capacity: 200 yds. 4 lb. Trilene XL
Gear Ratio: 4.1 to 1
Drag System: Disc
Ball Bearings: Yes

Model No.: 446
Line Capacity: 200 yds. 8 lb. Trilene XL
Gear Ratio: 4.1 to 1
Drag System: Disc
Ball Bearings: Yes

Model No.: 604
Line Capacity: 200 yds. 4 lb. Trilene XL
Gear Ratio: 3.6 to 1

Model No.: 612
Line Capacity: 250 yds. 8 lb. Trilene XL
Gear Ratio: 3.6 to 1
Spool Material: Aluminum

Model No.: 4201
Line Capacity: 375 yds. 8 lb. Trilene XL
Gear Ratio: 4.5 to 1
Ball Bearings: Yes

Model No.: 4201A. Same as Model 4201
except: instant line change adapter
Line Capacity: 100 yds. spool 6 lb. Trilene XL
(on spool); 100 yds. 10 lb. Trilene XL. Plus
regular spool wound with 150 yds. 17 lb.
Trilene XL

Model No.: 810
Lince Capacity: 225 yds. 17 lb. Trilene
Tensimatic
Gear Ratio: 4 to 1
Drag System: Disc
Ball Bearings: Yes

Model No.: 870
Line Capacity: 200 yds. 17 lb. Trilene
Tensimatic
Gear Ratio: 4 to 1
Ball Bearings: Yes

Model No.: 680
Line Capacity: 250 yds. 17 lb. Trilene
Tensimatic
Gear Ratio: 3.6 to 1
Drag System: Disc

Model No.: 690
Line Capacity: 300 yds. 20 lb. Trilene
Tensimatic
Gear Ratio: 3.6 to 1
Drag System: Disc
Spool Material: Magnum

Spin-Casting Reels

Model No.: Castamatic I
Line Capacity: 225 yds. 8 lb. Trilene XL

Model No.: 56
Line Capacity: 100 yds. 8 lb. Trilene XL
Gear Ratio: 3 to 1
Drag System: Star

Model No.: 290
Line Capacity: 80 yds. 8 lb. Trilene XL
Gear Ratio: 3 to 1

Model No.: 300
Line Capacity: 125 yds. 8 lb. Trilene XL
Gear Ratio: 3 to 1
Drag System: Star

Model No.: 350
Line Capacity: 125 yds. 17 lb. Trilene XL
Gear Ratio: 3.5 to 1
Drag System: Star

Fly Reels

Model No.: 500
Line Capacity: 25 yds. flyline; 50 yds.
braided or mono

Model No.: 510
Line Capacity: 30 yds. Berkley floating fly
line
Drag System: Adjustable

Model No.: 530
Line Capacity: 30 yds. #6 Berkley floating
fly line
Drag System: Adjustable
Spool Size: 2½″ diameter

Model No.: 540
Line Capacity: 30 yds. #6 Berkley floating
fly line with 50 yds. backing
Drag System: Adjustable
Spool Size: 2⅞″ diameter

Model No.: 550
Line Capacity: 30 yds. #6 Berkley floating
with 100 yds. backing
Drag System: Adjustable
Spool Size: 3¼″ diameter

Model No.: 570
Line Capacity: 30 yds. #6 fly line with
50 yds. 10 lb. test backing

Browning

Spinning Reels

Model No.: 1330
Line Capacity: 210 yds. 6 lb. test mono
Gear Ratio: 4.2 to 1
Weight: 8 oz.
Drag System: Multi-disc
Ball Bearings: Yes

Model No.: 5330
Line Capacity: 145 yds. 12 lb. test mono
Gear Ratio: 4.1 to 1
Weight: 12 oz.
Drag System: Multi-disc
Ball Bearings: Yes

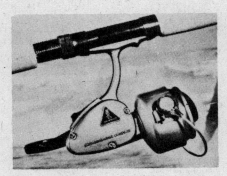

Model No.: 5430
Line Capacity: 130 yds. 20 lb. test mono
Gear Ratio: 3.8 to 1
Weight: 15 oz.
Drag System: 6 disc system
Ball Bearings: Yes

Spin Casting Reels

Model No.: 1130
Line Capacity: 90 yds. 10 lb. test mono
Gear Ratio: 2.71 to 1
Weight: 8.4 oz.
Drag System: Star Multi-disc
Ball Bearings: Yes

Model No.: 5130
Line Capacity: 90 yds. 12 lb. test mono
Gear Ratio: 3.6 to 1
Weight: 12.5 oz.
Drag System: Star Multi-disc
Ball Bearings: Yes

Fly Reels

Model No.: 1230
Line Capacity: 25 yds. 15 lb. test braided mono
Weight: 4 oz.
Spool Material: Aluminum

Model No.: 5230
Line Capacity: 50 yds. 15 lb. test braided mono
Weight: 5 oz.

Continental

Spinning Reels

Model No.: Alcedo Mark IV
Line Capacity: 700 yds. 14 lb. test
Ball Bearings: Yes

Model No.: Alcedo Mark V
Line Capacity: 600 yds. 20 lb. test
Weight: 26 oz.
Ball Bearings: Yes

Model No.: Alcedo 2 C/S
Line Capacity: 350 yds. 26 lb. mono
Gear Ratio: 4 to 1
Weight: 11½ oz.
Ball Bearings: Yes
Spool Material: Duraluminum

Model No.: Alcedo Micron
Line Capacity: 260 yds. 4 lb. test mono
Gear Ratio: 5¼ to 1
Weight: 6⅓ oz.
Ball Bearings: Yes
Spool Material: Duraluminum

Daiwa

Spinning Reels

Model No.: 2500
Line Capacity: 280 yds. 12 lb. test
Gear Ratio: 4.8 to 1
Weight: 15 oz.
Ball Bearings: Yes
Spool Material: Aluminum, skirted

Model No.: 4000
Line Capacity: 300 yds. 15 lb. test
Gear Ratio: 4.7 to 1
Weight: 16 oz.
Ball Bearings: Yes
Spool Material: Aluminum, skirted

Model No.: 4300
Line Capacity: 320 yds. 10 lb. test

Gear Ratio: 3.8 to 1
Weight: 13 oz.
Drag System: Spring loaded
Ball Bearings: Yes

Model No.: 7000
Line Capacity: 200 yds. 25 lb. test
Gear Ratio: 4.4 to 1
Weight: 21 oz.
Ball Bearings: Yes
Spool Material: Aluminum, skirted

Model No.: 7200 H
Line Capacity: 200 yds. 6 lb. test mono
Gear Ratio: 4.7 to 1
Weight: 7 oz.
Drag System: Spring loaded

Model No.: 7250 RL
Line Capacity: 300 yds. 6 lb. test
Gear Ratio: 4.5 to 1
Weight: 8 oz.
Ball Bearings: Yes

Model No.: 7270
Line Capacity: 220 yds. 8 lb. test
Gear Ratio: 3.2 to 1
Weight: 7 oz.

Model No.: 7280
Line Capacity: 200 yds. 8 lb. test mono
Gear Ratio: 3.2 to 1
Weight: 8½ oz.

Model No.: 7290 C
Line Capacity: 25 yds. 8 lb. test mono
Gear Ratio: 3.3 to 1
Weight: 10½ oz.

Model No.: 7300
Line Capacity: 250 yds. 10 lb. test
Gear Ratio: 3.4 to 1
Weight: 12 oz.

Model No.: 7300 H
Line Capacity: 300 yds. 10 lb. test
Gear Ratio: 4.5 to 1
Weight: 12 oz.
Drag System: Spring loaded
Ball Bearings: Yes

Model No.: 7350 RL
Line Capacity: 250 yds. 12 lb. test
Gear Ratio: 3.8 to 1
Weight: 13 oz.
Drag System: Spring loaded

Model No.: 7450 HRL
Line Capacity: 255 yds. 10 lbs. test mono
Gear Ratio: 4.1 to 1

Daiwa (cont'd.)

Weight: 13 oz.
Drag System: Spring loaded
Ball Bearings: Yes

Model No.: 7500 H
Line Capacity: 240 yds. 12 lb. test
Gear Ratio: 4.5 to 1
Weight: 15 oz.

Model No.: 7600
Line Capacity: 230 yds. 18 lb. test
Gear Ratio: 3.4 to 1
Weight: 15 oz.

Model No.: 7600 H
Line Capacity: 250 yds. 15 lb. test
Gear Ratio: 4.5 to 1
Weight: 16 oz.
Drag System: Spring
Ball Bearings: Yes

Model No.: 7650 HRL
Line Capacity: 250 yds. 15 lb. test mono
Gear Ratio: 4.1 to 1
Weight: 17¾ oz.
Drag System: Spring loaded
Ball Bearings: Yes

Model No.: 7700
Line Capacity: 225 yds. 25 lb. test
Gear Ratio: 3.4 to 1
Weight: 22 oz.

Model No.: 7850 RL
Line Capacity: 300 yds. 30 lb. test
Gear Ratio: 3.5 to 1
Weight: 23 oz.
Ball Bearings: Yes

Model No.: 8100
Line Capacity: 200 yds. 6 lb. test
Gear Ratio: 4.6 to 1
Weight: 9 oz.
Ball Bearings: Yes

Model No.: 8300
Line Capacity: 200 yds. 12 lb. test
Gear Ratio: 3.7 to 1
Weight: 11 oz.
Ball Bearings: Yes

Model No.: 8600
Line Capacity: 250 yds. 15 lb. test
Gear Ratio: 3.7 to 1
Weight: 17 oz.
Ball Bearings: Yes

Spin Casting Reels

Model No.: 2100
Line Capacity: 85 yds. 8 lb. mono with
  practice plug
Gear Ratio: 2.7 to 1
Weight: 6 oz.
Drag System: Star

Model No.: 2200
Line Capacity: 100 yds. 8 lb. test mono
Gear Ratio: 2.3 to 1
Weight: 6½ oz.
Drag System: Star

Model No.: 5400 RL
Line Capacity: 100 yds. 12 lb. test mono

Gear Ratio: 3.9 to 1
Weight: 13.4 oz.

Model No.: 5500 RL
Line Capacity: 120 yds. 15 lb. test mono
Gear Ratio: 3.9 to 1
Weight: 14½ oz.

Model No.: 6400
Line Capacity: 100 yds. 8 lb. test mono
Gear Ratio: 3.2 to 1
Weight: 10 oz.
Drag System: Star

Model No.: 6600
Line Capacity: 100 yds. 12 lb. test mono
Gear Ratio: 4.1 to 1
Weight: 12 oz.
Drag System: Star

Model No.: 6700
Line Capacity: 120 yds. 15 lb. test mono
Gear Ratio: 4.2 to 1
Weight: 13.4 oz.
Drag System: Star

Model No.: 9300
Line Capacity: 80 yds. 8 lb. test mono
Gear Ratio: 2.5 to 1
Weight: 7 oz.

Model No.: 9550
Line Capacity: 80 yds. 8 lb. test
Gear Ratio: 2.5 to 1
Weight: 9 oz.

Model No.: 9600
Line Capacity: 100 yds. 8 lb. test
Gear Ratio: 2.7 to 1
Weight: 11 oz.

Model No.: 9850
Line Capacity: 120 yds. 15 lb. test
Gear Ratio: 2.7 to 1
Weight: 14 oz.
Drag System: Star

Fly Reels

Model No.: 252
Weight: 8½ oz.
Drag System: Shoe type

Model No.: 254
Weight: 8½ oz.
Drag System: Shoe type
Ball Bearings: Yes

Model No.: 700
Weight: 3½ oz.
Spool Size: 2½" diameter, ⅝" width

Model No.: 710
Weight: 4 oz.
Spool Size: 2⅞" diameter, ⅝" width

Model No.: 720
Weight: 5 oz.
Spool Size: 3⅛" diameter, ⅞" width

Model No.: 740
Weight: 6 oz.
Spool Size: 3⅜" diameter, ⅞" width

Trolling Reels

Model No.: Millionaire V
Drag System: Star
Ball Bearings: Yes

Eagle Claw

Spinning Reels

Model No.: Blue Pacific 125 Ultra Light
Gear Ratio: 4.1 to 1
Weight: 8.5 oz.
Drag System: Multi-disc
Ball Bearings: Yes

Model No.: Blue Pacific 225 Light Fresh
  Water
Gear Ratio: 3.4 to 1
Weight: 10 oz.

Model No.: Blue Pacific 425 Medium Fresh
  Water
Gear Ratio: 3.5 to 1
Weight: 16.5 oz.

Model No.: Blue Pacific 525 Light Surf
Gear Ratio: 3.5 to 1
Weight: 20.5 oz.

Model No.: Blue Pacific 625 Heavy Salt Water
Gear Ratio: 3.5 to 1
Weight: 24 oz.

Model No.: Ultra Light Model ECO
Gear Ratio: 5½ to 1
Weight: 6 oz.

Model No.: ECS
Gear Ratio: 4¼ to 1
Weight: 11½ oz.

Model No.: ECRU
Gear Ratio: 5½ to 1
Weight: 10 oz.

Model No.: ECP
Gear Ratio: 4 to 1
Weight: 9½ oz.

Model No.: ECQ
Gear Ratio: 5½ to 1
Weight: 9½ oz.

Model No.: ECR
Weight: 10 oz.

Model No.: 10 BC Freline
Line Capacity: 150 yds. 4 lb. test; 120 yds. 6 lb. test; 100 yds. 8 lb. test; 90 yds. 10 lb. test

Salt Water Spinning

Model No.: ECU
Gear Ratio: 3½ to 1
Weight: 21 oz.

Model No.: ECT
Gear Ratio: 3½ to 1
Weight: 20 oz.

Spin Casting Reels

Model No.: 102 Light Weight Push Button
Drag System: Star

Model No.: 103 Light to Medium Lures Push Button
Drag System: Star

Model No.: 104 Medium to Heavy Lures Push Button (Oscillating Spool)

Fly Reels

Model No.: EC10
Weight: 4½ oz.

Model No.: EC3B Single Action Fly Reel
Spool Material: Aluminum

Model No.: EC11 Medium Single Action
Weight: 4 oz.

Model No.: EC12 Large Single Action
Weight: 3½ oz.

Model No.: ECD
Line Capacity: 30 yds. D line
Spool Material: Aluminum

Feurer Bros.

Spinning Reels

Model No. FB 410
Line Capacity: 240 yds. 6 lb. test; 150 yds. 8 lb. test; 140 yds. 10 lb. test
Gear Ratio: 3.44 to 1
Weight: 9 oz.
Ball Bearings: Yes

Model No.: FB 412
Line Capacity: Large Spool: 200 yds. 8 lb. test; 175 yds. 10 lb. test; 125 yds. 15 lb. test. Small Spool: 140 yds. 8 lb. test; 125 yds. 10 lb. test
Gear Ratio: 3.44 to 1
Weight: 12 oz.

Model No.: FB 414
Line Capacity: 240 yds. 6 lb. test; 150 yds. 8 lb. test; 140 yds. 10 lb. test
Gear Ratio: 3.44 to 1
Weight: 10 oz.

Model No.: FB 417
Line Capacity: 240 yds. 6 lb. test; 150 yds. 8 lb. test; 140 yds. 10 lb. test
Gear Ratio: 3.44 to 1
Weight: 9.6 oz.
Drag System: Nylon expansion
Ball Bearings: Yes

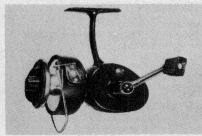

Model No.: FB 430
Line Capacity: 240 yds. 6 lb. test; 150 yds.

8 lb. test; 140 yds. 10 lb. test
Gear Ratio: 3.39 to 1
Weight: 11 oz.

Salt Water Spinning Reels

Model No.: FB 400
Line Capacity: 300 yds. 12 lb. test; 200 yds. 15 lb. test; 150 yds. 20 lb. test
Gear Ratio: 3.2 to 1
Weight: 14 oz.
Drag System: Rear

Model No.: FB 450
Line Capacity: 350 yds. 10 lb. test; 200 yds. 15 lb. test; 185 yds. 20 lb. test
Gear Ratio: 3.88 to 1
Weight: 19 oz.

Spin Casting Reels

Model No.: FB 426
Line Capacity: 100 yds. prewound
Gear Ratio: 2.75 to 1
Weight: 7 oz.
Drag System: Adjustable

Model No.: FB 427. Same as Model FB 426 except: chrome finish

Fly Reels

Model No.: FB 473
Line Capacity: 50 yds. #3 or #4 fly line
Weight: 5½ oz.
Spool Material: Aluminum
Spool Size: 2⅞"

Model No.: FB 475
Line Capacity: 50 yds. #3 or #4 fly line
Weight: 6½ oz.
Spool Material: Aluminum
Spool Size: 3½"

Model No.: FB 480 GS
Line Capacity: 250 yds. 20 lb. test mono or braided line
Weight: 12 oz.

Spinning Reels

Model No.: GK10
Line Capacity: 200 yds. 8 lb. test mono
Gear Ratio: 3.1 to 1
Weight: 10 oz.
Drag System: Multi-disc
Ball Bearings: Yes

Model No.: GK22
Line Capacity: 180 yds. 6 lb. test mono
Gear Ratio: 4 to 1
Weight: 9 oz.
Drag System: Adjustable
Ball Bearings: Yes

Model No.: GK24
Line Capacity: 200 yds. 10 lb. test mono
Gear Ratio: 4 to 1
Drag System: Adjustable
Ball Bearings: Yes

Model No.: GK26
Line Capacity: 280 yds. 15 lb. test mono
Gear Ratio: 4 to 1
Drag System: Adjustable
Ball Bearings: Yes, carbon steel

Model No.: 300
Line Capacity: 300 yds. 8 lb. test mono
Gear Ratio: 3.7 to 1
Weight: 11.25 oz.
Drag System: Teflon
Ball Bearings: Yes
Spool Material: Aluminum

Model No.: 300C
Line Capacity: 300 yds. 8 lb. test mono
Gear Ratio: 3.7 to 1
Weight: 11.25 oz.
Drag System: Teflon friction disc
Ball Bearings: Yes
Spool Material: Aluminum

Model No.: 300DL
Line Capacity: 300 yds. 8 lb. test mono
Gear Ratio: 3.7 to 1
Weight: 11.25 oz.
Drag System: Teflon friction disc
Ball Bearings: Yes
Spool Material: Aluminum

Model No.: 306
Line Capacity: 400 yds. 10 lb. test mono
Gear Ratio: 3.9 to 1
Weight: 14.4 oz.
Drag System: Fiber friction disc
Ball Bearings: Yes
Spool Material: Aluminum

Model No.: 308
Line Capacity: 300 yds. 4 lb. test mono
Gear Ratio: 4.6 to 1
Weight: 7.4 oz.
Drag System: Fiber friction disc
Ball Bearings: Yes
Spool Material: Aluminum

Model No.: 320
Line Capacity: 225 yds. 6 lb. test mono
Gear Ratio: 3.6 to 1
Weight: 9.9 oz.
Drag System: Fiber friction disc
Ball Bearings: Yes

Model No.: 324
Line Capacity: 225 yds. 6 lb. test mono
Gear Ratio: 3.6 to 1
Weight: 10.4 oz.
Drag System: Fiber friction disc
Ball Bearings: Yes
Spool Material: Aluminum

Model No.: 330
Line Capacity: 200 yds. 4 lb. test mono
Gear Ratio: 3.7 to 1
Weight: 11.3 oz.
Drag System: Teflon and fiber friction disc
Ball Bearings: Yes
Spool Material: Aluminum

Model No.: 406
Line Capacity: 330 yds. 15 lb. royal bonnyl
Gear Ratio: 4.5 to 1
Weight: 19.4 oz.
Drag System: Teflon and fiber friction disc
Ball Bearings: Yes
Spool Material: Aluminum

Model No.: 408
Line Capacity: 300 yds. 4 lb. test mono
Gear Ratio: 5.5 to 1
Weight: 7.8 oz.
Drag System: Teflon friction disc
Ball Bearings: Yes
Spool Material: Aluminum

Model No.: 410
Line Capacity: 300 yds. 8 lb. test mono
Gear Ratio: 4.8 to 1
Weight: 11.5 oz.
Drag System: Teflon friction disc
Ball Bearings: Yes
Spool Material: Aluminum

Model No.: 440
Line Capacity: 200 yds. 4 lb. test mono
Gear Ratio: 4.8 to 1
Weight: 11.8 oz.
Drag System: Teflon friction disc

Ball Bearings: Yes
Spool Material: Aluminum

Spin Casting Reels

Model No.: GK32
Line Capacity: 100 yds. 8 lb. test mono
Gear Ratio: 2¾ to 1
Weight: 8 oz.
Drag System: Dial

Model No.: GK34
Line Capacity: 100 yds. 10 lb. test mono
Gear Ratio: 3½ to 1
Drag System: Star
Ball Bearings: Yes

Bait Casting Reels

Model No.: 6500C
Line Capacity: 275 yds. 15 lb. test
Gear Ratio: 4.7 to 1
Drag System: Adjustable star
Ball Bearings: Yes, stainless steel

Model No.: 1750
Line Capacity: 150 yds. 10 lb. test mono
Gear Ratio: 3.3 to 1
Weight: 6.3 oz.

Model No.: 5000
Line Capacity: 200 yds. 15 lb. royal bonnyl
Gear Ratio: 3.6 to 1
Weight: 8.5 oz.
Drag System: Adjustable star

Model No.: 5000B
Line Capacity: 220 yds. 15 lb. royal bonnyl
Gear Ratio: 3.6 to 1
Weight: 8.5 oz.
Drag System: Star

Model No.: 5000C
Line Capacity: 165 yds. 15 lb. test mono
Gear Ratio: 3.6 to 1
Weight: 10.7 oz.
Drag System: Multi-disc star
Ball Bearings: Yes

Model No.: 5000D
Line Capacity: 100 yds. 20 lb. test mono
Gear Ratio: 3.6 to 1
Weight: 8.5 oz.
Drag System: Adjustable

Model No.: 5001C
Line Capacity: 165 yds. 15 lb. test mono
Gear Ratio: 3.6 to 1
Weight: 10.7 oz.
Drag System: Multi-disc star
Ball Bearings: Yes

Model No.: 5500C
Line Capacity: 225 yds. 10 lb. test mono
Gear Ratio: 4.7 to 1
Weight: 10.3 oz.
Drag System: Adjustable
Ball Bearings: Yes

Model No.: 6000
Line Capacity: 275 yds. 15 lb. royal bonnyl
Gear Ratio: 3.6 to 1
Weight: 9.7 oz.
Drag System: Star

Model No.: 6000C
Line Capacity: 270 yds. 10 lb. test mono
Gear Ratio: 3.6 to 1
Weight: 11.9 oz.
Drag System: Multi-disc star
Ball Bearings: Yes

Model No.: 6500C
Line Capacity: 275 yds. 15 lb. royal bonnyl
Gear Ratio: 4.7 to 1
Weight: 12.5 oz.
Drag System: Adjustable star
Ball Bearings: Yes

Model No.: 7000
Line Capacity: 350 yds. royal bonnyl
Gear Ratio: 4 to 1
Weight. 17.5 oz.
Drag System: Adjustable star
Ball Bearings: Yes
Spool Material: Aluminum

Fly Reels

Model No.: 120
Line Capacity: 165 yds. 6 lb. test mono
Gear Ratio: 3 to 1
Weight: 9 oz.
Drag System: Tamper proof syncro

Model No.: 150
Line Capacity: 150 yds. 10 lb. test mono
Gear Ratio: 3 to 1
Weight: 11 oz.
Drag System: Tamper proof syncro

Model No.: 170
Line Capacity: 150 yds. 10 lb. test mono
Gear Ratio: 3 to 1
Weight: 11 oz.
Drag System: Adjustable star

Model No.: 270
Line Capacity: 150 yds. 10 lb. test mono

Gear Ratio: 3 to 1
Weight: 12 oz.
Drag System: Knurled

Model No.: 290
Line Capacity: 190 yds. 10 lb. test mono
Gear Ratio: 3 to 1
Weight: 13 oz.
Drag System: Knurled

Model No.: 710
Line Capacity: 50 yds. 20 lb. test mono or
 braided
Weight: 9.9 oz.

Model No.: 752
Line Capacity: 100 yds. 15 lb. test mono
Gear Ratio: 1 to 1
Weight: 5.7 oz.
Drag System: Adjustable

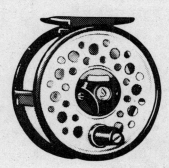

Model No.: 754
Line Capacity: 100 yds. 15 lb. test mono
Gear Ratio: 1 to 1
Weight: 5.7 oz.
Drag System: Adjustable

Model No.: GK42
Weight: 5 oz.
Drag System: Adjustable shoe type

Model No.: GK50
Line Capacity: 35 yds. 6 wt.

Saltwater Reels

Model No.: 302
Line Capacity: 400 yds. 20 lb. royal bonnyl
Gear Ratio: 3.9 to 1
Weight: 20 oz.
Drag System: Pressure washers with
 friction disc
Ball Bearings: Yes
Spool Material: Aluminum

Model No.: 386
Line Capacity: 575 yds. 15 lb. test royal
 bonnyl
Gear Ratio: 3.6 to 1
Weight: 22.8 oz.
Drag System: Ferodo friction disc
Ball Bearings: Yes
Spool Material: Aluminum

Model No.: 402
Line Capacity: 420 yds. 15 lb. test mono
Gear Ratio: 4.5 to 1
Weight: 21.7 oz.

Drag System: Pressure washers with Teflon
Ball Bearings: Yes
Spool Material: Aluminum

Model No.: 440
Line Capacity: 300 yds. 8 lb. test mono
Gear Ratio: 4.8 to 1
Weight: 11.8 oz.
Drag System: Teflon friction disc
Ball Bearings: Yes
Spool Material: Aluminum

Model No.: 486
Line Capacity: 400 yds. 20 lb. royal bonnyl
Gear Ratio: 4.1 to 1
Weight: 24 oz.
Drag System: Ferodo friction disc
Ball Bearings: Yes
Spool Material: Aluminum

Model No.: 488
Line Capacity: 525 yds. 20 lb. royal bonnyl
Gear Ratio: 4.1 to 1
Weight: 26.5 oz.
Drag System: Ferodo friction disc
Ball Bearings: Yes
Spool Material: Aluminum

Model No.: 600A
Line Capacity: 400 yds. 30 lb. test royal
 bonnyl
Gear Ratio: 3 to 1
Weight: 19.7 oz.
Drag System: Star
Spool Material: Metal or plastic

Model No.: 9000
Line Capacity: 300 yds. 20 lb. test mono
Gear Ratio: 4.2 to 1
Weight: 15.4 oz.
Drag System: Adjustable star
Ball Bearings: Yes

Model No.: 10,000C
Line Capacity: 600 yds. 20 lb. test mono
Gear Ratio: 4.2 to 1
Weight: 16.1 oz.
Drag System: Adjustable star
Ball Bearings: Yes

Big Game Reels

Model No.: 10,000C
Line Capacity: 475 yds. 30 lb. test
Gear Ratio: 4.2 to 1
Drag System: Star
Ball Bearings: Yes, stainless steel

Model No.: 622
Line Capacity: 500 yds. 20 lb. mono test
Gear Ratio: 3 to 1
Weight: 20.5 oz.
Drag System: Star
Spool Size: 2⅝" diameter, 1¾" width

Gladding

Spinning Reels

Model No.: 610
Line Capacity: 200 yds. 6 lb. test mono
Drag System: Adjustable disc
Spool Material: Plastic

Model No.: 630
Line Capacity: 190 yds. 8 lb. test mono
Drag System: Adjustable
Spool Material: Plastic

Model No.: 730A Freshwater
Line Capacity: 225 yds. 8 lb. test
Gear Ratio: 3.5 to 1

Model No.: 725A Ultralight
Line Capacity: 200 yds. 4 lb. test
Gear Ratio: 4.2 to 1

Model No.: 750A Heavy Duty
Line Capacity: 250 yds. 15 lb. test
Gear Ratio: 3.5 to 1

Model No.: 760A Saltwater
Line Capacity: 250 yds. 25 lb. test mono
Gear Ratio: 3.7 to 1

Model No.: Classic 925 Ultralight
Line Capacity: 200 yds. 6 lb. test
Gear Ratio: 4.75 to 1

Model No.: Classic 930 Freshwater
Line Capacity: 250 yds. 8 lb. test
Gear Ratio: 3.7 to 1

Model No.: Classic 935 Freshwater Saltwater
Line Capacity: 265 yds. 10 lb. test mono
Gear Ratio: 3.7 to 1

Model No.: Classic 960 Heavy Saltwater
Line Capacity: 250 yds. 20 lb. test
Gear Ratio: 3.5 to 1

Spin Cast Reels

Model No.: 120 Norseman
Line Capacity: 125 yds. 15 lb. test
Gear Ratio: 3.2 to 1
Drag System: Power clutch
Ball Bearings: Yes, bronze

Model No.: Spin Cast 25
Line Capacity: 100 yds. 8 lb. test mono
Drag System: Star

Model No.: Spin Cast 30A
Line Capacity: 100 yds. 8 lb. test mono

Model No.: Spin Cast 40
Line Capacity: 100 yds. 8 lb. test mono

Model No.: Spin Cast 60
Line Capacity: 100 yds. 8 lb. test mono
Drag System: Star

Model No.: Spin Cast 85
Line Capacity: 100 yds. 10 lb. test mono
Gear Ratio: 4 to 1
Drag System: Star

Model No.: Spin Cast 90
Line Capacity: 100 yds. 12 lb. test mono
Gear Ratio: 3.1 to 1
Drag System: Star

Model No.: Spin Cast 95
Line Capacity: 100 yds. 15 lb. test mono
Gear Ratio: 3.1 to 1
Drag System: Multi-disc star

Bait Casting Reels

Model No.: 3 Casting Reel
Line Capacity: 100 yds. 15 lb. test
Gear Ratio: 4 to 1

Model No.: 5 Casting Reel
Line Capacity: 110 yds. 12 lb. test
Gear Ratio: 4 to 1

Fly Reels

Model No.: 1033 Lightweight Gladding-South
 Bend Gear Fly Reel
Line Capacity: 75 yds. HEH; 100 yds. HDF

Model No.: 1044 Regular Gladding-South
 Bend Gear Fly Reel
Line Capacity: 100 yds. HDH; 125 yds. HCF
Gear Ratio: 2.66 to 1

Model No.: 1055 Kingsize Gladding-South
 Bend Gear Fly Reel
Line Capacity: 100 yds. GBC; 125 yds. GAF
Gear Ratio: 2.66 to 1

Model No.: 1122 Economy Finalist
Line Capacity: 35 yds. #5 fly line
Spool Diameter: 2½"

Model No.: 1130 Oreno-Matic
Line Capacity: 25 yds. #6 fly line
Weight: 8.5 oz.

Model No.: 1140 Oreno-Matic
Line Capacity: 35 yds. #6 fly line
Weight: 9.5 oz.

Model No.: 1155 Saltwater Finalist
Line Capacity: 40 yds. 11 Super Aerofloat
 Saltwater Taper backed with 200 yds.
 18 lb. class Trident
Spool Size: 3½" diameter

Model No.: 1180 Flat-Mounting Automatic
Line Capacity: 35 yds. #6 fly line
Weight: 9 oz.

Model No.: 1190 Oreno-Matic
Line Capacity: 35 yds. #6 fly line
Weight: 9.5 oz.

Hardy Bros.

Fly Reels

Model No.: Featherweight
Gear Ratio: 1⅔ to 1
Weight: 3 oz.

Model No.: The Husky
Gear Ratio: 1⅔ to 1
Weight: 7¾ oz.

Model No.: The Princess
Gear Ratio: 1⅔ to 1
Weight: 4¾ oz.

Model No.: Zenith
Gear Ratio: 1⅔ to 1
Weight: 6½ oz.

Model No.: L.R.H. Lightweight
Gear Ratio: 1⅔ to 1
Weight: 2 oz.

James Heddon's Sons

Spinning Reels

Model No.: 212
Line Capacity: 200 yds. 15 lb. test mono
Weight: 15 oz.
Drag System: Multi-disc
Spool Material: Metal

Model No.: 222
Line Capacity: 200 yds. 8 lb. test mono
Weight: 12 oz.
Drag System: Multi-disc
Spool Material: Metal

Model No.: 281
Line Capacity: 100 yds. 6 lb. test mono
Gear Ratio: 4.5 to 1
Drag System: Multi-disc
Ball Bearings: Yes
Spool Material: Metal

Model No.: 282
Line Capacity: 200 yds. 8 lb. test mono
Gear Ratio: 4.5 to 1
Drag System: Multi-disc
Ball Bearings: Yes
Spool Material: Metal

Model No.: 283
Line Capacity: 200 yds. 15 lb. test mono
Gear Ratio: 4.5 to 1
Drag System: Multi-disc
Ball Bearings: Yes
Spool Material: Metal

Model No.: 284
Line Capacity: 200 yds. 20 lb. test mono
Gear Ratio: 4.5 to 1
Drag System: Multi-disc
Ball Bearings: Yes
Spool Material: Metal

Model No.: 266
Line Capacity: 200 yds. 25 lb. test mono
Weight: 18 oz.
Drag System: Multi-disc
Spool Material: Metal

Spin Casting Reels

Model No.: 112
Line Capacity: 100 yds. 6 lb. test mono
Weight: 7 oz.
Drag System: Adjustable drag

Model No.: 152
Line Capacity: 100 yds. 8 lb. test mono
Weight: 10 oz.
Drag System: Star

Model No.: 185
Gear Ratio: 4 to 1
Weight: 11 oz.
Drag System: Star
Ball Bearings: Yes

Saltwater Trolling Reels

Model No.: 409
Line Capacity: 300 yds. 20 lb. test mono
Gear Ratio: 3 to 1
Weight: 20 oz.
Drag System: Star
Spool Material: Metal
Spool Size: 3¹⁄₁₆″ plate diameter, 2⅛″ width

Model No.: 421
Line Capacity: 225 yds. 20 lb. test dacron or mono
Gear Ratio: 3 to 1
Weight: 18 oz.
Drag System: Star
Spool Material: Metal
Spool Size: 3¼″ plate diameter, 2½″ width

Model No.: 422
Line Capacity: 250 yds. 20 lb. dacron
Gear Ratio: 2½ to 1
Weight: 22 oz.
Drag System: Star
Spool Material: Metal
Spool Size: 3¾″ plate diameter, 2½″ width

Model No.: 445
Line Capacity: 300 yds. 20 lb. test
Gear Ratio: 3 to 1
Weight: 20 oz.
Drag System: Star
Spool Material: Metal
Spool Size: 3¹⁄₁₆″ plate diameter, 2⅛″ width

Model No.: 450
Line Capacity: 200 yds. 36 lb. test
Weight: 19 oz.
Drag System: Star
Spool Material: Metal
Spool Size: 2⅝″ plate diameter, 2½″ width

Model No.: 499
Line Capacity: 250 yds. 15 lb. test mono
Gear Ratio: 3 to 1
Weight: 14 oz.
Drag System: Star
Spool Size: 2⅝″ plate diameter, 1¾″ width

Johnson

Spin Casting Reels

Model No.: 088A
Line Capacity: 240 ft. 10 lb. test mono.
    Handles 6 lb. to 12 lb. test
Gear Ratio: 3 to 1
Weight: 8 oz.
Drag System: Star

Model No.: 100B
Line Capacity: 200 ft. 10 lb. test mono.
    Handles 6 lb. to 10 lb. test

Johnson (cont'd.)

Weight: 9 oz.
Drag System: Multiple shoe
Ball Bearings: Yes, bronze

Model No.: 110B
Line Capacity: 410 ft. 10 lb. test mono.
   Handles 8 lb. to 15 lb. test
Weight: 11½ oz.
Drag System: Multiple shoe
Ball Bearings: Yes

Model No.: 125
Line Capacity: 240 ft. 10 lb. test mono.
   Handles 6 lb. to 12 lb. test
Gear Ratio: 3 to 1
Weight: 10 oz.
Drag System: Adjustable audible

Model No.: 130B
Line Capacity: 310 ft. 15 lb. test mono.
   Handles 10 lb. to 20 lb. test
Weight: 15 oz.
Drag System: Automatic fish-tiring drag
Ball Bearings: Yes, bronze

Model No.: 140B
Line Capacity: 200 ft. 10 lb. test mono.
   Handles 6 lb. to 12 lb. test
Gear Ratio: 3 to 1
Weight: 10 oz.
Drag System: Full drag adjustment with
   automatic click

Model No.: 150A
Line Capacity: 250 ft. 12 lb. test mono
Weight: 10½ oz.
Drag System: Automatic fish-tiring

Model No.: 160 (oscillating spool)
Line Capacity: 300 ft. 15 lb. test mono
Weight: 15½ oz.
Drag System: Double
Ball Bearings: Yes, precision retrieve

Model No.: 710B
Line Capacity: 280 ft. 10 lb. test mono.
   Handles 6 lb. to 15 lb. test
Weight: 11 oz.
Drag System: Fish-tiring

Martin

Spinning Reels

Model No.: Ultra Light 104
Line Capacity: 150 to 200 yds. 6 lb. test
Gear Ratio: 5 to 1
Weight: 9 oz.
Drag System: Spring loaded
Ball Bearings: Yes

Model No.: 207A
Line Capacity: 200 yds. 6 lb. test
Weight: 10 oz.
Ball Bearings: Yes

Model No.: 400
Line Capacity: 200 yds. 6 lb. test
Gear Ratio: 3.8 to 1
Weight: 11 oz.
Drag System: Multi-disc
Ball Bearings: Yes

Model No.: 807
Line Capacity: 175 yds. 20 lb. test
Gear Ratio: 4 to 1
Weight: 12 oz.
Drag System: Multi-disc
Ball Bearings: Yes

Model No.: 804SRM
Line Capacity: 300 yds. 8 lb. test
Gear Ratio: 4.75 to 1
Weight: 11 oz.
Ball Bearings: Yes

Model No.: 904
Line Capacity: 250 yds. 20 lb. test
Weight: 28 oz.
Drag System: Multi-disc
Ball Bearings: Yes

Model No.: 902
Line Capacity: 200 yds. 20 lb. test
Weight: 26 oz.
Drag System: Multi-disc
Ball Bearings: Yes

Model No.: 905
Line Capacity: 395 yds. 20 lb. test
Drag System: Multi-disc
Ball Bearings: Yes
Spool Diameter: 3½"

Spin Casting Reels

Model No. 220
Line Capacity: 80 yds. 6 lb. test mono
Drag System: Star

Model No.: 500
Line Capacity: 100 yds. 8 lb. test mono
Weight: 9 oz.
Drag System: Star

Model No.: 500R. Same as Model 500 except:
   in black and red two tone
Line Capacity: 85 yds. 10 lb. test mono
Weight: 9 oz.
Drag System: Star

Model No.: 700
Line Capacity: 100 yds. 8 lb. Martin "Tuffy"
   mono
Weight: 9 oz.
Drag System: Star

Fly Reels

Model No.: 6
Line Capacity: 30 yds. DT6F
Weight: 9¼ oz.

Model No.: 8
Line Capacity: 300 yds. DT6F

Model No.: 38G
Line Capacity: 30 yds. DT6F
Weight: 8¾ oz.

Model No.: 39G
Line Capacity: 30 yds. DT8F or WF8F
Weight: 9¼ oz.

Model No. 47
Line Capacity: Designed for 8 lb. test mono
Weight: 8½ oz.

Model No.: 48
Line Capacity: 30 yds. DT6F
Weight: 9 oz.

Model No.: Fly-Wate 49
Line Capacity: 30 yds. DT8F; 35 yds. WF8F
Weight: 9¼ oz.

Model No.: 60
Line Capacity: 30 yds. DT6F
Weight: 3½ oz.

Model No.: 61
Line Capacity: 35 yds. WF8F
Weight: 3¾ oz.

Model No.: 62
Line Capacity: 30 yds. DT6F
Weight: 3½ oz.

Model No.: 63
Line Capacity: 35 yds. WF8F
Weight: 3¾ oz.

Model No.: 64
Line Capacity: 35 yds. WF9F plus 150 yds. 18 lb. test dacron backing
Weight: 6¼ oz.
Drag System: Adjustable

Model No.: 65
Line Capacity: 35 yds. WF9F plus 130 yds. 18 lb. test braided dacron backing
Weight: 5 oz.

Model No.: 66
Line Capacity: 35 yds. WF9F plus 130 yds. 18 lb. test dacron backing
Weight: 5½ oz.

Model No.: Martin Model 68
Line Capacity: 35 yds. WF9F plus 150 yds. 18 lb. test
Gear Ratio: 3 to 1
Weight: 7 oz.

Model No.: 81
Line Capacity: 30 yds. DT8F; 35 yds. WF8F
Weight: 9 oz.

Model No.: 83
Line Capacity: 30 yds. DT8F; 35 yds. WF8F
Weight: 9¼ oz.

Model No.: 94
Line Capacity: 30 yds. DT6F
Weight: 8¾ oz.

Trolling Reels

Model No.: Sovereign 23
Line Capacity: 100 yds. 14 lb. test mono plus 230 yds. 18 lb. test dacron backing; 30 yds. DT6F
Weight: 10 oz.

Model No.: Trol-O-Matic 35A
Line Capacity: 35 yds. WF9F plus 150 yds. 18 lb. test backing
Weight: 15¾ oz.

Shakespeare

Spinning Reels

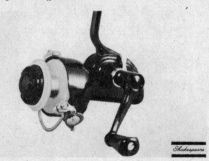

Model No.: 2052NL
Line Capacity: 350 yds. 2 lb. test mono; 220 yds. 4 lb. test mono; 155 yds. 6 lb test mono; 100 yds. 8 lb. test mono; 90 yds. 10 lb. test mono
Gear Ratio: 4.7 to 1
Weight: 9 oz.
Ball Bearings: Yes
Spool Material: Aluminum

Model No.: 2062NL
Line Capacity: 360 yds. 6 lb. test mono; 235 yds. 8 lb. test mono; 200 yds. 10 lb. test mono
Gear Ratio: 3.7 to 1

Weight: 10.7 oz.
Spool Material: Aluminum

Model No.: 2400
Line Capacity: 180 yds. 6 lb. test
Gear Ratio: 5.2 to 1

Model No.: 2410
Line Capacity: 270 yds. 8 lb. test mono
Gear Ratio: 4.5 to 1

Model No.: 2430
Line Capacity: 300 yds. 10 lb. test mono
Gear Ratio: 4.2 to 1

Model No.: 2450
Line Capacity: 400 yds. 12 lb. test mono
Gear Ratio: 4.1 to 1

Model No.: 2500
Line Capacity: 170 yds. 6 lb. test mono
Gear Ratio: 4.3 to 1

Model No.: 2510
Line Capacity: 160 yds. 10 lb. test mono
Gear Ratio: 4 to 1

Spin Casting Reels

Model No.: 1756
Line Capacity: 220 yds. 6 lb test mono; 145 yds. 8 lb. test mono; 120 yds. 10 lb. test mono
Gear Ratio: 4 to 1
Weight: 9 oz.
Spool Size: 2" diameter

Model No.: 1810
Line Capacity: 280 yds. 6 lb. test mono; 190

yds. 8 lb. test mono; 160 yds. 10 lb. test
mono
Gear Ratio: 4 to 1
Weight: 11.8 oz.
Spool Size: 2" diameter

Model No.: 2200LH
Line Capacity: 245 yds. 4 lb. test mono;
170 yds. 6 lb. test mono; 115 yds. 8 lb.
test mono; 100 yds. 10 lb. test mono
Gear Ratio: 5 to 1
Weight: 7 oz.
Spool Material: Die-cast aluminum

Model No.: 2210LH
Line Capacity: 390 yds. 4 lb. test mono;
270 yds. 6 lb. test mono; 180 yds. 8 lb.
test mono; 150 yds. 10 lb. test mono
Gear Ratio: 3.75 to 1
Weight: 11 oz.
Spool Material: Die-cast aluminum

Model No.: 7503
Line Capacity: 140 yds. 6 lb. test mono; 90
yds. 8 lb. test mono; 75 yds. 10 lb. test
mono
Gear Ratio: 4 to 1
Weight: 11.2 oz.
Spool Size: 1⅞" diameter

Model No.: 7504
Line Capacity: 170 yds. 12 lb. test mono;
125 yds. 15 lb. test mono; 85 yds. 20 lb.
test mono
Gear Ratio: 4 to 1
Weight: 12.5 oz.
Spool Size: 2" diameter

Fly Reels

Model No.: 1822 O.K. Automatic
Line Capacity: 30 yds. L8F
Weight: 8.5 oz.
Spool Size: 2⅞" diameter, ⅞" width

Model No.: 1824
Line Capacity: 34 yds. L6F

Weight: 8.9 oz.
Spool Size: 2⅞" diameter, ⅞" width

Model No.: 1826
Line Capacity: 34 yds. L6F
Weight: 9.4 oz.
Spool Size: 2⅞" diameter, ⅞" width

Model No.: 1827
Line Capacity: 34 yds. L6F
Weight: 9.4 oz.
Spool Size: 2⅞" diameter, ⅞" width

Model No.: 1836
Line Capacity: 34 yds. L6F
Weight: 9.3 oz.
Spool Size: 2⅞" diameter, ⅞" width

Model No.: 7594 Purist
Line Capacity: Up to 7 wt. level
Gear Ratio: 1 to 1
Weight: 4⅞ oz.
Drag System: 1 way drag can be set for
right or left hand use
Spool Size: 2¹¹⁄₁₆" diameter, ¹³⁄₁₆" width

Model No.: 7595
Line Capacity: Up to 8 wt. level
Gear Ratio: 1 to 1
Weight: 5⅝ oz.
Spool Size: 2¹¹⁄₁₆" diameter, 1" width

Model No.: 7596
Line Capacity: Up to 11 wt. level
Gear Ratio: 1 to 1
Weight: 5⅝ oz.
Drag System: 1 way drag can be set for
right or left hand use
Spool Size: 3¹⁄₁₆" diameter, ¹³⁄₁₆" width

Model No.: 7597
Line Capacity: Up to 12 wt. level

Gear Ratio: 1 to 1
Weight: 6⅜ oz.
Spool Material: Aluminum with Purist gray
epoxy enamel
Spool Size: 3¹⁄₁₆" diameter, 1" width

Level Wind Reels

Model No.: 599
Line Capacity: 125 yds. 12½ lb. braided
nylon; 100 yds. 15 lb. braided nylon
Weight: 3.9 oz.
Spool Size: 1⅜" diameter

Model No.: 1924MS Direct Drive Reel
Line Capacity: 100 yds. 15 lb. braided nylon
without arbor
Weight: 9.0 oz.
Ball Bearings: Yes
Spool Size: 1½" diameter

Model No.: 1950 Direct Drive Level Wind
Line Capacity: 50 yds. 15 lb. braided nylon
with arbor; 100 yds. 15 lb. braided nylon
without arbor
Weight: 8.7 oz.
Spool Size: 1½" diameter

Model No.: 1973A Direct Drive Sportcast
Line Capacity: 12½ lb. braided nylon with
arbor; 12½ lb. braided nylon without
arbor; 15 lb. test mono
Weight: 5.5 oz.
Ball Bearings: Yes, stainless steel
Spool Size: 1½" diameter

Model No.: 1960 Free Spool Service Reel
Line Capacity: 400 yds. 20 lb. test mono;
325 yds. 30 lb. test mono
Weight: 1 lb. 4 oz.
Drag System: Adjustable, positive
non-reverse
Spool Material: Glass-filled ABS Cycolac
Spool Size: 2⅛" diameter

Model No.: 1961 Free Spool Salt Water
Service Reel
Line Capacity: 400 yds. 20 lb. test mono;
325 yds. 30 lb. test mono
Weight: 1 lb. 1 oz.
Spool Material: Glass filled ABS Cycolac
Spool Size: 2⅛" diameter

Spinning Reels

Model No.: 8000
Line Capacity: 150 yds. 4 lb. test mono
Gear Ratio: 4.8 to 1
Weight: 8 oz.
Ball Bearings: Yes

Model No.: SC-2
Line Capacity: 6 lb. to 12 lb. test
Gear Ratio: 3 to 1
Drag System: Adjustable

Model No.: SL110
Line Capacity: 150 yds. 4 lb. test mono
Gear Ratio: 4.8 to 1
Weight: 8 oz.
Drag System: Multi-disc Teflon
Ball Bearings: Yes

Model No.: SL110A
Line Capacity: 200 yds. 6 lb. test
Gear Ratio: 4 to 1
Weight: 10 oz.
Drag System: Multi-disc Teflon
Ball Bearings: Yes

Model No.: SL111
Line Capacity: 200 yds. 10 lb. test mono
Gear Ratio: 4 to 1
Weight: 12 oz.
Drag System: Multi-disc Teflon
Ball Bearings: Yes

Model No.: SL113
Line Capacity: 225 yds. 20 lb. test mono
Gear Ratio: 3.6 to 1
Weight: 17 oz.
Drag System: Multi-disc Teflon
Ball Bearings: Yes

Model No.: SL114
Line Capacity: 250 yds. 30 lb. test mono
Gear Ratio: 4 to 1
Weight: 28 oz.

Drag System: Multi-disc Teflon
Ball Bearings: Yes

Model No.: FS850
Line Capacity: 200 yds. 4 lb. mono
Gear Ratio: 3.3 to 1
Weight: 6 oz.

Model No.: FS860
Line Capacity: 200 yds. 6 lb. test mono
Weight: 7 oz.

Model No.: FS870
Line Capacity: 200 yds. 6 lb. mono
Gear Ratio: 3.48 to 1
Weight: 10 oz.

Model No.: FS880
Line Capacity: 200 yds. 8 lb. test mono
Gear Ratio: 3.5 to 1
Weight: 10 oz.
Drag System: Multi-disc
Ball Bearings: Yes

Model No.: FS890
Line Capacity: 300 yds. 20 lb. mono
Gear Ratio: 3.5 to 1
Weight: 12 oz.

Spin Casting Reels

Model No.: RF70
Line Capacity: 90 yds. 8 lb. test mono
Weight: 7 oz.

Model No.: RF72
Line Capacity: 90 yds. 10 lb. test mono
Weight: 10 oz.

Model No.: RF76
Line Capacity: 180' 10 lb. test mono.
   Handles 6 lb. to 12 lb. test
Gear Ratio: 3 to 1
Drag System: Adjustable star

Model No.: SC1
Line Capacity: 240' 10 lb. test mono.
   Handles 6 lb. to 12 lb. test
Gear Ratio: 3 to 1
Drag System: Star

Model No.: SC2
Line Capacity: 200' 10 lb. test. Handles
   6 lb. to 12 lb. test
Gear Ratio: 3 to 1
Drag System: Audible adjustable

Model No.: SC3 Mustang
Line Capacity: 410' 10 lb. test deluxe mono;
   570' 8 lb. test; 410' 10 lb. test; 300' 12 lb.
   test; 260' 15 lb. test

Model No.: 37
Line Capacity: 80 yds. 6 lb. test mono
Gear Ratio: 3 to 1
Drag System: Star

Model No.: 212
Line Capacity: 90 yds. 8 lb. test mono
Gear Ratio: 3 to 1
Weight: 6.7 oz.
Drag System: Long range pressure-type

Model No.: 238
Line Capacity: 90 yds. 8 lb. test
Gear Ratio: 3 to 1
Weight: 6.7 oz.
Drag System: Star

Model No.: 248
Line Capacity: 110 yds. 10 lb. test
Gear Ratio: 3 to 1
Weight: 8.3 oz.
Drag System: Star

Model No.: 252
Line Capacity: 110 yds. 10 lb. test mono
Gear Ratio: 3 to 1
Weight: 10 oz.
Drag System: Pressure-type

Model No.: 262
Line Capacity: 110 yds. 10 lb. mono
Gear Ratio: 3 to 1
Weight: 10 oz.
Drag System: Pressure-type

Model No.: 268
Line Capacity: 100 yds. 10 lb. test
Gear Ratio: 3.5 to 1
Weight: 12.5 oz.

Bait Casting Reels

Model No.: 33
Line Capacity: 100 yds. 15 lb. braided line

Weight: 4 oz.
Drag System: Fingertip

Model No.: 44A
Line Capacity: 100 yds. 15 lb. test braided line
Weight: 6 oz.
Spool Material: Metal

Model No.: 62
Line Capacity: 50 yds. 15 lb. test
Gear Ratio: 4 to 1
Weight: 5.5 oz.

Fly Reels

Model No.: 25
Line Capacity: 30 yds. HCH taper; 25 yds. "C" level
Weight: 4½ oz.
Drag System: 2 position adjustable

Model No.: 29
Line Capacity: 40 yds. "C" level line
Weight: 9½ oz.

Model No.: 47
Line Capacity: Up to and including 11 wt.
Weight: 10 oz.
Drag System: Adjustable

Trolling Reels

Model No.: 1000
Line Capacity: 320 yds. 12 lb. test
Gear Ratio: 3 to 1
Weight: 14.1 oz.
Drag System: Star
Spool Size: 1⁴⁵⁄₆₄"

Model No.: 2000
Line Capacity: 270 yds. 25 lb. test
Weight: 15.2 oz.

Model No.: 3000
Line Capacity: 300 yds. 30 lb. test
Gear Ratio: 3 to 1
Weight: 19.5 oz.
Spool Size: 2³¹⁄₆₄"

Model No.: 5000
Line Capacity: 250 yds. 30 lb. test mono
Gear Ratio: 2.3 to 1
Weight: 17 oz.
Drag System: Star
Spool Material: Metal

#6000 TROLLING REEL

Model No.: 6000
Line Capacity: 350 yds. 30 lb. test mono
Gear Ratio: 2.4 to 1
Weight: 20 oz.
Drag System: Multi-disc star

#7000 TROLLING REEL

Model No.: 7000
Line Capacity: 300 yds. 35 lb. test
Gear Ratio: 2.4 to 1
Weight: 29.6 oz.
Spool Size: 2³¹⁄₆₄"

True Temper

Spinning Reels

Model No.: 507
Line Capacity: 200 yds. 8 lb. test mono
Gear Ratio: 3.5 to 1
Weight: 10 oz.
Drag System: Multiple
Ball Bearings: Yes
Spool Material: Aluminum

Model No.: 527
Line Capacity: 200 yds. 10 lb. test mono
Gear Ratio: 3.7 to 1
Weight: 12 oz.
Drag System: Multiple
Ball Bearings: Yes
Spool Material: Aluminum

Model No.: 537
Line Capacity: 200 yds. 15 lb. test mono
Gear Ratio: 3.87 to 1
Weight: 17 oz.
Drag System: Multiple
Ball Bearings: Yes
Spool Material: Aluminum

Model No.: 707
Line Capacity: 200 yds. 6 lb. test mono
Gear Ratio: 4.4 to 1
Weight: 7¾ oz.
Ball Bearings: Yes

Model No.: 727
Line Capacity: 200 yds. 10 lb. test mono
Gear Ratio: 4.1 to 1
Weight: 11½ oz.
Drag System: Adjustable
Ball Bearings: Yes
Spool Material: Aluminum

Model No.: 737
Line Capacity: 200 yds. 15 lb. test mono
Gear Ratio: 4.1 to 1
Weight: 13½ oz.
Ball Bearings: Yes

Model No.: 747
Line Capacity: 300 yds. 20 lb. test mono
Gear Ratio: 4.2 to 1
Weight: 21 oz.
Ball Bearings: Yes

Spin Casting Reels

Model No.: 327
Line Capacity: 100 yds. 10 lb. test mono
Gear Ratio: 3.2 to 1
Weight: 9½ oz.

Drag System: Wheel type
Spoon Material: Metal

Model No.: 337
Line Capacity: 100 yds. 15 lb. test mono
Gear Ratio: 3.5 to 1
Weight: 13 oz.
Drag System: Star
Ball Bearings: Yes

Fin-Nor

Spinning Reels

Model No.: Fin-Nor #3
Line Capacity: 300 yds. 8 lb. test; 225 yds. 10 lb. test

Model No.: Fin-Nor #4
Line Capacity: 400 yds. 15 lb. test; 300 yds. 8 lb. test

Fly Reels

Model No.: 1 "The Trout"
Line Capacity: 30 yds. #6 fly line; 150 yds. 12 lb. test

Model No.: 2 "The Salmon"
Line Capacity: 40 yds. #9 fly test; 200 yds. 15 lb. test

Model No.: 3 "The Tarpon"
Line Capacity: 40 yds. #10 fly line; 250 yds. 20 lb. test backing

Trolling Reels

Model No.: Big Game 12-20 lb. class
Line Capacity: 1,200 yds. 12 lb. test; 850 yds. 20 lb. test
Gear Ratio: 4 to 1
Size: 2½/0

Model No.: Big Game 30 lb. class
Gear Ratio: 4 to 1
Size: 4/0

Model No.: Big Game
Line Capacity: 650 yds. 50 lb. test
Gear Ratio: 3 to 1
Spool Size: 6/0

Model No. Big Game 50 lb. class
Line Capacity: 1,000 yds. 15 lb. test
Gear Ratio: 3 to 1
Size: 7½/0

Model No.: Big Game 80 lb. class reel
Line Capacity: 800 yds.
Gear Ratio: 2¾ to 1
Size: 9/0

Model No.: Big Game 50 lb. class
Line Capacity: 850 yds. 130 lb. test
Gear Ratio: 1 to 1, 2 to 1, 3 to 1
Size: 12/0

Model No.: Golden Regal 20
Line Capacity: 1,000 yds. 12 lb. test; 800 yds. 20 lb. test

Model No.: Golden Regal 30
Line Capacity: 800 yds. 30 lb. test

Model No.: Golden Regal 50
Line Capacity: 600 yds. 50 lb. test

Zebco

Spinning Reels

Model No.: Cardinal 3
Line Capacity: 178 yds. 4 lb. test

Gear Ratio: 5 to 1
Drag System: Multi-disc
Ball Bearings: Yes

Model No.: Cardinal 6
Line Capacity: 180 yds. 17 lb. test
Drag System: Multi-disc
Ball Bearings: Yes

Model No.: Cardinal 4
Line Capacity: 200 yds. 8 lb. test
Gear Ratio: 5 to 1
Drag System: Multi-disc
Ball Bearings: Yes

Model No.: Cardinal 7
Line Capacity: 180 yds. 20 lb. test
Drag System: Multi-disc
Ball Bearings: Yes

Model No.: XBL39
Line Capacity: 280 yds. 8 lb. test mono
Gear Ratio: 3.4 to 1
Drag System: Disc
Ball Bearings: Yes
Spool Material: Aluminum

Spin Casting Reels

Model No.: 700 "Hoss"
Line Capacity: 198' 25 lb. Dupont Stren mono

Specifications: Hooks and Lures

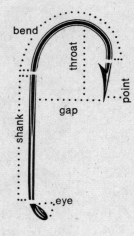

In the illustration at the left, the various parts of a fish hook are shown together with their names. The two important dimensions of the hook are made clear: its gap and its throat. The hook shown here is a Mustad-Viking hook. Note the width of the gap, the clearance between point and shank, and the depth of the throat of the hook. These generous dimensions make for a bigger bite, for deeper penetration of the point, and for better holding power. The weight of the fish is carried high up on the centre of the bend.

HOOK TERMINOLOGY

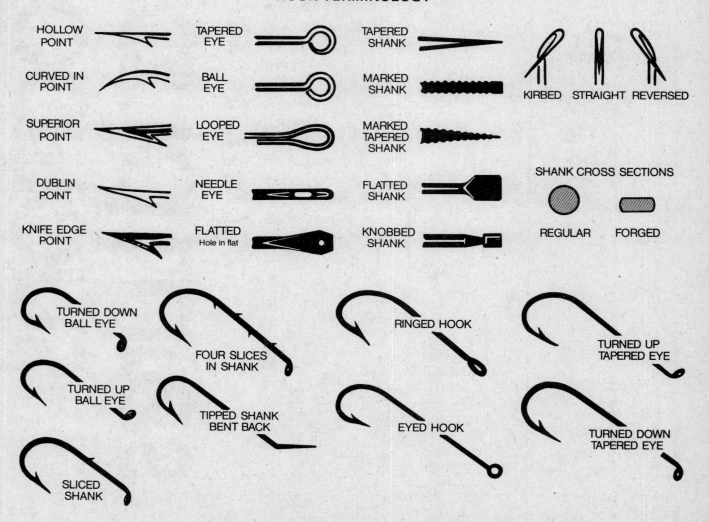

Lures

Fred Arbogast

Name: Jig Hoods
Type: Jig
Color(s): 5 assorted
Length(s): Not specified
Weight(s): ¼ oz.; ⅜ oz.; ½ oz.
Material: Plastic; lead

Name: Poly-Demon Lures
Type: Jig
Color(s): 5 assorted
Weight(s): 1/16 oz.; ⅛ oz.
Material: Lead; polyvinyl

Name: Pug-Nose
Type: Pug
Color(s): 18 assorted
Length(s): 3¼"
Weight(s): ⅝ oz.

Name: Hammerhead
Type: Plug
Color(s): 7 assorted
Length(s): 5½"; 7½"
Weight(s): 1 oz.; 2½ oz.

Name: Triton
Type: Plug
Color(s): 6 assorted
Weight(s): ¾ oz.; 1 oz.; 2 oz.

Name: Jitterbug
Type: Plug
Color(s): 16 assorted
Length(s): 1¼"; 2"; 2½"; 3"
Weight(s): ⅛ oz.; ¼ oz.; ⅜ oz.; ⅝ oz.

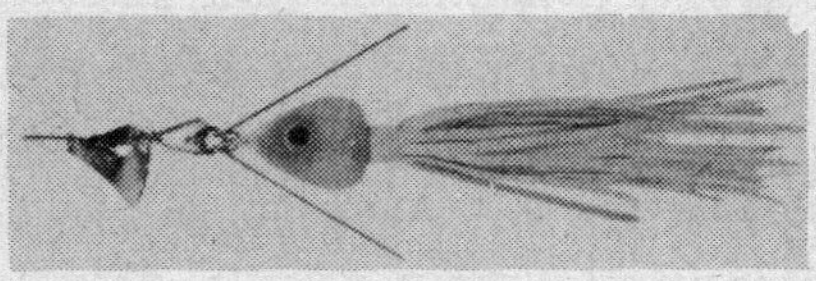

Name: Tournament Hawaiian Wiggler
Type: Spinner
Color(s): Assorted
Weight(s): ⅝ oz.

Name: Mini Twister Spin
Type: Spinner bait
Color(s): 8 assorted
Weight(s): ¼ oz.; ⅛ oz.; 1/32 oz.

Name: Leadbelly
Type: Spoon
Color(s): 6 assorted
Weight(s): ⅝ oz.; ⅜ oz.; ⅛ oz.

Name: K-B 3 Dimensional Spoon
Type: Spoon
Color(s): Nickel; gold; copper; coho blue
Length(s): 3½"; 4½"
Weight(s): 1 oz.; 1¾ oz.

Name: The Doctor Spoon
Type: Spoon

Color(s): 5 assorted
Length(s): 4¼"; 3¾"
Weight(s): 1³⁄₁₆ oz.; ⅝ oz.
Material: Solid brass

Name: Flash Eye
Type: Spoon
Length(s): 2"; 2¾"; 3⅜"; 3"
Weight(s): ¼ oz.; 9/16 oz.; ¾ oz.

Name: Hi-tail Worms
Type: Worm
Color(s): 8 assorted
Length(s): 6"; 7½"; 9"

Jim Bagley

Name: Hustle Bug
Type: Jig
Color(s): 8 assorted
Weight(s): 1/16 oz.; ⅛ oz.
Material: Plastic

Name: Regular Salty Dog
Type: Jig
Color(s): Assorted
Weight(s): ¼ oz.
Material: Lead, plastic

Name: Salty Dog Shrimp
Type: Jig
Color(s): Assorted
Weight(s): 5/16 oz.; 1 oz.; 2 oz.
Material: Plastic

Name: Salty Dog Spoon
Type: Jig
Color(s): 5 assorted
Weight(s): 1 oz.; 2 oz.
Material: Lead body

Name: Bug Eye Shrimp
Type: Jig
Color(s): 8 assorted
Weight(s): 1 oz.; 2 oz.; 3 oz.

Name: Balsa Bang-O-Lure
Type: Plug
Color(s): 3
Length(s): 4¼"; 5¼"
Material: Balsa wood

Name: Dub'L-07 Fish Agent
Type: Plug
Color(s): 5
Length(s): 3½"; 5½"
Material: Balsa wood

Name: Switch Blade
Type: Spinner bait
Color(s): 7
Weight(s): ¼ oz.; ½ oz.

Name: Spinner Bug
Type: Spinner bait
Color(s): 7
Weight(s): ¼ oz.; ½ oz.

Name: Purty Bug
Type: Spinner bait
Color(s): Assorted
Weight(s): ⅛ oz.; ¼ oz.
Material: Plastic tail

Name: Submarine Shad
Type: Spinner bait
Color(s): 6 assorted

Weight(s): ⅛ oz.; ¼ oz.; ½ oz.; ¾ oz.

Name: Hardhead Baby Fly Worms
Type: Worms rigged, non weedless
Color(s): 5
Length(s): 2½"; 4½"

Name: Medium 6" Hardhead Worms
Type: Worm, rigged, weedless
Color(s): Assorted
Length(s): 6"
Material: Gold plated nonweedless hooks

Name: King Size 8" Hardhead Worms
Type: Worm
Color(s): 6 assorted
Length(s): 8"
Material: 2 gold plated weedless hooks

Name: Ol' Monster 9" Hardhead Worms
Type: Worm, rigged, weedless
Color(s): Assorted
Length(s): 9"

Name: King Size 8" Eager Beaver
Type: Worms
Color(s): Black; purple; blue
Length(s): 8"

Name: 16" Awful Worms
Type: Worm
Color(s): 3 black; purple; blue
Length(s): 16"

Name: Spring Tail Worms
Type: Worm
Color(s): 7 assorted
Material: Plastic

Name: Spring Tail 9" Mag-num Worms
Type: Worm
Color(s): Assorted
Length(s): 9"
Material: Plastic

Name: Flat Tail Molly
Type: Worm, rigged, weedless
Color(s): Assorted
Length(s): 8"

Name: Salt Water Eel
Type: Worm
Color(s): 6 assorted
Length(s): 10"
Material: Stainless steel chain, chrome-plated head

Bass Buster

Name: Worm Jig
Type: Jig
Color(s): Black; blue; purple; red
Length(s): 2"; 4"; 6"
Weight(s): ¼ oz.; ⅜ oz.
Material: Plastic

Name: Beetle
Type: Jig
Color(s): Assorted
Weight(s): ¼ oz.; 3/16 oz.; ⅛ oz.; 1/16 oz.; 1/32 oz.; 1/64 oz.
Material: Plastic

Name: Mini Twister
Type: Jig
Color(s): 8 assorted

Weight(s): ¼ oz.; ⅛ oz.; ¹⁄₃₂ oz.

Name: Maribou Jigs
Type: Jig
Color(s): 9 assorted
Weight(s): ¹⁄₆₄ oz.; ¹⁄₃₂ oz.; ¹⁄₁₆ oz.; ⅛ oz.;
  ¼ oz.; ⅜ oz.; ½ oz.; ⅝ oz.
Material: Gold plated hook, maribou body

Name: Bucktail Jig
Type: Jig
Color(s): 8 assorted
Weight(s): ⅛ oz.; ¼ oz.; ⅜ oz.; ½ oz.
Material: Gold plated hook, fiber guard

Name: Beetle
Type: Jig
Color(s): 19 assorted
Weight(s): ¼ oz.; ³⁄₁₆ oz.; ⅛ oz.; ¹⁄₁₆ oz.;
  ¹⁄₃₂ oz.; ¹⁄₆₄ oz.
Material: Gold plated hook, plastic body

Name: Crappie Buster Jigs
Type: Jig
Color(s): Assorted
Weight(s): ⅛ oz.; ¹⁄₁₆ oz.; ¹⁄₃₂ oz.
Material: Gold plated hook, chenille body

Name: Mini Twister Spin
Type: Spinner bait
Color(s): 8 assorted
Weight(s): ¼ oz.; ⅛ oz.; ¹⁄₃₂ oz.

Name: Tandem Spin
Type: 2 Blade spinner bait
Color(s): 11 assorted
Weight(s): ¼ oz.; ⅜ oz.; ½ oz.; ⅝ oz.
Material: Copper blades, nickel plated hook,
  vinyl skirt

Name: Scorpion
Type: Spinner bait
Color(s): 8 assorted
Weight(s): ½ oz.; ⅜ oz.; ¼ oz.; ⅛ oz.
Material: Chrome or copper spinner, nickel
  plated hook and plastic skirt

Name: Beetle spin
Type: Spinner bait
Color(s): 20 assorted
Weight(s): ¼ oz.; ⅛ oz.; ¹⁄₃₂ oz.; ³⁄₁₆ oz.
Material: Gold plated hook, chrome blade,
  plastic blade

Name: Tarantula
Type: Spinner bait
Color(s): Assorted
Weight(s): ½ oz.; ⅜ oz.; ¼ oz.
Material: Nickel plated hook, chrome blade

Name: Slinky Worm
Type: Worm
Color(s): Assorted
Length(s): 4"; 6"; 7½"; 9"
Material: Plastic

Bead

Name: Mackerel Jigs
Type: Jig
Color(s): Metal finish
Length(s): 2¼"; 2"; 1¾"
Weight(s): ¾ oz.; ½ oz.; ⅜ oz.
Material: Metal finish

Name: Long Slim
Type: Jig
Color(s): Nickel finish
Weight(s): 3 oz.
Material: Nickel finish

Name: Diamond Squids
Type: Jig
Color(s): Polished nickel finish
Length(s): 2"; 3"; 4"; 5"
Weight(s): 1 oz.; 3 oz.; 4¾ oz.; 8 oz.
Material: Brass

Name: Surfer
Type: Jig
Weight(s): 2 oz.

Name: Keel & Diamond Spinners
Type: Spinner
Color(s): Silver; gold
Weight(s): ⅛ oz.; ¼ oz.

Name: Wemac-Feathered Spoon
Type: Spoon
Weight(s): ⅜ oz.

Blakemore

Name: Crappie's Delight
Type: Jig
Color(s): Assorted
Weight(s): ¹⁄₆₄ oz.; ¹⁄₃₂ oz.; ¹⁄₁₆ oz.
Material: Marabou skirt

Name: Road Runner
Type: Jig
Color(s): Assorted
Weight(s): ¹⁄₁₆ oz.; ⅛ oz.; ¼ oz.

Name: Trout & Panfish Worm
Type: Worm
Color(s): Assorted
Length(s): 2"
Material: Plastic

Name: Cheese Treated Worm
Type: Worm
Color(s): White; red
Length(s): 3¼"
Material: Plastic

Name: Spinner Bait
Type: Single spin
Color(s): Assorted
Weight(s): ¼ oz.; ⅜ oz.
Material: Nickel or copper blade

Name: Single-spin
Type: Spinner bait
Color(s): Fluorescent, standard
Weight(s): ¼ oz.; ⅜ oz.
Material: Nickel or copper blades

Name: Split Tail Spin
Type: Spinner bait
Color(s): Assorted
Weight(s): ¹⁄₁₆ oz.; ⅛ oz.

Name: Twister
Type: Spinner bait
Color(s): Assorted
Weight(s): ¾ oz.

Bomber

Name: Jig
Type: Jig
Color(s): Assorted
Length(s): 2¼"; 3"; 3¼"; 3½"
Weight(s): ¼ oz.; ½ oz.; ¾ oz.; 1 oz.

Name: Speed Shad
Type: Plug
Color(s): 20 assorted
Length(s): 3½"; 4½"; 5½"
Weight(s): ¼ oz.; ½ oz.; ⅝ oz.

Name: Pinfish
Type: Plug
Color(s): Assorted
Length(s): 2"; 2½"; 3"
Weight(s): ¼ oz.; ⅜ oz.; ½ oz.

Name: Waterdog
Type: Plug
Color(s): 20 assorted
Length(s): 3½"; 4½"; 5½"
Weight(s): ¼ oz.; ½ oz.; ⅝ oz.

Name: The Bomber, Baby, Midget, Small,
  Medium, Large
Type: Plug
Color(s): Assorted
Length(s): 2½"; 2¾"; 3¼"; 3¾"; 4¼"
Weights: ¼ oz.; ⅜ oz.; ½ oz.; ⅝ oz.; ¾ oz.

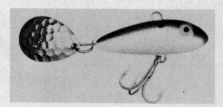

Name: Spinstick
Type: Spinner
Color(s): Assorted
Length(s): 2½"; 3½"
Weight(s): ¼ oz.; ⅜ oz.

Name: Bushwacker
Type: Spinner bait
Color(s): Assorted
Weight(s): ¼ oz.; ½ oz.

Name: Slab Spoon
Type: Spoon
Color(s): Assorted
Length(s): 1½"; 1¾"; 2⅛"
Weight(s): ⅝ oz.; ⅞ oz.; 1¼ oz.

Burke

Name: Wig Wag Worm
Type: Worm
Color(s): Assorted
Length(s): 4"; 7"

Creek Chub

Name: Creek Chub Ding Bat
Type: Jig
Color(s): Assorted
Length(s): 2"
Weight(s): ¼ oz.
Material: Plastic

Name: Striper Strike
Type: Plug
Color(s): Assorted
Weight(s): ½ oz.; ¾ oz.; 1 oz.; 1½ oz.
Material: Plastic

Name: Mouse
Type: Plug
Color(s): Assorted
Weight(s): ¼ oz.
Material: Plastic

Name: Darter
Type: Plug
Color(s): Assorted
Length(s): 1⅝"; 2¼"; 3"; 3¾"
Weight(s): ⅛ oz.; ¼ oz.; ⅜ oz.; ½ oz.; ⅝ oz.
Material: Wood; plastic

Name: Plunker
Type: Plug
Color(s): Assorted
Length(s): 1⅝"; 2"; 2½"
Weight(s): ⅛ oz.; ¼ oz.; ⅜ oz.; ½ oz.
Material: Wood; plastic

Name: Nikie
Type: Plug
Color(s): Assorted
Weight(s): ¼ oz.; ⅛ oz.
Material: Plastic

Name: Wiggle Diver
Type: Plug
Color(s): Assorted
Weight(s): 1½ oz.
Material: Plastic

Name: Creek Chub Mouse
Type: Plug
Color(s): Assorted
Length(s): 2¼"; 2½"; 2¾"
Weight(s): ¼ oz.; ⅜ oz.; ½ oz.
Material: Plastic

Name: Creek Chub Striper Strike
Type: Plug
Color(s): Amber
Length(s): 2½"; 3"; 4½"; 5¼"
Weight(s): ½ oz.; ¾ oz.; 1 oz.; 1½ oz.; 2¼ oz.
Material: Plastic

Name: Creek Chub Wiggle Diver
Type: Plug
Length(s): 5"
Weight(s): 1½ oz.
Material: Plastic

Name: Creek Chub Huskie Jointed Pikie
Type: Plug
Length(s): 6"
Weight(s): 1½ oz.
Material: Plastic; wood

Name: Creek Chub Giant Straight Pikie
Type: Plug
Length(s): 8"
Weight(s): 3½ oz.
Material: Wood

Name: Creek Chub Jointed Snook Pikie
Type: Plug
Length(s): 4⅞"
Weight(s): 1⅛ oz.
Material: Wood

Name: Creek Chub Wiggle Diver
Type: Plug
Length(s): 5"
Weight(s): 1½ oz.
Material: Plastic

Name: Creek Chub Super Pikie
Type: Plug
Length(s): 4⅞"
Weight(s): 1⅛ oz.

Name: Streeker
Type: Spinner
Weight(s): ⅜ oz.
Material: Plastic

Name: Injured Minnow
Type: Spinner
Color(s): Assorted
Weight(s): ¼ oz.; ⅛ oz.
Material: Plastic; wood

Name: Pikie
Type: Spinner
Color(s): Assorted
Weight(s): ¼ oz.; ⅛ oz.
Material: Plastic

Name: Straight Pikie
Type: Spinner
Color(s): Assorted
Weight(s): ½ oz.; ¾ oz.; 1⅛ oz.; 1½ oz.; 3¼ oz.; 3½ oz.
Material: Plastic; wood

Name: Creek Chub Injured Minnow
Type: Spinner
Color(s): Assorted
Length(s): 1⅝"; 2"; 3¾"; 2¾
Weight(s): ⅛ oz.; ¼ oz.; ⅝ oz.; ½ oz.
Material: Plastic; wood

Name: Creek Chub Streeker
Type: Spinner
Color(s): Assorted
Length(s): 5½"
Weight(s): ½ oz.
Material: Plastic

Name: Creek Chub Cohokie
Type: Spoon
Color(s): Assorted
Length(s): 2"; 2¾"
Weight(s): ¼ oz.; ½ oz.
Material: Metal

Creme

Name: Caddis Fly
Type: Fly
Color(s): Brown; yellow

Name: Brown Frog
Type: Fly

Name: Bee
Type: Fly

Name: Sand Crab
Type: Fly

Name: Grasshopper
Type: Fly

Name: Spent Wing Salmon Fly
Type: Fly

Name: Ratlin' Grub
Type: Jig
Color(s): Assorted
Weight(s): ¼ oz.

Name: Soda Straw
Type: Worm
Color(s): Assorted
Length(s): 10"

Name: Scoundrel
Type: Worm
Color(s): Assorted
Length(s): 6"

Name: Shimmy Gal
Type: Worm
Color(s): Assorted
Length(s): 7¼"

Name: Shimmy Tail
Type: Worm
Color(s): Assorted 2 tone
Length(s): 3"

Name: Ratlin' Spin
Type: Spinner Bait
Color(s): Assorted

Name: Nite-Mare
Type: Spinner bait
Color(s): Assorted
Weight(s): ½ oz.

Lou J. Eppinger

Name: Thindervle
Type: Spoon
Length(s): 3¼" x ¾"
Weight(s): ⅓ oz.
Material: Metal

Name: Dardevle; Dardevlet; Dardevle Imp; Dardevle Spinnie; Dardevle Midget
Type: Spoon
Color(s): Not specified
Length(s): 3⅝" x 1¼"; 2⅞" x 1$\frac{1}{16}$"; 2¼" x ⅞"; 1¾" x ¾"; 1⅜" x ⅝"
Weight(s): 1 oz.; ⅗ oz.; ⅖ oz.; ¼ oz.; $\frac{1}{16}$ oz.
Material: Metal

Name: Seadevle
Type: Spoon
Length(s): 4" x ⅞"
Weight(s): 1½ oz.
Metal: Metal

Name: Rok't-Devle Imp
Type: Spoon
Length(s): 2¼" x ⅞"
Weight(s): ⅘ oz.
Material: Metal

Fenwick

Name: Knucklehead
Type: Jig on skirt
Length(s): 5"; 6"; 9½"; 12"; 16½"

Name: Psychohex
Type: Jig
Length(s): 18"

Name: Hexhead
Type: Jig
Length(s): 3¾"; 4½"; 5"; 7½"
Weight(s): ¾ oz.; 1 oz.; 2 oz; 4 oz.

Gaines

Name: Minnie — Pop 200
Type: Popper
Color(s): Standard color assort.

Name: Pan Popp 1100
Type: Popper
Color(s): Standard color assortment

Name: Bee Bug 1700
Type: Poppers
Color(s): Standard color assortment

Name: Gnat 3200
Type: Popper
Color(s): Standard color assortment

Name: Froggie
Type: Popper
Color(s): Standard color assortment

Gapen

Name: Crappie Bait
Type: Jig
Color(s): Assorted
Weight(s): 1/32 oz.
Material: Vinyl body, nickel-plated head

Name: Weedcutter I
Type: Spinner bait
Color(s): 5 assorted
Material: Rubber skirt

Name: Weedcutter III
Type: Spinner bait
Color(s): 5 assorted

Name: Leeches
Type: Worms
Color(s): Assorted
Length(s): 2"; 3½"
Material: Vinyl

Gudebrod

Name: Sniper
Type: Jig
Color(s): 8 assorted
Length(s): 3⅜"; 2⅞"; 5¼"
Weight(s): ⅛ oz.; ½ oz.; 1⅛ oz.
Material: Plastic

Name: Bippie
Type: Plug
Color(s): Assorted
Length(s): 2¼"
Weight(s): ⅝ oz.

Name: Bassprin
Type: Plug
Color(s): 12 assorted
Weight(s): ⅛ oz.; ⅜ oz.; ½ oz.

Name: Firebacks
Type: Plug
Color(s): 3 fluorescent

Name: Bump 'N' Grind
Type: Plug
Color(s): 3 fluorescent
Length(s): 2⅜"; 2⅞"; 5½"
Weight(s): ⅛ oz.; ½ oz.; 1⅛ oz.

Name: Maverick
Type: Plug
Color(s): 7 standard, 3 fluorescent
Length(s): 3¼"; 4¼"
Weight(s): ¼ oz.; ⅜ oz.

Name: Goodie
Type: Plug

Color(s): 12 assorted
Length(s): 2⅞"
Weight(s): ¼ oz.

Name: Blabber Mouth
Type: Plug
Color(s): Assorted
Length(s): 1¾"; 3"
Weight(s): ⅛ oz.; ½ oz.

Name: Trouble Maker
Type: Plug
Color(s): 14 assorted
Length(s): 1½"; 2"; 2⅝"; 3¾"; 5¼"
Weight(s): ⅛ oz.; ¼ oz.; ½ oz.; 1¼ oz.; 1¾ oz.

Name: Sinner Spinner
Type: Spinner
Color(s): 14 assorted
Length(s): 1¾"; 2⅞"
Weight(s): ½ oz.; ⅜ oz.

Name: Gudespoon
Type: Spoon
Color(s): Nickel
Length(s): 2½"; 3"; 3½"; 4¾"; 6"
Weight(s): ³⁄₁₆ oz.; ⁵⁄₁₆ oz.; ⅜ oz.; 1 oz.; 1½ oz.
Material: Brass, nickelchrome finish

James Heddon's Sons

Name: Surface lure 210
Type: Plug
Color(s): 8 assorted
Weight(s): ⅝ oz.
Material: Stainless steel fittings

Name: Crackleback
Type: Plug
Color(s): Assorted, crackle- textured finish
Length(s): 3⅞"; 4½"
Weight(s): ⅜ oz.; ⅝ oz.

Name: Southern Tadpolly
Type: Plug
Color(s): 6 chrome and assorted
Length(s): 2⅞"
Weight(s): ½ oz.

Name: Big Eye
Type: Plug
Color(s): 6
Weight(s): ⅜ oz.; ⅝ oz.

Name: Big Bud 9410
Type: Plug
Weight(s): ⅝ oz.

Name: Big Chugger Spook
Type: Plug
Color(s): Assorted

Name: Big Prowler
Type: Plug
Color(s): Assorted
Length(s): 6½"
Weight(s): 1⅝ oz.

Name: Cousin 1
Type: Plug
Color(s): Assorted
Length(s): 4¾"
Weight(s): ⅜ oz.

Name: Prowler
Type: Plug
Color(s): 6 assorted
Length(s): 2⅝"; 3⅝"; 4⅝"

Weight(s): ¼ oz.; ⅜ oz.; ⅝ oz.

Name: Heddon Big Hedd
Type: Plug
Weight(s): ⅝ oz.

Name: Zara Spook
Type: Plug
Length(s): 4½"
Weight(s): ¾ oz.

Name: Brush Popper Model 5440
Type: Spinner
Color(s): 8 assorted
Weight(s): ½ oz.
Material: Epoxy finish, brass and stainless steel hardware

Name: Smokey Joe
Type: Spinner
Color(s): Assorted
Weight(s): ³⁄₁₆ oz.; ¼ oz.

Name: Wounded Spook
Type: Spinner
Length(s): 3⅛"
Weight(s): ⅝ oz.

Helin

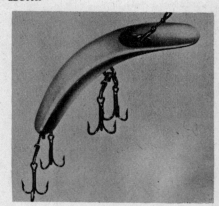

Name: Flatfish
Type: Plug
Color(s): 37 assorted
Length(s): 21 assorted
Material: Wood or plastic

Name: Fishcake
Type: Plug
Color(s): Assorted
Length(s): 1¾"; 2¼"; 2¾"
Weight(s): ¼ oz.; ⅜ oz.; ⅝ oz.

Name: Swimmerspoon
Type: Spoon
Color(s): 16 assorted
Length(s): Assorted

Hopkins

Name: Shorty Lures
Type: Jig
Color(s): Stainless steel finish
Length(s): Assorted
Weight(s): ⅛ oz.; ¼ oz.; ¾ oz.; 1½ oz.; 2¼ oz.
Material: Stainless steel

Name: No-Eql
Type: Jig
Color(s): Stainless steel finish
Length(s): Assorted
Weight(s): ⅓ oz.; ½ oz.; 1¼ oz.; 2 oz.; 2¾ oz.; 3¼ oz.
Material: Stainless steel

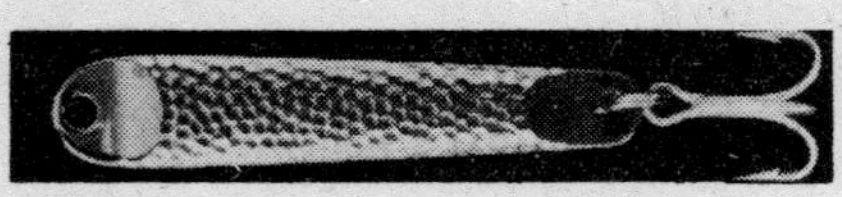

Name: Hammered Spoons
Type: Spoon
Color(s): All white; red/white; stainless steel
Length(s): 2⅜″; 3⅞″; 5½″
Weight(s): ¼ oz.; ¾ oz.; 1¾ oz.
Material: Stainless steel hardware

Louis Johnson

Name: Silver Minnow Weedless
Type: Jig

Name: Lucky Lujon
Type: Jig
Material: Brass

Name: Silver Salmon Sprite
Type: Plug
Color(s): Trout like spots

Name: Sprite-Weedless and Non-Weedless
Type: Spoon

Name: Sea Silver Minnow Non-Weedless
Type: Spoon

Name: Caper
Type: Spoon with replaceable flared weed guard

Name: Bucktail Spoon
Type: Spoon
Color(s): 7
Weight(s): ⅛ oz.; ¼ oz.; ½ oz.; ¾ oz.; 1⅜ oz.

Lazy Ike

Name: Li'l Wigly
Type: Jig
Color(s): 6
Weight(s): ¼ oz.

Name: Wigly Jig
Type: Jig
Color(s): 4
Weight(s): ¼ oz.; ⅜ oz.; ¾ oz.

Name: Wigly Squid
Type: Jig
Color(s): 6
Length(s): 6½″
Weight(s): ⅞ oz.

Name: Super Jigs
Type: Jig
Color(s): Assorted
Weight(s): 1⁄16 oz.; ⅛ oz.; ¼ oz.; ⅜ oz.; ½ oz.
Material: Bucktail hair, marabow feathers

Name: Wigly Crawler
Type: Jig-Semi-weedless
Color(s): 5
Weight(s): ¼ oz.; ⅜ oz.; ½ oz.; ¾ oz.

Name: Chug Ike
Type: Plug
Color(s): 6 standard, 6 metallic
Length(s): 2″; 3″
Weight(s): ¼ oz.; ½ oz.

Name: Sail Shark
Type: Plug
Color(s): 12 standard, 6 metallic
Length(s): 1⅝″
Weight(s): ¾ oz.

Name: Flex Ike
Type: Plug
Color(s): 12 standard, 12 metallic
Length(s): 2¾″; 3″
Weight(s): ⅙ oz.; ¼ oz.

Name: Snappertail
Type: Plug
Color(s): 6 standard, 6 metallic
Length(s): 3¼″
Weight(s): ½ oz.

Name: Snapper
Type: Plug
Color(s): 6 standard, 6 metallic
Length(s): 2¾″
Weight(s): ⅜ oz.
Material: Plastic

Name: Tail Shark
Type: Plug
Color(s): 6 standard, 6 metallic
Length(s): 2½″
Weight(s): ½ oz.

Name: Lazy Ike KL Series
Type: Plug
Color(s): Assorted combinations
Length(s): 1 1⁄16″; 1¾″; 2″; 2½″; 3″; 3½″
Weight(s): 1⁄32 oz.; 1⁄15 oz.; ⅛ oz.; ¼ oz.; ⅓ oz.; ⅝ oz.

Name: HS Hippy Spinners
Type: Spinner bait
Color(s): 6 assorted
Weight(s): ¼ oz.; ⅜ oz.; ½ oz.

L & S

Name: 52m Family
Type: Plug
Length(s): 3⅝″; 4¼″
Weight(s): ⅜ oz.; 9⁄16 oz.; ½ oz.; ⅝ oz.; ⅞ oz.; ⅝ oz.; ⅞ oz.; ⅝ oz.; ⅞ oz.; ¾ oz.; 1 oz.

Name: Tiny Trout Family
Type: Plug
Length(s): 2⅛″; 3⅝″
Weight(s): ¼ oz.; 9⁄16 oz.; ⅜ oz.

Name: Double Scat
Type: Spinner
Length(s): 3⅝″
Weight(s): ½ oz.

Name: Popular Spinner Models
Type: Spinner
Length(s): 3⅝″
Weight(s): ½ oz.; ⅝ oz.

Mann's

Name: Jelly Worm Grub
Type: Jig
Weight(s): 1⁄16 oz.

Name: Fat Albert
Type: Plug

Name: Super George
Type: Plug
Weight(s): ½ oz.
Material: Plastic body, nickle blade

Name: Little George
Type: Plug
Color(s): Pearl lustre

Name: Big George
Type: Plug
Color(s): Pearl lustre
Weight(s): ½ oz.
Material: Plastic

Name: Wally Bully
Type: Spinner bait
Color(s): 11 assorted

Name: Jelly Worm
Type: Worm
Length(s): 3″; 4″; 6″; 7″; 8″; 9″

Mepps

Name: Comet Mino
Type: Plug
Color(s): Lifelike
Length(s): 1⅞″; 2⅛″; 2⅝″; 2⅞″; 3⅜″; 4½″
Weight(s): ⅐ oz.; ⅕ oz.; ⅓ oz.; ½ oz.; ¾ oz.; 1 oz.

Name: Musky Killer
Type: Spinner or Jig
Color(s): Assorted
Weight(s): ½ oz.

Name: Giant Killer Mino
Type: Spinner
Color(s): Lifelike
Weight(s): 1½ oz.

Name: Black Fury Plain
Type: Spinner
Color(s): 1
Weight(s): ⅛ oz.; ⅙ oz.; ¼ oz.; ⅓ oz.

Name: Aglia Long Mino
Type: Spinner
Length(s): 1⅞″; 2⅛″; 2⅝″; 2⅞″; 3⅜″; 4½″
Weight(s): ⅙ oz.; ⅕ oz.; ⅓ oz.; ½ oz.; ⅚ oz.; 1⅛ oz.

Name: Aglia
Type: Spinner

Color(s): Assorted standard and metallic
Weight(s): 1/12 oz.; ⅛ oz.; ⅙ oz.; ¼ oz.; ⅓ oz.; ½ oz.

Name: Aglia Long
Type: Spinner
Color(s): Assorted
Weight(s): ⅛ oz.; ⅙ oz.; ¼ oz.; ⅓ oz.; ½ oz.

Name: Aglia Streamer
Type: Spinner
Color(s): Assorted
Weight(s): 1/12 oz.; ⅛ oz.; ⅙ oz.; ¼ oz.; ⅓ oz.; ½ oz.

Name: Aglia Dressed
Type: Spinner
Color(s): Assorted
Weight(s): 1/12 oz.; ⅛ oz.; ⅙ oz.; ¼ oz.; ⅓ oz.; ½ oz.

Name: Comet Dressed
Type: Spinner
Color(s): Assorted
Weight(s): 1/10 oz.; ⅛ oz.; ⅕ oz.; ⅓ oz.; ⅜ oz.

Name: Aglia Mino-Spin
Type: Spinner bait
Color(s): 5
Weight(s): 3/16 oz.; ⅜ oz.; ⅞ oz.

Name: Kriss
Type: Spoon
Color(s): Gold or silver
Weight(s): 1/10 oz.; 1/7 oz.; ¼ oz.

Norman

Name: Flasher
Type: Plug
Length(s): 2″
Weight(s): ¼ oz.

Name: Chugger-Flash
Type: Plug
Length(s): 3½″
Weight(s): ⅜ oz.

Name: Rat-Lur
Type: Plug
Length(s): 3½″
Weight(s): ⅝ oz.

Name: Quarter-Back Deep Runner
Type: Plug
Length(s): 1¾″; 4½″; 5½″
Weight(s): ¼ oz.; ½ oz.; 1 oz.

Name: Jointed-Minnow Series
Type: Plug
Length(s): 2½″; 3½″; 4½″; 5½″
Weight(s): ⅛ oz.; ¼ oz.; ⅜ oz.; ⅝ oz.

Name: Linebacker Series
Type: Plug
Length(s): 2½″; 3½″; 4½″; 5½″; 7″
Weight(s): ⅛ oz.; ¼ oz.; ⅜ oz.; ⅝ oz.; 1 oz.

Name: Super Scooper
Type: Plug
Color(s): Assorted
Length(s): 2″
Weight(s): ⅜ oz.

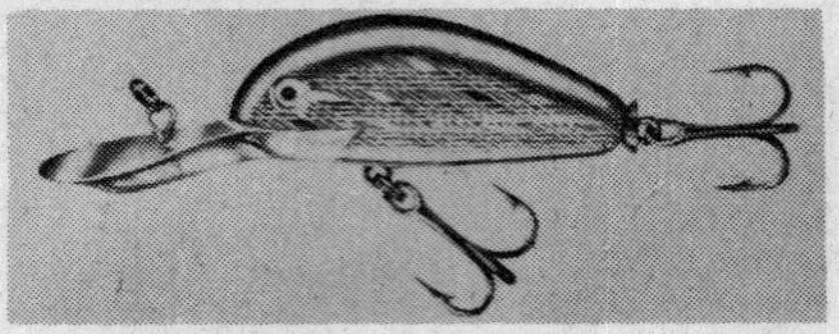

Name: Little Scooper
Type: Plug
Color(s): Assorted
Length(s): 1¾″
Weights(s): ¼ oz.

Name: Baby N
Type: Plug
Color(s): Assorted
Length(s): 2″
Weight(s): ¼ oz.

Name: Little N #1900
Type: Plug
Color(s): Assorted
Length(s): 2½″
Weight(s): ⅜ oz.

Name: Big N
Type: Plug
Color(s): Assorted
Length(s): 3″
Weight(s): ⅝ oz.

Name: Woundedflash
Type: Spinner
Length(s): 2¼″; 3½″
Weight(s): ¼ oz.; ½ oz.

Name: Spinnerbait
Type: Spinner bait
Color(s): 6
Weight(s): ¼ oz.; ½ oz.
Material: Nylon skirt, steel hook

Name: The Ranger Worm
Type: Worm
Color(s): 10 assorted
Length(s): 6″; 8″

Normark

Name: Countdown Sinking Models
Type: Jig
Color(s): Assorted
Length(s): 2″; 2¾″; 3½″; 4⅜″
Weight(s): ¼ oz.; ⅜ oz.; ½ oz.; ⅝ oz.

Name: Original Floating Models
Type: Plug
Color(s): Silver; Gold; Blue; Fluorescent Red
Length(s): 2″; 2¾″; 3½″; 4⅜″; 5¼″; 7″
Material: Balsa wood body, stainless steel wire

Name: Rapala Jigging Lure
Type: Plug
Color(s): Silver; gold; fluorescent red
Length(s): 1½″; 2″; 2¾″; 3½″
Weight(s): 3/16 oz.; 5/16 oz.; ½ oz.; ¾ oz.

Name: Jointed Rapala
Type: Plug
Color(s): Silver; gold; blue; fluorescent red
Length(s): 3½″

Name: Rapala Deep Diver
Type: Plug
Color(s): Silver; gold; blue; fluorescent red
Length(s): 2¾″; 3½″
Weight(s): ⅜ oz.; ½ oz.

Name: Magnum Rapalas
Type: Plug
Color(s): Silver; gold; blue; fluorescent red
Length(s): 5¼″; 7″
Weight(s): ¾ oz.; ⅞ oz.; 1½ oz.; 2 oz.
Material: Odoum wood bodies

Padre Island

Name: Hondo Jig
Type: Jig
Color(s): Assorted
Weight(s): ⅜ oz.; ⅝ oz.

Name: Pico Pop
Type: Plug
Length(s): 3¼″
Weight(s): ½ oz.

Name: Pico Side-Shad
Type: Plug
Color(s): Assorted
Length(s): 2½″
Weight(s): ½ oz.

Name: Hot Pants
Type: Spinner bait
Color(s): Assorted
Weight(s): ½ oz.
Material: Wire; plastic

Name: Piggy Boat
Type: Spinner bait
Color(s): Assorted
Weight(s): ⅓ oz.
Material: Rubber; nickel

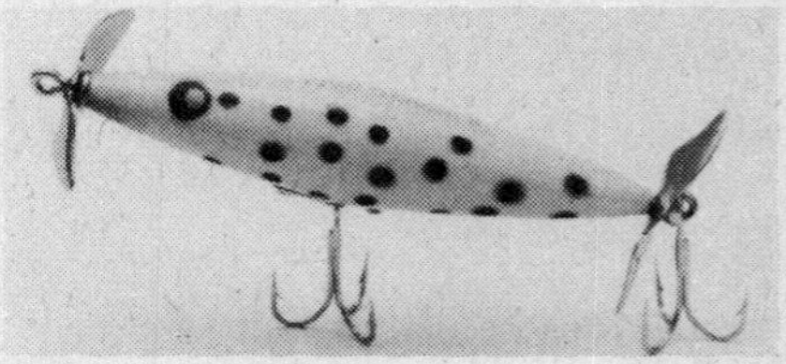

Name: Pico Slasher
Type: Spinner bait
Color(s): Assorted
Length(s): 4″
Weight(s): ½ oz.
Material: Plastic

Name: Jigging Spoon
Type: Spoon
Color(s): Assorted
Weight(s): ⅝ oz.

Name: Jigging Spoon
Type: Spoon
Color(s): Silver
Weight(s): ⅝ oz.
Material: Silver

Name: Wild Card Worm
Type: Worm
Color(s): Assorted
Length(s): 4″; 5″; 6″

Name: Pico Grub
Type: Worm
Color(s): Assorted
Length(s): 3″

Rogers

Name: Teeny Bee
Type: Jig
Color(s): Assorted
Weight(s): ⅛ oz.

Name: Flutter Tail Jig
Type: Jig
Color(s): Assorted
Weight(s): ¹⁄₁₆ oz.; ⅛ oz.; ¼ oz.

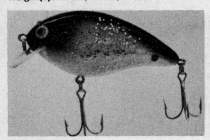

Name: Big Jim
Type: Plug
Color(s): Assorted
Weight(s): ⅜ oz.; ½ oz.; ¾ oz.

Name: Vib-r-fin
Type: Plug
Color(s): 17 assorted
Weight(s): ½ oz.

Name: Super Craw-Pap
Type: Plug
Color(s): 17 assorted
Weight(s): ¾ oz.

Name: Craw Pap
Type: Plug
Color(s): 17 assorted
Weight(s): ½ oz.

Name: Spin Worms
Type: Spinner
Color(s): Assorted
Length(s): 4″; 6″; 7¼″; 9¼″; 10″

Name: Spinwinder
Type: Spinner bait
Color(s): 13 assorted
Weight(s): ¹⁄₁₆ oz.; ⅛ oz.; ¼ oz.

Name: Ambusher
Type: Spinner bait
Color(s): Assorted
Weight(s): ⅜ oz.

Name: Gumbo Worms
Type: Worm
Color(s): 9 assorted
Length(s): 6″; 7¼″

Name: Hooktail
Type: Worm

Color(s): Assorted
Length(s): 3″; 4″; 6″

Name: Rogers Wooly Worm
Type: Worm
Color(s): Assorted
Weight(s): 2 oz.; 6 oz.; 8 oz.

Name: 2 Inch Rogers Grub
Type: Worm
Color(s): 13 assorted
Length(s): 2″

Jack K. Smithwick & Son

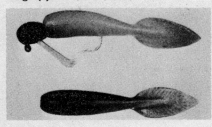

Name: Tail Gater
Type: Jig
Weight(s): ¼ oz.

Name: Wood Chug
Type: Jig
Weight(s): ¼ oz.

Name: Fishing Lure
Type: Plug
Length(s): 2¾″
Weight(s): ³⁄₁₆ oz.

Name: Rogue
Type: Plug
Length(s): 5½″
Weight(s): ½ oz.

Name: Devils Horse
Type: Spinner
Weight(s): ½ oz.

Name: Devils Horse
Type: Spinner
Weight(s): ⅜ oz.

Name: Chug Horse
Type: Spinner
Weight(s): ½ oz.

Name: Fishing Lures
Type: Spinner
Length(s): 3¼″
Weight(s): ¼ oz.

Name: Buck and Bawl
Type: Spinner
Weight(s): ⅜ oz.

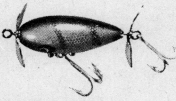

Name: Buck and Bawl
Type: Spinner
Weight(s): ¼ oz.

Name: King Snipe
Type: Spinner
Weight(s): ⅜ oz.

Stembridge

Name: Fuddlebug Regular, Fuddlebug Junior
Type: Worm
Color(s): 20 assorted
Length(s): 1¾″; 2⅞″
Material: Plastic, stainless steel clip

Name: Fliptail Family: Daddy; Regular;
Junior; Lizard; Baby
Type: Worm
Color(s): 20 assorted
Length(s): 2⅜″; 6½″; 6″; 7¼″; 9¼″
Material: Plastic

Name: Lizard
Type: Worm
Color(s): Assorted
Length(s): 6½″
Weight(s): ⅜ oz.
Material: Plastic

Bill Upperman

Name: Bucktails
Type: Jigs
Color(s): Assorted
Weight(s): 2 oz.; 1 oz.; ⅝ oz.; ½ oz.; ⅜ oz.

Zebco

Name: Doll-E-Pop
Type: Plug
Color(s): 6 color patterns
Weight(s): ½ oz.; ¾ oz.; 1 oz.; 1½ oz.

Name: Z-Plug
Type: Plug
Color(s): 12 colors
Weight(s): ⅜ oz.

Name: The Super Secret
Type: Plug
Color(s): 12 assorted
Weight(s): ½ oz.
Material: Aluminum lip

Name: Top Secret With Skirt
Type: Plug
Color(s): Assorted

Name: Z-spin
Type: Spinner bait
Color(s): 10 color combinations
Weight(s): ⅜ oz.; ⅝ oz.
Material: Stainless steel wire

Specifications: Lines and Leaders

Lines

Ande

Type: Tournament monofilament line
Breaking Strength (in lbs): 2 to 600
Color(s): 5
Packaging: Not specified

Belvin — Wilcox

Type: Spin cast monofilament line
Breaking Strength (in lbs.): 4; 6; 8; 10; 12;
15; 20; 25; 30; 40; 50; 60
Color(s): Blue; green
Packaging: 100 yd. narrow, spools, 12 per
box; 8 lb. spools; 4 lb. spools; 2 lb. spools;
1 lb. spools

Type: Beu-flex monofilament line
Breaking Strength (in lbs.): 4; 6; 8; 10; 12;
15; 20; 25; 30; 40; 50; 60
Color(s): Blue; green; smoketone; clear
Packaging: 100 yd. wide spools, 2 per box;
100 yd. wide spools, 12 per box; 100 yd.
wide spools; 8 lb. spools; 4 lb. spools;
2 lb. spools; 1 lb. spools

Type: Perlene monofilament line
Breaking Strength (in lbs.): 4; 6; 8; 10; 12;
15; 20; 25; 30; 40; 50
Color(s): Pearl gray
Packaging: 100 yd. wide spools, 2, 6 or 12
per box; 8 lb. spools; 4 lb. spools; 2 lb.
spools; 1 lb. spools

Type: Pilot dacron salt water surf and
trolling lines
Breaking Strength (in lbs.): 12; 20; 30; 40;
50; 60; 70; 80; 96; 130
Color(s): Greenspot; tan
Packaging: 50 yd., 6 per box; 50 yd. wide,
12 per box; 100 yd., 6 per box; 200 yd.;
300 yd.; 500 yd.; 600 yd.; 800 yd.;
1,000 yd.; 1,200 yd.

Type: Cast-ezy casting lines
Breaking Strength (in lbs.): 10; 12; 15; 20;
25; 30; 35; 40; 50
Color(s): Black; camouflage
Packaging: 50 yd. wide spools, 1, 2, 6 or 12
per box

Berkley

Type: Crusader braided canepole line
Breaking Strength (in lbs.): Assorted test
weights
Color(s): Assorted colors
Packaging: 10 yd. winders, 12 per box

Type: Spin Chief nylon monofilament line
Breaking Strength (in lbs.): 4; 6; 8; 10; 12;
15; 20; 25; 30; 40; 50;
60; 75; 100; 125; 150
Color(s): Mist blue
Packaging: 100 yds., 2, 6 or large capacity
bulk spools per box

Type: Depth-o-Matic nylon monofilament line
Breaking Strength (in lbs.): 15; 20; 25; 30; 40
Color(s): Bright, visible colors change
every 10 feet
Packaging: ¼ lb. spools, 1 lb. spools

Type: Mill Ends nylon monofilament line
Breaking Strength (in lbs.): 2; 4; 6; 8; 10; 12;
15; 20; 25; 30; 40; 50; 60
Color(s): Assorted colors
Packaging: Not specified

Type: Medallion braided nylon bait
casting line
Breaking Strength (in lbs.): 10; 12; 15; 20;
25; 30; 40; 50
Color(s): Black; camouflage
Packaging: 50 yd. spools, 2 per box

Type: Medallion lines dacron trolling and
surfing braided lines
Breaking Strength (in lbs.): 10; 18; 27; 45;
72; 117
Color(s): Green fleck
Packaging: 50 yd. spools, 6 per box; 100
yd. spools, 6 per box; 1,000 yd. spools

Type: Crusader braided nylon bait casting
lines
Breaking Strength (in lbs.): 10; 12; 15; 20;
25; 30; 40; 50
Color(s): Black; camouflage
Packaging: 50 yd. spools, 2 or 6 per box

Type: Crusader braided nylon squidding line
Breaking Strength (in lbs.): 18; 27; 36; 45;
54; 63; 72; 90; 110
Color(s): Sand
Packaging: 50 yd. spools, 6 per box

Type: Dew Flex nylon monofilament line
Breaking Strength (in lbs.): 4; 6; 8; 10; 12;
15; 20; 25; 30; 40; 50;
60; 75; 100; 125; 150
Color(s): Mist blue
Packaging: 100 yd. spools; large capacity
or bulk

Type: Trilene XL casting line
Breaking Strength (in lbs.): 2; 4; 6; 8; 10;
12; 14; 17; 20; 25; 30;
40; 50; 60; 80

Color(s): Crystal clear
Packaging: 100 yd. spools, 2 or 6 per box;
1,000 yd. spools

Type: Trilene Tensimatic heavy-duty line
Breaking Strength (in lbs.): 2; 4; 6; 8; 10; 12;
14; 17; 20; 25; 30; 40;
50; 60; 80
Color(s): Green
Packaging: 100 yd. spools, 2 or 6 per box

Type: Trilene Dura Tuff
Breaking Strength (in lbs.): 2; 4; 6; 8; 10; 12;
14; 17; 20; 25; 30; 40;
50; 60; 80
Color(s): Copper; sea mist green
Packaging: Popular filler spools

Type: Trilene monofilament
Breaking Strength (in lbs.): 2; 4; 6; 8; 10; 12;
14; 17; 20; 25; 30; 40;
50; 60; 80
Color(s): Mist blue; smoke
Packaging: 100 yd. spools, 2 or 6 per box;
1,000 yd. spools

Cortland

Type: Premium monofilament imported
nylorfi line
Breaking Strength (in lbs.): 4; 6; 8; 10; 12;
15; 20; 25; 30
Color(s): Neutral grey
Packaging: 100 meter (109.3 yds.), 2
connected

Type: Cortland monowire solid wire
deep trolling line
Breaking Strength (in lbs.): 10; 15; 20; 30;
40; 50
Color(s): Not specified
Packaging: 100 yd. spools, 2 connected

Type: Micron braided casting line
Breaking Strength (in lbs.): 10; 12; 15; 20;
25; 30; 40; 50
Color(s): Surgical white
Packaging: 50 yd. spools, 2 connected

Type: Heart-o-Gold braided nylon surface
casting line
Breaking Strength (in lbs.): 10; 12; 15; 18;
20; 25; 30; 35; 40; 50
Color(s): Gold-flecked black
Packaging: 50 yd. spools, 2 connected

Type: Wormer casting line blend of
polyester fibers
Breaking Strength (in lbs.): 10; 12; 15; 20;
25; 30; 35

Color(s): Two-tone green
Packaging: 50 yd. spools, 2 connected; 100 yd. spools, 2 connected

Type: Micron braided trolling line
Breaking Strength (in lbs.): 5½; 10; 27; 45; 72; 117
Color(s): Surgical white
Packaging: 100 yd. spools, 6 connected; 150 yd. spools, 6 connected

Type: Mono-worm flat monofilament casting line
Breaking Strength (in lbs.): 12; 15; 20; 25; 30; 35
Color(s): Two-tone green
Packaging: 100 yd. spools, 2 connected

Type: Cam-o-flage braided nylon casting line
Breaking Strength (in lbs.): 10; 12; 15; 18; 20; 25; 30; 35; 42; 50
Color(s): Camouflaged
Packaging: 50 yd. spools, 2 connected

Type: Braided dacron trolling line
Breaking Strength (in lbs.): 10; 18; 27; 36; 45; 72
Color(s): Greenspot
Packaging: 50 yd. spools, 6 per box

Type: Micron braided spinning line
Breaking Strength (in lbs.): 10; 12; 15; 20; 25; 30
Color: Not specified
Packaging: 100 yd. spools, 6 connected; 30 yd. spools

Type: Kerplunk braided nylon over lead core deep trolling line
Breaking Strength (in lbs.): 18; 27; 36; 45; 60
Color(s): Not specified
Packaging: 100 yd. spools, 2 connected

Type: Cam-o-flage limp monofilament
Breaking Strength (in lbs.): 4; 6; 8; 10; 12; 15; 20; 25; 30
Color(s): Camouflaged
Packaging: 100 yd. spools, 2 or 6 per box

Daiwa

Type: Mono-Dex monofilament
Breaking Strength (in lbs.): 4 to 40
Color(s): Clear; fume green
Packaging: Blister pack; bulk spool; new tube-pack

Danielson

Type: Nylon line
Breaking Strength (in lbs.): 6; 8; 10; 12; 15
Color(s): Not specified
Packaging: ⅛ lb. spools, 6 per box

Type: Nylon line
Breaking Strength (in lbs.): 20; 30; 40; 60
Color(s): Not specified
Packaging: ¼ lb. spools, 6 per box

Type: Nylon line
Breaking Strength (in lbs.): 6; 8; 10; 12; 15
Color(s): Not specified
Packaging: ¼ lb. spools, 12 per box

Type: Nylon
Breaking Strength (in lbs.): 20; 30; 40; 50
Color(s): Not specified
Packaging: ¼ lb. spools, 6 per box

Dragon Fly

Type: Superior monofilament spinning line
Breaking Strength (in lbs.): 6; 8; 10; 12; 15; 20; 25; 30
Color(s): Mist; smoke
Packaging: 100 yd. spools, 2 connected

Type: Braided waterproofed nylon casting line
Breaking Strength (in lbs.): 15; 20; 25; 30; 35; 40; 50; 63; 72
Color(s): Black; camouflage
Packaging: 50 yd. spools, 2 connected

Type: Monofilament spinning line
Breaking Strength (in lbs.): 6; 8; 10; 12; 15; 20
Color(s): Mist; smoke
Packaging: 100 yd. spools, 2 connected

DuPont

Type: Stren monofilament line
Breaking Strength (in lbs.): 2 to 30
Color(s): Clear; blue fluorescent
Packaging: 220-350 yds. (depending on lb. test); 100 yd. spools, 2 connected

Type: Stren monofilament line
Breaking Strength (in lbs.): 2 to 30
Color(s): Golden fluorescent
Packaging: 220-350 yds. (depending on lb. test)

Type: Stren monofilament line
Breaking Strength (in lbs.): 6 to 80
Color(s): Golden fluorescent
Packaging: 2,400 yd. spools; 4,800 yd. spools; 150 yd. spools

Type: Stren monofilament line
Breaking Strength (in lbs.): 2 to 40
Color(s): Clear; blue fluorescent
Packaging: 2,400 yd. spools; 4,800 yd. spools; 100 yd. spools, 6 connected or 2 connected

Garcia

Type: Royal bonnyl monofilament line
Breaking Strength (in lbs.): 2; 4; 6; 8; 10; 12; 15; 20; 25; 30; 40; 50; 80
Color(s): Not specified
Packaging: 100 yd. spools; long-length spools; royal

Type: Super-platyl spinning monofilament line
Breaking Strength (in lbs.): 1; 2; 3; 4; 6; 8; 10; 12; 15; 20; 25; 30; 40
Color(s): Soft mist
Packaging: 100 yd. spools; long-length spools; leader material

Type: Braided casting sinking dacron line of high-tenacity DuPont dacron
Breaking Strength (in lbs.): 10; 12; 15; 20; 25; 30; 35; 40; 45; 50
Color(s): Not specified
Packaging: 50 yd. spools; 1,000 yd. spools

Type: Invisible monofilament line
Breaking Strength (in lbs.): 2; 4; 6; 8; 10; 12; 15; 20; 25; 30; 40; 50; 60
Color(s): Visible in air, invisible in water
Packaging: 100 yd. spools; long-length

Type: Braided casting floating nylon line with braided-in lubrication
Breaking Strength (in lbs.): 10; 12; 15; 20; 25; 30; 35; 40; 45; 50
Color(s): Camouflage; black
Packaging: 50 yd. spools; 1,000 yd. spools

Type: Lead cove trolling line
Breaking Strength (in lbs.): 18; 25; 40; 60
Color(s): Color-coded every ten yards
Packaging: 50 yd. coils, 2 per box; 100 yd. coils, 2 per box

Type: Squidding line
Breaking Strength (in lbs.): 18; 27; 36; 45; 54; 63; 72
Color(s): Not specified
Packaging: 50 yd. spools, 2 or 6 connected; 1,000 yd. bulk spools

Type: Braided dacron trolling line
Breaking Strength (in lbs.): 6; 12; 20; 30; 50; 80; 130; 162
Color(s): Not specified

Packaging: 50 yds.; 500 yds.; 600 yds.; 800 yds.; 1,000 yds.; 1,200 yds.

Gladding

Type: Invincible-braided floating nylon bait casting line
Breaking Strength (in lbs.): 6; 9; 12; 15; 18; 20; 25; 30; 35; 40; 45; 50
Color(s): Black; white
Packaging: 50 yd. spools; 1,000 yd. spools

Type: Mercury ultra-soft monofilament
Breaking Strength (in lbs.): 2; 4; 6; 8; 10; 15; 20; 25; 30; 35; 40
Color(s): Gunmetal
Packaging: 100 yd. spools, 2 or 6 per box

Type: Super monofilament spinning-casting line
Breaking Strength (in lbs.): 4; 6; 8; 10; 12; 15; 20
Color(s): Mist green
Packaging: 100 yd. spools, 1 or 2 per box

Type: Gladyl monofilament siliconized finish
Breaking Strength (in lbs.): 2; 4; 6; 8; 10; 12; 15; 20; 25; 30; 40; 50
Color(s): Aqua mist
Packaging: 100 yd. spools, 2 per box

Type: Special Mark V braided dacron leadcore line
Breaking Strength (in lbs.): 20; 30; 45; 60
Color(s): New color every 10 yds.
Packaging: 100 yd. spools, 2 per box

Type: Clearon monofilament siliconized finish line
Breaking Strength (in lbs.): 4; 6; 8; 10; 12; 15; 20; 25
Color(s): Clear
Packaging: 100 yd. spools, 2 per box

Type: Champion monofilament line
Breaking Strength (in lbs.): 4; 6; 8; 10; 12; 15; 20; 25; 30; 40; 50; 60
Color(s): Mist green
Packaging: 100 yd. spools

Type: Dreadnaught nylon braided casting line
Breaking Strength (in lbs.): 12; 15; 20; 25; 30
Color(s): Multicolor
Packaging: 50 yd. spools, 2 per box

Type: South Bend Black Oreno braided nylon casting trolling line
Breaking Strength (in lbs.): 10; 12; 15; 18; 20; 25; 30; 35; 40
Color(s): Midnight blue
Packaging: 50 yd. spool, 2 connected

Type: Super casting line
Breaking Strength (in lbs.): 12; 15; 20; 25
Color(s): Black
Packaging: 50 yd. spools, 1 or 2 per box

Type: Beachcomber braided nylon-sand line
Breaking Strength (in lbs.): 18; 27; 36; 45; 50; 63
Color(s): Not specified
Packaging: 50 yd. spools, 12 connected; 150 yd. spools, 6 connected

Type: Trident-braided greenspot dacron line
Breaking Strength (in lbs.): 12; 18; 27; 36; 45; 72; 117
Color(s): Greenspot
Packaging: 50 yd. spools, 6 per box; 150 yd.

spools, 6 per box; 300 yd. spools; 600 yd. spools; 1,000 yd. spools; 1,200 yd. spools

Type: Mark V-deep trolling nylon braided over lead core line
Breaking Strength (in lbs.): 18; 25; 45; 60
Color(s): Color code decal in every box
Packaging: 50 yd. spools, 2 per box; 100 yd. spools, 2 per box

Type: Snag King braided dacron line
Breaking Strength (in lbs.): 63; 72; 90; 108
Color(s): Ivory
Packaging: 50 yd. spools, 6 per box; 1,000 yd. spools

Type: Cor-Les dacron line
Breaking Strength (in lbs.): 20; 30; 45; 60
Color(s): Color code decal in every box
Packaging: 100 yd. spools, 2 per box

Type: Bass in man "All Pro" magnum bass nylon monofilament line
Breaking Strength (in lbs.): 10; 12; 14; 18; 22
Color(s): Invisible smoke grey
Packaging: 300 yd. spools; 275 yd. spools; 250 yd. spools; 200 yd. spools; 150 yd. spools

Type: Gladding depth-finder monofilament line
Breaking Strength (in lbs.): 6; 8; 10; 12; 15; 20; 25; 30
Color(s): Color code decals packed with each spool
Packaging: 100 yd. spools; 200 yd. spools

Type: Gladding L-B nylon monofilament line
Breaking Strength (in lbs.): 4; 6; 8; 10; 12;

15; 20; 25; 30; 40; 50
Color(s): Water blue
Packagng: 100 yd. spools, 12 per box

Herter's

Type: Lock stitch spinning and casting limp monofilament nylon line
Breaking Strength (in lbs.): 4; 6; 8; 10; 12; 15; 18
Color(s): Camouflage
Packaging: 100 yd. spools, 2 connected

Type: Pylon monofilament line
Breaking Strength (in lbs.): 1; 2; 4; 6; 8; 10; 12; 15; 20; 25; 30
Color(s): British fog grey
Packaging: 100 yd. spools

Type: Trolling line monel wire
Breaking Strength (in lbs.): 20; 25; 40
Color(s): Not specified
Packaging: 100 yds.; 200 yds.

Type: Depth finder monofilament line
Breaking Strength (in lbs.): 15; 20; 25; 30; 40
Color(s): 5 bright colors change every 10'
Packaging: ¼ lb. spools

Type: Chalk stream nylon monofilament
Breaking Strength (in lbs.): 4; 6; 8; 10; 12; 15; 20; 25; 30
Color(s): Natural translucent; mist blue
Packaging: 100 yd. spools, maximum 6 spools connected

Type: Limp bulk monofilament
Breaking Strength (in lbs.): 4; 6; 8; 10; 12; 15; 20; 25; 30
Color(s): Mist blue
Packaging: ¼ lb. spools

Ideal

Type: Braided nylon casting line
Breaking Strength (in lbs.): 10 to 30
Color(s): Assorted
Packaging: 12 per box

Type: Jet nylon monofilament spinning line
Breaking Strength (in lbs.): 6; 8; 10; 15; 20; 25
Color(s): Mist blue
Packaging: ¼ lb. spools; 2,150 yds.; 1,775 yds.; 1,500 yds.; 956 yds.; 663 yds.; 488 yds.

Lakeland

Type: Nylon monofilament line
Breaking Strength (in lbs.): 8; 10; 15; 20; 30
Color(s): Not specified
Packaging: Not specified

Martin

Type: Depth-O-Meter nylon monofilament fishing line
Breaking Strength (in lbs.): 4; 6; 8; 10; 12; 15; 20; 25; 30; 40
Color(s): 25 ft. of each color: clear, yellow, red, blue. Repeated every 100 ft. throughout length of line
Packaging: 200 yd. spool

Bruce B. Mises

Type: Chameleon maxi-spool
Breaking Strength (in lbs.): 4; 6; 8; 10; 12; 15; 20; 25; 30; 40

Color(s): Not specified
Packaging: 660 yd. spools

Type: Foam green maxi-spool monoline
Breaking Strength (in lbs.): 4; 6; 8; 10; 12; 15; 20; 25; 30; 40; 50; 60
Color(s): Foam green
Packaging: 660 yd. spools

Type: Chameleon "one shot" filling spool
Breaking Strength (in lbs.): 2; 4; 6; 8; 10; 12; 15; 20; 25; 30; 40
Color(s): Color-changing
Packaging: 2 lb., 4 lb.: 280 yds.; 6 lb., 20 lb., 25 lb., 30 lb., 40 lb.: 250 yds.; 8 lb., 12 lb., 15 lb.: 220 yds.

Type: Blue mist mono line
Breaking Strength (in lbs.): 4; 6; 8; 10; 12; 15; 20; 25; 30; 40; 50; 60; 80
Color(s): Blue
Packaging: 4 lb., 6 lb., 8 lb., 10 lb., 12 lb.: 3,200 yds.; 15 lb., 20 lb., 25 lb., 30 lb., 40 lb.: 2,600 yds.; 50 lb., 60 lb.: 1,900 yds.; 80 lb.: 1,300 yds.

Type: Super soft "one shot" filling spool mono line
Breaking Strength (in lbs.): 2; 4; 6; 8; 10; 12; 15; 20; 25; 30; 40
Color(s): Not specified
Packaging: 2 lb., 4 lb.: 280 yds.; 6 lb., 20 lb., 25 lb, 30 lb, 40 lb.: 250 yds.; 8 lb., 10 lb., 12 lb., 15 lb.: 220 yds.

Quick

Type: Damyl monofilament line
Breaking Strength (in lbs.): 2 to 60; 4 to 10; 12 to 60; 2 to 130
Color(s): Transparent
Packaging: 100 yd. spools, 6 per box

Saunders

Type: Braided nylon cord
Breaking Strength (in lbs.): 80
Color(s): Not specified
Packaging: 50', 6 per box

Shakespeare

Type: Super 700 mono nylon
Breaking Strength (in lbs.): 2; 4; 6; 8; 10; 12; 15; 17; 20; 25; 30; 40; 50
Color(s): Water blue
Packaging: 110 yd. spools, 2 or 6 per box

Type: Saltwater nylon monofilament
Breaking Strength (in lbs.): 8; 10; 12; 15; 20; 25; 30; 40; 50; 60; 80; 100
Color(s): Green
Packaging: ¼ lb. spools, 6 per box

Type: Nylon monofilament for spinning and bait casting

Breaking Strength (in lbs.): 6; 8; 10; 12; 15; 17; 20; 25; 30
Color(s): Gold
Packaging: 100 yd. spools, 2 per box

Shurkatch

Type: Light hand nylon monofilament line
Breaking Strength (in lbs.): 12; 40; 25
Color(s): Green
Packaging: 35'; 50'; 75'

Type: Light duty salt water hand nylon monofilament line
Breaking Strength (in lbs.): 100; 200; 250
Color(s): Brown
Packaging: 50'; 100'

Type: Heavy duty salt water hand line, twisted nylon
Breaking Strength (in lbs.): 100; 200; 250
Color(s): Brown
Packaging: 50' on 5" x 5" wood winder

Type: Cane pole twisted nylon line
Breaking Strength (in lbs.): 12
Colors(s): Green
Packaging: 15'

Tycoon/Fin-Nor

Type: Gold bond dacron
Breaking Strength (in lbs.): 20; 30; 50; 80; 130
Color(s): Not specified
Packaging: 600 yds.; 800 yds.; 1,000 yds.; 1,200 yds.

Type: Tournament monofilament
Breaking Strength (in lbs.): 12; 20; 30; 50; 80
Color(s): Not specified
Packaging: 600 yd. spools; 1,000 yd. spools

Weber

Type: Bulk limp nylon monofilament
Breaking Strength (in lbs.): 2; 3; 4; 6; 8; 10; 12; 15; 20; 25; 30; 40; 50; 75; 90; 125; 150; 175; 200
Color(s): Camouflaged
Packaging: ⅛ lb. spools; ¼ lb. spools; ½ lb. spools; 1 lb. spools.

Type: Redi-pak limp nylon
Breaking Strength (in lbs.): 1; 2; 3; 4; 5; 6; 7; 8; 9; 10; 12; 15; 20; 25; 30; 40; 60
Color(s): Camouflaged; mist
Packaging: 4 yd. spools; 5 yd. spools; 7 yd. spools; 8 yd. spools; 10 yd. spools; 15 yd. spools; 20 yd. spools; 30 yd. spools

Type: SS limp nylon monofilament spinning line
Breaking Strength (in lbs.): 2; 3; 4; 6; 8; 10; 12; 15; 20
Color(s): Camouflaged; mist
Packaging: 100 yd. spools, 2 connected

Type: Limp nylon monofilament
Breaking Strength (in lbs.): 1; 2; 3; 4; 5; 6; 7; 8; 9; 10; 12; 15; 20; 25; 30; 40; 50; 75; 90; 125; 150; 175; 200
Color(s): Camouflaged
Packaging: 100 yd. spools, 4 connected; 50 yd. spools, 8 connected

Type: BB limp nylon monofilament spinning line
Breaking Strength (in lbs.): 4; 6; 8; 10; 12; 15; 20
Color(s): Gray mist
Packaging: 100 yd. spools, 4 connected

Fly Lines

Berkley

Type: Specialist qwik-sink sinking fly line
Length: L: 25 yds.; WF: 30 yds.; DT: 30 yds.; ST: 30'
Color(s): High visibility yellow; bright white; light green; sky blue; cocoa brown; deep brown
AFTMA Designation: L-5-S; L-6-S; L-7-S; L-8-S; L-9-S; WF-6-S; WF-7-S; WF-8-S; WF-9-S; WF-10-S; DT-5-S; DT-6-S; DT-7-S; DT-8-S; DT-9-S; DT-10-S; ST-7-S; ST-8-S; ST-9-S; ST-10-S; ST-11-S

Type: Specialist floating fly line
Length: L: 25 yds.; WF: 30 yds.; DT: 25 yds., 30 yds.
Color(s): High visibility yellow; bright white; light green; sky blue; cocoa brown; deep brown
AFTMA Designation: L-4-F; L-5-F; L-6-F; L-7-F; L-8-F; L-9-F; WF-8-F; WF-9-F; WF-10-F; WF-11-F; DT-3-F; DT-4-F; DT-5-F; DT-6-F; DT-7-F; DT-8-F; DT-9-F; DT-10-F

Type: Specialist floating/sinking fly line weight forward qwik sink tip
Length: 30 yds.
Color(s): High visibility yellow; bright white; light green; sky blue; cocoa brown; deep brown
AFTMA Designation: WF-5-E/S; WF-6-F/S; WF-7-F/S; WF-8-F/S; WF-9-F/S; WF-10-F/S

Type: Perma-float sinking fly line
Length: 25 yds.

Color(s): Ivory
AFTMA Designation: L-4-S; L-5-S; L-6-S

Type: Perma-float floating fly line
Length: L: 25 yds.; WF: 30 yds.; DT: 30 yds.
Color(s): Ivory
AFTMA Designation: L-4-F; L-5-F; L-6-F; L-7-F; WF-6-F; WF-7-F; WF-8-F; WF-9-F; WF-10-F; DT-4-F; DT-5-F; DT-6-F; DT-7-F

Type: Golden zephyr floating fly line sinking fly line
Length: 25 yds.
Color(s): Green
AFTMA Designation: L-4-S; L-5-S; L-6-S

Type: Golden zephyr floating fly line
Length: L: 25 yds.; WF: 30 yds.; DT: 30 yds.
Color(s): Green
AFTMA Designation: L-4-F; L-5-F; L-6-F; L-7-F; WF-6-F; WF-7-F; WF-8-F; WF-9-F; WF-10-F; DT-4-F; DT-5-F; DT-6-F; DT-7-F

Cortland

Type: Micro-Foam floating fly line
Length: L: 25 yd. coil; DT: 30 yd. coil
Color(s): Not specified
AFTMA Designation: L-5-F; L-6-F; L-7-F; L-8-F; L-9-F; L-10-F; DT-4-F; DT-5-F; DT-6-F; DT-7-F; DT-8-F; DT-9-F

Type: Micro-Foam floating fly line rocket taper
Length: 35 yd. coils
Color(s): Yellow
AFTMA Designation: WF-5-F; WF-6-F; WF-7-F; WF-8-F; WF-9-F; WF-10-F

Type: Micro-Foam bug tapers
Length: 35 yd. coils
Color(s): Yellow
AFTMA Designation: WF-7-F; WF-8-F; WF-9-F; WF-10-F

Type: Micro-Foam salt water tapers
Length: 35 yd. coils
Color(s): Yellow
AFTMA Designation: WF-7-F; WF-8-F; WF-9-F; WF-10-F; WF-11-F

Type: "333"
Length: L: 25 yd. coil; DT: 30 yd. coil
Color(s): Mist green; dark amber; white
AFTMA Designation: L-3-F; L-4-F; L-5-F; L-6-F; L-7-F; L-8-F; L-9-F; DT-4-F; DT-5-F; DT-6-F; DT-7-F; DT-8-F; DT-9-F

Type: "333" bug tapers
Length: 35 yd. coils
Color(s): Mist green; dark amber; white
AFTMA Designation: WF-7-F; WF-8-F; WF-9-F; WF-10-F; WF-11-F

Type: "333" rocket tapers
Length: 35 yd. coils
Color(s): Mist green; dark amber; white
AFTMA Designation: WF-5-F; WF-6-F; WF-7-F; WF-8-F; WF-9-F; WF-10-F; WF-11-F

Type: "333" sink-tip taper
Length: 35 yds.
Color(s): Dark green sink tip, light green balance
AFTMA Designation: WF-5-F/S; WF-6-F/S; WF-7-F/S; WF-8-F/S; WF-9-F/S; WF-10-F/S; WF-11-F/S

Garcia

Type: Lee Wulff long belly fly line
Length: 30 yds.
Color(s): Ivory; aqua; grey
AFTMA Designation: WF-5-S; WF-6-S; WF-7-S; WF-8-S; WF-9-S; WF-10-S; WF-5-F; WF-6-F; WF-7-F; WF-8-F; WF-9-F; WF-10-F; WF-5-F/S; WF-6-F/S; WF-7-F/S; WF-8-F/S; WF-9-F/S; WF-10-F/S

Type: Kingfisher floating fly line
Length: L: 25 yds.; WF: 30 yds.; DT: 30 yds.
Color(s): Not specified
AFTMA Designation: L-4-F; L-5-F; L-6-F; L-7-F; L-8-F; L-9-F; WF-4-F; WF-5-F; WF-6-F; WF-7-F; WF-8-F; WF-9-F; DT-4-F; DT-5-F; DT-6-F; DT-7-F; DT-8-F; DT-9-F

Type: Garcia sinking fly line
Length: L: 25 yds; WF: 37 yds.; WF-5-S: 30 yds; DT: 30 yds.
Color(s): Mahogany; aqua
AFTMA Designation: L-3-S; L-4-S; L-5-S; L-6-S; L-7-S; WF-5-S; WF-6-S; WF-7-S; WF-8-S; DT-4-S; DT-5-S; DT-6-S; DT-7-S

Type: Garcia floating fly line
Length: L: 25 yds.; WF: 30 yds.; DT: 30 yds.
Color(s): Mahogany; aqua; ivory
AFTMA Designation: L-3-F; L-4-F; L-5-F; L-6-F;
L-7-F; WF-5-F; WF-6-F; WF-7-F; WF-8-F;
WF-9-F; WF-10-F; DT-4-F; DT-5-F; DT-6-F;
DT-7-F

Gladding

Type: Magistrate
Length: L: 25 yd. coil; WF: 40 yd. coil; DT:
30 yd. coil
Color(s): Green
AFTMA Designation: L-1-F; L-2-F; L-3-F; L-5-F;
L-6-F; L-7-F; L-8-F; WF-6-F; WF-7-F; WF-8-F;
WF-9-F; DT-5-F; DT-6-F; DT-7-F; DT-8-F

Type: Aqua sink
Length: L: 25 yd. coil; WF: 35 yd. coil; DT:
30 yd. coil; ST: 33' coil
Color(s): Dark green
AFTMA Designation: L-3-S; L-4-S; L-5-S; L-6-S;
L-7-S; L-8-S; L-9-S; L-10-S; WF-5-S; WF-6-S;
WF-8-S; WF-9-S; WF-10-S; DT-5-S; DT-6-S;
DT-8-S; DT-9-S; DT-10-S; ST-9-S; ST-11-S

Type: Super-aerofloat
Length: L: 25 yd. coil; WF: 35 yd. coil; DT:
30 yd. coil; ST: 33' coil
Color(s): White; green
AFTMA Designation: L-3-F; L-4-F; L-5-F; L-6-F;
L-7-F; L-8-F; L-9-F; WF-6-F; WF-7-F; WF-8-F;
WF-9-F; WF-10-F; DT-5-F; DT-6-F; DT-7-F;
DT-8-F; DT-9-F; ST-9-F; ST-10-F

Type: Super-aerofloat salt water taper
Length: 40 yd. coils; 100 yds. with 18 lb.

test backing; 200 yds. with 18 lb. test
backing
Color(s): White; green
AFTMA Designation: WF-9-F; WF-10-F;
WF-11-F

Type: Salmon taper
Length: 40 yd. coils, 100 yd. backing; 40 yd.
coils, 200 yd. backing
Color(s): Dark green
AFTMA Designation: WF-9-S; WF-10-S;
WF-11-S; WF-12-S

Type: Super line levels
Length: 25 yd. coils
Color(s): Green
AFTMA Designation: Not specified

Type: Super line double tapers
Length: 30 yd. coils
Color(s): Green
AFTMA Designation: Not specified

Type: Ideal fly line
Length: 25 yd. spools
Color(s): Dark green
AFTMA Designation: L-3-F; L-5-F; L-6-F; L-7-F

Herter's

Type: Professional fly line
Length: L: 25 yds.; DT: 30 yds.; WF: 30 yds.
Color(s): Ivory
AFTMA Designation: L-4-F; L-5-F; L-6-F; L-7-F;
DT-4-F; DT-5-F; DT-6-F; DT-7-F; WF-6-F;
WF-7-F; WF-8-F

Type: Masterweave sinking fly line
Length: DT: 90'; L: 75'; WF: 105'
Color(s): Dark brown
AFTMA Designation: L-8-S; L-9-S; DT-6-S;
DT-8-S; WF-9-S; WF-10-S

Type: Masterweave floating fly line
Length: DT: 90'; WF: 105'; L: 75'
Color(s): Green; tan
AFTMA Designation: L-5-F; L-6-F; L-7-F;
DT-5-F; DT-6-F; DT-7-F; DT-9-F; WF-7-F;
WF-8-F; WF-9-F

Type: Imperial sinking fly lines
Length: L: 75'; DT: 90'; WF: 105'
Color(s): Brown
AFTMA Designation: L-7-S; L-8-S; L-9-S;
DT-5-S; DT-6-S; DT-8-S; WF-6-S; WF-8-S;
WF-9-S

Type: Imperial floating fly line
Length: L: 75'; WF: 105'; DT: 90'
Color(s): Green
AFTMA Designation: L-4-F; L-5-F; L-6-F; L-7-F;
DT-4-F; DT-5-F; DT-6-F; DT-7-F; WF-6-F;
WF-7-F; WF-8-F

Ideal

Type: Floating fly rocket taper nylon
Length: 35 yds.
Color(s): Glo-white
AFTMA Designation: WF-5-F; WF-6-F

Type: Floating fly line
Length: 30 yd. coils
Color(s): Light green
AFTMA Designation: L-6-F; L-8-F

Type: Nylon fly line
Length: 30 yd. coils
Color(s): Light green
AFTMA Designation: DT-6-F; DT-8-F; DT-5-F

Pflueger

Type: Supreme floating fly line
Length: Not specified
Color(s): Light gray
AFTMA Designation: L-4-F; L-5-F; L-7-F; L-8-F

Type: Supreme floating fly line
Length: Not specified
Color(s): Light gray
AFTMA Designation: WF-7-F; WF-8-F; WF-9-F;
WF-10-F

Type: Supreme floating fly line
Length: Not specified
Color(s): Light gray
AFTMA Designation: DT-4-F; DT-5-F

Type: Mono-fly, mono-sink
Length: 105'
Color(s): Not specified
AFTMA Designation: WF-8-S; WF-9-S;
WF-10-S; WF-11-S

Type: Medalist mono-fly slow sinking inner
core of extruded monofilament
Length: 35 yd. coils
Color(s): Translucent
AFTMA Designation: WF-6-S; WF-7-S; WF-8-S;
WF-9-S; WF-10-S; WF-11-S; WF-12-S

Type: Medalist mono-fly slow sinking inner
core of extruded monofilament
Length: 35 yd. coils
Color(s): Translucent
AFTMA Designation: DT-5-S; DT-6-S; DT-7-S;
DT-8-S

Type: Medalist mono-fly floating inner core
of extruded monofilament
Length: 35 yd. coils
Color(s): White
AFTMA Designation: WF-6-F; WF-7-F; WF-8-F;
WF-9-F; WF-10-F; WF-11-F

Type: Medalist mono-fly inner core of
extruded monofilament
Length: 35 yd. coils
Color(s): White
AFTMA Designation: DT-5-F; DT-6-F; DT-7-F;
DT-8-F

Scientific Anglers

Type: Wet Cel I slow sinking
Length: 25 yd. coils
Color(s): Medium green
AFTMA Designation: L-5-S; L-6-S; L-7-S; L-8-S;
L-9-S; L-10-S; L-11-S; L-12-S

Type: Wet Cel I slow sinking
Length: 30 yd. coils
Color(s): Medium green
AFTMA Designation: WF-5-S; WF-6-S; WF-7-S;
  WF-8-S; WF-9-S; WF-10-S; WF-11-S;
  WF-12-S

Type: Wet Cel I slow sinking
Length: 30 yd. coils
Color(s): Medium green
AFTMA Designation: DT-5-S; DT-6-S; DT-7-S;
  DT-8-S; DT-9-S; DT-10-S; DT-11-S; DT-12-S

Type: Wet Cel I slow sinking
Length: 30 yd. coils
Color(s): Medium green
AFTMA Designation: ST-6-S; ST-7-S; ST-8-S;
  ST-9-S; ST-10-S; ST-11-S

Type: Wet Cel II fast sinking
Length: 30 yd. coils
Color(s): Dark green
AFTMA Designation: DT-4-S; DT-5-S; DT-6-S;
  DT-7-S; DT-8-S; DT-9-S; DT-10-S; DT-11-S;
  DT-12-S

Type: Wet Cel wet head
Length: 30 yd. coils
Color(s): Two-tone green
AFTMA Designation: WF-7-F/S; WF-8-F/S;
  WF-9-F/S; WF-10-F/S; WF-11-F/S;
  WF-12-F/S

Type: Air Cel
Length: 25 yd. coils
Color(s): White; light green; dark brown
AFTMA Designation: L-1-F; L-2-F; L-3-F; L-4-F;
  L-5-F; L-6-F; L-7-F; L-8-F; L-9-F; L-10-F

Type: Air Cel
Length: 30 yd. coils
Color(s): White; light green; dark brown
AFTMA Designation: WF-5-F; WF-6-F; WF-7-F;
  WF-8-F; WF-9-F

Type: Air Cel
Length: 30 yd. coils
Color(s): White; light green; dark brown
AFTMA Designation: DT-4-F; DT-5-F; DT-6-F;
  DT-7-F; DT-5-F; DT-6-F

Type: Air Cel
Length: 30′ coils
Color(s): White
AFTMA Designation: ST-7-F; ST-8-F; ST-9-F;
  ST-10-F; ST-11-F

Type: Air Cel bass bug taper
Length: 30 yd. coils
Color(s): Light green
AFTMA Designation: WF-6-F; WF-7-F; WF-8-F;
  WF-9-F

Type: Air Cel wet tip
Length: 30 yd. coils
Color(s): Two-tone green
AFTMA Designation: WF-5-F/S; WF-6-F/S;
  WF-7-F/S; WF-8-F/S; WF-9-F/S;
  WF-10-F/S

Type: Air Cel wet tip
Length: 30 yd. coils
Color(s): Two-tone green
AFTMA Designation: DT-4-F/S; DT-5-F/S;
  DT-6-F/S; DT-7-F/S; DT-8-F/S; DT-9-F/S;
  DT-10-F/S

Type: Air Cel wet tip hi-d
Length: 30 yd. coils
Color(s): Yellow; dark green

AFTMA Designation: WF-5-F/S; WF-6-F/S;
  WF-7-F/S; WF-8-F/S; WF-9-F/S;
  WF-10-F/S; WF-11-F/S; WF-12-F/S

Type: Air Cel supreme
Length: 30 yd. coils
Color(s): Ivory; mahogany; fluorescent
  orange
AFTMA Designation: WF-4-F; WF-5-F; WF-6-F;
  WF-7-F; WF-8-F; WF-9-F; WF-10-F

Type: Air Cel supreme saltwater taper
Length: 30 yd. coils
Color(s): Ivory; non-glare grey
AFTMA Designation: WF-8-F; WF-9-F;
  WF-10-F; WF-11-F; WF-12-F

Type: Air Cel supreme
Length: 30 yd. coils
Color(s): Ivory; mahogany; fluorescent
  orange
AFTMA Designation: DT-3-F; DT-4-F; DT-5-F;
  DT-6-F; DT-7-F; DT-8-F; DT-9-F; DT-10-F;
  DT-11-F

Type: Air Cel fisherman
Length: 25 yd. coils
Color(s): Kelly green
AFTMA Designation: L-5-I; L-6-I; L-7-I;
  L-8-I; L-9-I

Type: Air Cel fisherman
Length: 30 yd. coils
Color(s): Kelly green
AFTMA Designation: WF-6-I; WF-7-I; WF-8-I;
  WF9-I; WF-10-I; WF-11-I (saltwater
  taper); WF-12-I (saltwater taper)

Type: Air Cel fisherman
Length: 30 yd. coil
Color(s): Kelly green
AFTMA Designation: DT-5-I; DT-6-I; DT-7-I;
  DT-8-I; DT-9-I; DT-10-I

Type: Wet Cel Hi-D extra fast sinking
Length: 30 yd. coils
Color(s): Greenish black
AFTMA Designation: WF-7-S; WF-8-S; WF-9-S;
  WF-10-S; WF-11-S; WF-12-S

Type: Wet Cel Hi-D extra fast sinking
Length: 30 yd. coils
Color(s): Greenish black
AFTMA Designation: DT-7-S; DT-8-S; DT-9-S;
  DT-10-S; DT-11-S; DT-12-S

Type: Wet Cel Hi-D extra fast sinking
Length: 30′ coils
Color(s): Greenish black
AFTMA Designation: ST-7-S; ST-8-S; ST-9-S;
  ST-10-S; ST-11-S

Type: Wet Cel II fast sinking
Length: 25 yd. coils; *also 50 yd. coils
Color(s): Dark green
AFTMA Designation: L-4-S; L-5-S; L-6-S*;
  L-7-S*; L-8-S*; L-9-S*; L-10-S; L-11-S

Type: Wet Cel II fast sinking
Length: 30 yd. coil
Color(s): Dark green
AFTMA Designation: WF-4-S; WF-5-S; WF-6-S;
  WF-7-S; WF-8-S; WF-9-S; WF-10-S;
  WF-11-S; WF-12-S

Type: Wet Cel II fast sinking
Length: 30′ coils
Color(s): Dark green
AFTMA Designation: ST-6-S; ST-7-S; ST-8-S;
  ST-9-S; ST-10-S; ST-11-S

Shakespeare

Type: Presidential fast sinking
Length: 25 yds.
Color(s): Dark green
AFTMA Designation: L-6-S; L-7-S; L-8-S; L-9-S

Type: Presidential fast sinking
Length: 40 yds.
Color(s): Dark green
AFTMA Designation: WF-11-S; WF-12-S

Type: Presidential fast sinking
Length: 30 yds.
Color(s): Dark green
AFTMA Designation: WF-6-S; WF-7-S; WF-8-S;
  WF-9-S; WF-10-S

Type: Presidential fast sinking
Length: 30 yds.
Color(s): Dark green
AFTMA Designation: DT-6-S; DT-7-S; DT-8-S;
  DT-9-S

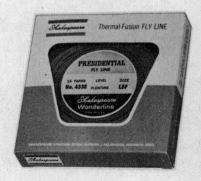

Type: Presidential floating fly line
Length: 25 yds.
Color(s): Green
AFTMA Designation: L-4-F; L-5-F; L-6-F; L-7-F;
  L-8-F; L-9-F

Type: Presidential floating fly line
Length: 30 yds.; WF-10-F: 40 yds.
Color(s): Green
AFTMA Designation: WF-5-F; WF-6-F; WF-7-F;
  WF-8-F; WF-9-F; WF-10-F

Type: Presidential floating fly line
Length: 30 yds.
Color(s): Green
AFTMA Designation: DT-4-F; DT-5-F; DT-6-F;
  DT-7-F; DT-8-F; DT-9-F

Leaders

Berkley

Type: Steelon nylon leader with a heart of steel
Diameter: Not specified
Breaking Strength (in lbs.): 6; 10; 20
Length: 3"; 4"; 5"; 6"; 9"; 12"; 18"; 24"
Color(s): Not specified

Type: Steelon nylon leaders with a heart of steel
Diameter: Not specified
Breaking Strength (in lbs.): 20; 30; 45; 60
Length: 6"; 9"; 12"; 18"; 24"; 36"; 48"; 72"
Color(s): Clear

Type: Qwik sink tippet material
Diameter: 0X to 6X
Breaking Strength (in lbs.): 1¾ to 8
Length: 20 yd. lengths
Color(s): Camouflage

Type: Qwik sink knotless tapered nylon
Diameter: 0X; 1X; 2X; 3X; 4X; 5X; 6X
Breaking Strength (in lbs.): 6; 5; 4; 3; 2½; 2; 1¾
Length: 6'; 7½'; 9'
Color(s): Clear

Type: Knotless heavy tapered nylon
Diameter: 4X; 3X; 2X; 1X; 0X; 8/5; 6/5
Breaking Strength (in lbs.): 2½; 3; 4; 5; 6; 8; 10
Length: 7½'; 9'
Color(s): Clear

Type: Flat butt knotless tapered
Diameter: 0X; 1X; 2X; 3X; 4X; 5X; 6X
Breaking Strength (in lbs.): 6; 5; 4; 3; 2½; 2; 1¾
Length: 9'
Color(s): Camouflage

Cortland

Type: Tapered nylon leaders
Diameter: 6X; 5X; 4X; 3X; 2X; 1X; 0X; 8/5; 6/5
Breaking Strength (in lbs.): 1.5; 2; 3; 3.5; 4.5; 6; 8; 11; 13
Length: 7½'; 9'
Color(s): Mist blue

Danielson

Type: Salmon egg leaders
Diameter: Not specified
Breaking Strength (in lbs.): 1¼; 1¾; 2¼; 2¾; 3
Length: 3'
Color(s): Gold

Type: Mooching rigs
Diameter: Not specified
Breaking Strength (in lbs.): 8-10; 10-12-15; 12-15-20; 15-20-25-30; 25-30-40
Length: 7'
Color(s): Clear

Dragon Fly

Type: Nylon leaders
Diameter: Not specified
Breaking Strength (in lbs.): 30
Length: 24"
Color(s): Clear

Type: Nylo-steel leaders
Diameter: Not specified
Breaking Strength (in lbs.): 30
Length: 6"; 9"; 12"
Color(s): Clear

Type: Stainless steel leaders
Diameter: Not specified
Breaking Strength (in lbs.): 40
Length: 24"
Color(s): Clear

Garcia

Type: Garcia knotless tapered fly leaders
Diameter: 6X; 5X; 4X; 3X; 2X; 1X; 0X
Breaking Strength (in lbs.): 1½; 2; 4; 5; 6; 7; 8
Length: 7½'; 9'
Color(s): Clear

Gladding

Type: Gladding-South Bend knotless tapered leaders

Diameter: Not specified
Breaking Strength (in lbs.): 8; 9; 6.3; 2.1; 12.6
Length: 7½'; 9'
Color(s): Not specified

Type: Gladyl knotless tapered leaders
Diameter: 7X; 6X; 5X; 4X; 3X; 2X; 1X; 0X
Breaking Strength (in lbs.): Not specified
Length: 6' (5X, 4X only); 7½'; 9'
Color(s): Not specified

Type: Clearon knotless tapered nylon fly
Diameter: 6X; 5X; 4X; 3X; 2X; 1X; 0X
Breaking Strength (in lbs.): Not specified
Length: 7½'; 9'
Color(s): Water clear

Herter's

Type: Knotless taper for trout and panfish
Diameter: 4X; 3X; 2X; 1X; 0X
Breaking Strength (in lbs.): 2½; 3; 4½; 5½; 6½
Length: 7½'; 6'; 9'
Color(s): Camouflage; natural translucent

Type: Magnum butt tapered nylon
Diameter: 4X; 3X; 2X; 1X; 0X; 8/5; 6/5
Breaking Strength (in lbs.): 2½; 3; 4; 5; 6; 8
Length: 9'; 12'
Color(s): Camouflage

Type: Nylon covered stainless steel
Diameter: Not specified
Breaking Strength (in lbs.): 10; 20; 30
Length: 3"; 6"; 9"; 12"; 18"; 24"
Color(s): Not specified

Type: Imperial ball bearing swivel nylon covered stainless steel
Diameter: Not specified
Breaking Strength (in lbs.): 10; 20; 30
Length: 3"; 6"; 9"
Color(s): Not specified

Ideal

Type: Knotless tapered leaders
Diameter: 2X; 3X; 4X; 5X
Breaking Strength (in lbs.): Not specified
Length: 7½'
Color(s): Mist grey

Type: Steel core leaders
Diameter: Not specified
Breaking Strength (in lbs.): 15
Length: 4"; 5"; 6"
Color(s): Clear

Type: Steel core leaders
Diameter: Not specified
Breaking Strength (in lbs.): 30
Length: 6"; 9"; 12"
Color(s): Clear

Type: Steel core leaders
Diameter: Not specified
Breaking Strength (in lbs.): 40
Length: 24"
Color(s): Clear

Type: Super-soft monofilament leader
Diameter: Not specified
Breaking Strength (in lbs.): 2; 4; 6; 8; 10
Length: Not specified
Color(s): Mist grey

Kassnar

Type: Nylon coated wire with size 4 swivel & ¾" snap
Diameter: Not specified
Breaking Strength (in lbs.): 40
Length: 6"; 9"; 12"
Color(s): Not specified

Type: Nylon coated wire with size 10 swivel & size 2 interlock snap
Diameter: Not specified
Breaking Strength (in lbs.): 30
Length: 6"; 9"
Color(s): Not specified

Martin

Type: Herring rig with stainless steel leader
Diameter: Not specified
Breaking Strength (in lbs.): Not specified
Length: 18"; 24"; 30"
Color(s): Clear

Type: Mooching leaders
Diameter: Not specified
Breaking Strength (in lbs.): 10 lb. thru 30 lb.
Length: 7'
Color(s): Clear

Type: Dodger leaders
Diameter: Not specified
Breaking Strength (in lbs.): 25 lb. treble
Length: 33"
Color(s): Clear

Orvis

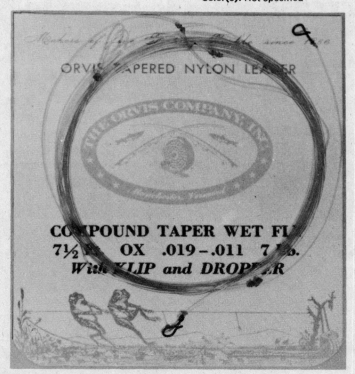

Type: Compound taper wet fly leaders with kwik-klips
Diameter: OX; 1X; 2X; 3X
Breaking Strength (in lbs.): 6; 5; 4; 3½
Length: 7½'; 9'
Color(s): Not specified

Sampo

Type: Steelheart leaders
Diameter: Not specified
Breaking Strength (in lbs.): 6; 10; 20; 30; 45
Length: 3"; 4"; 5"; 6"; 9"; 12"; 18"; 24"; 36"
Color(s): Not specified

MUSKY LEADER

Type: Ball-bearing muskie leaders
Diameter: Not specified
Breaking strength (in lbs.): 45
Length: 9"
Color(s): Not specified

Type: Ball-bearing striper leaders
Diameter: Not specified
Breaking Strength (in lbs.): 45
Length: 18"; 24"; 36"
Color(s): Not specified

Type: Rosco steelheart leader
Diameter: Not specified
Breaking Strength (in lbs.): 6; 10; 20; 30; 45
Length: 3"; 4"; 5"; 6"; 9"; 12"; 18"; 24"; 36"
Color(s): Not specified

SAMPO BALL-BEARING STRIPER LEADERS

Type: Rosco striper leaders
Diameter: Not specified
Breaking Strength (in lbs.): 45
Length: 18"; 24"; 36"
Color(s): Not specified

St. Croix

Type: Golden salmon egg leaders
Diameter: Not specified
Breaking Strength (in lbs.): Not specified
Length: 36"
Color(s): Gold

Type: Nylon steel leader
Diameter: Not specified
Breaking Strength (in lbs.): 20
Length: 6"; 9"; 12"; 18"
Color(s): Clear

Type: Nylon steel leader
Diameter: Not specified
Breaking Strength (in lbs.): 30
Length: 6"; 9"; 12"; 18"
Color(s): Clear

Type: Monofilament snelled leader
Diameter: Not specified
Breaking Strength (in lbs.): 10; 20
Length: 6"; 9"; 12"
Color(s): Clear

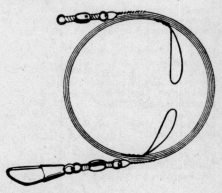

Type: Surf leaders
Diameter: Not specified

Breaking Strength (in lbs.): 10; 15; 20; 30; 40; 50
Length: 36″
Color(s): Clear

Type: Mooching leaders
Diameter: Not specified
Breaking Strength (in lbs.): 20
Length: Not specified
Color(s): Clear

Universal

Type: Sinking Tippet Material
Diameter: 6X; 5X; 4X; 3X; 2X; 1X; 0X; 00X
Breaking Strength (in lbs.): Not specified
Length: 30′ spools
Color(s): Not specified

Type: Knotless sinking tapered leader
Diameter: 5X; 4X; 3X; 2X; 1X; 0X; 00X
Breaking Strength (in lbs.): Not specified
Length: 7½′; 9′ (0X and 00X available in 9′ only)
Color(s): Green

Weber

Type: Trolorcast nylon leaders
Diameter: Not specified
Breaking Strength (in lbs.): 10; 15; 20
Length: 6″; 9″; 12″
Color(s): Camouflaged; mist

Type: Tied tapered nylon leaders
Diameter: 5X; 4X; 3X; 2X; 1X; 0X
Breaking Strength (in lbs.): 1½; 2; 2½; 3; 3½; 4½
Length: 6′; 7½′; 9′
Color(s): Camouflaged; mist; natural

Type: Kwik-cast nylon leaders
Diameter: Not specified

Breaking Strength (in lbs.): 6; 8; 10; 12; 15; 20
Length: 3′; 4½′; 6′
Color(s): Camouflaged; mist

Type: 3″ "shorty" kant kink wire leaders
Diameter: Not specified
Breaking Strength (in lbs.): 10
Length: 3″
Color(s): Clear nylon over bright wire

Type: Kant kink wire leaders
Diameter: Not specified
Breaking Strength (in lbs.): 20; 30
Length: 6″; 9″; 12″; 18″; 24″; 36″; 72″
Color(s): Clear nylon over bright wire

Type: "Big butt" knotless tapered nylon leaders
Diameter: 6X; 5X; 4X; 3X; 2X; 1X
Breaking Strength (in lbs.): 1¼; 2; 2½; 3; 4; 5
Length: 7½′; 9′
Color(s): Camouflaged

Type: "Sink" knotless tapered nylon trout leaders
Diameter: 5X; 4X; 3X; 2X; 1X
Breaking Strength (in lbs.): 2.8; 3.5; 4.2; 5.6; 7.0
Length: 7½′; 9′; 12′
Color(s): Camouflaged glint-free

Type: "No-sheen" knotless tapered nylon leaders
Diameter: 6X; 5X; 4X; 3X; 2X; 1X; 0X; 8/5; 6/5
Breaking Strength (in lbs.): 1¼; 2; 2½; 3; 4; 5; 6; 8; 10
Length: 7½′; 9′
Color(s): Camouflaged

Type: Knotless level nylon leaders
Diameter: Not specified

Breaking Strength (in lbs.): 2; 3; 4; 6; 8; 10; 15; 20
Length: 3′; 4½′; 6′; 7½′
Color(s): Camouflaged; mist; natural

Worth

Type: Stainless steel wire covered nylon leaders with durable nylon
Diameter: Not specified
Breaking Strength (in lbs.): 10; 20; 30
Length: 6″; 9″; 12″; 18″
Color(s): Not specified

WORTH PIANO WIRE LEADERS

Type: Piano wire leader with attached snap and swivel
Diameter: .018
Breaking Strength (in lbs.): Not specified
Length: 6″; 9″; 12″; 18″; 24″
Color(s): Not specified

Type: Heavy duty knotless tapered
Diameter: 6X; 5X; 4X; 3X; 2X; 1X; 0X; 9/5; 8/5; 7/5; 6/5; 5/5
Breaking Strength (in lbs.): 1.5; 2.5; 3; 3.5; 4.5; 6.8; 7.5; 9; 10.3; 11; 12.5
Length: 7½′; 9′; 12′
Color(s): Not specified

Type: Sinking knotless tapered
Diameter: 6X; 5X; 4X; 3X; 2X; 1X; 0X; 8/5; 6/5
Breaking Strength (in lbs.): 1.7; 2.5; 3.5; 4.5; 5.5; 7.5; 9.5; 11.5
Length: 7½′; 9′; 12′
Color(s): Clear

Specifications: Accessories

Bait Boxes

Mfr.: The American Import Company
Model No.: 55065
Size: Not specified
Tray(s): 1
Compartment(s): 2
Material: Plastic

Mfr.: Flambeau Products Corporation
Model No.: 5130
Size: ½" x 6⅛" x 1½"
Tray(s): 1
Compartment(s): Not specified
Material: Tenite with metal rust-proof
   hinges

Mfr.: Gladding Corporation
Model No.: 7-001-600
Size: Not specified
Tray(s): Not specified
Compartment(s): Not specified
Material: Polyolefin

Mfr.: Old Pal
Model No.: 10
Size: 6" x 3½" x 2"
Tray(s): Not specified
Compartment(s): 1
Material: Steel

Mfr.: Old Pal
Model No.: P30
Size: 7⅜" x 4⅝" x 7½"
Tray(s): Not specified
Compartment(s): Not specified
Material: Polypropylene

Mfr.: Old Pal
Model No.: 300
Size: 6" x 3½" x 2"
Tray(s): Not specified
Compartment(s): 2
Material: Polyethylene

Mfr.: Outers Laboratories, Inc.
Model No.: 590
Size: Not specified
Tray(s): Not specified
Compartment(s): Not specified
Material: Polypropylene

Mfr.: H. S. Ross
Model: Bait Baffler
Size: Not specified
Tray(s): Not specified
Compartment(s): Not specified
Material: Lightweight aluminum

Baskets

Mfr.: The American Import Company
Model No.: 55043
Material: ⁹⁄₁₆" unichrome-plated wire mesh
Length: 24"
Diameter: 14½"

Mfr.: The American Import Company
Model No.: 55047
Material: ⁹⁄₁₆" unichrome-plated wire mesh
Length: 22½"
Diameter: 17" oval

Mfr.: The American Import Company
Model No.: 55048
Material: Unichrome-plated mesh with
   polypropylene trap door
Length: 24"
Diameter: 14½"

Mfr.: The Danielson Company
Model No.: W-6
Material: Wire
Length: 18"
Diameter: 13½"

Mfr.: Dragon Fly Company, Inc.
Model No.: 3ZDT
Material: Zinc plated
Size: 13½" x 18½"

Mfr.: Gladding Corporation
Model No.: MB-3
Material: Wire mesh
Width: 16"
Depth: 20"

Mfr.: Ideal Products, Inc.
Model No.: N-19
Material: Collapsible wire
Length: 19"
Diameter: 14"

Mfr.: Ideal Products, Inc.
Model No.: N-22
Material: Collapsible metal
Length: 21"
Diameter: 15"

Mfr.: Kassnar Imports
Model No.: FK1101
Material: Wire
Length: 24"
Diameter: 14"

Mfr.: Lindy/Little Joe
Model No.: AC231
Material: ⅝" wire mesh
Length: 24"
Diameter: 14"

Mfr.: Nylon Net Co.
Model No.: 430
Material: Polyethylene plastic
Length: 14½"
Diameter: 19" top, 14½" bottom

Mfr.: Nylon Net Co.
Model No.: WB-1
Material: Wire
Length: 21"
Diameter: 15"

Mfr.: St. Croix Corporation
Model No.: W-6
Material: Not specified
Length: 24"
Diameter: 14"

Mfr.: St. Croix Corporation
Model No.: W-18
Material: Not specified
Length: 28"
Diameter: 15"

Mfr.: St. Croix Corporation
Model No.: W-51
Material: Not specified
Length: 20"
Diameter: 12"

Crab Traps

Mfr.: The American Import Company
Model No.: 55055
Material: Unichrome Welded steel
Size: Bottom: 12½" x 11½";
   side: 10½" x 10½"
Net: 1" x 2" mesh

Mfr.: The American Import Company
Model No.: 55056
Material: Not specified
Size: Star shaped, bottom: 16" x 16";
   height: 15"
Net: 1" x 2" mesh

Mfr.: Back Porch Industries, Inc.
Model: Crabnapper
Material: Galvanized wire
Size: 16" x 16" x 7½"
Net: ½" sq. mesh

Mfr.: The Danielson Company
Model No.: JWB-16
Material: Unichrome-plated mesh
Size: 16" x 16"
Net: Not specified

Mfr.: The Danielson Company
Model No.: JWB-1000
Material: Plastic ring, wire bottom
Size: 15½" x 24"
Net: Knotted

Mfr.: Dragon Fly Company, Inc.
Model No.: 510T
Material: Not specified
Size: 10½" x 10½" x 10½"
Net: Not specified

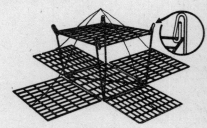

Mfr.: Isaac Franklin Co., Inc.
Model No.: 120
Material: Galvanized wire
Size: 12" x 12" x 10"
Net: Galvanized wire

Mfr.: Old Pal
Model No.: 666
Material: Plastic

Size: 15" x 16" x 10"
Net: Green

Creels

Mfr.: The American Import Company
Model No.: 55373
Size: 11½" x 17½"
Material: Nylon and rubber

Mfr.: The American Import Company
Model No.: 56863
Size: 13" wide
Material: Rattan

Mfr.: The American Import Company
Model No.: 57651
Size: 19" x 12"
Material: Rubberized rayon

Mfr.: Colorado Tent & Awning Company
Model No.: 1 ArtiCreel
Size: 9" x 15" x 4"
Material: Flax water bag canvas with
   plastic sealer

Mfr.: Colorado Tent & Awning Company
Model No.: 20 ArtiCreel
Size: 10" x 14" x 4"
Material: Flax water bag canvas with
   plastic sealer

Mfr.: The Danielson Company
Model No.: G-20
Size: 12½" x 20"
Material: Canvas

Mfr.: The Danielson Company
Model No.: 8381
Size: 9½" x 15"
Material: Canvas

Mfr.: Gladding Corporation
Model No.: DL15
Size: 15" long
Material: Split willow

Mfr.: Herter's Inc.
Model No.: LE8A5A
Size: 14" x 6½" x 8"
Material: Split willow

Mfr.: Herter's Inc.
Model No.: LE8A7
Size: 11½" x 6" x 6½"
Material: Polyethylene

Mfr.: Ideal Products, Inc.
Model No.: 41

Size: 16" x 9" x 6"
Material: Fiberglass screen poly form lining

Mfr.: Ideal Products, Inc.
Model No.: 40
Size: 14" x 8½" x 2"
Material: Rubberized cloth

Mfr: Kassnar Imports
Model No.: FP1001
Size: 12" x 17"
Material: Varnished rattan

Mfr.: Pueblo Tent & Awning Co., Inc.
Model No.: KK-1
Size: 15" x 11" x 4"
Material: Scotch flax with plastic liner

Mfr.: Pueblo Tent & Awning Co., Inc.
Model No.: KK-10
Size: 15" x 11" x 14"
Material: Scotch flax with plastic liner

Mfr.: Rogue River Fishing Creel, Inc.
Model: Creel
Size: 15" x 7" x 7½"
Material: Polypropylene plastic

Mfr.: St. Croix Corporation
Model No.: F390
Size: 17" x 10½"
Material: Canvas

Mfr.: St. Croix Corporation
Model No.: F393
Size: 15½" x 9½"
Material: Canvas

Mfr.: St. Croix Corporation
Model No.: F395
Size: 18" x 11½"
Material: Canvas

Mfr.: Fritz Von Schlegell
Model No.: 103 Artic Creel
Size: Not specified
Material: Plastic inner liner

Mfr.: Fritz Von Schlegell
Model No.: K-340
Size: Not specified
Material: Rubberized nylon

Electronic Depth-Sounding Equipment

Mfr.: Apelco
Model No.: MS110

Depth Range: 100'
Size: 7" x 5¼" x 5¾"
Type: Flasher

Mfr.: Fishmaster Products, Inc.
Model No.: DF-7
Depth Range: Not specified
Size: Not specified
Type: Flasher

Mfr.: Fishmaster Products, Inc.
Model No.: DM-100S
Depth Range: Not specified
Size: Not specified
Type: Meter

Mfr.: Gladding
Model No.: 1200
Depth Range: 240'
Size: Not specified
Type: Flasher

Mfr.: Gladding
Model No.: 1060
Depth Range: 120'
Size: Not specified
Type: Flasher

Mfr.: Ray Jefferson Div., Jetronic Industries
Model No.: Depthmeter 400
Depth Range: 12' low, 120' high
Size: 7" x 9½" x 2¾"
Type: Meter

Mfr.: Lowrance
Model No.: LFP150
Depth Range: 100'
Size: Not specified
Type: Flasher

Mfr.: Lowrance
Model No.: LFG150
Depth Range: 100'
Size: Not specified
Type: Flasher

Mfr.: Lowrance
Model No.: LFP300
Depth Range: 100'
Size: 6" wide, 9" deep
Type: Flasher

Mfr.: Lowrance
Model No.: LFG305
Depth Range: 100'
Size: 8" high, 5" deep
Type: Flasher

Mfr.: Lowrance
Model No.: LFG325
Depth Range: 200'
Size: 8" high, 5" deep
Type: Flasher

Mfr.: Raytheon Co.
Model No.: DE732
Depth Range: 120'
Size: 7¾" x 6¾" x 5¾"
Type: Flasher

Mfr.: Shakespeare
Model No.: DF-1
Depth Range: 200'
Size: Not specified
Type: Flasher

Mfr.: Shakespeare
Model No.: DF-3
Depth Range: 100'
Size: Not specified
Type: Flasher

Mfr.: Shakespeare
Model No.: DF-4
Depth Range: 6'-360'
Size: Not specified
Type: Flasher

Mfr.: Shakespeare
Model: ScanMaster
Depth Range: 200'
Size: 5 lbs.
Type: Flasher

Mfr.: Telisons International Corporation
Model No.: AS-100B
Depth Range: 780' with 40° beam angle
Size: 10¾" x 6¾" x 3" (less transducer)
Type: Flasher

Mfr.: Telisons International Corporation
Model No.: AS-100C
Depth Range: 780' with 8° beam angle
Size: 10¾" x 6¾" x 3" (less transducer)
Type: Flasher

Mfr.: Telisons International Corporation
Model No.: AS-100STC
Depth Range: 780'
Size: 10¾" x 6¾" x 3" (less transducer)
Type: Flasher

Mfr.: Vexilar, Inc.
Model No.: 360
Depth Range: Not specified
Handle: Pakawood
Type: Flasher

Mfr.: Vexilar, Inc.
Model No.: 510
Depth Range: 200'
Size: Not specified
Type: Flasher

Mfr.: Waller Corporation
Model No.: 102
Depth Range: 100' +
Size: 6½" x 6" x 11"
Type: Flasher

Mfr.: Waller Corporation
Model No.: 202
Depth Range: 200' +
Size: 6½" x 6" x 11"
Type: Flasher

Mfr.: Waller Corporation
Model No.: 204
Depth Range: Not specified
Size: 8" x 6" x 8¼"
Type: Flasher

Mfr.: Waller Corporation
Model No.: 301
Depth Range: 200' +
Size: Not specified
Type: Flasher

Mfr.: Waller Corporation
Model No.: 303
Depth Range: 200' +
Size: 5½" x 6" x 9"
Type: Flasher

Mfr.: Waller Corporation
Model No.: 304
Depth Range: Not specified
Size: 8" x 6" x 8¼"
Type: Flasher

Mfr.: Waller Corporation
Model No.: 404
Depth Range: 60'
Size: 8" x 6" x 8¼"
Type: Flasher

Mfr.: Waller Corporation
Model No.: 530
Depth Range: 100'
Size: Not specified
Type: Digital meter

Mfr.: Waller Corporation
Model No.: 550

Depth Range: 100'
Size: Not specified
Type: Meter

Mfr.: Waller Corporation
Model No.: 600
Depth Range: 80'
Size: 12¾" x 2¼" x 6½" folded
Type: Meter

Gaff Hooks

Mfr.: The American Import Company
Model No.: 55158
Overall Length: 11¾" extended, 6½" closed
Gaff: Stainless steel
Grip: Plastic

Mfr.: The American Import Company
Model No.: 55161
Overall Length: 11½"
Gaff: Stainless steel
Grip: Not specified

Mfr.: The Danielson Company
Model No.: 1
Overall Length: 26"
Gaff: Not specified
Grip: Not specified

Mfr.: The Danielson Company
Model No.: 2
Overall Length: 18½"
Gaff: Not specified
Grip: Not specified

Mfr.: Gladding Corporation
Model No.: 1SS-12
Overall Length: Not specified
Gaff: Stainless steel
Grip: 12" wooden

Mfr.: Gladding Corporation
Model No.: 7-900-100
Overall Length: Not specified
Gaff: Stainless steel
Grip: 10" rosewood nylon wrapped

Mfr.: Herter's Inc.
Model No.: GA3D4
Overall Length: 24"
Gaff: 4½" with 2⅞" bite, 2½" gap
cadmium-plated hooks
Grip: Ash

Mfr.: Ideal Products, Inc.
Model No.: 357
Overall Length: 24½"
Gaff: Chrome-plated
Grip: Wood

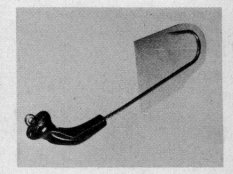

Mfr.: Jet-Aer
Model No.: 2080
Overall Length: 19"
Gaff: Tempered stainless steel
Grip: 6" sure-grip, non-slip

Mfr.: Jet-Aer
Model No.: 2090
Overall Length: 13"
Gaff: Tempered stainless steel
Grip: 6" sure-grip, non-slip

Mfr.: Martin Tackle & Manufacturing Co.
Model No.: G55
Overall Length: 6" x 2" x 16"
Gaff: Cadmium-plated steel
Grip: Wood

Mfr.: Martin Tackle & Manufacturing Co.
Model No.: G66
Overall Length: 6" x 2" x 30"
Gaff: Cadmium-plated steel
Grip: Wood

Mfr.: Martin Tackle & Manufacturing Co.
Model No.: G77
Overall Length: 7" x 3" x 36"
Gaff: Tempered steel
Grip: Wood

Mfr.: Pompanette, Inc.
Model No.: 38
Overall Length: 8"
Gaff: 3" stainless steel
Grip: Aluminum

Mfr.: Pompanette, Inc.
Model No.: 56
Overall Length: Not specified
Gaff: 5" stainless steel
Grip: 6" aluminum

Mfr.: Pompanette, Inc.
Model: Fiberglass gaff
Overall Length: Not specified
Gaff: 2" stainless steel
Grip: 3" fiberglass

Mfr.: Sampo
Model No.: G44
Overall Length: Not specified
Gaff: 5/16" diameter, forged stainless steel
Grip: 36" aluminum; 1 1/8" diameter

Mfr.: Shurkatch Fishing Tackle Co., Inc.
Model No.: 11-L
Overall Length: 14"
Gaff: 2" baked enamel finish on spring steel
Grip: 8" turned

Mfr.: Shurkatch Fishing Tackle Co., Inc.
Model No.: 11-SS
Overall Length: 9 1/2"
Gaff: Nickel-chromium stainless steel
Grip: Wood

Mfr.: Shurkatch Fishing Tackle Co., Inc.
Model No.: 24
Overall Length: Not specified
Gaff: 3" baked enamel finish
Grip: 24"

Mfr.: Shurkatch Fishing Tackle Co., Inc.
Model No.: 20SS
Overall Length: 5 1/2"

Gaff: 2" gap
Grip: 7/32" wire

Mfr.: True Temper
Model No.: G9
Overall Length: Not specified
Gaff: Plated 5/16" steel rod
Grip: 9" ash

Mfr.: True Temper
Model No.: G36
Overall Length: Not specified
Gaff: Plated 5/16" steel rod
Grip: 24"

Mfr.: True Temper
Model No.: G48
Overall Length: Not specified
Gaff: Plated 5/16" steel rod
Grip: 48" ash

Knives

American Import

Model No.: 55110
Overall Length: 10" closed
Blade Length: 3 1/2"
Blade(s): 1 (cutting, scaler)
Handle: Wooden (square)
Sheath: Wooden (square)

Model No.: 55111
Overall Length: 8 1/4"
Blade Length: 4 1/4"
Blade(s): 1 stainless steel with scaler
Handle: Not specified
Sheath: Plastic

Model No.: 55112
Overall Length: 8"
Blade Length: 3 3/4"
Blade(s): 1 stainless steel with scaler
Handle: Wooden

Model No.: 55113
Overall Length: 8 1/4"
Blade Length: 3 5/8"
Blade(s): 1 stainless steel
Handle: Wooden

Model No.: 55116
Overall Length: 5"
Blade Length: 4"
Blade(s): 2 stainless steel (cutting; disgorger, scaler)
Handle: Imitation pearl

Model No.: 57714
Overall Length: 10 1/2"
Blade Length: 6"
Blade(s): 1 stainless steel
Handle: Wooden

Model No.: 57716
Overall Length: 11"
Blade Length: 5 3/4"
Blade(s): 1 stainless steel
Handle: Wooden
Sheath: Plastic

Buck

Model No.: 102
Overall Length: Not specified
Blade Length: 4"
Blade(s): 1 high carbon steel
Handle: Ebony

Sheath: Genuine saddle leather

Model No.: 121
Overall Length: Not specified
Blade Length: 5 1/2"
Blade(s): 1 high carbon steel
Handle: Ebony
Sheath: Genuine saddle leather

Camillus

Model No.: 5
Overall Length: 5" closed
Blade Length: Not specified
Blade(s): 1 chrome-plated sabre clip
Handle: Maize

Model No.: 25
Overall Length: 5" closed
Blade Length: Not specified
Blade(s): 2 stainless steel sabre clip (serrated tip; hook disgorger, scaler, bottle cap lifter)
Handle: Genuine maize

Model No.: 31
Overall Length: 5" closed
Blade Length: Not specified
Blade(s): 2 stainless steel sabre clip (cutting; hook disgorger-fish scaler, cap lifter)
Handle: Indian stag

W. R. Case & Sons

Model No.: 116-8" F w/sh
Overall Length: Not specified
Blade Length: 8"
Blade(s): 1 stainless steel
Handle: Walnut
Sheath: Leather

Model No.: 124-6" w/sh
Overall Length: Not specified
Blade Length: 6"
Blade(s): 1 stainless steel
Handle: Rosewood
Sheath: Leather

Model No.: P203-6" w/sh
Overall Length: Not specified
Blade Length: 6"
Blade(s): 1 chrome-plated
Handle: Pakawood
Sheath: Leather

Model No.: 32095 FSS
Overall Length: 5" closed
Blade Length: Not specified
Blade(s): 2 stainless steel (cutting; disgorger, scaler)
Handle: Composition

Model: Fly Fisherman SS
Overall Length: 3 7/8" closed
Blade Length: Not specified
Blade(s): 4 stainless steel (cutting; scissors; pick; file)
Handle: Stainless steel

Danielson

Model No.: 311-C
Overall Length: 12 1/4"
Blade Length: 6"
Blade(s): 1 stainless steel (waved edge)
Handle: Not specified

Model No.: 4018-A

Overall Length: 6¼"
Blade Length: 3"
Blade(s): 1 carbon steel
Handle: Not specified

Model No.: 9719
Overall Length: 10¼"
Blade Length: 3⅜"
Blade(s): 1 stainless steel with scaler
Handle: Cherrywood with brown lacquered finish
Sheath: Cherrywood with brown lacquered finish

Model No.: 10215-A
Overall Length: 9"
Blade Length: 4"
Blade(s): Not specified
Handle: Not specified
Sheath: Not specified

Gladding

Model No.: 6FK
Overall Length: Not specified
Blade Length: Not specified
Blade(s): 1 stainless steel
Handle: Hardwood
Sheath: Leather

Model No.: 9FK
Overall Length: Not specified
Blade Length: Not specified
Blade(s): 1 stainless steel
Handle: Not specified
Sheath: Unbreakable

Model No.: 10FK
Overall Length: Not specified
Blade Length: Not specified
Blade(s): 2 (cutting; scaler)
Handle: Cork

Model No.: 14CK
Overall Length: Not specified
Blade Length: Not specified
Blade(s): Not specified
Handle: Wood

Model No.: 15BK
Overall Length: Not specified
Blade Length: 4¼"
Blade(s): 1 stainless steel (serrated)
Handle: Wooden

Model No.: 17
Overall Length: 4¾" closed
Blade Length: Not specified
Blade(s): 2 (cutting; scaler, disgorger, bottle opener, screwdriver)
Handle: Not specified

Model No.: 32
Overall Length: 10½"
Blade Length: 6"
Blade(s): 1 stainless steel (cutting, scaler)
Handle: Hardwood

Model No.: 431
Overall Length: 11"
Blade Length: 6"
Blade(s): 1 stainless steel
Handle: Hardwood

Model No.: CSS
Overall Length: Not specified
Blade Length: 3½"
Blade(s): 1 stainless steel
Handle: Wood

Model No.: 7-9000-002 Norseman
Overall Length: Not specified
Blade Length: Not specified
Blade(s): 1 stainless steel
Handle: Rosewood
Sheath: Included

Model: Feather-Edge
Overall Length: Not specified
Blade Length: Not specified
Blade(s): 1 stainless steel
Handle: Rosewood
Sheath: Safety

Herter's

Model No.: AJ50
Overall Length: Not specified
Blade Length: 8"
Blade(s): Carona plus carbon steel
Handle: Rosewood

Model No.: AJFA2
Overall Length: 9½"
Blade Length: 5"
Blade(s): 1 carona plus carbon steel
Handle: African tiger wood

Model No.: AJ5S1
Overall Length: 11"
Blade Length: 6"
Blade(s): 1 Swedish stainless steel
Handle: Wood
Sheath: Leather

Model No.: AJ5S2. Same as Model AJ5S1 except:
Overall Length: 8½"
Blade Length: 4"

Ideal

Model No.: 64
Overall Length: Not specified
Blade Length: 6"
Blade(s): 1 stainless steel
Handle: Vista fiber
Sheath: Leather

Model No.: 71
Overall Length: 9½"
Blade Length: 5"
Blade(s): 1 stainless steel
Handle: Wood
Sheath: Rubber-vinyl

Model No.: 73
Overall Length: Not specified
Blade Length: 3½"
Blades(s): 1 stainless steel (cutting, scaler)
Handle: Wood

Model No.: 75
Overall Length: Not specified
Blade Length: 5"
Blades(s): 1 stainless steel (cutting, scaler)
Handle: Wood

Model No.: 89
Overall Length: Not specified
Blade Length: 3¾"
Blade(s): 2 (cutting; disgorger, scaler, cap lifter)
Handle: Plastic

Model No.: 93
Overall Length: 5" closed
Blade Length: Not specified
Blade(s): 2 (cutting; disgorger, scaler, cap lifter)
Handle: Black stag

Model No.: 94
Overall Length: 10½"
Blade Length: 4½"
Blades(s): 1 stainless steel (cutting, scaler, cap lifter)
Handle: Wood
Sheath: Wood

Model No.: 95
Overall Length: 4½"
Blade Length: Not specified
Blade(s): 3 stainless steel (cutting; scaler, disgorger, cap lifter; scissors)
Handle: Simulated pearl

International

Model No.: R14010
Overall Length: 11"
Blade Length: 6½"
Blade(s): 1 stainless steel
Handle: Wood
Sheath: Molded

Model No.: R14030
Overall Length: Not specified
Blade Length: 3¼"
Blade(s): 1 stainless steel
Handle: Not specified

Model No.: R14040
Overall Length: Not specified
Blade Length: 4⅝"
Blade(s): 1 stainless steel
Handle: Paulownia wood
Sheath: Paulownia wood

Model No.: R14050
Overall Length: Not specified
Blade Length: Not specified
Blade(s): 2
Handle: Pearl plastic

Model No.: R14070
Overall Length: Not specified
Blade Length: 4⅝"
Blade(s): 1
Handle: Not specified
Sheath: Not specified

Model No.: R14350
Overall Length: Not specified
Blade Length: 6"
Blade(s): 1 stainless steel
Handle: Hardwood
Sheath: Leather

IPCO

Model No.: Mark I
Overall Length: Not specified
Blade Length: 6"
Blade(s): 1 Swedish stainless steel
Handle: Hardwood
Sheath: Ebony

Model No.: Mark V
Overall Length: Not specified
Blade Length: 6"
Blade(s): 1 Swedish high carbon steel
Handle: Hardwood
Sheath: Leather

Model No.: Mark IX
Overall Length: Not specified
Blade Length: 9"
Blade(s): 1 Swedish high carbon steel

Handle: Hardwood
Sheath: Leather

Model No.: Pro-6
Overall Length: Not specified
Blade Length: 6″
Blade(s): 1 Swedish high carbon steel
Handle: Ebony
Sheath: Leather

Model No.: OB-6
Overall Length: Not specified
Blade Length: 6″
Blade(s): 1 Swedish high carbon steel
Handle: Pearl
Sheath: Leather

Jet-Aer

Model No.: 2000
Overall Length: 9½″
Blade Length: 4¾″
Blade(s): 1 rustproof steel
Handle: Not specified
Sheath: Plastic

Model No.: 2010
Overall Length: 11″
Blade Length: 6¼″
Blade(s): 1 rustproof steel
Handle: Not specified
Sheath: Plastic

Model No.: 2020
Overall Length: 11½″
Blade Length: 6¾″
Blade(s): 1 rustproof steel
Handle: Not specified
Sheath: Plastic

Model No.: 2030
Overall Length: 12¾″
Blade Length: 8″
Blade(s): 1 rustproof steel
Handle: Not specified
Sheath: Plastic

Model No.: 2040
Overall Length: 12¾″
Blade Length: 7¾″
Blade(s): 1 rustproof steel (cutting, scaler)
Handle: Not specified
Sheath: Plastic

Model No.: 2050
Overall Length: 16¼″
Blade Length: 11¼″
Blade(s): 1 rustproof steel (cutting, scaler)
Handle: Not specified
Sheath: Plastic

Model No.: 2060
Overall Length: 12¼″
Blade Length: 7¼″
Blade(s): 1 rustproof steel (cutting, scaler)
Handle: Not specified
Sheath: Plastic

Model No.: 2070
Overall Length: 4⅞″ closed
Blade Length: 4″
Blade(s): 2 (cutting; hook remover)
Handle: Brass and Pacca wood
Sheath: Not specified

Kassnar

Model No.: FI0554
Overall Length: 11½″
Blade Length: 6¼″
Blade(s): 1 stainless steel
Handle: Rosewood
Sheath: Not specified

Model No.: FI0058
Overall Length: 10½″
Blade Length: 6″
Blade(s): 1 stainless steel (cutting, scaler)
Handle: Rosewood

Model No.: FI1151
Overall Length: 10¾″
Blade Length: 6″
Blade(s): 1 stainless steel
Handle: Laminated pakawood
Sheath: Leather

Model No.: FI5408
Overall Length: Not specified
Blade Length: 4″
Blade(s): 3 (cutting; disgorger, scaler and bottle opener; folding scissors)
Handle: Not specified

Model No.: FI5602
Overall Length: Not specified
Blade Length: 4″
Blade(s): 2 (cutting; combination disgorger, scaler and bottle opener)
Handle: Not specified

Model No.: FI6005
Overall Length: Not specified
Blade Length: 3½″
Blade(s): 1 stainless steel (cutting, scaler)
Handle: Wood

Model No.: FI6102
Overall Length: Not specified
Blade Length: 2⅜″
Blade(s): Not specified
Handle: Wood

M. C. Matthews

Model No.: 8 piece Trout Fisherman's Knife
Overall Length: 4″ closed
Blade Length: Not specified
Blade(s): 8 (2 cutting; file; pick; scissor; tweezer; cork screw; cap lifter)
Handle: Stainless steel
Sheath: Leather

Normark

Model No.: DP306
Overall Length: 10¾″
Blade Length: 6″
Blade(s): 1 carbon, molybdenum and chromium steel
Handle: Ebony
Sheath: Tooled Oxide

Model No.: FNF-4
Overall Length: 7¾″
Blade Length: 4″
Blade(s): 1 stainless steel
Handle: Reinforced birch
Sheath: Tooled leather

Model No.: FNF-6. Same as Model FNF-4 except:
Overall Length: 10¾″
Blade Length: 6″

Model No.: FNF-9. Same as Model FNF-4 except:
Overall Length: 14¼″
Blade Length: 9″

Olsen

Model No.: 109
Overall Length: Not specified
Blade Length: Not specified
Blade(s): 2 (cutting; hook disgorger, straightener)
Handle: Not specified

Model No.: 213-F
Overall Length: Not specified
Blade Length: 6″
Blade(s): 1 high carbon steel
Handle: Not specified

Model No.: 251
Overall Length: Not specified
Blade Length: 3½″
Blade(s): 1
Handle: Not specified

Model No.: 265
Overall Length: Not specified
Blade Length: 5″
Blade(s): 1 high carbon steel
Handle: Not specified

Name: Fisherman Swiss Army Knife
Overall Length: 3½″ closed
Blade Length: Not specified
Blade(s): 8 (2 cutting; reamer; hook disgorger; scaler; can opener; cap lifter; phillips screwdriver; scissors; tweezers)
Handle: Elsinid plastic

Model: CK Coho Knife
Overall Length: Not specified
Blade Length: Not specified
Blade(s): 1 high carbon steel
Handle: Not specified

Model: Champion Swiss Army Knife
Overall Length: 3½″ closed
Blade Length: Not specified
Blade(s): 11 (2 cutting; can opener; cap lifter; reamer; phillips screwdriver; tweezer; pick; double-cut saw; scaler, hook disgorger; nail file, metal file; scissors)
Handle: Elsinid plastic

Sampo

Model No.: K706B
Overall Length: Not specified
Blade Length: 6″
Blade(s): 1 carbon steel (cutting, scaler)
Handle: Hardwood
Sheath: Leather

Model No.: K736B
Overall Length: Not specified
Blade Length: 6″
Blade(s): 1 stainless steel
Handle: Hardwood
Sheath: Leather

Model No.: K755B
Overall Length: Not specified
Blade Length: 6″
Blade(s): 1 tungsten steel

Handle: Agatewood
Sheath: Leather

Model No.: K756B
Overall Length: Not specified
Blade Length: 6″
Blade(s): 1 tungsten steel
Handle: Agatewood
Sheath: Leather

Model No.: K757B. Same as K755B except:
Blade Length: 7½″

Model No.: K759B
Overall Length: Not specified
Blade Length: 9″
Blade(s): 1 tungsten stainless steel
Handle: Agatewood
Sheath: Leather

Smith & Wesson

Model No.: 6040
Overall Length: 11½″
Blade Length: 6½″
Blade(s): 1 stainless steel
Handle: Rosewood
Sheath: Cowhide

Model No.: 6050
Overall Length: 10½″
Blade Length: 5½″
Blade(s): 1 stainless steel
Handle: Rosewood
Sheath: Cowhide

Syl-Mark Enterprises

Model No.: 660
Overall Length: Not specified
Blade Length: 3½″
Blade(s): 1 stainless steel (cutting, scaler)
Handle: Leather
Sheath: Leather

Tru-Nord

Model No.: S-9156-PK
Overall Length: 11″
Blade Length: 6″
Blade(s): 1 Swedish stainless steel
Handle: Polypropen
Sheath: Not specified

Western Cutlery

Model No.: S-751
Overall Length: 4⅜″
Blade Length: Not specified
Blade(s): 2 (cutter; scaler, disgorger and cap lifter)
Handle: Composition

Model No.: SW769-Super Fillet
Overall Length: 14″
Blade Length: 9″
Blade(s): 1 stainless steel
Handle: Hardwood

Model No.: SW766
Overall Length: 11″
Blade Length: 6″
Blade(s): 1
Handle: Hardwood

Lure Boxes

Mfr.: Dragon Fly Company, Inc.
Model No.: 556
Size: 4¼″ x 8¼″
Compartments: 6
Material: Plastic

Mfr.: Gladding Corp.
Model No.: 7-000-006
Size: 3¼″ x ¾″
Compartments: 6
Material: Plastic

Mfr.: Herter's
Model No.: AC7E2
Size: 3¾″ x 2¾″ x ⅞″
Compartments: Not specified
Material: Duraluminum

Mfr.: Old Pal
Model No.: 380
Size: 9¼″ x 4″ x 2″
Compartments: 9
Material: Plastic

Mfr.: Old Pal
Model No.: 360
Size: 4⅝″ x 3″ x 1³⁄₁₆″
Compartments: 4
Material: Plastic

Mfr.: Old Pal
Model No.: 365A
Size: 11″ x 6¾″ x 1¾″
Compartments: 18
Material: Plastic

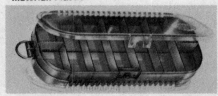

Mfr.: Old Pal
Model No.: P31
Size: 7⅜″ x 4⁵⁄₁₆″ x 7½″
Compartments: Not specified
Material: Polypropylene

Mfr.: Sampo
Model No.: 26A
Size: 8¼″ x 4¼″ x 1⅛″
Compartments: 18
Material: Butyrate

Nets

Type of net: Landing
Mfr.: The American Import Company
Model No.: 596
Overall Length: 17″
Handle: Rubber grip
Frame: 10½″ x 12½″ aluminum
Net: Cotton
Net Depth: 18″

Type of net: Minnow Bucket Dip
Mfr.: The American Import Company
Model No.: 55050
Overall Length: Not specified

Handle: 7″
Frame: 3⅝″ x 4⅞″ wire, D-shaped
Net: Nylon
Net Depth: 2½″

Type of net: Minnow Bucket Dip
Mfr.: The American Import Company
Model No.: 55049. Same as Model 55050 except:
Net: Cotton

Type of net: Minnow Bucket Dip
Mfr.: Dragon Fly Company, Inc.
Model No.: MBN-9
Overall Length: Not specified
Handle: Gauge wire
Frame: Gauge wire
Net: Nylon
Net Depth: Not specified

Type of net: Minnow
Mfr.: Herter's Inc.
Model No.: AK5P21
Overall Length: Not specified
Handle: Wire
Frame: Wire
Net: Nylon
Net Depth: Not specified

Type of net: Landing
Mfr.: Herter's Inc.
Model No.: LF6A3
Overall Length: 48″ x 19″
Handle: 30″ duraluminum
Frame: 19″ x 17″
Net: Nylocable
Net Depth: 36″

Type of net: Landing
Mfr.: Herter's Inc.
Model No.: LF6A4
Overall Length: Not specified
Handle: 48″ closed, 73″ extended
Frame: Aluminum tubing
Net: 20″ x 23″ green nylon
Net Depth: Not specified

Type of net: Landing
Mfr.: Herter's Inc.
Model No.: LF6A6
Overall Length: 20″
Handle: Plastic
Frame: 10½″ x 13¾″ duraluminum
Net: Fine mesh
Net Depth: 24″

Type of net: Minnow
Mfr.: Ideal Products, Inc.
Model No.: 1550
Overall Length: Not specified
Handle: Not specified
Frame: Not specified
Net: Vinlon
Net Depth: 27″

Type of net: Trout landing
Mfr.: Ideal Products, Inc.
Model No.: 1600
Overall Length: Not specified
Handle: Not specified
Frame: Not specified
Net: ¾″ square mesh nylon
Net Depth: 20″

Type of net: Landing
Mfr.: Ideal Products, Inc.
Model No.: N-3
Overall Length: Not specified
Handle: Rubber
Frame: Aluminum

Net: ¾″ square mesh cotton
Net Depth: 24″

Type of net: Promotional Boat
Mfr.: Ideal Products, Inc.
Model No.: N-13
Overall Length: 34½″
Handle: 17½″ aluminum
Frame: 15″ diameter, aluminum
Net: Cotton
Net Depth: 24″

Type of net: Fishing
Mfr.: Ideal Products, Inc.
Model No.: N-17
Overall Length: Not specified
Handle: 42″ sliding aluminum
Frame: 19″ x 20″ aluminum
Net: Cotton cord
Net Depth: 30″

Type of net: Trout
Mfr.: Isaac Franklin Co., Inc.
Model No.: ATZ
Overall Length: Not specified
Handle: 4½′ aluminum with plastic grip
Frame: 13½″ x 16″ aluminum
Net: Waxed cotton
Net Depth: 24″

Type of net: Crab
Mfr.: Isaac Franklin Co., Inc.
Model No.: AKC54P
Overall Length: Not specified
Handle: 4½′ long, 1″ diameter aluminum
Frame: 13″ steel
Net: Not specified
Net Depth: 16″

Type of net: Minnow Shrimp
Mfr.: Isaac Franklin Co., Inc.
Model No.: ADS5-54A
Overall Length: Not specified
Handle: 4½′ steel
Frame: 15½″ aluminum, 1″ diameter
Net: Nylon
Net Depth: 24″

Type of net: Bass Landing
Mfr.: Kassnar Imports
Model No.: FJ0452
Overall Length: Not specified
Handle: Rubber
Bow: 15″ x 12½″ aluminum
Net: Not specified
Net Depth: Not specified

Type of net: Landing
Mfr.: Kassnar Imports
Model No.: FJ0657
Overall Length: 25″ closed, 61″ opened
Handle: Telescoping
Frame: Not specified
Net: Not specified
Net Depth: Not specified

Type of net: English Landing
Mfr.: Kassnar Imports
Model No.: FJ0754

Overall Length: Not specified
Handle: Wood
Frame: 15″ x 10½″ wood
Net: Glazed
Net Depth: Not specified

Type of net: Minnow
Mfr.: Kassnar Imports
Model No.: FJ0053
Overall Length: 11″
Handle: Not specified
Frame: 3½″ x 4½″
Net: Nylon
Net Depth: Not specified

Type of net: Trout
Mfr.: Nova Products, Inc.
Model No.: V11
Overall Length: Not specified
Handle: 6″ aluminum
Bow: 10″ x 13″
Net: Not specified
Net Depth: 16″

Type of net: Bass
Mfr.: Nova Products, Inc.
Model No.: V22
Overall Length: Not specified
Handle: 18″ aluminum
Bow: 15″
Net: Nylon
Net Depth: 24″

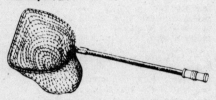

Type of net: Bait Dealer Dip
Mfr.: Nova Products, Inc.
Model No.: BD1
Overall Length: Not specified
Handle: 24″ aluminum
Bow: 16″
Net: Fine mesh nylon
Net Depth: 16″

Type of net: Landing
Mfr.: Nova Products, Inc.
Model No.: Q56PE
Overall Length: Not specified
Handle: 30″ aluminum
Bow: 19½″ R
Net: Polypropylene
Net Depth: 30″

Type of net: Landing
Mfr.: Nova Products, Inc.
Model No.: Q40Y
Overall Length: Not specified
Handle: 24″ aluminum
Bow: 16″ R
Net: Nylon
Net Depth: 24″

Type of net: Landing
Mfr.: Nova Products, Inc.
Model No.: Q50PL
Overall Length: Not specified
Handle: 30″ aluminum
Bow: 17½″ R
Net: Plastic
Net Depth: 30″

Type of net: Drop
Mfr.: Nylon Net Company

Name: Nylon Lift Net
Overall Length: Not specified
Handle: Not specified
Frame: 4′ x 4′ spring steel
Net: Nylon
Net Depth: Not specified

Type of net: Landing
Mfr.: Nylon Net Company
Model No.: NY0-0
Overall Length: Not specified
Handle: 18″ aluminum
Frame: 15″ diameter aluminum
Net: Nylon mesh
Net Depth: 18″

Type of net: Minnow Bucket Dip
Mfr.: Nylon Net Company
Name: Minnow Bucket Dip Net
Overall Length: 11″
Handle: 7″ wire
Frame: Wire
Net: ⅛″ square mesh
Net Depth: 3″

Type of net: Dip
Mfr.: Nylon Net Company
Model No.: HDS-1
Overall Length: 47″
Handle: 30″ long, 1″ diameter aluminum
Frame: 16″ x 17″
Net: Nylon
Net Depth: 12″

Type of net: Smelt
Mfr. Sampo
Model No.: WSN4
Overall Length: Not specified
Handle: 48″ aluminum
Frame: 14″ diameter aluminum
Net: Aluminum wire
Net depth: Not specified

Type of net: Shrimp & Minnow
Mfr.: Sampo
Model No.: SM60
Overall Length: Not specified
Handle: 4″ ribbed aluminum, 1″ diameter
Frame: 15″ x 16″, ⅜″ aluminum tubing
Net: ¼″-½″ graduated vinylon
Net Depth: 22″

Type of net: Heavy Landing
Mfr.: Shurkatch Fishing Tackle Co., Inc.
Model No.: 900
Overall Length: Not specified
Handle: 1⁵⁄₁₆″ x 48″ hardwood
Frame: 15″ diameter
Net: ¾″ mesh polyethylene
Net Depth: 20″

Type of net: Smelt
Mfr.: Shurkatch Fishing Tackle Co., Inc.
Model No.: 910W
Overall Length: Not specified
Handle: 1⅛″ x 72″ wood
Frame: 18″ diameter hoop
Net: ½″ mesh wire, cadmium plated
Net Depth: 18″

Type of net: Trout Bow
Mfr.: Shurkatch Fishing Tackle Co., Inc.
Model No.: ATB-1
Overall Length: 14½″
Handle: Rubber grip
Frame: Aluminum alloy tubing
Net: ¾″ knotted mesh
Net Depth: Not specified

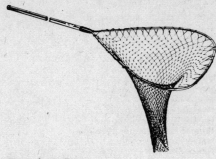

Type of net: Boat
Mfr.: Shurkatch Fishing Tackle Co., Inc.
Model No.: AL-30PY
Overall Length: 36″
Handle: Rubber grip
Frame: Aluminum tube
Net: Green polyethylene net, ¾″ mesh
Net Depth: 30″

Type of net: Minnow Dip
Mfr.: St. Croix Corporation
Model No.: F777
Overall Length: Not specified
Handle: Wire
Frame: Not specified
Net: Nylon
Net Depth: Not specified

Rod Holders

Mfr.: Bystrom Bros.
Model No.: 500
Size: Not specified
Bracket(s): Permanent mount
Material: Aluminum

Mfr.: Bystrom Bros.
Model No.: 501
Size: Not specified
Bracket(s): 1
Material: Aluminum

Mfr.: Dorbo Manufacturing Co.
Model No.: Hook-Amatic Angler
Size: Not specified
Bracket(s): Not included
Material: Aluminum and carbon steel

Mfr.: Herter's
Model No.: AM7A1
Size: Not specified
Bracket(s): Not specified
Material: Steel

Mfr.: Herter's
Model No.: AM7J
Size: Not specified
Bracket(s): 1
Material: Plastic coated tensaloy aluminum

Mfr.: Jorgensen Bros.
Model No.: 100
Size: Not specified
Bracket(s): 1
Material: Not specified

Mfr.: Klamerus & Company
Model No.: 202
Size: Not specified
Bracket(s): Not specified
Material: Steel with rubber

Mfr.: Klamerus & Company
Model No.: 500

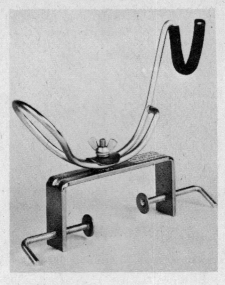

Size: Not specified
Bracket(s): Not specified
Material: Steel with rubber plate

Mfr.: Joseph Mennen Company, Inc.
Model No.: 1302
Size: 1 ⅞″ (inside diameter) x 9″
Bracket(s): Aluminum
Material: Vinyl

Mfr.: Joseph Mennen Company, Inc.
Model No.: 1303
Size: 1 ⅞″ (inside diameter) x 9″
Bracket(s): Stainless steel
Material: Vinyl

Mfr.: Joseph Mennen Company, Inc.
Model No.: 1312
Size: 1 ⅞″ (inside diameter) x 9″
Bracket(s): Not specified
Material: Not specified

Mfr.: Penguin Industries Inc.
Model No.: MA-1
Size: Not specified
Bracket(s): 1
Material: Aluminum with plastic coating

Mfr.: Reece Enterprises
Model: Your Pal
Size: Not specified
Bracket(s): Not specified
Material: Plated steel

Mfr.: St. Croix Corporation
Model No.: FM-111
Size: Not specified
Bracket(s): Not specified
Material: Steel

Mfr.: St. Croix Corporation
Model No.: FM-113
Size: Not specified
Bracket(s): Not specified
Material: Cadmium finish

Scales

Mfr.: The Danielson Company
Model No.: 8-24
Tape Length: 27″
Scale Capacity: Up to 8 lbs.

Mfr.: The Danielson Company
Model No.: 28-42
Tape Length: 38″
Scale Capacity: Up to 28 lbs.

Stringers

Mfr.: The American Import Company
Model No.: 55191
Length: 46″
Snaps: 9
Material: Unichrome

Mfr.: The Danielson Company
Model No.: 9304PT
Length: 6′
Snaps: Not specified
Material: Twisted polyethylene

Mfr.: The Danielson Company
Model No.: 9320
Length: 46″
Snaps: 9
Material: Cadmium plated

Mfr.: Dragon Fly Company, Inc.
Model No.: SCS-9
Length: Not specified
Snaps: 9
Material: Metal plated

Mfr.: Herter's Inc.
Model No.: LF5A3
Length: 59″
Snaps: 9
Material: Polycord

Mfr.: Herter's Inc.
Model No.: LF5A2
Length: 60″
Snaps: 8
Material: Not specified

Mfr.: Ideal Products. Inc.
Model No.: 350
Length: 40″
Snaps: 7
Material: Unichrome plated

Mfr.: Ideal Products. Inc.
Model No: 352
Length: 63″
Snaps: 9
Material: Coated rust-resistant metal

Mfr.: Kassnar Imports
Model No.: FF5118
Length: 46″
Snaps: 9

Mfr.: Lindy/Little Joe
Model No.: ST81
Length: 9′
Snaps: Not specified
Material: Nylon

Mfr.: Lindy/Little Joe
Model No.: ST115
Length: 60″
Snaps: 9
Material: Zinc-plated steel chain

Mfr.: Martin Tackle & Manufacturing Co.
Model No.: FT83
Length: Not specified
Snaps: 3
Material: Chain

Mfr.: Sampo
Model No.: 300
Length: 6′
Snaps: 8
Material: Nylon

Mfr.: Sampo
Model No.: 502
Length: Not specified
Snaps: Not specified
Material: Floating polypropylene with polyethylene cord

Mfr.: Sampo
Model No.: 310. Same as 300 except:
Length: 10′

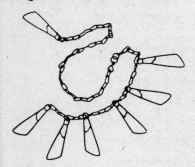

Mfr.: St. Croix Corporation
Model No.: FS-3
Length: 45″
Snaps: 7
Material: Cadmium plated

Mfr.: St. Croix Corporation
Model No. FS-2
Length: 48″
Snaps: 9
Material: Cadmium plated

Tackle Boxes

Mfr.: The American Import Company
Model No. 50067
Size: 6¼″ x 3¾″ x 1⅞″
Tray(s): 1
Compartment(s): 5
Material: Plastic

Mfr.: L. L. Bean
Model No.: 6861
Size: 15″ x 5¼″ x 9½″
Tray(s): 0
Compartment(s): 4
Material: Waterproof duck, leather reinforced

Mfr.: Flambeau Products Corp.
Model No.: 5129
Size: 12½″ x 6⅛″ x 1⅜″
Tray(s): 1
Material: Tenite

Mfr.: Flambeau Products Corp.
Model No.: 5138
Size: 6½″ x 3¾″ x 2″
Tray(s): 1
Material: Not specified

Mfr.: Herter's Inc.
Model No.: 25-6000-C2G
Size: 16½″ x 7½″ x 8¼″
Tray(s): 3
Compartment(s): 26
Material: Plastic

Mfr.: Herter's Inc.
Model No.: 25-6000-C2J
Size: 16⅞″ x 9¼″ x 9″
Tray(s): 6
Compartment(s): 45
Material: ABS thermoplastic

Mfr.: Ideal Products, Inc.
Model No.: 1561-8
Size: 14″ x 11″ x 9½″
Tray(s): 8
Compartment(s): 41
Material: Plastic

Mfr.: Ideal Products, Inc.
Model No.: 1561-3
Size: 13½″ x 7″ x 7½″
Tray(s): 3
Compartment(s): 22
Material: Plastic

Mfr.: Ideal Products, Inc.
Model No.: 1561
Size: 12″ x 5″ x 4″
Tray(s): 2 removable
Compartment(s): 6
Material: Plastic

Mfr.: Kassnar Imports
Model No.: FG1505
Size: 14⅜″ x 6½″ x 6″
Tray(s): 2
Compartment(s): 12
Material: Plastic

Mfr.: Outers Laboratories Inc.
Model No.: 585
Size: 1″ x 3″ x 5″
Tray(s): 1
Compartment(s): 7
Material: Polypropylene

Mfr.: Plano
Model No.: 727
Size: 19⅛″ x 10″ x 10¾″
Tray(s): 3
Compartment(s): 29
Material: ABS top, polypropylene bottom

Mfr.: Plano
Model No.: 747
Size: 20⅜″ x 11½″ x 12¾″
Tray(s): 3
Compartment(s): 29
Material: ABS

Mfr.: Plano
Model No.: 6500
Size: Not specified
Trays: 3
Compartment(s): 20
Material: Polypropylene

Mfr.: Stratton & Terstegge Co.
Model No.: 453
Size: 15″ x 6½″ x 7″
Tray(s): 3
Compartment(s): 36
Material: Aluminum

Mfr.: Stratton & Terstegge Co.
Model No.: 9314
Size: 14½″ x 8¼″ x 8″
Tray(s): 3
Compartment(s): 21
Material: Copolymer

Mfr.: Stratton & Terstegge Co.
Model No.: 1352
Size: 13½″ x 6½″ x 5¾″
Tray(s): 2
Compartment(s): 6
Material: Steel

Mfr.: Stratton & Terstegge Co.
Model No.: 8820
Size: 20″ x 11″ x 10½″
Tray(s): 8
Compartment(s): 52
Material: Plastic

Mfr.: UMCO Corp.
Model No.: 131A
Size: 13½″ x 7″ x 5¾″
Tray(s): 1
Compartment(s): 7
Material: Aluminum

Mfr.: UMCO Corp.
Model No.: 3500 UPB
Size: 21½″ x 12½″ x 19″
Tray(s): 10
Compartment(s): 84
Material: Plastic

Mfr.: Vlchek Plastics Company
Model No.: 1203
Size: 12⅜″ x 7″ x 6″
Tray(s): 0
Compartment(s): Not specified
Material: Copolymer

Mfr.: Vlchek Plastics Company
Model No.: 1726
Size: 16½″ x 8¾″ x 7½″
Tray(s): 3
Compartment(s): 24
Material: Copolymer

Mfr.: Vlchek Plastics Company
Model No.: 1985
Size: 18½″ x 10¼″ x 10⅜″
Tray(s): 5
Compartment(s): 26
Material: Copolymer

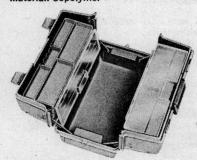

Mfr.: Vlchek Plastics Company
Model No.: 1986

Size: 18½" x 10¼" x 10⅜"
Tray(s): 6
Compartment(s): 40
Material: Copolymer

Mfr.: VIchek Plastics Company
Model No.: 2000
Size: 19" x 10¾" x 10⅛"
Tray(s): 1
Compartment(s): (9 cartridge boxes)
Material: Copolymer

Mfr.: VIchek Plastics Company
Model No.: 1043
Size: 12⅜" x 7" x 4⅝"
Tray(s): 3
Compartment(s): 12
Material: Copolymer

Mfr.: Woodstream Corporation
Model No.: PF 1585
Size: 16⅛" x 9⅜" x 9¼"
Tray(s): 3
Compartment(s): 29
Material: Not specified

Mfr.: Woodstream Corporation
Model No.: PF 1450
Size: 12⅞" x 7⅜" x 6½"
Tray(s): 3
Compartment(s): 23
Material: Not specified

Mfr.: Woodstream Corporation
Model No.: PF 1636
Size: 15¼" x 9⅛" x 7¼"
Tray(s): 3
Compartment(s): 11
Material: Not specified

Mfr.: Woodstream Corporation
Model No.: PF 3300
Size: 18½" x 10" x 9¾"
Tray(s): 3
Compartment(s): 35
Material: Not specified

Mfr.: Woodstream Corporation
Model No.: PF 4000
Size: 15" x 9" x 10"
Tray(s): 6
Compartment(s): 36
Material: Not specified

Mfr.: Woodstream Corporation
Model No.: PF 2300
Size: 15" x 8⅞" x 9⅜"
Tray(s): 3
Compartment(s): 23
Material: Not specified

Thermometers

Mfr.: Fishmaster Products, Inc.
Model No.: FT-100
Size: Not specified
Reading Cable Depth: 100'
Temp. Reading Range: 90°F

Mfr.: Fishmaster Products, Inc.
Model No.: SFT-1 Surface Fishthometer

Size: 3½" x 6"
Reading Cable Depth: 20'
Temp. Reading Range: 90°F

Mfr.: Lowrance Electronics
Model No.: LTP 100
Size: 3" x 2¼" x 5¾"
Reading Cable Depth: 100'
Temp. Reading Range: 30° to 90°F

Mfr.: Taylor Sybron Corporation
Model No.: 5100
Size: Not specified
Reading Cable Depth: Not specified
Temp. Reading Range: −50° to 120°F

Mfr.: Taylor Sybron Corporation
Model No.: 5280
Size: 5"
Reading Cable Depth: Not specified
Temp. Reading Range: 104°F

Mfr.: Vexilar, Inc.
Model No.: 104
Size: Not specified
Reading Cable Depth: Not specified
Temp. Reading Range: 120°F

Mfr.: Vexilar, Inc.

Model No.: 116
Size: Not specified
Reading Cable Depth: Not specified
Temp. Reading Range: 35° to 95°F

Mfr.: Waller Corporation
Model No.: 505
Size: Not specified
Reading Cable Depth: 50'
Temp. Reading Range: 80°F

Mfr.: Waller Corporation
Model No.: 510
Size: Not specified
Reading Cable Depth: 100'
Temp. Reading Range: 85°F

Mfr.: Waller Corporation
Model No.: 530
Size: Not specified
Reading Cable Depth: 200'
Temp. Reading Range: 85°F

Trolling Motors

Mfr.: Byrd Industries Incorporated
Model No.: S-500
Power: Electric 12V
Mount: Transom
Shaft Length: 27"
Weight: 9 lb.
Speed(s): 1
Thrust: 6½ lbs.
Reverse: 90°

Mfr.: Byrd Industries Incorporated
Model No.: S-1000
Power: Electric 12V
Mount: Transom
Shaft Length: 30"
Weight: 14 lbs.
Speed(s): 3
Thrust: 7 lbs.; 4½ lbs.; 2 lbs.
Reverse: Yes

Mfr.: Byrd Industries Incorporated
Model No.: S-2000
Power: Electric 12V
Mount: Transom
Shaft Length: 30" or 36"
Weight: 14½ lbs.
Speed(s): 3
Thrust: 12½ lbs.; 7 lbs.; 4 lbs.
Reverse: Yes

Mfr.: Byrd Industries Incorporated
Model No.: S-2250
Power: Electric 12V
Mount: Bow
Shaft Length: 30" or 36"
Weight: 30 lbs.
Speed(s): 3
Thrust: 12½ lbs.; 7 lbs.; 4 lbs.
Reverse: 90°

Mfr.: Byrd Industries Incorporated
Model No.: S-2275
Power: Electric 12V
Mount: Transom
Shaft Length: 30" or 36"
Weight: 22 lbs.
Speed(s): 3
Thrust: 12½ lbs.; 7 lbs.; 4 lbs.
Reverse: 90°

Mfr.: ESKA
Model No.: 1787
Power: Electric 12V
Mount: Transom
Shaft Length: 31½"
Weight: 8¾ lbs.
Speed(s): 10
Thrust: High
Reverse: 360°

Mfr.: ESKA
Model No.: 1854

Power: Electric 12V
Mount: Transom
Shaft Length 31½"
Weight: 8¾ lbs.
Speed(s): 20
Thrust: High
Reverse: 360°

Mfr.: Gladding Corporation
Model No.: 7-00-1005
Power: Electric 6V/12V
Mount: Transom
Shaft Length: Not specified
Weight: 4.5 lbs.
Speed(s): 2
Thrust: 5.5 lbs.; 2.21 lbs.
Reverse: 360°

Mfr.: Gladding Corporation
Model No.: 7-00-1006
Power: Electric 12V/24V
Mount: Transom
Shaft Length: Not specified
Weight: Not specified
Speed(s): 3
Thrust: 26 lbs. full
Reverse: Yes

Mfr.: Gladding Corporation
Model No.: 7-00-1007
Power: Electric 12V/24V
Mount: Bow
Shaft Length: Not specified
Weight: Not specified
Speed(s): 3
Thrust: 24V: 26 lbs.; 12 lbs.; 7 lbs.
   12V: 10.5 lbs.; 4.5 lbs.; 2.2 lbs.
Reverse: 180° right/left

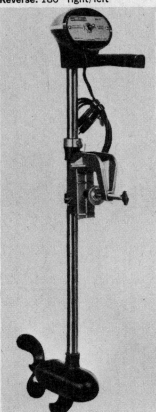

Mfr.: Pflueger
Model No.: M7

Power: Electric
Mount: Transom
Shaft Length: 27"
Weight: 6 lbs.
Speed(s): 2
Thrust: 6 lbs.; 2 lbs.
Reverse: 360°

Mfr.: Pflueger
Model No.: M15
Power: Electric
Mount: Transom
Shaft Length: 30"
Weight: Not specified
Speed(s): 3
Thrust: 8.4 lbs.; 4.5 lbs.; 2.5 lbs.
Reverse: Yes

Mfr.: Pflueger
Model No.: M40
Power: Electric 12V
Mount: Transom
Shaft Length: 36"
Weight: 15½ lbs.
Speed(s): 3
Thrust: 15 lbs.; 10 lbs.; 5 lbs.
Reverse: Yes

Mfr.: Pflueger
Model No.: M60
Power: Electric 12V/24V switch
Mount: Transom
Shaft Length: 36"
Weight: Not specified
Speeds(s): 3
Thrust: 20 lbs.; 12.5 lbs.; 5 lbs.
Reverse: Yes

Mfr.: Pflueger
Model No.: RM440
Power: Electric remote control
Mount: Bow
Shaft Length: 36"
Weight: Not specified
Speed(s): 3
Thrust: 15 lbs.; 10 lbs.; 5 lbs.
Reverse: Yes

Mfr.: Pflueger
Model No.: RM450
Power: Electric remote control
Mount: Bow
Shaft Length: 36"
Weight: Not specified
Speeds(s): 3
Thrust: 10.5 lbs.; 5 lbs.; 3 lbs.
Reverse: Yes

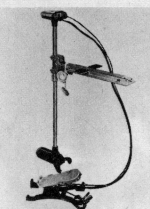

Mfr.: Pflueger
Model No.: RM460

Power: Electric 12V/24V switch remote control
Mount: Bow
Shaft Length: 36"
Weight: Not specified
Speed(s): 3
Thrust: 20 lbs.; 12.5 lbs.; 5 lbs.
Reverse: Yes

Mfr.: Shakespeare
Model No.: 51DJ
Power: Electric
Mount: Transom
Shaft Length: 27" chromed steel
Weight: 5½ lbs.
Speed(s): 1
Thrust: 5.5 lbs.
Reverse: 360°

Mfr.: Shakespeare
Model No.: 303DH
Power: Electric
Mount: Transom
Shaft Length: 30"
Weight: 9 lbs.
Speed(s): 3
Thrust: 8.4 lbs.; 4.5 lbs.; 2.5 lbs.
Reverse: 360°

Mfr.: Shakespeare
Model No.: 505
Power: Electric 12V
Mount: Not specified
Shaft Length: 30 "
Weight: 8 lbs.
Speed(s): Variable control
Thrust: 1½ to 7½ lbs.
Reverse: Yes

Power: Electric 6/12V
Mount: Transom
Shaft Length: Not specified
Weight: 11 lbs.
Speed(s): 3
Thrust: Not specified
Reverse: Yes

Mfr.: Shakespeare
Model No.: 612DH
Power: Electric 12V
Mount: Transom
Shaft Length: 36"
Weight: Not specified
Speed(s): 3
Thrust: 15 lbs.; 10 lbs.; 5 lbs.
Reverse: Not specified

Mfr.: Shakespeare
Model No.: 624
Power: Electric 12V/24V
Mount: Transom
Shaft Length: 36"
Weight: Not specified
Speed(s): 3
Thrust: 24V: 20 lbs.; 12.5 lbs.; 5 lbs.
  12V: 7 lbs.; 4 lbs.; 1 lb.
Reverse: Not specified

Mfr.: Shakespeare
Model No.: 808DH
Power: Electric 12V D.C.
Mount: Bow
Shaft Length: 36"
Weight: 15 lbs.
Speed(s): 3
Thrust: 10.5 lbs.; 5 lbs.; 3 lbs.
Reverse: Not specified

Power: Electric
Mount: Bow
Shaft Length: 36"
Weight: 22 lbs.
Speed(s): 3
Thrust: 10.5 lbs.; 5 lbs.; 3 lbs.
Reverse: Not specified

Mfr.: Shakespeare
Model No.: 909
Power: 12V
Mount: Transom
Shaft Length: 33"
Weight: 11 lbs.
Speed(s): Variable
Thrust: 10.5 lbs.
Reverse: Yes

Mfr.: Shakespeare
Model No.: 988
Power: Electric 12V
Mount: Bow
Shaft Length: Not specified
Weight: 26 lbs.
Speed(s): 4
Thrust: 10.6 lbs.; 5.1 lbs.; 2.9 lbs.
Reverse: 360°

Waders

Mfr.: Converse Rubber Company
Model No.: 13433
Height: Chest
Material: Cloth lined rubber surfaced

Mfr.: Converse Rubber Company
Model No.: 13931
Height: Chest
Material: Fabric and rubber

Mfr.: Converse Rubber Company
Model No.: Wadewell Hip Boot
Height: Hip
Material: Nylon cloth with wide rubber chafting tip

Mfr.: Converse Rubber Company
Model: Brighton Nylon Hip Boot
Height: Hip
Material: 2 rubberized layers of nylon cloth

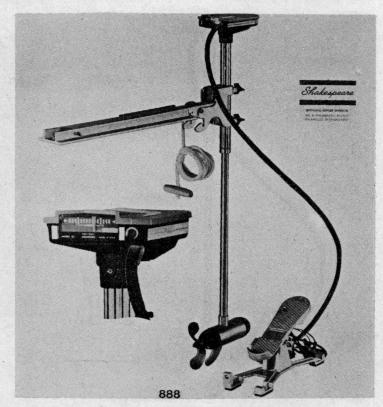

888

Mfr.: Shakespeare
Model No.: 606

Mfr.: Shakespeare
Model No.: 888DH

Mfr.: Converse Rubber Company
Model: Rod & Reel Wader
Height: Chest
Material: Cloth lined rubber surface

Mfr.: Converse Rubber Company
Model: Caster Wader
Height: Chest
Material: Not specified

Mfr.: Herter's Inc.
Model No.: DJ5F2D
Height: Chest
Material: Rubber fused to cotton

Mfr.: Ideal Products, Inc.
Model No.: 1364
Height: Chest
Material: Cloth supported rubber

Mfr.: Ideal Products, Inc.
Model No.: 1372

Height: Chest
Material: Double laminated nylon

Mfr.: Kassnar Imports
Model No.: FV3368
Height: Chest
Material: 3-ply nylon

Mfr.: Lasco Rubber Company
Model No.: 660-5676
Height: Not specified
Material: Rubber

Mfr.: Lasco Rubber Company
Model No.: 660-5654
Height: Thigh
Material: Rubber

Mfr.: Fritz von Schlegell
Model No.: Hipper with Wade Safe Soles
Height: Hip
Material: Not specified

Mfr.: Fritz von Schegell
Model No.: 123
Height: Chest
Material: Nylon and rubber

Reference and Directory Section

The Angler's Bookshelf

Artificial Flies

Bates, Joseph C., Jr. **Atlantic Salmon Flies & Fishing.** (Illus.). 1970. 14.95. Stackpole.

Bates, Joseph D., Jr. **Streamer Fly Tying & Fishing.** (Illus.). 1966. 7.95. Stackpole.

Bay, Kenneth E. & Vinciguerra, Matthew M. **How to Tie Freshwater Flies.** 1974. 10.00. Winchester Pr.

Bergman, Ray. **Trout.** rev. ed. (lIlus.). 1952. 12.50 Knopf.

Fulsher, Keith. **Fishing the Thunder Creek Series.** (Illus.). 1973. 7.95. Freshet Pr.

Gerlach, Rex. **Creative Fly Tying & Fishing.** 1974. 10.00. Winchester Pr.

Hyndman, James H. **Modern Fly Craft.** rev. & enl. ed. (Illus.). 1952. 3.50. Binfords.

Jennings, Preston. **Book of Trout Flies.** Lyons, Nick, ed. (Illus.). 1970. 7.50. Crown.

Jorgenson, Poul. **Dressing Flies for Fresh & Salt Water.** (Illus.). 1973. 12.95. Freshet Pr.

Kessler, Herman & Bay, Kenneth. **Salt Water Flies: Popular Patterns & How to Tie Them.** (Illus.). 1972. 8.95. Lippincott.

Lawrie, William H. **All Fur Flies & How to Dress Them.** (Illus.). 1968. 5.95. A S Barnes.

Leonard, J. Edson. **Flies.** (Illus.). 1950. 9.95. A S Barnes.

McDonald, John. **Quill Gordon.** 1972. 10.95. Knopf.

Orvis, Charles F. & Cheney, A. Nelson, eds. **Fishing with the Fly: Sketches by Lovers of the Art with Illustrations of Standard Flies.** (Illus.). 1967. Repr. 8.25. C E Tuttle.

Schwiebert, Ernest G., Jr. **Matching the Hatch.** (Illus.). 1962. 7.50. Macmillan.

Shaw, Helen. **Fly-Tying Materials-Tools-Technique.** (Illus.). 1963. 8.95. Ronald.

Sturgis, William B. **Fly-Tying.** (Illus.). 1940. 8.95. Scribner.

Swisher, Doug & Richards, Carl. **Selective Trout.** (Illus.). 1971. 6.95. Crown.

Veniard, John & Downs, Donald. **Fly-Tying Problems & Their Answers.** (Illus.). 1972. 4.95. Crown.

Bait

Earp, Samuel A. & Wildeman, William J. **The Blue Water Bait Book: Secrets of Successful Big Game Fishing.** (Illus.). 1974. 7.95. Little.

Harris, John R. **An Angler's Entomology.** (Illus.). 1973. 8.95. A S Barnes.

Ovington, Ray. **Introduction to Bait Fishing.** (Illus.). 1971. 5.95. Stackpole.

— — **Introduction to Bait Fishing.** 1974. Repr. pap. 2.95. Stackpole.

Bass Fishing

Bauer, Erwin. **Bass in America.** 1955. 4.95. S&S.

Bauer, Erwin A. **Bass Fisherman's Bible.** (Illus.). 1961. pap. 2.50. Doubleday.

Bergman, Ray. **Fresh-Water Bass.** (Illus.). 1942. 8.95. Knopf.

Dalrymple, Byron. **Modern Book of the Black Bass.** (Illus.). 1972. 6.95. Winchester Pr.

Fagerstrom, Stan. **Catch More Bass.** (Illus.). 1973. pap. 7.95. Caxton.

Gresham, Grits. **Complete Book of Bass Fishing.** 1966. 7.95. Har-Row.

Gresham, Grits L. **Complete Book of Bass Fishing.** (Illus.). Repr. of 1967 ed. 7.95. Har-Row.

Grigsby, Red. **Bass, & How to Catch Them.** 1966. pap. 0.50. Claitors.

Hawk, Dave. **One Hundred Years on Bass.** (Illus.). 1970. 6.00. Naylor.

Hornsey, Bill. **Bass Fishing: Strategy & Tactics.** 1967. 2.00. Claitors.

Livingston, A. D. **Fishing for Bass: Modern Tactics & Tackle.** 1974. 8.95. Lippincott.

McKinnis, Jerry. **Jerry McKinnis Bass Fishing.** (Illus.). 1974. pap. 2.95. Stoeger.

Rosko, Milt. **Secrets of Striped Bass Fishing.** 1966. 6.95. Macmillan.

Sosin, Mark & Dance, Bill. **Practical Black Bass Fishing.** (Illus.). 1974. 7.95. Crown.

Bibliographies

A Bibliography of African Freshwater Fish. 1974. pap. 10.00. (FAO). Unipub.

Dean, Bashford. **A Bibliography of Fishes,** 3 vols. (Vols. 1 & 2 enl. & edited by C. R. Eastman, vol. 3 enl. & edited by E. W. Gudger & A. W. Henn). 1972. Repr. of 1923 ed. 168.00. Hafner Service.

Fishing Industry Index International 1974. 17.50. Intl. Pubns. Serv.

Huver, Charles W., ed. **A Bibliography of the Genus Fundulus.** 1973. 18.00. G K Hall.

Lauche, R. **World Bibliography of Agricultural Bibliographies.** 1957. pap. 24.50. Adler.

Cod

Jensen, Albert C. **The Cod.** 1972. 7.95. T Y Crowell.

Cod Fisheries

Lounsbury, Ralph G. **British Fishery at Newfoundland, 1634 to 1763.** 1969. Repr. of 1934 ed. 11.50. Shoe String.

Dictionaries and Encyclopedias

Bates, Joseph D., Jr. **Fishing: An Encyclopedic Guide to Tackle & Tactics for Fresh & Salt Water.** 1974. 14.95. Dutton.

Brander, Michael. **Dictionary of Sporting Terms.** (Illus.). 1968. 6.50. Fernhill.

McClane, Albert J., ed. **McClane's New Standard Fishing Encyclopedia & International Angling Guide.** (Illus.). 1974. 40.00. HR&W.

Marston, A. N. **Encyclopedia of Angling.** 2nd ed. 1963. 15.00. Transatlantic.

Fish Anatomy

Chiasson, Robert B. **Laboratory Anatomy of the Perch.** rev. 2nd ed. Booth, Ernest S., ed. (illus.). 1974. pap. 3.95. Wm C Brown.

Craigie, E. Horne. **Laboratory Outline for the Dissection of the Lamprey, of the Dogfish, & the Skate.** 1957. pap. 3.50. U of Toronto Pr.

Gans, Carl & Parsons, Thomas S. **Photographic Atlas of Shark Anatomy: The Gross Morphology of Squalus Acanthias.** 1964. 4.50 Acad Pr.

Gilbert, Stephen G. **Pictorial Anatomy of the Dogfish.** (Illus.). 1973. pap. 4.95. U of Wash Pr.

Kindred, James E. **Skull of Amiurus.** (Illus.). 1919. 8.50. Johnson Repr.

Kusaka, Takaya. **The Urohyal of Fishes.** new ed. (Illus.). 1974. 50.00. Intl Schol Bk Serv.

Ribelin, William E. & Migaki, George, eds. **Pathology of Fishes.** 1974. 27.50. U of Wis Pr.

Wright, James E., et al. **Biochemical Genetics of Fish, 1.** 1974. 15.00. Mss Info.

Fish as Food

Borgstrom, G., ed. **Fish As Food,** 4 vols. Incl. Vol. 1. **Production, Biochemistry & Microbiology.** 1961. 39.50. Vol. 2. **Nutrition, Sanitation & Utilization.** 1926. 37.50. Vol. 3. **Processing Part 1.** 1965. 30.00. Vol. 4. **Processing. Part 2.** 1965. 30.00. Acad Pr.

Heen, E. & Kreuzer, R., eds. **Fish in Nutrition.** 1962. pap. 19.00 (FAO). Unipub.

Moore, Remedios W., et al. **Progress in Fishery & Food Science.** (Illus.). 1972. text ed. 15.00. U of Wash Pr.

Quick Frozen Fillets of Cod & Haddock. 1972. pap. 1.00. (FAO). Unipub.

Quick Frozen Fillets of Ocean Perch. 1972. pap. 1.00. (FAO). Unipub.

Quick Frozen Gutted Pacific Salmon. 1970. pap. 1.00. (FAO). Unipub.

Fish as Laboratory Animals

Institute of Laboratory Animal Resources. **Fishes: Guidelines for the Breeding Care & Management of Laboratory Animals.** (Illus.). 1974. pap. 5.00. Natl Acad Sci.

Neuhaus, O. W. & Halver, J. E., eds. **Fish in Research.** 1969. 13.00. Acad Pr.

Shul'man, G. E. **Life Cycles of Fish.** Hardin, Hillary, ed. Kaner. Nathan, tr. from Rus. (Illus.). 1974. 30.00. Halsted Pr.

Fish Behavior

Greenwood, P. H., et al, eds. **Interrelationships of Fishes: Supplement No. 1 to the Zoological Journal of the Linnean Society, Vol. 53.** 1973. 31.00. Acad Pr.

Ingle, David, ed. **Central Nervous System & Fish Behavior.** 1968. 15.00. U of Chicago Pr.

Kleerekoper, Herman. **Olfaction in Fishes.** (Illus.). 1969. 14.95. Ind U Pr.

Lateral Line Sense Organs & Their Importance in Fish Behavior. 1973. 21.10. Intl Schol Bk Serv.

Neil, E. H. **An Analysis of Color Changes & Social Behavior of Tilapia Mossambica.** 1964. pap. 1.25. U of Cal Pr.

Simon, Hilda. **Strange Breeding Habits of Aquarium Fish.** (Illus.). 1974. 5.95. Dodd.

Sosin, Mark & Clark, John. **Through the Fish's Eye.** (Illus.). 1973. 7.95. Har-Row.

Wickler, Wolfgang. **Breeding Behavior of Aquarium Fishes.** (Illus.). 1973. pap. 6.95. TFH Pubns.

Williams, Russ & Cadieux, Charles L. **The Ways of Game Fish.** (Illus.). 1973. 24.95. Doubleday.

Fish Collection

Gulland, J. A. **Manual of Methods for Fish Stock Assessment Part 1: Fish Population Analysis.** (Illus.). 1969. pap. 5.00 (FAO). Unipub.

Fish Cookery

Aberson, Sarah D. **Blue Sea Cookbook.** Porter, Eleanor, ed. (Illus.). 1968. 8.95. Hastings.

Allyn, Rube. **How to Cook Your Catch.** pap. 1.00. Great Outdoors.

Angier, Bradford. **Wilderness Cookery.** (Illus.). 1970. pap. 1.95. Stackpole.

Beard, James A. **James Beard's Fish Cookery.** (Illus.). 1954. 6.95. Little.

— —**James Beard's Fish Cookery.** pap. 0.95. Paperback Lib.

Beaton, I. M. **Fish Cookery.** (Illus.). 4.00. Soccer.

Better Homes & Gardens Books, ed. **Better Homes & Gardens Fish & Seafood Cookbook.** 1971. 3.95. BH&G.

Brown, Helen E. **Shrimp & Other Shellfish Recipes.** Brown, Philip S., ed. 1972. Repr. of 1966 ed. 3.95. pap. 2.95. Ritchie.

— —**Some Oyster Recipes.** 1951. 2.50. Grant Dahlstrom.

— —**Some Shrimp Recipes.** 1951. 2.50. Grant Dahlstrom.

Chekenian, Jane & Meyer, Monica. **Shellfish Cookery.** (Illus.). 1971. 12.50. Macmillan.

The Complete Fish Cookbook. pap. 1.50. Hippocrene Bks.

Dahlem, Ted. **How to Smoke Seafood.** pap. 1.00. Great Outdoors.

Davis, Charles J., **2nd. Fish Cookery.** 1967. 2.98. A S Barnes.

Day, Bunny. **Hook 'em & Cook 'em.** (Illus.). pap. 0.95. Paperbooks. Funk & W.

Dunaway, Vic. **From Hook to Table: An Angler's Guide to Good Eating.** (Illus.). 1974. 4.95. Macmillan.

Festive Seafood Cookery. 1.95. Peter Pauper.
Fish & Shell Fish. new ed. (Illus.). 1973. 29.50. Radio City.
Fish & Shellfish Cookbook. (Illus.). pap. 1.95. Oxmoor Hse.
Frederick & Joyce. Long Island Seafood Cookbook. 1971. pap. 2.50. Dover.
Froud, Nina & Lo, Tamara. International Fish Dishes. 1974. 7.95. Hippocrene Bks.
Hamilton, Dorothy R. How to Catch & Cook Shellfish. (Illus.). 1973. pap. 1.50. Great Outdoors.
Hawkins, Arthur. Complete Seafood Cookbook. (Illus.). 1970. 6.95. P-H.
Heath, Ambrose. Madame Prunier's Fishery Cook Book. (Illus.). 4.50. Peter Smith.
Hull, Raymond & Sleight, Jack. Home Book of Smoke-Cooking Meat, Fish & Game. (Illus.). 1971. 7.95. Stackpole.
Kaufman, William I. Fish & Shellfish Cookbook. 1968. 2.95. Doubleday.
Kelley, Carolyn T. Carolyn's Seafood Recipes. (Illus.). 1972. 5.95. Intl Marine.
Knight, Jacqueline E. The Cook's Fish Guide. 1973. 11.95. Dutton.
Leamer, Robert B., et al. Bottoms Up Cookery. (Illus.). 1971. pap. 5.00. Fathom Ents.
Lewin, Esther & Lewin, Birdina. Stewed to the Gills. (Illus.). 1972. 7.95. Nash Pub.
Lose Weight Deliciously with Fish. 1969. pap. 0.95. Univ Pub & Dist.
McGrail, William & McGrail, Joie. Catch & the Feast. (Illus.). 1969. 20.00. Weybright.
MacIlquham, Frances. Fish Cookery of North America. 1974. 8.95. Winchester Pr.
Mason, Phillip. Shellfish Cookbook. (Illus.). 1974. 8.95. Drake Pubs.
Miloradovich, Milo. Art of Fish Cookery. rev. ed. 1970. 5.95. Doubleday.
—Art of Fish Cookery. pap. 1.00. Bantam.
Morris, Dan & Morris, Inez Complete Fish Cookbook. 1972. 10.00. Bobbs.
Patten, Marguerite. Fish, Meat, Poultry, & Game. rev. ed. (Illus.). 1970. 5.25. Intl Pubns Serv.
Priestland, Gerald. Frying Tonight: The Saga of Fish & Chips. (Illus.). 1974. 12.50. Intl Pubns Serv.
Prunier, S. B. Madame Prunier's Fish Cookery Book. 1971. pap. 2.50. Dover.
Reidpath, Stewart. The Angler's Cookbook: Trout, Salmon & Eel. 1973. spiral bdg. 3.50. Reed.
Simon, Andre L. Lobsters, Crabs, Etc. 1957. 1.00. Wehman.
Steindler, Geraldine. Game Cookbook. (Illus.). 1965. 6.95. softbound 4.95. Stoeger.
Sunset Editors. Sunset Seafood Cook Book. (Illus.). 1967. pap. 1.95. Lane.
Townsend, Sally & Ericson, Virginia. Sea Cook. pap. 2.95. Funk & W.
Vilkitis, James & Uhlinger, Susan. Fish Cookery. (Illus.). 1974. pap. 1.25. Greene.
Wall, Roy. Game & Fish: From Field to Table. 1972. 5.95. Naylor.
World's Fifty Best Fish Recipes. 1971. pap. 1.50. Hippocrene Bks.
Zachary, Hugh. Beachcomber's Handbook of Seafood Cookery. (Illus.). 1972. 4.95. Blair.

Fish Culture

Atz, James W. Aquarium Fishes: Their Beauty, History & Care. (Illus.). 1971. 12.50. Intl Pubns Serv.
Davis, H. S. Culture & Diseases of Game Fishes. (Illus.). 1953. 9.50. U of Cal Pr.
Hickling, C. F. The Farming of Fish. (Illus.). 1968. 4.00. pap. 2.00. Pergamon.
Hoedeman, J. J. Naturalists' Guide to Fresh-Water Aquarium Fish. (Illus.). 1974. 30.00. Sterling.
Lee, Jasper S. Commercial Catfish Farming. (Illus.). 1973. 9.25. Interstate.
Lewis, William M. Maintaining Fishes for Experimental & Instructional Purposes. 1963. 5.00. pap. 1.45. S Ill U Pr.

Ostermoeller, Wolfgang. Fish Breeding Recipes. (Illus.). 1973. pap. 3.95. TFH Pubns.

Fish Diseases and Pests

Anderson, Douglas P. Diseases of Fishes, Book 4: Fish Immunology. Snieszko, S. F. & Axelrod, Herbert R. eds. (Illus.). 1974. pap. 9.95. TFH Pubn.
Bauer, O. N., et al. Disease of Pond Fishes. Theodor, O., ed. Mercado, A., tr. from Rus. (Illus.). 1974. 21.00. Intl Schol Bk Serv.
Davis, H. S. Culture & Diseases of Game Fishes. (Illus.). 1953. 9.50. U of Cal Pr.
Fish Diseases: Crustaceans. pap. 9.95. TFH Pubns.
Fish Diseases (Immunology). pap. 9.95. TFH Pubns.
Fish Diseases Textbook. (Illus.). pap. 9.95. TFH Pubns.
Geisler, Rolf. Aquarium Fish Diseases. (Illus.). 1963. pap. 1.29. TFH Pubns.
Goldstein, R. J. Diseases of Aquarium Fishes. (Illus.). pap. 4.95. TFH Pubns.
Mawdesley-Thomas, Lionel E., et al. Diseases of Fish. 1974. 17.50. Mss Info.
Reichenbach-Klinke, H. H. Fish Pathology. (Illus.). 1973. pap. 20.00. TFH Pubns.
Sinderman, C. J. Principal Diseases of Marine Fish & Shellfish. 1970. 23.00. Acad Pr.
Sindermann, C. J. Diseases of Marine Fishes. (Illus.). pap. 3.95. TFH Pubns.
Sniezko, S., et al. Fish Diseases: Bacteria. (Illus.). pap. 9.95. TFH Pubns.
Van Duijn, C. Diseases of Fishes, 3rd ed. 1973. 12.95. C C Thomas
Zoological Society of London - 30th Symposium. Diseases of Fish. Mawdesley-Thomas, Lionel E., ed. 1972. 21.00. Acad Pr.

Fish Embryology

Armstrong, Philip B. & Child, Julia S. Stages in the Development of Ictalurus Nebulosus. (Illus.). 1962. 4.95. Syracuse U Pr.

Fish Finding

Dunlap, G. Dale. Navigating & Finding Fish with Electronics. (Illus.). 1972. Intl Marine.
Fishing with Electricity: Its Applications to Biology & Management. 1967. pap. 9.50. (Fao). Unipub.
Meyer-Waarden, P. F. Electric Fishing. 1965. Repr. 1.00 (Fao). Unipub.

Fish in Religion and Folklore

Ouwehand, C. Namazu-E & Their Themes: An Interpretive Approach to Some Aspects of Japanese Folk Religion. 1964. 13.75. Humanities.
Titcomb, Margaret. Native Use of Fish in Hawaii. 1972. 7.00. U Pr of Hawaii.
Trevelyan, Marie. Folk-Lore & Folk-Stories of Whales. 20.00. Norwood Edns.

Fish Migration

Harden, Jones, F. R. Fish Migration. (Illus.). 1968. 21.00. St Martin.

Fish Nomenclature

OECD, ed. Multilingual Dictionary of Fish & Fish Products. 1973. 1950. Intl Pubns Serv.

Fish Oils

Stansby, Maurice. Fish Oils. (Illus.). 1967. 20.00. Avi.

Fish Parasites

Dogiel, V. A., et al. Parasitology of Fishes. (Illus.). 14.95. TFH Pubns.
Hoffman, Glenn L. Parasites of North American Fresh Water Fishes. 1967. 19.25. U of Cal Pr.
Hoffman, Glen L. & Meyer, Fred P. Parasites of Freshwater Fishes. (Illus.). 1974. pap. 12.95. TFH Pubns.

Scott, T. & Scott, A. British Parasitic Copepoda, 2 Vols. in 1. 1913. 21.00. Johnson Repr.
Yamaguti, Satyu. Monogenetic Trematodes of Hawaiian Fishes. (Illus.). 1968. 15.00. U Pr of Hawaii.

Fish Physiology

Agricultural Board. Nutrient Requirements of Trout, Salmon & Catfish. 1973. pap. 3.25 Natl Acad Sci.
Alexander, R. McNeill. Functional Design in Fishes. (Illus.). 1967. 3.75. pap. 2.25. Hillary.
Chavin, Walter. Responses of Fish to Environmental Changes. (Illus.). 1973 19.75. C C Thomas.
Hoar, W.S. & Randall, D. J., eds. Fish Physiology, 6 vols 1969-71. Vol. 1. 31.00; Vol. 2. 31.00; Vol. 3. 31.00; Vol. 4. 33.00; Vol. 5. 38.00; Vol. 6. 36.00. Acad Pr.
Kleerekoper, Herman. Olfaction in Fishes. (Illus.). 1969. 14.95. Ind U Pr.
Love, M. R. Chemical Biology of Fishes. 1970. 23.50. Acad Pr.
Neuhaus, O. W. & Halver, J. E., eds. Fishes in Research. 1969. 13.00. Acad Pr.
Satchell, G. H. Circulation in Fishes. (Illus.). 1971. 8.00. Cambridge U Pr.

Fish Ponds

Betts, Leonard C. Garden Pools. (Illus.). 1952. pap. 1.50. TFH Pubns.
Nuffield Foundation. How to Build a Pond. (Mathematics Project Ser.). 1968. pap. 3.00. Wiley.

Fish Populations

Cushing, D. H. Fisheries Biology: A Study in Population Dynamics. (Illus.). 1968. 10.00. U of Wis Pr.
Gullard, J. A. Manual of Methods for Fish Stock Assessment Part 1: Fish Population Analysis. (Illus.). 1969. pap. 5.00 (FAO). Unipub.
Weatherly, A. H. Growth & Ecology of Fish Populations. 1972. 13.50. Acad Pr.

Fish Preservation

Burgess, G. H., et al. Fish Handling & Processing. (Illus.). 1967. 11.25. Chem Pub.
Mead, John T. Marine Refrigeration & Fish Preservation. (Illus.). 1973. 14.95. Busn News. Preservation of Fish by Irradiation. (Illus.). 1970. pap. 5.00 (IAEA). Unipub.
Rawson G. C. & Sai, F. A. Short Guide to Fish Preservation. 1966. 1.00 (FAO). Unipub.

Fish Trophies

Migdalski, Edward C. How to Make Fish Mounts & Other Fish Trophies. (Illus.). 1960. 6.95. Roland.
Pray, Leon. Nineteen Sixty-Five Fish Mounting Book. rev. & enl. ed. 1965. 2.00. Reel Trophy.

Fisheries

Bogdanov, A. S. Soviet-Cuban Fishery Research. 1973. 23.25. Intl Schol Bk Serv.
Browning, Robert. Fisheries of the North Pacific: History, Species, Gear, Processes. (Illus.). 1974. 24.95. Alaska Northwest.
Christy, Francis T., Jr. Alternative Arrangements for Marine Fisheries: An Overview. 1973. pap. 3.00. Johns Hopkins.
Christy, Francis T., Jr. & Scott, Anthony. Common Wealth in Ocean Fisheries: Some Problems of Growth & Economic Allocation. 1966. 10.00. Johns Hopkins.
Crutchfield, James A. & Pontecorvo, Giulio.

Pacific Salmon Fisheries: A study of Irrational Conservation. (Illus.). 1969. 8.50. Johns Hopkins.

Finn, William. Fishermen on Georges Bank. (Illus.). 1972. 5.75. Little.

Firth, Frank F. Encyclopedia of Marine Resources. (Illus.). 1969. 27.50. Van Nos Reinhold.

Food And Agriculture Organization. Fisheries in the Food Economy. 1968. 1.25 (FAO). Unipub.

Funk, John L., et al. Black River Studies. 1953. pap. 2.50. U of Mo Pr.

General Fisheries Council for the Mediterranean, 11th. Proceedings. 1973. pap. 3.00 (FAO). Unipub.

General Fisheries Council for the Mediterranean: Report of the Tenth Session. 1970. pap. 2.00 (FAO). Unipub.

Gulland, J. A. Manual of Methods for Fish Stock Assessment Part 1: Fish Population Analysis. (Illus.). 1969. pap. 5.00 (FAO). Unipub.

Gulland, John A. Population Dynamics of World Fisheries. (Illus.). 1972. 7.50. U of Wash Pr.

Harden-Jones, F. R., ed. Sea Fisheries Research. 32.50. Halsted Pr.

Hazelton, J. E. & Bell, F. W. Recent Developments & Research in Fisheries Economics. 1967. 12.00. Oceana.

Holliman, E. S. Financial Assistance Policies & Administration for Fisheries. 1962. pap. 1.00 (FAO). Unipub.

Idyll, C. P. Sea Against Hunger. 1970. 8.95. T Y Crowell.

Kasahara, Hiroshi & Burke, William. North Pacific Fisheries Management. 1973. pap. 3.00. Johns Hopkins.

Lang, Varly. Follow the Water. (Illus.). 1961. 4.50. Blair.

Mack, Jerry. Catfish Farming Handbook. 1971. 12.95. Educator Bks.

Manual of Methods for Fisheries Resource Survey & Appraisal, Pt. 2: The Use of Acoustic Instruments for Fish Detection. & Abundance estimation. (Illus.). 1973. pap. 4.00 (FAO). Unipub.

Manual on Fishermen's Cooperatives. (Fisheries Studies, No. 13). 1971. pap. 3.00 (FAO). Unipub.

Miles, Edward. Organizational Arrangements to Facilitate Global Management of Fisheries. 1974. pap. 1.00. Johns Hopkins.

Moore, Remedios W., et al. Progress in Fishery & Food Science. (Illus.). 1972. 15.00 U of Wash Pr.

Proper, Ida S. Mohegan, the Cradle of New England. (Illus.). 8.00 NH Pub Co.

Protasov, V. R. Vision & Near Orientation of Fishes. 1974. 15.85. Intl Schol Bk Serv.

Ricker, William E. Methods of Estimating Vital Statistics of Fish Populations. 1948. pap. 4.00. Kraus Repr.

Royce, William F. Introduction to the Fishery Sciences. 1971. 14.50. Acad Pr.

Russell-Hunter, W. D. Aquatic Productivity: An Introduction to Some Basic Aspects of Biological Oceanography & Limnology. (Illus.). 1970. 5.95. Macmillan.

Sabine, Lorenzo. Report on the Principal Fisheries of the American Seas. (Illus.). Repr. of 1853 ed. 15.00. Kelley.

Stansby, Maurice E. Industrial Fishery Technology. 1963. 14.50. Krieger.

Sunset Editors. Sea of Cortez. 1966. 14.95. Lane.

Symposium on the Oceanography & Fisheries Resources the Tropical Atlantic. Proceedings. (Illus.). 1969. 13.50 (UNESCO). Unipub.

Taevastu, T. Manual of Methods in Fisheries Biology. 1965. 5.00 (FAO). Unipub.

Trilingual Dictionary of Fisheries Technological Terms: Curing. 1972. pap. 3.00 (FAO). Unipub.

Tussing, Arlon R., et al, eds. Alaska Fisheries Policy: Economics, Resources & Management. 1972. pap. 10.00. U of Wash Pr.

Wharton, James. Bounty of the Chesapeake: Fishing in Colonial Virginia. (Illus.). 1957. pap. 1.25. U Pr of Va.

White, Donald J. New England Fishing Industry: A Study in Price & Wage Setting. (Illus.). 1954. 5.50. Harvard U Pr.

Yearbook of Fishery Statistics: Fishery Commodities. 1970. 1971. 9.00 (FAO). Unipub.

Fisheries—Africa

Crutchfield, James A. & Lawson, Rowena. West African Marine Fisheries: Alternatives for Management. 1974. pap. 3.00. Johns Hopkins.

Prins, A. H. Sailing from Lamu: A Study of Maritime Culture in Islamic East Africa. 1965. 15.50. Fernhill.

Rawson, G. C. & Sai, F. A. Short Guide to Fish Preservation. 1966. 1.00 (FAO). Unipub.

Symposium On Hydrobiology And Inland Fisheries—3rd—Lusaka—1960. Proceedings: Problems of Major Lakes. 6.25. Intl Pubn Serv.

Fisheries—Australia

Roughley, T. C. Fish & Fisheries of Australia. rev ed. (Illus.). 1966. 16.00. Verry.

Fisheries—Great Britain

March, Edgar J. Sailing Drifters. (Illus.). 1972. 22.50. Intl Marine.

Fisheries—Indian Ocean

Bogdanov, A. S. Soviet Fisheries Investigations in the Indian Ocean. Golek, B., ed. Kaner, N., tr. from Rus. (Illus.). 1974. lib. bdg. 13.00. Intl Schol Bk Serv.

Fisheries—Newfoundland

Lounsbury, Ralph G. British Fishery at Newfoundland, 1634 to 1763. (Illus.). 1969. Repr. of 1934 ed. 11.50. Shoe String.

Reeves, John. History of the Government of the Island of Newfoundland. 1793. 12.50. Johnson Repr.

Fisheries—Norway

Klausen, Arne Martin. Kerala Fishermen & the Indo-Norwegian Pilot Project. (Illus.). 1968. 8.00. Universitet.

Kobayashi, Teruo. Anglo-Norwegian Fisheries Case of 1951 & the Changing Law of the Territorial Sea. 1965. pap. 2.00 U of Fla Pr.

Fisheries—Nova Scotia

Denys, Nicolas. Description—Natural History of the Coasts of North America. Ganong, William F., ed. 1968. Repr. of 1908 ed. 42.25. Greenwood.

Farstad, Nelvin. Fisheries Development in Newfoundland: Aspects of Development, Location & Infrastructure. 1972. pap. 6.00. Universitet.

Ziner, Feenie. Bluenose, Queen of the Grand Banks. (Illus.). 1970. 5.50. Chilton.

Fisheries—Tropics

Tussing, Arlon R. & Hiebert, Robin A. Fisheries of the Indian Ocean: Issues of International Management & Law of the Sea. 1974. pap. 3.00. Johns Hopkins.

Fishermen

Clifford, Harold B. Charlie York: Maine Coast Fisherman. (Illus.). 1974. 7.95. Intl Marine.

Critchfield, Richard. The Golden Bowl Be Broken: Peasant Life in Four Cultures. (Illus.). 1974. 10.00. Ind U Pr.

Curtis, Elwood A. A Wet Butt & a Hungry Gut. 1974. 5.95. Blair.

De Gast, Robert. Oystermen of the Chesapeake. (Illus.). 1970. 16.00. Intl Marine.

Finn, William. Fishermen on Georges Bank. (Illus.). 1972. 5.75. Little.

Firth, Raymond. Malay Fishermen: Their Peasant Economy. 2nd ed. (Illus.). 1966. 10.00. Shoe String.

Forman, Shepard. Raft Fishermen: Tradition & Change in the Brazilian Peasant Economy. (Illus.). 1970. 10.00 Ind U Pr.

Grossinger, Richard. Book of the Cranberry Islands. 1974. 10.00. autographed edition. 15.00. Black Sparrow.

Jenkin, A. Hamilton. Cornwall & Its People. Repr. of 1945 ed. 13.50. Kelley.

Lang, Varley. Follow the Water. (Illus.). 1961. 4.50. Blair.

Mills, A. Graham. Fisherman's Breeze: The Log of the Ruth M. Martin. 1973. Repr. of 1929 ed. 2.50. South St Sea Mus.

Schwind, Phil. Cape Cod Fisherman. 1974. Intl Marine.

Fishery Law and Legislation

Johnston, Douglas M. International Law of Fisheries: A Framework for Policy-Oriented Inquiries. (Illus.). 1965. 25.00. Yale U Pr.

Kobayashi, Teruo. Anglo-Norwegian Fisheries Case of 1951 & the Changing Law of the Territorial Sea. 1965. pap. 2.00. U of Fla Pr.

Leonard, Leonard L. International Regulation of Fisheries. (Illus.). 1944. 1750. Johnson Repr.

Lounsbury, Ralph G. British Fishery at Newfoundland, 1634 to 1763. (Illus.). 1969. Repr. of 1934 ed. 11.50. Shoe String.

Portecorvo, Givlio, ed. Fisheries Jurisdiction & Enforcement: The Case of the North Atlantic Region. (Illus.). 1974. 11.50. Ballinger Pub.

Riesenfeld, Stefan A. Protection of Coastal Fisheries Under International Law. Repr. of 1942 ed. 28.00. Johnson Repr.

Rothschild, Brian J., ed. World Fisheries Policy: Multidisciplinary Views. (Illus.). 1972. 9.50. U of Wash Pr.

Tussing, Arlon R., et al, eds. Alaska Fisheries Policy: Economics, Resources, & Management. (Illus.). 1972. pap. 5.00. U Alaska Inst Res.

Fishery Products

Brody, Julius. Fishery By-Products Technology. (Illus.). 1965. 17.00. Avi.

Chichester, C. O. & Graham, H. D., eds. Microbial Safety of Fishery Products. 1973. 12.50. Acad Pr.

Food And Agriculture Organization. Fisheries in the Food Economy. 1968. 1.25 (FAO). Unipub.

Kreuzer, R., ed. Technology of Fish Utilization: Contributions from Research. 1965. 17.50 (FAO). Unipub.

OECD, ed. Multilingual Dictionary of Fish & Fish Products. 1973. 19.50. Intl Pubns Serv.

Tannenbaum, Steven & Stillings, Bruce, eds. Economics, Marketing & Technology of Fish Protein Concentrate. 18.50. MIT Pr.

Fishes

Allen, Gerald. Anemone Fishes. new ed. 20.00. TFH Pubns.

Allyn, Rube. Dictionary of Fishes. pap. 1.95. Great Outdoors.

Ames, Felicia. Fish You Care For. 1971. pap. 1.25. NAL.

Artedi, Peter. **Genera Piscium: Emendata et Aucta.** (Illus., Lat.). 1967. Repr. of 1792 ed. 33.00. Hafner Service.
— — **Ichthyologia Linnaeus, C.,** ed (Lat). 1961. Repr. of 1738 ed. 21,55. Hafner Service.
Axelrod, Herbert R. & Emmens, Cliff W. **Exotic Marine Fishes.** (Illus.). 1973. 15.00. TFH Pubn.
Bagenal, T. B., ed. **Ageing of Fish: Proceedings of an International Symposium.** 1974. 17.95. Haessner Pub.
Benirschke, K. & Hsu, T. C. eds. **Chromosome Atlas: Fish, Amphibians, Reptiles & Birds, Vol. 1.** (Illus.). 1972. loose leaf. 14.80. Springer-Verlag.
Blaxter, J. H. **The Early Life History of Fish.** (Illus.). 1974. 40.20. Springer-Verlag.
Bloch, E. M. **Systema Ichthyologiae,** 2 Vols. in 1. Schneider, J. G., ed. (Illus., Lat.). 1967. Repr. of 1801 ed. 55.00. Hafner Service.
Brittan, Martin. **Rasbora.** (Illus.). 1972. 12.95. TFH Pubns.

Cannon, Raymond. **How to Fish the Pacific Coast.** 3rd ed. (Illus.). 1967. pap. 2.95. Lane.
Cantor, Theodore F. **Catalogue of Malayan Fishes.** 1966. Repr. of 1849 ed. 35.00. Hafner Service.
Chaplin, Charles C. & Scott, Peter. **Fishwatcher's Guide to West Atlantic Coral Reefs.** Livingston, Robert A., ed. (Illus.). 1972. plastic 5.95. Livingston.
Check-List of the Fishes of the Northeastern Atlantic & of the Mediterranean: Clofnan, Vols. 1-2. 1974. Set. pap. 66.00. (UNESCO). Unipub.
Childress. **Conchy on the Halfshell.** 1973. pap. 0.75. G&D.
Clark, Eugenie. **Lady with a Spear.** 1974. pap. 2.00. Ballantine.
— — **Lady with a Spear.** (Illus.). 1953. lib. bdg. 5.92. Har-Row.
Cooper, Allan. **Fishes of the World.** (Illus.). 1972. pap. 1.45. Bantam.
— — **Fishes of the World.** Zappler, Georg. ed. (Illus.). 1970. 3.95. G&D.
Curtis, Brian. **Life of the Fish: His Manners & Morals.** (Illus.). 4.00. Peter Smith.
— — **Life Story of the Fish.** 2nd ed. 1949. pap. 2.50. Dover.
Cushing, David H. **Recruitment & Parent Stock in Fishes.** 1974. pap. 7.50. U of Wash Pr.
Cuvier, G. L. & Valenciennes. F. A. **Histoire Naturelle Des Poissons,** 22 Vols. (Illus., Fr.). 1969. Repr. of 1828 ed. Set. 780.00. Hafner Service.

Deemer, Philip, compiled by. **Fish Directory 1973.** 1973. pap. 1.00. Jarrow.
De Sylva, Donald P. **The Alfred C. Glassell Jr. University of Miami Argosy Expedition to Ecuador, Pt. 1: Introduction & Narrative.** (Illus.). 1972. 6.95. U of Miami Pr.
Dunaway, Vic. **From Hook to Table: An Angler's Guide to Good Eating.** (Illus.). 1974. 4.95. Macmillan.
Eddy, Samuel & Underhill, James C. **Northern Fishes.** rev. 3rd ed. (Illus.). 1974. 17.50. U of Minn Pr.
Fish, Marie P. & Mowbray, William H. **Sounds of Western North Atlantic Fishes: A Reference File of Biological Underwater Sounds.** (Illus.). 1970. 12.50. Johns Hopkins
Goldstein, Robert J. **Anabantoids Gouramis & Related Species.** (Illus.). pap. 5.95. TFH Pubns.
Goode, G. Brown. **Game Fishes of the United States.** (Illus.). 1972. Repr. of 1879 ed. 75.00. Winchester Pr.
Gosline, William A. **Functional Morphology & Classification of Teleostean Fishes.** (Illus.). 1971. pap. 6.00. U Pr. of Hawaii.
Greenfield, David, ed. **Systemic Ichthyology: A Collection of Readings.** 1972. 13.00. MCS Info.
Guenther, Albert C. **Catalogue of Fishes in the British Museum — Natural History,**

8 Vols. in 4. 1964. Repr. of 1859 ed. 115.50. Hafner Service.
— — **Introductioin to the Study of Fishes.** (Illus.). 1964. Repr. of 1880 ed. 10.00. Hafner Service.
Gulland, J. A. **The Fish Resources of the Ocean.** (Illus.). 1972. 27.00. (FAO). Unipub.
Herald, Earl S. **Living Fishes of the World.** (Illus.). 1961. 16.95. Doubleday.
Hopkirk, John D. **Endemism in Fishes of the Clear Lake Region.** pap. 5.50. U of Cal Pr.
Hvass, Hans. **Fishes of the World in Color.** Vevers, Gwynne, tr. (Illus.). 1965. 5.95. Dutton.
Innes, William T. **Exotic Aquarium Fishes.** 19th ed. (Illus.). 6.95. Dutton.
— — **Innes Exotic Aquarium Fish.** 4.95. TFH Pubns.
Jacobs, Kurt, **Livebearing Fishes.** (Illus.). 1974. pap. 9.95. TFH Pubns.
Janes, Edward C. **Fresh-Water Fishing Complete.** (Illus.). 1973. pap. 1.95. B&N.
Jocher, Willy. **Spawning Problem Fishes.** Incl. Book 1; Book 2. (Illus.). 1972. pap. 3.95 ea. TFH Pubns.
Jordan, David S. **Genera of Fishes & a Classification of Fishes.** 1963. 22.50. Stanford U Pr.
Juntunen, Erland T., et al. **Economic Icthyology.** 1973. pap. text ed. 3.75. Oreg St U Bkstrs.
Kyle, Harry M. **Biology of Fishes.** 1971. 12.95. TFH Pubns.
Lagler, Karl F., et al. **Ichthyology.** 1962. 16.75. Wiley.
Lampman, Ben H. **Coming of the Pond Fishes.** 6.50. Binfords.
Lanham, Urless N. **The Fishes.** (Illus.). 1967. pap. 2.25. Columbia U Pr.
Lindberg, G. U. **Fishes of the World: A Key to Famlies & a Checklist.** Mills, H., ed. (Illus.). 42.50. Halstead Pr.
Marshall, N. B. **Explorations in the Life of Fishes.** 1971. 6.50. Harvard U Pr.
— — **Life of Fishes.** 1966. 12.50. Universe.
Metzelaar, J. **Report on the Fishes Collected by J. Boeke in the Dutch West Indies 1904-05,** with Comparative Notes on Marine Fishes of Tropical West Africa. (Illus.). 1967. Repr. of 1919 ed. 35.00. Hafner Service.
Mills, Derek H. **Salmon & Trout: A Resource, Its Ecology, Conservation & Management.** 1972. 15.95. St Martin.
Morris, Dan & Strung, Norman. **Fisherman's Almanac.** (Illus.). 1970. 4.95. Macmillan.
Muus, Bent J. **Collins Guide to Sea Fishes.** (Illus.). 1974. 10.00. Scribner.
Myers, George S. **How to Become an Ichthyologist.** 1970. pap. 1.50. TFH Pubns.

Neugebauer, Wilbert. **Marine Aquarium Fish Identifier.** (Illus.). 1974. 3.95. Sterling.
Nikolsky, G. V. **Ecology of Fishes.** Birkett, L., tr. 1963. 17.00. Acad Pr.
Norman, J. R. **A History of Fishes.** 8.95. British Bk Ctr.
Ommanney, F. D. **Fishes.** (Illus.). 1968. 3.95. Time-Life.
— — **Fishes.** (Illus.). 1968. 8.80. Time-Life.
Perlmutter, Alfred. **Guide to Marine Fishes.** (Illus.). 1961. 6.50. NYU Pr.
— — **Guide to Marine Fishes.** (Illus.). pap. NYU Pr.
Rafinesque-Schmaltz, C. S. **Caratteri di Aleuni Nuovi Generi e Nuove Specie di Animali.** (Principalmente de Pesci) e Piante della Sicilia, con Varie Osservazioni Sopra i Medisimi. Bd. with Indice D'ittiologia Siciliana: Ossia Catalogo Metodico Dei Nomi Lathini, Italiani Che Si Rinveng Ono in Sicilia, etc. (Illus.). 10.50. (Illus.). 1967. Repr. of 1810 ed. Set. 25.20. Hafner Service.
Risso, Antoine. **Ichthyiologie De Nice, Une Histoire Des Poissons De Departement Des Alpes Maritimes.** 1967. Repr. of 1810 ed. 35.00. Hafner Service.
Saïla, Saul B. & Norton, Virgil J. **Tuna:**

Status, Trends & Alternative Management Arrangements. 1974. pap. text ed. 3.00. Johns Hopkins.
Stephens, J. S., Jr. **A Revised Classification of The Blennioid Fishes of the American Family Chaenopsidae.** 1963. pap. 3.50. U of Cal Pr.
Sullivan, Chester R. **Alligator Gar.** 1973. 6.95. Crown.
— — **Symposium on Icthygenetics, 1st. Genetics & Mutagenesis of Fish: Proceedings.** Schroder, J. H., ed. 1973. 18.50. Springer-Verlag.
Tirmizi, Khan. **Hand Book on a Pakistani Marine Prawn Panaeus.** 5.00. Panther Hse.
Trott, Lamarr B. **Contributions to the Biology of Carapid Fishes** (Paracanthopterygii, Gadiformes). 1970. pap. 2.00. U of Cal Pr.
Vessey-Fitzgerald, Brian. **World of Fishes.** 1973. 5.25. British Bk Ctr.
Weatherly, A. H. **Growth & Ecology of Fish Populations.** 1972. 13.50. Acad Pr.
What Fish Is That? (Illus.). 4.45. Purnell Lib Serv.

Fishes—Africa

Balon, Eugene K. **African Fishes of Lake Kariba.** (Illus.). 1974. 14.95. TFH Pubns.
Boulenger, G. A. **Catalogue of the Freshwater Fishes of Africa,** 4 Vols. in 2. 1964. Repr. of 1909 ed. 146.40. Hafner Service.
Fryer, Geoffrey & Iles, T. D. **Cichlids of the Great Lakes of Africa.** (Illus.). 1972. 20.00. TFH Pubns.
Lowe-McConnell, R. H. **Illustrated Key to Freshwater Fishes of the Volta Lake.** 1972. 6.00. Panther Hse.
Playfair, R. Lambert & Guenther, Albert C. **The Fishes of Zanzibar.** (Illus.). 1971. Repr. of 1866 ed. 125.00. N K Gregg.

Fishes—Atlantic Ocean

Beebe, William & Tee-Van, John. **Field Book of the Shore Fishes of Bermuda & the West Indies.** Orig. Title: Field Book of the Shore Fishes of Bermuda. (Illus.). 1970. pap. 3.00. Dover.
Breder, Charles M., Jr. **Fieldbook of Marine Fishes of the Atlantic Coast.** (Illus.). 1948. 5.95. Putnam.
Migdalski, Edward C. **Angler's Guide to the Salt Water Game Fishes: Atlantic & Pacific.** (Illus.). 1958. 10.95. Ronald.
Perlmutter, Alfred. **Guide to Marine Fishes.** (Illus.). pap. NYU Pr.
— — **Guide to Marine Fishes.** (Illus.). 1961. 6.50. NYU Pr.

Fishes—Australia

Deas, Walter. **Australian Fishes in Colour.** (Illus.). 1974. 6.50. Intl Pubns Serv.
Hale, R. **Australian Fishes in Color.** (Illus.). 1973. 6.75. Newbury Bks Inc.

Fishes—Egypt

Boulenger, George A. **Fishes of the Nile,** 2 Vols. (Zoology of Egypt, Vols. 3 & 4). (Illus.). 1964. Repr. of 1907 ed. 114.70. Hafner Service.

Fishes—Europe

Lythgoe, John & Lythgoe, Lillian. **Fishes of the Sea: The Coastal Waters of the British Isles, Europe & the Mediterranean, a Photographic Guide in Color.** 1972. 15.00. Intl Pubns Serv.
Vachon, Mrs. Claude, illus. **European Inland Water Fish: A Multilingual Catalogue.** (Illus.). 1972. 22.00. (FAO). Unipub.
Wheeler, Alwyne. **Fishes of the British Isles & Northwest Europe.** 1969. 25.00. Mich St U Pr.

Fishes—Great Britain

Bagenal, T. B. **Observer's Book of Fresh Water Fishes.** (Illus.). bds. 2.50. Warne.
— — **Observer's Book of Sea Fishes of the British Isles.** (Illus.). bds. 2.50. Warne.
Wheeler, Alwyne. **Fishes of the British Isles & Northwest Europe.** 1969. 25.00. Mich St U Pr.
Woodward, A. Smith. **Fishes of the English Chalk,** Part 1-7, Vols. 56-56, 61-65, Nos. 263, 266, 291, 300, 308, 313, 320. Repr. of 1912 ed. Set. pap. 40.50. Johnson Repr.

Fishes—Japan

Marr, John, ed., **Kuroshio: A Symposium on the Japan Current.** 1970. 17.50. U Pr of Hawaii.

Fisheries—Mediterranean

General Fisheries Council for the Mediterranean. **Proceedings & Technical Papers,** Vol. 7. 1964. pap. 10.00. (FAO). Unipub.
— — **Proceedings & Technical Papers,** Vol. 8. 1967. pap. 15.00. (FAO). Unipub.

Fishes—New Zealand

Bodeker, Philip. **The Sandgroper's Trail: An Angling Safari from Perth to the Kimberley.** (Illus.). 1971. 8.95. Reed.
Doak, Wade. **Fishes of the New Zealand Region.** (Illus.). 1974. 27.50. British Bk Ctr.
Moreland, John M. **Marine Fishes of New Zealand.** (Illus.). 1967. 5.50. Reed.

Fishes—North America

Beebe, William & Tee-Van, John. **Field Book of the Shore Fishes & the West Indies.** (Illus.). 5.50. Peter Smith.
Gabrielson, Ira N., ed. **New Fisherman's Encyclopedia.** rev. ed. (Illus.). 1963. 19.95. Stackpole.
Herald, Earl. **Fishes of North America.** (Illus.). 1972. 9.95. Doubleday.
Herbert, Henry W. **Frank Forester's Fish & Fishing in the United States & British Provinces of North America.** (Illus.). 1970. Repr. of 1850 ed. 16.00. Arno.
Jordan, David S. & Evermann, Barton W. **American Food & Game Fishes.** (Illus.). 1969. pap. 5.00. Dover.
Miracle, Leonard, et al. **New Hunter's Encyclopedia.** rev. ed. 1965. 24.95. Stackpole.
Schultz, Leonard P., et al. **Wondrous World of Fishes.** (Illus.). 1969. 9.95. Natl Geog.
Storer, David H. **A Synopsis of Fishes of North America.** 1972. Repr. of 1845 ed. 32.20. Hafner Service.
Westman, James. **Why Fish Bite & Why They Don't.** 1961. 4.95. P-H.
Zim, Herbert S. & Shoemaker, Hurst H. **Fishes.** 4.95; pap. 1.50. Western Pub.

Fishes—Pacific Ocean

Fitch, John E. & Lavenberg, Robert J. **Deep-Water Fishes of California.** (Illus.). 1968. pap. 2.25. U of Cal Pr.
Fowler, H. R. **Fishes of Oceania with Supplements I-III.** 1967. Repr. of 1881 ed. pap. 82.50. Hafner Service.
Fowler, H. W. **Fishes of Guam, Hawaii, Samoa, & Tahiti.** Repr. of 1925 ed. pap. 3.00. Kraus Repr.
— — **The Fishes of Oceania, Supplement 3.** pap. 12.00. Kraus Repr.
— — **Fishes of the Tropical Central Pacific.** Repr. of 1927 ed. pap. 3.00. Kraus Repr.
Fowler, H. W. & Ball, S. C. **Fishes of Hawaii, Johnston Island, & Wake Island.** Repr. of 1925 ed. pap. 3.00. Kraus Repr.
Fowler, Henry W. **Fishes of Oceania,** 4 Vols. in 1. (Illus.). 1928-1949. 105.00. Johnson Repr.

Gosline, William A. & Brock, Vernon E. **Handbook of Hawaiian Fishes.** (Illus.). 1960. pap. 7.50. U Pr of Hawaii.
Gotshall, Daniel W. & Zimbleman. **Fishes of the Pacific Coast: An Underwater Guide, Alaska to the Baja.** (Durabooks). (Illus.). 1974. 5.95. Livingston.
Guenther, A. **Andrew Garrett's Fische der Suedsee,** 3 Vols. in 1. 1966. Repr. of 1873 ed. 99.00. Hafner Service.
Howard, John K. & Ueyanagi, Shoji. **Distribution-Relative Abundance of Billfishes (Istiophoridae) of the Pacific Ocean.** (Illus., Atlas). 1965. Set. pap. 5.50. U of Miami Pr.
Jordan, David S. & Evermann, Barton W. **The Shore Fishes of Hawaii.** (Illus.). 1973. pap. 8.50. C E Tuttle.
Kizevetter, I. V. **Chemistry & Technology of Pacific Fish.** IPST Staff, tr. from Rus. (Illus.). 1974. 22.00. Intl Schol Bk Serv.
Migdalski, Edward C. **Angler's Guide to the Salt Water Game Fishes: Atlantic & Pacific.** (Illus.). 1958. 10.95. Ronald.
Pietschmann, V. **Remarks on Pacific Fishes.** Repr. of 1930 ed. pap. 3.00. Kraus Repr.
Schindler, O. **Sexually Mature Larval Hemiramphidae from the Hawaiian Islands.** Repr. of 1932 ed. pap. 3.50. Kraus Repr.

Fishes—Red Sea

Klausewitz, W. **Erforschung Der Ichthyofauna Des Roten Meeres.** (Illus.). pap. 2.20. Hafner Service.

Fishes—United States

Allyn, Rube. **Florida Fishes.** Allyn, Charles, ed. (Illus.). 1969. pap. 1.25. Great Outdoors.
Burgess, Warren E. & Axelrod, Herbert R. **Pacific Marine Fishes, Bk. 4.** (Illus.). 1974. 20.00. TFH Pubn.
Dahlberg, Michael. **Guide to Coastal Fishes of Georgia & Nearby States.** (Illus.). 1974. pap. 5.75. U of Ga. Pr.
Eddy, Samuel & Surber, Thaddeus. **Northern Fishes.** 5.75. Branford.
Fitch, John E. & Lavenberg, Robert J. **Deep-Water Fishes of California.** (Illus.). 1968. pap. 2.25. U of Cal Pr.
Funk, John L., et al. **Black River Studies.** 1953. pap. 2.50. U of Mo Pr.
Hubbs, Carl L. & Lagler, Karl F. **Fishes of the Great Lakes Region.** (Illus.). 1964. 9.95. U of Mich Pr.
Jordan, D. S. & Evermann, B. W. **American Food & Game Fishes.** (Illus.). 10.00. Peter Smith.
Jordan, David S. & Evermann, Barton W. **The Shore Fishes of Hawaii.** (Illus.). 1973. pap. 8.50. C E Tuttle.
Koster, William J. **Guide to the Fishes of New Mexico.** (Illus.). 1957. pap. 1.65. U of NM Pr.
Rafinesque, Constantine. **Ichthyologia Ohiensis, or, Natural History of the Fishes Inhabiting the River Ohio & Its Tributary Streams.** 1970. Repr. of 1820 ed. 8.00. Arno.
Ricciuti, Edward R. **Dancers on the Beach: The Story of the Grunion.** (Illus.). 1973. 3.95. T Y Crowell.
Schultz, Leonard P. **Keys to the Fishes of Washington, Oregon & Closely Adjoining Regions.** 136. pap. 2.00. U of Wash Pr.
Smith, Jerome V. C. **Natural History of the Fishes of Massachusetts.** (Illus.). 1970. boxed. 10.75. Freshet Pr.
Titcomb, Margaret. **Native of Fish in Hawaii.** 1972. 7.00. U Pr of Hawaii.

Fishing

All-Union Conference, Murmansk, Feb.-Mar., 1968. **Fish Behavior & Fishing Techniques: Proceedings.** 1973. 14.00. Intl Schol Bk Serv.
Allyn, Rube. **Fishermen's Handbook.** pap. 1.00. Great Outdoors.

Annesley, Patrick, ed. **Hardy's Book of Fishing.** (Illus.). 1971. 13.95. Dutton.
Arnov, Boris. **Fishing for Everyone.** (Illus.). 1970. 4.95. Hawthorn.

Babcock, Havilah. **Jaybirds Go to Hell on Friday.** 1964. 4.95. HR&W.
Babson, Stanley M. **Bonefishing.** rev. ed. 1973. 6.95. Winchester Pr.
Barrett, Peter. **In Search of Trout.** (Illus.). 1973. 7.95. P-H.
Bashline, L. James, ed. **The Eastern Trail.** (Illus.). 1972. 8.95. Freshet Pr.
Bates, Joseph D., Jr. **Complete Fishing Book.** new ed. (Illus.). 1973. Har-Row.
— — **Fishing: An Encyclopedic Guide to Tackle & Tactics for Fresh & Salt Water.** 1973. 14.95.
— — **How to Find & Make Them Strike.** (Illus.). 1974. 8.95.
Bauer, Erwin A., ed. **Fishermen's Digest.** 9th ed. 1973. pap. 6.95. Digest Bks.
Bayless, Kenneth M. **Complete Book of Sportfishing.** (Illus.). 1973. pap. 4.95. Petersen Pub.
Bennett, Tiny. **Art of Angling.** 1970. 9.95. P-H.
Bergman, Ray. **Fishing with Ray Bergman.** Janes, Edward C., ed. (Illus.). 1970. 8.95. Knopf.
Berlin, Sven. **Jonah's Dream: A Meditation on Fishing.** (Illus.). 1974. 8.00. W Kaufmann.
Blackwood, Elsie M. **Many Rivers.** (Illus.). 1968. 1.98. A S Barnes.
Blaisdell, Harold F. **Philosophical Fisherman.** 1969. 6.95. HM.
— — **Tricks That Take Fish.** (Illus.). 1954. 5.95. HR&W.
Bradford, Charles. **The Brook Trout & the Determined Angler.** (Illus.). 1970. boxed 6.75. Freshet Pr.
Bradner, Enos. **Fish-on!** 3.95. Superior Pub.
— — **Inside on the Outdoors.** (Illus.). 1973. 9.95. Superior Pub.
Briscoe, Lawrance. **Fisher's Alley.** 7.95. Vantage.
Brooks, Joe. **Complete Book of Fly Fishing.** rev. ed. 7.95. A S Barnes.
— — **Complete Guide to Fishing Across North America.** (Illus.). 1966. 9.95. Har-Row.
Brooks, Joseph W., Jr. **World of Fishing.** (Illus.). 1964. 9.75. Van Nos Reinhold.

Camp, Raymond, ed. **Fireside Book of Fishing.** (Illus.). 1959. 6.50. S&S.
Casson, Paul. **Decoys Simplified** (Illus.). 1973. 14.95. Freshet Pr.
Clark, Eugenie. **Lady with a Spear.** 1974. pap. 2.00. Ballantine.
— — **Lady with a Spear.** (Illus.). 1953. 5.92. Har-Row.
Clotfelter, Cecil F. **Hunting & Fishing.** 1974. 7.50. Libs Unl.
Code of Safety for Fishermen & Fishing Vessels: Pt. A. Safety & Health Practice for Skippers & Crews. 1973. 2.70. Intl. Labour Office.
Cole, Len. **Fishing All Waters.** 1973. pap. 1.50 Stadia Sports Pub.
Cone, Arthur L., Jr. **Fishing Made Easy.** (Illus.). 1968. 6.95. Macmillan.
Crahall, Joseph. **The Completest Angling Booke That Ever Was Writ.** (Illus.). 1970. boxed. 27.50. Freshet Pr.
Crowe, John. **Modern A B C's of Fresh Water Fishing.** pap. 0.95. Funk & W.
— — **Modern ABC's of Fresh Water Fishing.** (Illus.). 1973. 4.95; pap. 2.95. Stackpole.
Cullen, Anthony & Hemphill, Patrick. **Crash Strike.** (Illus.). 1971. pap. 8.75. Intl Pubns Serv.
Culley, M. B. **The Pilchard.** 1972. 27.00. Pergamon.
Cushing, D. H. **Detection of Fish.** (Illus.). 1973. 20.00 Pergamon.

Dahlem, Ted. **How to Make & Mend Cast Nets.** pap. 1.25. Great Outdoors.
Dalrymple, Byron. **Sportsman's Guide to Game Fish.** 3rd ed. 1971. 6.95. T Y Crowell.

Decker, Maurice H. **How to Take Fresh Water Fish in Lake, Pond & Stream.** rev. ed. (Illus.). 1958. pap. 2.25. Sentinel.

Denny, George. **The Dread Fishwish.** (Illus.). 1974. 8.95. Freshet Pr.

Dodd, Ed. **Mark Trail's Fishing Tips.** (Illus.). 1969. pap. 1.00. Essandess.

Doogue, Raymond. **Seafishing for Beginners.** 1974. pap. 3.50. Reed.

Downey, Earl. **How to Fish for Snook.** pap. 1.00. Great Outdoors.

Earp, Samuel A. & Wildeman, William J. **The Blue Water Bait Book: Secrets of Successful Big Game Fishing.** (Illus.). 1974. 7.95. Little.

Elliot, Bob. **Bass Fishing in New England.** new ed. (Illus.). 1973. 6.50; pap. 3.50. Stone Wall Pr.

Elliott, Charles. **Outdoor Observer: How to See, Hear & Interpret in the Natural World.** 1970. 4.50. Dutton.

Evanhoff. **Complete Guide to Fishing.** 2.00. Borden.

Evanoff, Vlad. **Another Thousand & One Fishing Tips & Tricks.** (Illus.). 1970. 6.95. Har-Row.

— — **Complete Guide to Fishing.** pap. 2.00. Wilshire.

— — **How to Fish in Salt Water.** (Illus.). 1974. 7.95. A S Barnes.

— — **One Thousand & One Fishing Tips & Tricks.** (Illus.). 1966. 6.95. Har-Row.

Fabian, John. **Fishing for the Beginner.** 1974. 5.95. Atheneum.

Fallon, John. **Teaching Your Children to Fish.** 1974. 6.95. Winchester Pr.

FAO Technical Conference, Reykjavik, 1970. **Modern Fishing Gear of the World Three: Fish Finding, Purse Seining, & Aimed Trawling.** Kristjonsson, H., ed. (Illus.). 1972. 38.00. (FAO). Unipub.

Farmer, Charles J. **Backpack Fishing.** (Illus.). 1974. 8.95. pap. 5.95. O'Hara.

— — **Creative Fishing.** (Illus.). 1973. 5.95. Stackpole.

Farrington, S. Kip, Jr. **Fishing with Hemingway & Glassell.** 1971. 5.95. McKay.

Fichter, George S. & Francis, Phil. **Fishing.** Zim, Herbert S., ed. 1974. 2.95. Western Pub.

Field & Stream. **Field & Stream Reader.** facs. ed. 1946. 13.50. Bks for Libs.

Fishing Ports & Markets. (Illus.). 1971. 30.00 (FAO). Unipub.

Flick, Art. **Art Flicks New Streamside Guide to Naturals & Their Imitations.** (Illus.). 1970. 4.95. Crown.

Forbes, David C. **Big-Game Fishing in British Waters.** (Illus.). 1973. 7.95. David & Charles.

— — **Successful Roach Fishing.** (Illus.). 1973. 7.59. David & Charles.

— — **Successful Sea Angling.** (Illus.). 1971. 4.95. David & Charles.

Freeman, Jim. **California Steelhead Fishing.** (Illus.). 1971. pap. 1.95. Chronicle Bks.

— — **California Trout Fishing.** (Illus.). 1971. pap. 1.95. Chronicle Bks.

— — **Fishing with Small Fry: A Parent's Guide to Teaching Children How to Fish.** (Illus.). 1973. pap. 2.95. Chronicle Bks.

— — **Klamath River Fishing.** (Illus.). 1971. pap. 1.95. Chronicle Bks.

— — **Shasta Lake Fishing.** (Illus.). 1971. pap. 1.95. Chronicle Bks.

— — **Trinity River Fishing.** (Illus.). 1971. pap. 1.95. Chronicle Bks.

Fridman, A. L. **Theory & Design of Commercial Fishing Gear.** Kondor, R., tr. from Rus. (Illus.). 1974. 35.00. Intl Schol Bk Serv.

Gerlach, Rex. **Creative Fly Tying & Fishing.** 1974. 10.00. Winchester Pr.

Gingrich, Arnold. **The Fishing in Print.** 1974. 12.95. Winchester Pr.

— — **Well Tempered Angler.** (Illus.). 1965. 6.95. Knopf.

Goadby, Peter. **Big Fish & Blue Water.** 1972. 14.95. HR&W.

Haig-Brown, Roderick. **Return to the River.** 1974. 7.50. Crown.

— — **River Never Sleeps.** 1974. 7.50. Crown.

Haines, R. G. **Echo Fishing.** (Illus.). 1970. 9.50. Transatlantic.

Hall, Henry M. **Idylls of Fishermen.** 1914. 9.50. AMS Pr.

Hardy, Arthur E. **Beginner's Guide to Coarse Fishing.** (Illus.). 1973. 8.75. Transatlantic.

Hawk, Dave. **One Hundred Years on Bass.** (Illus.). 1970. 6.00. Naylor.

Helm, Thomas. **Fishing Southern Salt Waters.** (Illus.). 1972. 10.00 Dodd.

Hilton, Jack. **Quest for Carp.** (Illus.). 1972. 9.95. Transatlantic.

Holm, Don. **Fishing the Pacific.** (Illus.). 1972. 6.95. Winchester Pr.

Hoover, Herbert. **Fishing for Fun.** 1963. 4.95. Random.

Horne, Bernard S., compiled by. **Compleat Angler. 1653-1967: A New Bibliography.** (Illus.). 1970. 25.00. U of Pittsburgh. Pr.

Hoyt, Murray. **Fish in My Life.** 1964. 3.95. Crown.

Hughes, Stephen O. **Tight Lines & Dragonflies.** (Illus.). 1972. 5.95. Lippincott.

Janes, E. C. **Fresh Water Fishing Complete.** (Illus.). 1961. 4.95. HR&W.

Janes, Edward C. **Fishing with Lee Wulff.** (Illus.). 1972. 8.95. Knopf.

Jenkins, J. Geraint. **Nets & Coracles.** (Illus.). 1974. 18.95. David & Charles.

Johnson, et al. **Outdoor Tips: A Remington Sportsmen's Library Bk.** pap. 2.95. Benjamin Co.

The Joy of Fishing. 1974. pap. 3.95. Rand.

Kelly, Florence F. **Flowing Stream.** 29.95. Gordon Pr.

Knap, Jerome & Richey, David. **Getting Hooked on Fishing: An Angler's Hand-book.** (Illus.). 1974. 7.95. Scribner.

Kostyunin, Yu N. & Nokonorou, I. V. **Trawling & New Methods of Continuous Fishing.** (Illus.). 1973. 16.00. Intl School Bk Serv.

Kreh, Lefty & Kessler, Hermann. **Fly Casting with Lefty Kreh.** (Illus.). 1974. 8.95. Lippincott.

Lamo, Dana S **Where the Pools Are Bright & Deep.** (Illus.). 1973. 8.95; limited ed. 15.00. Winchester Pr.

Lane, Billy & Graham, Colin. **Billy Lanes Encyclopaedia of Float Fishing.** (Illus.). 1971. 7.50. Transatlantic.

Laycock, George. **The Field & Stream Guide to Fishing.** 1973. pap. 1.25. Popular Lib.

Livingston, A. D. **Fishing for Bass: Modern Tactics & Tackle.** 1974. 8.95. Lippincott.

Lyman, Henry. **Successful Bluefishing.** (Illus.). 1974. 10.00 Intl Marine.

Lyman, Henry & Woolner, Frank. **Complete Book of Weakfishing.** (Illus.). 1973. 5.95. A S Barnes.

Lyons, Nick. **Seasonable Angler.** 1970. 5.95. Funk & W.

Lyons, Nick, ed. **Fisherman's Bounty: Treasury of Fascinating Lore & the Finest Stories from the World of Angling.** 1970. 6.95; deluxe ed. 8.50. Crown.

McClahe, A. J. **McClahe's New Standard Fishing Encyclopedia & International Angling Guide.** rev. ed. (Illus.). 1974. 40.00. HR&W.

McClane, A. J. **McClane's Standard Fishing Encyclopedia.** (Illus.). 19.95. Reel Trophy.

McClane, Albert J. **Field & Stream International Fishing Guide.** (Illus.). 1971. 8.95; pap. 4.95. HR&W.

McCristal, Vic. **Freshwater Fighting Fish.** (Illus.). 10.00. Soccer.

McDonald, John. **Quill Gordon.** 1972. 10.95. Knopf.

McGrail, William & McGrail, Joie. **Catch & the Feast.** (Illus.). 1969. 20.00. Weybright.

McInturff, Roy A. **Wilderness Fishing for Salmon & Steelhead.** 1974. 8.95. A S Barnes.

Major, Harlan. **Basic Fishing.** (Illus.). 1968. pap. 1.95. Funk & W.

Mendoza, George. **Lord, Suffer Me to Catch a Fish.** 1974. 6.95. Quadrangle.

Mitchell, John. **Better Fishing, Freshwater.** 1968. 5.00. Intl Pubns Serv.

Moe, Martin. **Florida Fishing Grounds.** Orig. Title: Off Shore Coastal Fishing: Florida. pap. 1.95. Great Outdoors.

Mohan, Peter. **Carp for Everyone.** (Illus.). 1972. 6.95. David & Charles.

Moore, Ed. **Fresh Water Fishing.** (Illus.). 1965. pap. 0.95. Macmillan.

Morris, Dan & Strung, Norman. **Fisherman's Almanac.** (Illus.). 1970. 4.95. Macmillan.

Moss, Frank T. **Successful Striped Bass Fishing.** (Illus.). 1974. 12.50. Intl Marine.

Nadaud, J. Peche. (Illus., Fr.). 18.50. Larousse.

Netherby, Steve, ed. **The Experts' Book of Freshwater Fishing.** 1974. 9.95. S&S.

Netting Materials for Fishing Gear. (Illus.). 1974. pap. 6.50 (FAO). Unipub.

Nibler, C. W. **Goodbye Mr. Trout.** 1973. 3.75. Vantage.

Norton, Mortimer, ed. **Angling Success, by Leading Outdoor Writers.** facs. ed. 1935. 11.50. Bks for Libs.

Outdoor Life Editors. Tacklebox Library, 5 Vols. (Illus.). 1971. Set. 5.95. Har-Row.

Ovington, Ray. **Fresh Water Fishing.** 1973. 5.95. Hawthorn.

— — **Introduction to Bait Fishing.** (Illus.). 1971. 5.95. Stackpole.

Parsons, P. Allen. **Complete Book of Fresh Water Fishing.** (Illus.). 1963. 7.95. Har-Row.

Peper, Eric & Rakhoff, Jim, eds. **Fishing Moments of Truth.** 1973. 8.95. Winchester Pr.

— — **Hunting & Fishing Moments of Truth.** 1973. limited ed. 25.00. Winchester Pr.

Pfeiffer, G. Boyd. **Making Your Own Fishing Tackle.** 1974. 6.95. Crown.

Piper, John. **All About Angling.** 1971. 7.50. Transatlantic.

Pobst, Richard. **Fish the Impossible Places.** (Illus.). 1974. 9.95. Freshet Pr.

Power, John & Brown, Jeremy. **Fisherman's Handbook.** 1972. 7.95. Scribner.

Puddepha, D. N. **Coarse Fishing Is Easy.** (Illus.). 1970. 4.95. David & Charles.

Radcliffe, W. **Fishing from the Earliest Time.** 1974. 15.00. Ares.

Radcliffe, William. **Fishing from the Earliest Times.** 1969. Repr. of 1921 ed. 14.95. B. Franklin.

Randolph, J. W. **World of Wood, Field & Stream.** 1962. 3.95. HR&W.

Raymond, Steve. **Year of the Angler.** 1973. 10.00. Winchester Pr.

Reiger, George, ed. **Zane Grey: Outdoorsman.** (Illus.). 1972. 9.95. P-H.

Reinfelder, Al. **Bait Tail Fishing.** (Illus.). 1969. 6.95. A S Barnes.

Ritz, Charles. **A Fly Fisher's Life.** 1973. 7.50. Crown.

Rosko, Milt. **Salt Water Fishing from Boats.** 1972. pap. 2.45. Macmillan.

Sams, Jonathan C. **Reflections of a Fishing Parson.** 1973. 2.95. Abingdon.

Samson, Jack. **Line Down: The Special World of Big Game Fishing.** 1973. 12.50. Winchester Pr.

Sawyer, Frank. **Nymphs & the Trout.** 1973. 5.95. Crown.

Schaldach, William J. **Coverts & Casts & Currents & Eddies,** 2 vols. (Illus.). boxed 25.00. Freshet Pr.

Schwiebert, Ernest. **Remembrances of Rivers Past.** (Illus.). 1972. 6.95. Macmillan.

Scott, Jack. **Greased Line Fishing.** (Illus.). 1970. boxed 10.75. Freshet Pr.

Seaman, Kenneth. **Big Fish from Small Waters.** (Illus.). 1973. 8.95. David & Charles.

Sharp, Hal. **Sportsman's Digest of Fishing.** 1963. pap. 1.75. B&N.

Situacion Demografica: No. 1 Agricultura, Ganaderia, Silvicultura, Caza y Pesca. (Span.). 1.00. OAS.

Smith, A. Paul. **How to Fish for Bass.** (Illus.). pap. 1.00. Great Outdoors.

Sosin, Mark & Clark, John. **Through the Fish's Eye.** (Illus.). 1973. 7.95. Har-Row.
Sosin, Mark & Dance, Bill. **Practical Bass Fishing.** 1974. 9.95. Crown.
Sparano, Vin T. **The Complete Outdoors Encyclopedia.** (Illus.). 1973. 13.95. Har-Row.
Spiller, Burton L. **Fishin' Around.** 1974. 10.00. Winchester Pr.
Sportsman's Guide to Game Fish. (Illus.). 1968. 6.95. T Y Crowell.
Tacklebox Library, 5 bks. Incl. **Angler's Safety & First Aid.** Sosin, Mark J; **Freshwater Tackle.** Hall, Baird; **Fish Cookery.** Marshall, Mel; **Selecting Lures, Flies & Baits.** Rice F. Philip; **Reading the Water.** Bates, Joseph D. (Illus.). pap. 5.95. slip case set. Har-Row.
Tapply, Horace G. **Sportsman's Notebook.** 1964. 7.95. HR&W.
Taylor, Fred J. **Fishing Here & There.** 1970. 8.75. Intl Pubns Serv.
Three Books on Fishing. 1962. Repr. of 1659 ed. 7.50. Schol Facsimiles.
Trench, Charles C. **The History of Angling.** (Illus.). 1974. 12.95. Follett.
Ulrich, Heinz. **How the Experts Catch Trophy Fish.** 1969. 6.95. A S Barnes.
Van De Water, Frederick F. **In Defense of Worms.** 1970. boxed 5.75. Freshet Pr.
Van Dyke, Henry. **Fisherman's Luck & Some Other Uncertain Things.** 1927. Repr. 14.00. Finch Pr.
Von Brandt, Andres. **Fish Catching Methods of the World** rev. & enlarged edition ed. (Illus.). 1972. 25.00. Heinman.
Wall, Roy. **Game & Fish: From Field to Table.** 1972. 5.95. Naylor.
Walton, Izaac & Cotton, Charles. **The Compleat Angler; or, the Contemplative Man's Recreation.** (Illus.). 1974. Repr. of 1962 ed. 7.50. Rowman.
Walton, Izaak. **Compleat Angler.** 3.95; pap. 1.50. Dutton.
Warner, Robert. **Don't Blame the Fish.** 1974. 8.95. Winchester Pr.
Waterman, Charles F. **The Fisherman's World.** 1972. 15.00. Random.
— — **Modern Fresh & Salt Water Fly Fishing.** (Illus.). 1974. pap. 3.95. Macmillan.
Weeks, Edward. **Fresh Waters.** (Illus.). 1968. 7.95. Little.
Welle-Strand, E. **Angling in Norway.** (Illus.). 1971. pap. 4.00. Vanous.
Westman, James. **Secret of Why Fish Bite.** pap. 2.00. Wilshire.
Whitaker, Ralph R. **Song of the Outriggers: Big Game Fishing on the Ocean Surface.** Amos, William E., ed. (Illus.) 1972. 8.95. Green.
Willock, Colin, ed. **A B C of Fishing.** (Illus.). 1971. 9.50; deluxe ed. 15.00. Transatlantic.
Wood, E. J. **Inshore Dinghy Fishing.** pap. 1.95. Transatlantic.
Wood, James. **Sport Fishing for Beginners.** 5.95. British Bk Ctr.
Wrangles, Alan, ed. **The Complete Guide to Coarse Fishing.** (Illus.). 1973. 12.50. David & Charles.
— — **The Complete Guide to Sea Angling.** (Illus.). 12.50. David & Charles.
Wright, D. Macer. **A Fish Will Rise.** (Illus.). 1972. 6.95. David Charles.
Wright. Leonard, Jr. **Thinking Man's Guide to Trout Angling.** 1972. 6.95. Dutton.
Zern, Ed. **A Fine Kettle of Fish Stories.** (Illus.). 1972. 5.95. Winchester Pr.
Zwirz, Bob. **A B C's of Fishing.** pap. 5.95. Digest Bks.

Fishing—Africa

Organization of African Unity. **Report on the Guinean Trawling Survey.** Lagos 1968, 3 vols. 62.50. Intl Pubns Serv.

Fishing—Australia

Colwell, Max. **Whaling Around Australia.** (Illus.). 1969. 8.00. Verry.

Fishing—British Honduras

Craig, Alan K. **Geography of Fishing in British Honduras & Adjacent Coastal Waters.** (Illus.). 1966. pap. 4.00. La State U Pr.

Fishing—Great Britain

Fysh, Hudson. **Round the Bend in the Stream.** (Illus.). 1968. 11.00. Verry.
Marston, A. N. **Encyclopedia of Angling.** 2nd ed. 1963. 15.00. Transatlantic.
Willock, Colin, ed. **A B C of Fishing.** (Illus.). 1971. 9.50; deluxe ed. 15.00. Transatlantic.

Fishing—Hawaii

Hosaka, Edward. **Shore Fishing in Hawaii.** pap. 4.50. Petroglyph.
Mackeller, Jean S. **Hawaii Goes Fishing.** (Illus.). 1968. Repr. of 1956 ed. bds. 3.50. C E Tuttle.

Fishing—Japan

Fysh, Hudson. **Round the Bend in the Stream.** (Illus.). 1968. 11.00. Verry.

Fishing—New Zealand

Doogue, Raymond & Moreland, John. **New Zealand Sea Angler's Guide.** (Illus.). 1974. 8.50. Reed.
Draper, Keith. **Trout Flies in New Zealand.** (Illus.). 1971. 8.50. Reed.
Ferris, George. **Fly Fishing in New Zealand.** 1972. 8.50. Intl Pubns Serv.
Fysh, Hudson. **Round the Bend in the Stream.** (Illus.). 1968. 11.00. Verry.

Fishing—North America

Bradner, Enos. **Northwest Angling.** 2nd ed. (Illus.). 1969. 6.50. Binfords.
Cramond, Michael. **Hunting & Fishing in North America.** (Illus.). 1953. 9.95. U of Okla Pr.
Evanoff, Vlad, ed. **Fresh-Water Fisherman's Bible.** (Illus.). 1964. pap. 2.50. Doubleday.
Gabrielson, Ira N., ed. **New Fisherman's Encyclopedia.** rev. ed. (Illus.). 1963. 19.95. Stackpole.
Herbert, Henry W. **Frank Forester's Fish & Fishing in the United States & British Provinces of North America.** (Illus.). 1970. Repr. of 1850 ed. 16.00. Arno.
Knap, Jerome. **Where to Fish & Hunt in North America: A Complete Sportsmen's Guide.** (Illus.). 7.95. Pagurian.
McClane, Albert J. **American Angler.** (Illus.). 1954. 5.00. HR&W.
Matthiessen, Peter. **Wildlife in America.** (Illus.). 1964. pap. 2.25. Viking Pr.
Migdalski, Edward C. **Angler's Guide to the Fresh Water Sport Fishes of North America.** (Illus.). 1962. 9.50. Ronald.
Miracle, Leonard, et al. **New Hunter's Encyclopedia.** rev. ed 1965. 24.95. Stackpole.
Power, John & Brown, Jeremy. **Fisherman's Handbook.** 1972. 7.95. Scribner.
Rostlund, Erhard. **Freshwater Fish & Fishing in Native North America.** Repr. of 1952 ed. pap. 21.00. Johnson Repr.
Westman, James. **Why Fish Bite & Why They Don't.** 1961. 4.95. P-H.

Fishing—Pacific Ocean

Cannon, Raymond. **How to Fish the Pacific Coast.** 3rd ed. (Illus.). 1967. pap. 2.95. Lane.
Holm, Don. **Fishing the Pacific.** (Illus.). 1972. 6.95. Winchester Pr.
— — **Pacific North.** Orig. Title: Sport Fishing in the North Pacific. 1969. 12.50. Caxton.
Tracy, J. P. Low. **Man on a Gill-Netter.** (Illus.). 1974. pap. 3.95. Alaska Northwest.

Fishing—United States

Ames, Francis H. **Fishing the Oregon Country.** (Illus.). 1966. 6.95. Caxton.
Anderson, Tommy. **The Complete Guide to Florida Fishing.** (Illus.). 1973. 8.95. A S Barnes.
Babcock, Havilah. **My Health Is Better in November.** (Illus.). 1960. 5.95. HR&W.
Bascom, Dave. **How to Fish Good.** (Illus.). 1971. pap. 2.95. Winchester Pr.
Becker, A. C., Jr. **Gulf Coast Fishing.** (Illus.). 1970. 8.50. A S Barnes.
Dietz, Lew. **Touch of Wildness: A Maine Woods Journal.** 1970. 5.95. HR&W.
Donaldson, Ivan & Cramer, Frederick. **Fishwheels of the Columbia.** (Illus.). 1971. 10.00. Binfords.
Duffy, M. **Hunting & Fishing in Louisiana.** 1969. 3.95. Pelican.
Dunaway, Vic. **Vic Dunaway's Fishing Guide to Florida - Fresh & Salt Water.** (Illus.). 1974. 8.95; pap. 5.95. O'Hara.
Elliot, Bob. **Bass Fishing in New England.** newed. (Illus.). 1973. 6.50; pap. 3.50. Stone Wall Pr.
Fagerstrom, Stan. **Catch More Bass.** (Illus.). 1973. pap. 7.95. Caxton.
Fellegy, Joe, Jr. **Walleyes & Walleye Fishing.** (Illus.). 1973. 6.95. Dillon.
Freeman, Jim. **How to Catch California Trout.** (Illus.). 1972. pap. 1.95. Chronicle Bks.
— — **Lake Berryessa Fishing.** (Illus.). 1971. pap. 1.95. Chronicle Bks.
— — **North Sierra Trout Fishing.** (Illus.). 1972. pap. 1.95. Chronicle Bks.
Fysh, Hudson. **Round the Bend in the Stream.** (Illus.). 1968. 11.00. Verry.
Gallo, Philip S., Jr. **Guidebook to Saltwater Fishing in Southern California.** 1973. pap. 1.95. Ritchie.
Gilbert, De Witt, ed. **The Future of the Fishing Industry of the United States.** (Illus.). 1968. pap. 10.00. U of Wash Pr.
Gresham, Grits. **Fishes & Fishing in Louisiana.** 1965. 5.00; pap. 4.00. Claitors.
— — **Fishing & Boating in Louisiana.** pap. 2.00. Claitors.
— — **Fishing & Boating in Louisiana.** 1965. 4.00. Claitors.
Grey, Hugh, ed. **Field & Stream Treasury.** 1971. 12.95. HR&W.

Hayden, Mike. **Fishing the California Wilderness.** (Illus.). 1974. pap. 2.95. Chronicle Bks.
Holm, Donald R. **One-Hundred One Best Fishing Spots in Oregon.** (Illus.). 1970. pap. 3.95. Caxton.
Klink, Jerry. **The Mighty Cortez Fish Trap.** (Illus.). 1973. 8.95. A S Barnes.
Konizeski, Dick. **The Montanan's Fishing Guide, Vol. 1: Waters West of the Continental Divide.** 2nd ed. (Illus.). 1974. pap. 4.95. Mountain Pr.
— — **The Montanans' Fishing Guide: Vol. 2, Waters East of Continental Divide.** 1971. 4.95. (Illus.); pap. 3.95. Mountain Pr.
Konizeski, Richard. **The Montanan's Fishing Guide, Vol. 1. Montana Waters West of Continental Divide.** (Illus.) 1970. 4.95. Mountain Pr.
Lewis, Gordon. **Book of Florida Fishing: Fresh & Salt Water.** (Illus.). 1957. pap. 1.75. Great Outdoors.
McTeer, Ed. **Adventures in the Woods & Waters of the Low Country.** 4.95. Beaufort.
Morrison, Morie. **Fresh Water Fishing Illustrated.** 1965. pap. 1.95. Lane.
Murray, William H. **Adventures in the Wilderness.** Verner, William K., ed. (Illus.). 1970. Repr. 10.50. Syracuse U Pr.
Neasham, V. Aubrey. **Wild Legacy: California Hunting & Fishing Tales.** (Illus.). 1973. 6.50. Howell-North.
Rice, William. **Fishing the San Diego Bass Lakes.** (Illus.). 1972. pap. 1.95. Chronicle Bks.

Scharp, Hal. **Florida's Game Fish & How to Land Them.** (Illus.). 1968. 8.50. A S Barnes.

Schwind, Phil. **Striped Bass & Other Cape Cod Fish.** (Illus.). 1972. pap. 3.95. Chatham Pr.

Ulrich, Heinz. **America's Best Lake, Stream, & River Fishing.** 5.95. A S Barnes.

Wharton, James. **Bounty of the Chesapeake: Fishing in Colonial Virginia.** (Illus.). 1957. pap. 1.25. U Pr of Va.

White, Donald J. **New England Fishing Industry: A Study in Price & Wage Setting.** (Illus.). 1954. 5.50. Harvard U Pr.

Wienecke, Lou & Peterson, John. **Guide to Far West Fishing.** (Illus.). 1973. pap. 3.50. P-H.

Wilcoxson, Kent H. **Angler's Guide to Fresh Water Fishing in New England.** (Illus.). 1973. pap. 4.50. Book Prod Serv.

Fishing Boats

Andrews, Ralph W. & Larssen, A.K. **Fish & Ships.** 7.95. Superior Pub.

Blair, Carvel H. & Ansel, William D. **Guide to Fishing Boats & Their Gear.** 1968. 6.00. Cornell Maritime.

Chapelle, Howard I. **The American Fishing Schooners: 1825-1935.** (Illus). 1973. 20.00. Norton.

Fishing Boats of the World-2. 1960. pap. 22.00. (FAO). Unipub.

Fishing Boats of the World-3. 1967. pap. 24.00. (FAO). Unipub.

Gillmer, Thomas C. **Working Watercraft.** (Illus.). 1972. 15.95. Intl Marine.

Silverton, Walter F. **Sport's-Fisherman Paradise: Adventures of a Sport's-Fisherman on Vancouver Island.** (Illus.). 9.95. Pageant-Poseidon.

Fishing Stories

Brister, Bob. **Moss, Mallards & Mules: And Other Hunting & Fishing Stories.** 1973. 8.95. Winchester Pr.

Ford, Corey. **You Can Always Tell a Fisherman.** (Illus.). 1959. 2.95. HR&W.

Fox, Charles K., ed. **Armchair Adventure for the Angler.** 1970. 6.95. A S Barnes.

Gray, William B. **Fish Tales & Ocean Odd Balls.** (Illus.). 1970. 5.95; pap. 2.45. A S Barnes.

Humphrey, William. **Spawning Run.** (Illus.). 1970. 4.50. Knopf.

Lamb, Dana S. **Where the Pools Are Bright & Deep.** (Illus.). 1973. 8.95; limited ed. 15.00. Winchester Pr.

Lariar, Lawrence. **Fish & Be Damned.** 1953. 3.95. P-H.

Lyons, Nick, ed. **Fisherman's Bounty: Treasury of Fascinating Lore & the Finest Stories from the World of Angling.** 1970. 6.95. 8.50. Crown.

Lyons, Nick. **Fishing Widows.** (Sportsmen's Classics Ser.). 1974. 5.95. Crown.

Woolner, Frank. **My New England.** new ed. (Illus.). 1972. 6.50. Stone Wall Pr.

Fishing Lures

Becker, A. C., Jr. **Lure Fishing.** (Illus.). 1970. 3.95. A S Barnes.

Reinfelder, Al. **Bait Tail Fishing.** (Illus.). 1969. 6.95. A S Barnes.

Fishing Tackle

Burrell, Leonard F. **Beginner's Guide to Home Coarse Tacklemaking.** (Illus.). 1973. 8.75. Transatlantic.

Clemens, Dale P. **Fiberglass Rod Making.** 1974. 10.00. Winchester Pr.

De Rohan-Csermak, Geza. **Sturgeon Hooks of Eurasia.** (Illus.). 1963. 8.50. Aldine.

Evanoff, Vlad. **Modern Fishing Tackle.** (Illus.). 1961. 6.95. A S Barnes

FAO Catalogue of Fishing Gear Designs. (Illus.). 1973. 13.00 (FAO). Unipub.

Graumont, Raoul & Wenstrom, Elmer. **Fisherman's Knots & Nets.** (Illus.). 1948. 5.00. Cornell Maritime.

Hoover, Robert L. **Chumash Fishing Equipment.** (Illus.). 1973. pap. 1.50. Ballena Pr.

Lewers, Dick. **Understanding Fishing Tackle.** (Illus.). 1972. 14.50. Reed.

McCristal, Vic. **Great Fishing with Lures.** (Illus.). 1972. 13.50. Soccer.

McNally, Tom. **Tom McNally's Complete Book of Fishermen's Knots.** (Illus.). 1974. 6.95; pap. 3.95. O'Hara.

Melner, Sam & Kessler, Herman. **Great Fishing Tackle Catalogs of the Golden Age.** (Illus.). 1972. 6.95. Crown.

Modern Fishing Gear of the World: 2. 1964. 22.00 (FAO). Unipub.

Pfeiffer, C. Boyd. **Tackle Craft.** 1974. 9.95. Crown.

Publications International Ltd. **The Complete Buying Guide to Fishing Equipment.** 1973. pap. 1.95. PB.

Sosin, Mark & Kreh, Lefty. **Practical Fishing Knots.** (Illus.). 1972. 5.95. Crown.

Von Brandt, Andres. **Fish Catching Methods of the World.** rev. & enlarged edition ed. (Illus.). 1972. 25.00. Heinman.

Wilson, James. **The Rod & the Gun.** (Illus.). 1973. Repr. of 1844 ed. 16.95. British Bk Ctr.

Fly Fishing

Annesley, Patrick, ed. **Hardy's Book of Fishing.** (Illus.). 1971. 13.95. Dutton.

Atherton, John. **The Fly & the Fish.** (Illus.). 1971. boxed 12.95. Freshet Pr.

Ball, John W. **Casting & Fishing the Artificial Fly.** (Illus.). 1972. pap. 3.95. Caxton.

Bates, Joseph D., Jr. **Streamer Fly Tying & Fishing.** (Illus.). 1966. 7.95. Stackpole.

Bay, Kenneth E. & Vinciguerra, Matthew M. **How to Tie Freshwater Flies.** 1974. 10.00. Winchester Pr.

Brooks, Joe. **Complete Book of Fly Fishing.** rev. ed. 1968. 5.95. A S Barnes.

Bucknall, Geoffrey. **Fly-Fishing Tactics on Rivers.** (Illus.). 1968. 5.25. Intl Pubns Serv.

Cairns, Bill. **Fly Casting with Bill Cairns.** (Illus.). 1974. 7.95. Scribner.

Cross, Reuben. **The Completest Fly Tier.** (Illus.). 1971. 7.95. Freshet Pr.

Cullen, Anthony & Hemphill, Patrick. **Crash Strike.** (Illus.). 1971. pap. 8.75. Intl Pubns Serv.

Dick, Lenox. **Art & Science of Fly Fishing.** 2nd ed. (Illus.). 1972. 6.95. Winchester Pr.

Esquire, D. J. **Secrets of Angling.** 1970. 6.75. Freshet Pr.

Gerlach, Rex. **Fly Fishing the Lakes.** (Illus.). 1972. 6.95. Winchester Pr.

Gingrich, Arnold. **The Joys of Trout.** (Illus.). 1973. 7.50. Crown.

Goldberg, Howard. **The Angler's Book on Fly-Tying & Fishing.** (Illus.). 1973. 9.95. Scribner.

Hidy, V. S. **The Pleasures of Fly Fishing.** (Illus.). 1972. 10.00. Winchester Pr.

Hidy, Vernon S. & Sports Illustrated Editors. **Sports Illustrated Fly Fishing.** rev. ed. (Illus.). 1972. 4.50; pap. 1.75. Lippincott.

Hills, John W. **History of Fly Fishing for Trout.** 1971. boxed 8.95. Freshet Pr.

Ivens, T. C. **Still Water Fly Fishing: A Modern Guide to Angling in Reservoirs & Lakes.** 3rd ed. (Illus.). 1971. 21.50. Transatlantic.

Knight, John A. & Knight, Richard A. **Complete Book of Fly Casting.** 1963. 6.95. Putnam.

Koch, Ed. **Fishing the Midge.** (Illus.). 1973. 7.95. Freshet Pr.

Kreh, Bernard L. **Fly Fishing in Salt Water.** 1974. 8.95. Crown.

Latham, Roger, et al. **There's No Fishing Like Fly Rod Fishing.** (Illus.). 1972. 6.95. Rosen Pr.

Leisenring, James & Hidy, Vernon S. **Art of Tying the Wet Fly & Fishing the Flymph.** (Illus.). 1971. 4.50. Crown.

Leonard, Edson. **Feather in the Breeze.** (Illus.). 1974. 7.95. Freshet Pr.

Lynde, John G. **Thirty-Four Ways to Cast a Fly.** (Illus.). 1969. 5.95. A S Barnes.

McDonald, John. **Quill Gordon.** 1972. 10.95. Knopf.

Marinaro, Vincent C. **Modern Dry-Fly Code.** (Illus.). 1970. 10.00. Crown.

Mendoza, George. **Fishing the Morning Lonely.** (Illus.). 1974. 7.95. Freshet Pr.

Nix, Sam. **Salt-Water Fly-Fishing Handbook.** (Illus.). 1973. 6.95. Doubleday.

Orvis, Charles F. & Cheney, A. Nelson, eds. **Fishing with the Fly: Sketches by Lovers of the Art with Illustrations of Standard Flies.** (Illus.). 1967. Repr. 8.25. C E Tuttle

Ovington, Roy. **Basic Fly Fishing & Fly Tying.** 1973. 5.95; pap. 2.95. Stackpole.

Peper, Eric & Rikhoff, Jim, eds. **Fishing Moments of Truth.** 1973. 8.95. Winchester Pr.

Puddepha, D. N. **Fly Fishing Is Easy.** (Illus.). 1973. 4.94. David & Charles.

Quick, James. **Fishing the Nymph.** (Illus.). 1960. 6.50. Ronald.

Reid, John. **Clyde-Style Flies & Their Dressings.** (Illus.). 1971. 4.95. David & Charles.

Sand, George X. **Salt Water Fly Fishing.** (Illus.). 1970. 8.95. Knopf.

Slaymaker, S. R., 2nd. **Simplified Fly Fishing.** (Illus.). 1969. 6.95. Har-Row.

Veniard, John. **Fly Dresser's Guide.** new ed. (Illus.). 1973. 17.50. St. Martin.

Walker, C. F. **Art of Chalk Stream Fishing.** (Illus.). 1969. 6.50. Stackpole.

Wallace, Bill. **Fly Fishing Digest.** 1973. pap. 4.95. Digest Bks.

Waterman, Charles F. **Modern Fresh & Salt Water Fly Fishing.** (Illus.). 1972. 8.95. Winchester Pr.

Fossil Fishes

Herre, Albert. **Notes on Fishes in the Zoological Museum of Stanford University.** 1974. 6.95. N K Gregg.

Traquair, R. H. **Fishes of the Old Red Sandstone,** Pt. 2, Nos. 2-4. 1914. Set. pap. 14.75. Johnson Repr.

— —**Ganoid Fishes of British Carboniferous Formations,** Pt. 1, Nos. 2-7. 1914. Set. pap. 31.50. Johnson Repr.

Woodward, A. Smith. **Wealden & Pubeck Fishes,** Pts. 1-3. 1916-19. Set. pap. 35.00. Johnson Repr.

Fresh-Water Fishes

Berndt, A. C. **Fresh-Water Fish Handbook.** (Illus.). 1966. 2.00. Reel Trophy.

Boulenger, G. A. **Catalogue of the Freshwater Fishes of Africa.** 4 Vols. in 2. 1964. Repr. of 1909 ed. 146.40. Hafner Service.

Branson, Branley A. & Batch, Donald A. **Fishes of the Red River Drainage, Eastern Kentucky.** (Illus.). 1974. map. 4.00. U Pr of Ky.

Carlander, Kenneth D. **Handbook of Freshwater Fishery Biology, Vol. 1.** 3rd ed. (Illus.). 1969. 15.00. Iowa St U Pr.

Eddy, Samuel. **How to Know the Freshwater Fishes.** 2nd ed. (Illus.). 1970. 6.00; pap. 4.50. Wm C Brown.

Evanoff, Vlad, ed. **Fresh-Water Fisherman's Bible.** (Illus.). 1964. pap. 2.50. Doubleday.

Everett, Charles. **Fresh Water Fishes.** (Illus.). pap. 1.00. Binfords.

Hervey, George F. & Hems, Jack. **Illustrated Encyclopedia of Freshwater Fish.** (Illus.). 1973. 14.95. Doubleday.

Lagler, Karl F. **Freshwater Fishery Biology.** 1956. 8.95. Wm C Brown.

Lowe-McConnell, R. H. **Illustrated Key to Freshwater Fishes of the Volta Lake.** 1972. 6.00. Panther Hse.

Migdalski, Edward C. **Angler's Guide to the Fresh Water Sport Fishes of North America.** (Illus.). 1962. 9.50. Ronald.

Moore, Ed. **Fresh Water Fishing.** (Illus.). 1965. pap. 0.95. Macmillan.

Pet Library Ltd. **Know Your Bettas.** 1973. pap. 1.00. Doubleday.

Scott, W. B. & Carrick, W. H. **Freshwater Fishes of Eastern Canada.** 2nd ed. (Illus.). 1967. pap. 3.50. U of Toronto Pr.

Sterba, Gunther. **Sterba-Freshwater Fishes,** 2 vols. (Illus.). 1974. pap. 16.95. TFH Pubns.

Ulrich, Heinz. **America's Best Lake, Stream, & River Fishing.** 5.95. A S Barnes.

Vostradovsky, J. **Freshwater Fishes.** (Illus.). 1974. 3.75. Transatlantic.

Walden, Howard T. **Familiar Fresh Water Fishes of America.** (Illus.). 1964. 6.27. Har-Row.

Wilcoxson, Kent H. **Angler's Guide to Fresh Water Fishing in New York.** (Illus.). 1973. pap. 3.25. Book Prod Serv.

Flies

Harris, John R. **An Angler's Entomology.** 1973. 8.95. A S Barnes.

Schwiebert, Ernest G., Jr. **Matching the Hatch.** (Illus.). 7.50. Macmillan.

Harpoons

Mason, Otis T. **Aboriginal American Harpoons.** (Illus.). 1902. pap. 7.50. Shorey.

Indians of North America—Fishing

American Friends Service Committee. **Uncommon Controversy: Fishing Rights of the Muckleshoot, Puyallup & Nisqually Indians.** (Illus.). 1970. 5.95; pap. 2.95. U of Wash Pr.

Lobsters

Cook, Joseph J. **Nocturnal World of the Lobster.** (Illus.). 1971. 4.50. Dodd.

Dueland, Joy. **The Book of the Lobster.** (Illus.). 1973. 7.95; pap. 4.95. NH Pub Co.

Johnson, Martin W. **The Palinurid & Scyllarid Lobster Larvae of the Tropical Eastern Pacific & Their Distribution As Related to the Prevailing Hydrography.** 1971. pap. 2.00. U of Cal Pr.

Prudden, T. M. **About Lobsters.** (Illus.). 1973. pap. 4.95. Wheelwright.

Lobster Fisheries

Doliber, Earl. **Lobstering Inshore & Offshore.** 1973. 5.95. Intl Marine.

Doliber, Earl L. **Lobstering Inshore & Offshore.** (Illus.). 1973. 5.95. Assn Pr.

Dueland, Joy. **The Book of the Lobster.** (Illus.). 1973. 7.95; pap. 4.95. NH Pub Co.

Dueland, Joy V. **The Book of the Lobster.** (Illus.). 1974. pap. 4.95. Scribner.

Marine Biology

Agassiz, Elizabeth & Agassiz, Alexander. **Seaside Studies in Natural History: Marine Animals of Massachusetts Bay.** (Illus.). 1970. Repr. of 1865 ed. 10.00. Arno.

Atlas of the Living Resources of the Seas. (Illus.). 1973. 12.00 (FAO). Unipub.

Barnes, Harold. **Oceanography & Marine Biology Vol. 12.** 1974. text ed. 36.95. Hafner.

Barnes, Harold, ed. **Oceanography & Marine Biology. Vol 11.** 1973. text ed. 32.95. Hafner.

— — **Oceanography & Marine Biology: A Book of Techniques.** (Illus.). 1968. Repr. of 1959 ed. 9.00. Hafner.

— — **Oceanography & Marine Biology: An Annual Review.** 11 vols. Incl. Vol. 1. 12.00; Vol. 2. 12.00; Vol. 3. 14.50; Vol. 4. 15.50; Vol. 5. 20.00; Vol. 6. 22.00; Vol. 7. 22.00; Vol. 8. 22.00; Vol. 9. 24.00; Vol. 10. 29.95; Vol. 11. 32.95; Vol. 12. 36.95. 1963-70. Hafner.

— — **Some Contemporary Studies in Marine Biology.** (Illus.). 1966. 16.25. Hafner.

Berrill, N. J. **Life of the Ocean.** 1966. 5.50; by subscription 3.95. McGraw.

Boehme, Eckart, ed. **From the Law of the Sea Towards an Ocean Space Regime: Practical & Legal Implications of the Marine Revolution.** 1972. pap. 15.00. Intl Pubns Serv.

Boolootian, R. A. & Thomas. **Marine Biology.** (gr. 9-12). 1967. pap. text ed. 2.48. HR&W.

Bush, Eric W., ed. **Flowers of the Sea.** 1970. 7.50. Naval Inst. Pr.

Carson, Rachel. **Under the Sea Wind: A Naturalist's Picture of Ocean Life.** 1952. 7.50. Oxford U Pr.

Carson, Rachel L. **Under the Sea Wind.** pap. 1.25. NAL.

Coker, Robert E. **This Great & Wide Sea: An Introduction to Oceanography & Marine Biology.** (Illus.). pap. 2.95. Har-Row.

Conference on Marine Biology. Proceedings, Vol. 2-4. Incl. Vol. 2. Phytoplankton: Second Conference. Oppenheimer, C. H., ed. 1966. 15.50; Vol 3. Ecology of Invertebrates: Third Conference. Edmondson, W. T., ed. 1966. 11.25; Vol. 4. Unresolved Problems in Marine Microbiology: Fourth Conference. Oppenheimer, C. H., ed. 1968. 21.50. Gordon.

Cousteau, Jacques. **The Living Sea.** (Illus.). 1973. pap. 2.00. Ballantine.

Cousteau, Jacques & Dumas, Frederic. **The Silent World.** 1973. pap. 2.00. Ballantine.

Cousteau, Jacques Y. **Oasis in Space.** new ed. (Illus.). 1972. 7.95. Collins-World.

Cousteau, Jacques-Yves & Dugan, James. **Living Sea.** (Illus.) (gr. 10 up). 1963. 10.00. Har-Row.

Cox, Graham F. **Tropical Marine Aquaria.** (Illus.). 1972. 3.95. G&D.

Crane, Jules M. **Introduction to Marine Biology** (a Laboratory Text). 1973. pap. 6.95. Merrill.

Deacon, Margaret **Scientists & the Sea, 1650-1900: A History of Marine Science.** 1971. 17.25. Acad Pr.

Dunbar, Maxwell J., ed. **Marine Distributions.** (Illus.). 1963. 6.00. U of Toronto Pr.

Emery, K. O. **Coastal Pond-Studied by Oceanographic Methods.** 1969. 5.50. Am Elsevier.

European Marine Biology Symposium, 4th Proceedings. Crisp. D. J., ed. (Illus.). 1971. 39.50. Cambridge U Pr.

— — **Proceedings.** Crisp, D. J., ed. 39.50. Cambridge U Pr.

Evans, Idrisyn O. **Observer's Book of the Sea & Seashore.** (Illus.). 1962. bds. 2.50. Warne.

Falconer, William. **Falconer's Marine Dictionary.** Repr. of 1780 ed. 25.00. David & Charles.

Friedrich, Hermann. **Marine Biology On Introduction to Its Problems & Results.** (Illus.). 1970. 9.50. U of Wash Pr.

Galbraith, Robert & Boehler Ted. **Marine Biology for California Divers.** (Illus.). 1974. 6.95; pap. 3.95. Naturegraph.

Hardy, Alister. **Open Sea: Its Natural History.** 1971. 20.00. HM.

Harvey, Hildebrande W. **Chemistry & Fertility of Sea Waters.** 2nd ed. 1957. 14.95. Cambridge U Pr.

Hass, Hans. **Challenging the Deep: Thirty Years of Undersea Adventure.** Osers, Ewald, tr. from Ger. (Illus.). 1972. 11.95. Morrow.

Humm, Harold & Lane, Charles E., eds. **Bioactive Compounds from the Sea.** 1974. 18.75. Dekker.

Idyll, C. P. **Abyss: The Deep Sea & the Creatures That Live in It.** rev. ed. (Illus.). 1971. 7.95. T Y Crowell.

Johnson, Alexander B. **Deep Sea Soundings & Explorations of the Bottom.** 1861. Repr. 7.00. Greenwood.

Kinne, O. & Bulnheim, H. P., eds. **Cultivation of Marine Organisms & Its Importance for Marine Biology. 1972-73.** Repr. of 1970 ed. 86.00. Hafner Service.

Kyle, Harry M. **Biology of Fishes.** 1971. 12.95. TFH Pubns.

Lucas, Joseph. **Life in the Oceans.** 1974. 8.95. Dutton.

McConnaughey, Bayard H. **Introduction to Marine Biology.** 2nd ed. (Illus.). 1974. text ed. 13.95. Mosby.

Macdonald, A. G. **Physiological Aspects of Deep Sea Biology.** (Illus.). 1975. 35.00. Cambridge U Pr

Marine Biological Laboratory & Woods Hole Oceanographic Institution. **Catalog of the Library of the Marine Biological Laboratory & the Woods Hole Oceanographic Institution,** 12 Vols. 1971. lib. bdg. 980.00. set. G K Hall.

Marine Biology. Inc. Vol. 2. Phytoplanviton. International Interdisciplinary Conference, 2nd. Oppenheimer, H. C., ed. 1966. 18.50; **Vol. 3. Ecology of Intertebrates. International Interdisciplinary Conference, 3rd.** Edmondson, W. T., ed. 1966. 16.25; **Vol. 4. Unresolved Problems in Marine Microbiology. International Interdisciplinary Conference. 4th.** Oppenheimer, C. H., ed. 1968. 25.25; **Vol. 5. International Interdisciplinary Conference, 5th.** Costlow, John D., Jr., ed. 1969. 52.25; pap. 21.00. Gordon.

National ISA Marine Science Instrumentation Symposium, 5th Proceedings. Murdock, L.C., ed. 1973. 9.00. Instru Soc.

Platt, Rutherford. **Water: The Wonder of Life.** 1971. 8.95. P-H.

Polikarpov, G. G. **Radio-Ecology of Aquatic Organisms.** 1966. 18.50. Van Nos Reinhold.

R. V. Pillsbury. **Deep-Sea Biological Expedition to the Gulf of Guinea, 1964-1965, Pt. 2.** (Illus.). 1970. pap. 7.95. U of Miami Pr.

Ray, Carleton & Ciampi, Elgin. **Underwater Guide to Marine Life.** (Illus.). 6.98. A S Barnes.

Raymont, J. E. **Plankton & Productivity in the Oceans.** 1963. 21.00. Pergamon.

Reish, Donald J. **Biology of the Oceans.** 1969. pap. 8.65; pap. text ed. 6.95. Dickenson.

Remane, Adolf & Schlieper, Carl. **Biology of Brackish Water.** 1973. 21.75. Halsted Pr.

Rheinheimer, Gerhard. **Aquatic Microbiology.** 1974. price not set. Wiley.

Robbins, Sarah F. & Yentsch, Clarice M. **The Sea Is All About Us.** (Illus.). 1973. spiral bdg. 5.95. U Pr of New Eng.

Russell, F. S., ed. **Advances in Marine Biology.** Incl. Vol. 1. 1963. 15.50; Vol. 2. 1964. 13.50; Vol. 3. 1965. 19.00; Vol. 4. 1966. 16.50; Vol. 5. 1967. 22.00; Vol. 6. Russell, F. S. & Yonge, Maurice, eds. 1968. 21.00; Vol. 7. 1969. 21.00; Vol. 8. 1970. 24.00; Vol. 9. 1971. 24.50; Vol. 10. 1972. 29.00. Acad Pr.

— — **Advances in Marine Biology, Vol. 11,** 1973. 19.75. Acad Pr.

Russell, Findlay E. **Poisonous Marine Animals.** (Illus.). 1972. 8.95. TFH Pubns.

Russell-Hunter, W.D. **Aquatic Productivity: An Introduction to Some Basic Aspects of Biological Oceanography & Limnology.** (Illus.). 1970. text ed. 5.95. Macmillan.

Shilling, Charles W. & Werts, Margaret F. **Underwater Medicine & Related Sciences: A Guide to the Literature.** 1973. 37.50. IFI Plenum.

Smith, Bertie W. **The World Under Sea: A Concise Account of the Marine World.** 1940. Repr. 13.00. Finch Pr.

Society for Experimental Biology - 26th Symposium. **Effects of Pressure on Organisms.** 24.50. Acad. Pr.

Steele, J. H., ed. **Marine Food Chains.** (Illus.). 1973. Repr. of 1970 ed. 54.00. Hafner Serv.

Storr, John F. **Ecology & Oceanography of the Coral-Reef Tract, Abaco Island, Bahamas.** (Illus.). 1964. pap. 4.00. Geol Soc.

Ward, Ritchie. **Into the Ocean World.** 1974. 10.00. Knopf.

Wilber, Charles G. **Biological Aspects of Water Pollution.** (Illus.). 1971. 23.75. C C Thomas.

Yentsch, A., et al. **Marine & Estuarine Environments Organisms & Geology of the Cape Cod Region 1665-1965.** 1966. 6.00. Marine Bio.

Zeitzschel, B., ed. **The Biology of the Indian Ocean.** LC 72-90196. (Ecological Studies, Vol. 3). (Illus.). 1973. 50.50. Springer-Verlag.

Zenkevitch, L. **Biology of the Seas of the U.S.S.R.** Botcharskaya, S., tr. (Illus.). 1963. 26.75. Hafner.

Zoological Society Of London - 19th Symposium. **Aspects of Marine Zoology.** Marshall, N. B., ed. 1967. 14.00. Acad Pr.

Marine Biology—Antarctic Regions

Biology of the Antarctic Seas II. 12.00. Am Geophysical.

Biology of the Antarctic Seas III. 13.50. Am Geophysical.

Hardy, Alister. **Great Waters.** 1967. 10.95. HarpT. Har-Row.

Llano, George A. & Wallen, I. Eugene, eds. **Biology of the Antarctic Seas Four.** (Illus.). 1971. 30.00. Am Geophysical.

Marine Biology—Atlantic Ocean

Butler, James N., et al. **Pelagic Tar from Bermuda & the Sargasso Sea.** (Illus.). pap. 5.00. Harvard Eng.

Morris, Byron F. & Mogelberg, Deborah D. **Identification Manual to the Pelagic Sargassum Fauna.** 1973. pap. 2.00. Harvard Eng.

Morris, Byron F. & Schroeder, Elizabeth. **Hydrographic Observations in the Sargasso Sea of Bermuda: 1967-1973.** 1973. pap. 1.00. Harvard Eng.

Murray, John & Hjort, J. **Depths of the Ocean.** (Illus.). 1964. Repr. of 1912 ed. 52.50. Hafner Service.

Pocklington, Roger. **Variability in the Ocean off Bermuda.** 1972. 1.00. Harvard Eng.

R. V. Pillsbury. **Deep-Sea Biological Expedition to the Gulf of Guinea, 1964-1965, Pt. 1.** (Studies in Tropical Oceanography No. 4, Pt. 1). (Illus.). 1966. pap. 5.00. (ISBN 0-87024-085-4). U of Miami Pr.

Taylor, William R. & Bernatowicz, Albert J. **Distribution of Marine Algae About Bermuda.** (Bermuda Biological Station Special Pubn. No. 1). (Illus.). 1969. pap. 2.00. Harvard Eng.

Marine Biology—Pacific Ocean

Biology Colloquium, 33rd, Apr. 1972. **The Biology of the Oceanic Pacific: Proceedings.** Miller, Charles, ed. (Illus.). 1974. 6.00. Oreg St U Pr.

Coastal Aquaculture in the Indo-Pacific Region. (Illus., Orig.). 1974. 25.00 (FAO). Unipub.

Committee On Oceanography. **Scientific Exploration of the South Pacific.** 1970. 10.50; text ed. 11.50. Natl Acad Sci.

De Sylva, Donald P. **The Alfred C. Glassell Jr. University of Miami Argosy Expedition to Ecuador, Pt. 1: Introduction & Narrative.** (Illus.). 1972. 6.95. U of Miami Pr.

Galtsoff, P. S. **Pearl & Hermes Reef, Hawaii, Hydrographical & Biographical Observations.** Repr. of 1933 ed. pap. 4.00. Kraus Repr.

Johnson, Myrtle E. & Snook, Harry J. **Seashore Animals of the Pacific Coast.** (Illus.). pap. 4.50. Dover.

Marine Ecology

Arnov, Boris, Jr. **Homes Beneath the Sea: An Introduction to Ocean Ecology.** (Illus.). (gr. 6-10). 1969. 4.95. Little.

Costlow, John D., ed. **Fertility of the Sea,** 2 vols. (Illus.). 1971. Vol. 1. lib. bdg. 29.50; Vol. 2. lib. bdg. 29.50; Set. lib. bdg. 54.95. Gordon.

Cushing, D. H. **Marine Ecology & Fisheries.** Cambridge U Pr.

Dunbar, Maxwell J., ed. **Marine Distributions.** (Illus.). 1963. 6.00. U of Toronto Pr.

Fay, Rimmon C. **Southern California's Deteriorating Marine Environment: An Evaluation of the Health of the Benthic Marine Biota of Ventura, Los Angeles & Orange Counties.** (Illus.). 1972. pap. 3.50. Ctr Calif Public.

Galtsoff, Paul S., ed. **Bibliography of Oysters & Other Marine Organisms Associated with Oyster Bottoms & Estuarine Ecology.** 1972. lib. bdg. 74.00. G K Hall.

Green, J. **Biology of Estuarine Animals.** 1968. 9.50. U of Wash Pr.

Hedgpeth, Joel W. & Ladd, Harry S., eds. **Treatise on Marine Ecology & Paleoecology,** 2 vols. 1963. Repr. of 1957 ed. Vol. 1. 25.00; Vol. 2. 23.00; Set. 45.00. Geol Soc.

Kaill, Michael & Frey, John. **Environments in Profile: An Aquatic Approach.** (Illus.). 1973. pap. 4.95. Canfield Pr.

Kinne, O. **Marine Ecology,** 3 pts, Vol. 1. 1970. Pt. 1. 38.50; Pt. 2. 33.50; Pt. 3, 35.75. Wiley.

McLusky, Donald S. **Ecology of Estuaries.** (Illus.). 1972. 6.00. Hillary.

Menzies, Robert J., et al. **Abyssal Environment & Ecology of the World Oceans.** 1973. 27.50. Wiley.

Moore, Hilary B. **Marine Ecology.** (Illus.). 1958. 16.50. Wiley.

Nelson-Smith, A. **Oil Pollution & Marine Ecology.** 1973. 14.50. Plenum Pub.

Nybakken, James W. **Readings in Marine Ecology.** 1971. pap. 9.95. Har-Row.

Olsen, T. & Burgess, F. **Pollution & Marine Ecology.** 1967. 16.75. Wiley.

Radakov, D. V. **Schooling in the Ecology of Fish.** Mills, H., tr. from Rus. (Illus.). 1973. 19.75. Halsted Pr.

Reid, George K. **Ecology of Inland Waters & Estuaries.** (Illus.). 1961. 11.65. Van Nos Reinhold.

Sokolov, V. E. & Chapskii, K. K. eds. **Morphology & Ecology of Marine Mammals: Seals, Dolphins, Porpoises.** 1973. 24.00. Halsted Pr.

Steele, John H. **The Structure of Marine Ecosystems.** 1974. text ed. 7.95. Harvard U Pr.

Storr, John F. **Ecology & Oceanography of the Coral-Reef Tract, Abaco Island, Bahamas.** (Illus.). 1964. pap. 4.00. Geol Soc.

Tait, E. V. **Elements of Marine Ecology.** (Illus.). 1973. 12.80. Springer-Verlag.

Thorson, Gunner. **Life in the Sea.** LC 73-118405. (Illus.). 1971. 4.95; pap. 2.95. McGraw.

Vernberg, W. B. & Vernberg, F. J. **Environmental Physiology of Marine Animals.** (Illus.). 1972. 19.80. Springer-Verlag.

Vernberg, Winena, ed. **Symbiosis in the Sea.** 1974. 25.00. U of SC Pr.

Yentsch, A., et al. **Marine & Estuarine Environments Organisms & Geology of the Cape Code Region 1665-1965.** 1966. 6.00. Marine Bio.

Zottoli, Robert. **Introduction to Marine Environments.** (Illus.). 1973. pap. 4.95. Mosby.

Marine Fauna

Arnold, Augusta F. **Sea-Beach at Ebb-Tide.** (Illus.). 1968. pap. 4.00. Dover.

Barnard, J. Laurens, et al. **Abyssal Crustacea.** 1962. 15.00. Columbia U Pr.

Baslow, M. H. **Marine Pharmacology.** 1969. 19.75. Williams & Wilkins.

Briggs, John C. **Marine Zoogeography.** new ed. (Illus.). 1974. text ed. 25.00. McGraw.

Christiansen, Marit E. **Crustacea Decapoda Brachyura.** (Illus.). 1969. 8.00. Universitet.

Clark, A. H. **Ophiuroidea of the Hawaiian Islands.** Repr. of 1949 ed. pap. 9.00. Kraus Repr.

Clark, Ailsa. **Echinodermata Crinodea.** 1971. 8.00. Universitet.

Cromie, William J. **Living World of the Sea.** (Illus.). 1966. 7.95. P-H.

Edmondson, C. H., et al. **Marine Zoology of Tropical Central Pacific.** Repr. of 1925 ed. pap. 9.00. Kraus Repr.

Ely, C. A. **Shallow-Water Asteroidea & Ophiuroidea of Hawaii.** Repr. of 1942 ed. pap. 6.00. Kraus Repr.

Fowler, H. W. & Ball, S. C. **Fishes of Hawaii, Johnston Island, & Wake Island.** Repr. of 1925 ed. pap. 3.00. Kraus Repr.

Gosner, Kenneth L. **Guide to Identification of Marine & Estuarine Invertebrates: Cape Hatteras to the Bay of Fundy.** 1971. 31.50. Wiley.

Gotto, R. V. **Marine Animals.** 1969. 4.25. Am Elsevier.

Gray, William B. **Fish Tales & Ocean Odd Balls.** (Illus.). 1970. 5.95; pap. 2.45. A S Barnes.

Great Britain Challenger Office. **Report on the Scientific Results of the Voyage of H. M. S. Challenger During the Years 1873-1876,** 50 Vols. (Illus.). 1880-1895. Set. 3850.00. Johnson Repr.

Green, J. **Biology of Estuarine Animals.** (Illus.). 1968. 9.50. U of Wash Pr.

Gulland, John A. **The Management of Marine Fisheries.** (Illus.). 1974. 16.50. U of Wash Pr.

Holly, M. **Polychaeta from Hawaii.** Repr. of 1935 ed. pap. 3.00. Kraus Repr.

Howell, A. Brazier. **Aquatic Mammals.** (Illus.). 1970. pap. 3.00. Dover.

Jorgensen, C. B. **Biology of Suspension Feeding.** (Illus.). 1965. 17.00. Pergamon.

Krogh, August. **Osmotic Regulation in Aquatic Animals.** (Illus.). pap. 2.50. Dover.

— — **Osmotic Regulation in Aquatic Animals.** 4.75. Peter Smith.

Liburdi, Joe & Truitt, Harry. **Guide to Our Underwater World.** LC 73-79358. 5.95 Superior Pub.

MacGintie, G. E. & MacGintie, N. **Natural History of Marine Animals.** 2nd ed. 1968. text ed. 14.95. McGraw.

Millar, R. H. **British Ascidians.** (Synopses of British Fauna, No. 1). 1970. 3.50. Acad Pr.

Miner, Roy W. **Field Book of Seashore Life.** (Illus.). 1950. 9.00. Putnam.

Newell, R. C. **Biology of Intertidal Animals,** 1970. 23.75. Am Elsevier.

Pequegnat, Willis E. & Chance, Fenner A., Jr., eds. **Contributions on the Biology of the Gulf of Mexico.** (Texas A&M University Oceanographic Studies, Vol 1). (Illus.). 1970. 17.95. Gulf Pub.

Ravensdale, T. **Coral Fishes: Their Care & Maintenance.** (Illus.). 1973. 7.95. Great Outdoors.

Ricketts, Edward F. & Calvin, Jack. **Between Pacific Tides.** 4th ed. Hedgpeth, Joel W., ed. (Illus.). 1968. 10.95; text ed: 8.25. Stanford U Pr.

Rudloe, Jack. **Sea Brings Forth.** (Illus.). 1968. 6.95. Knopf.

Smith, R. I., et al. **Keys to Marine Invertebrates of the Woods Hole Region.** (Illus.). 1964. 5.00. Marine Bio.

Straughan, Robert P. **The Marine Collector's Guide.** (Illus.). 1973. 17.50. A S Barnes.

Sweeney, James B. **Pictorial History of Sea Monsters & Other Dangerous Marine Life.** 1972. 9.95. Crown.

Vernberg, W. B. & Vernberg, F. J. **Environmental Physiology of Marine Animals.** (Illus.). 1972. 19.80. Springer-Verlag.

Winberg, G. G. **Methods for the Estimation of Production of Aquatic Animals.** 1971. 9.00. Acad Pr.

Winn, H. E. & Olla, B. L. **Behavior of Marine Animals, Vol. 1: Invertebrates.** 1972. 16.00. Plenum Pub.

Marine Fauna—Atlantic Ocean

Schroeder, Robert. **Something Rich & Strange.** 1965. 5.95. Har-Row.

Marine Fauna—Pacific Ocean

Burgess, Warren E. & Axelrod, Herbert R. **Pacific Marine Fishes, Bk. 3.** (Illus.). 1973. 20.00. TFH Pubns.

Fitch, John E. & Lavenberg, Robert J. **Marine Food & Game Fishes of California.** (Illus.). 1971. pap. 2.35. U of Cal Pr.

Guberlet, Muriel L. **Animals of the Seashore.** 3rd ed. (Illus.). 1962. 7.50. Binfords.

Kozloff, Eugene N., et al. **Keys to the Marine Invertebrates of Puget Sound, the San Juan Archipelago, & Adjacent Regions.** (Illus.). 1968. pap. 4.00. U of Wash Pr.

Ricketts, Edward F. & Calvin, Jack. **Beween Pacific Tides.** 4th ed. Hedgpeth, Joel W., ed. (Illus.). 1968. 10.95, 8.25. Stanford U Pr.

Steinbeck, John. **Log from the Sea of Cortez.** 1962. pap. 2.25. Viking Pr.

Marine Fauna—Red Sea

Cousteau, Jacques-Yves. **World Without Sun.** Dugan, James, ed. (Illus.). (gr. 7 up). 1965. 15.00. Har-Row.

Marine Flora

Arber, A. **Water Plants: Study of Aquatic Angiosperms.** (Illus.). 1963. Repr. of 1920 ed. 12.40. Hafner Service.

Arnold, Augusta F. **Sea-Beach at Ebb-Tide.** (Illus.). 1968. pap. 4.00. Dover.

Baslow, M. H. **Marine Pharmacology.** 1969. 19.75. Williams & Wilkins.

Boney, A. D. **Biology of Marine Algae.** (Illus.). 1966. pap. 5.00. Hillary.

Botanica Marina: Internationale Zeitschrift fuer die Erforschung und Auswertung Von Meeresalgen, Vol. 17. (International Review for Seaweed Research & Utilization). (Ger., Fr. & Eng.). 1974. 100.00. De Gruyter.

Cavaliere, A. R. & Johnson, T. W. **Marine Ascomycetis, Asocarp Morphology & Its Application to Taxonomy.** pap. 6.30. Hafner Service.

Church, Arthur H. **Thalassiophyta & the Subaerial Transmigation.** 1968. Repr. of 1919 ed. 6.95. Hafner.

Coker, W. C. & Couch, J. N. **Stipitate Hyndums of the Eastern U.S.** 1970. Repr. of 1951 ed. 22.40. Hafner Service.

Dawson, E. Yale. **Seashore Plants of Northern California.** 1966. pap. 2.45. U of Cal Pr.

— — **Seashore Plants of Southern California.** 1966. pap. 1.75. U of Cal Pr.

Dawson, Elmer Y. **Marine Botany: An Introduction.** 1966. 13.50. HR&W.

Fitch, John E. & Lavenberg, Robert J. **Marine Food & Game Fishes of California.** (Illus.). 1971. pap. 2.35. U of Cal Pr.

Gerloff, J. **Die Marinen Braunalgen der Europaeischen Kuesten.** 1973. 28.00; subsc. 22.40. Hafner Service.

Hulten, E. **The Amphi-Atlantic Plants & Their Phytogeographic Connections.** (Illus.). 1973. Repr. of 1958 ed. 84.00. Hafner Service.

Johnson, T. W. & Sparrow, F. K. **Fungi in Oceans & Estuaries.** 1971. 1970. pap. 27.50. Hafner Service

Kinne, O. & Bulnheim, H. P., eds. **Cultivation of Marine Organisms & Its Importance for Marine Biology.** 1972-73. Repr. of 1970 ed. 86.00. Hafner Service.

Lyngbye, H. C. **Tentamen Hydrophytologia Danicae. Continens Omnia Hydrophyta Cryptogama Daniae. Holsatize, Faeroae, Islandiae, Groenlandiae Hvcusque Cognita, Systematice Deposita, Descripta Et Iconibus Illustrata, Adjectis Simul Speciebus Norvegicis.** 1972. Repr. of 1819 ed. 100.80. Hafner Service.

Sculthorpe, C. Duncan. **Biology of Aquatic Vascular Plants.** (Illus.). 1967. 35.00. St. Martin.

Marine Microbology

Colewell, R. **Marine & Estuarine Microbiology Laboratory Manual.** 9.50. Univ Park.

Droop, M. & Wood, F., eds. **Advances in Microbiology of the Sea, Vol. 1.** 1968. 11.00. Acad Pr.

Rodina, A. G. **Methods in Marine Microbiology. Proceedings.** Oppenheimer, Carl H., ed. (Illus.). 1963. 22.50. C C Thomas.

Wood, E. Ferguson. **Microbiology of Oceans & Estuaries.** 1967. 27.50. Am Elsevier.

Marine Pollution

Barros, James & Johnston, Douglas M. **International Law of Pollution.** 1974. text ed. 14.95. Free Pr.

Brown, E. D. **Legal Regime of Hydrospace.** 1971. 14.50. B&N.

Dye, Lee. **Blowout at Platform A: The Crisis That Awakened a Nation.** (Illus.). 1971. 5.95. Doubleday.

Hood, Donald W., ed. **Impingement of Man on the Oceans.** 1971. 30.25. Wiley.

Moorcraft, Colin. **Must the Seas Die?** (Illus.). 1973. 6.95. Gambit.

Nash, A. E., et al. **Oil Pollution & the Public Interest: A Study of the Santa Barbara Oil Spill.** (Illus.). 1972. pap. 3.75. Inst Gov Stud Berk.

Shinn, Robert A. **The International Politics of Marine Pollution Control.** (Illus.). 1974. text ed. 16.50. Praeger.

Skinner, Brian J. & Turekian, Karl K. **Man & the Ocean.** (Illus.). 1973. 7.95; pap. 2.95. P-H.

Marlin

Howard, John K. & Ueyanagi, Shoji. **Distribution - Relative Abundance of the Billfishes (Istiophoridae) Pacific Ocean.** (Illus., Atlas). 1965. Set. pap. 5.50. U of Miami Pr.

Primitive Fishing

Rau, Charles. **Prehistoric Fishing in Europe & North America.** 1884. 61.00. AMS Pr.

Titcomb, Margaret. **Native Use in Hawaii.** 1972. 7.00. U Pr of Hawaii.

Salmon

Burgner, Robert L., ed. **Further Studies of Alaska Sockeye Salmon.** 1968. pap. 3.60. U of Wash Pr.

Jordan, David S. **Trout & Salmon of the Pacific Coast.** facs. ed. pap. 1.25. Shorey.

Koo, Ted S., ed. **Studies of Alaska Red Salmon.** (Illus.). 1962. 8.50. U of Wash Pr.

Netboy, Anthony. **Atlantic Salmon: A Vanishing Species.** (Illus.). 1968. 6.95. HM.

— — **The Salmon: Their Fight for Survival.** (Illus.). 1974. 15.00. HM.

— — **Salmon of the Pacific Northwest.** (Illus.). 5.50. Binfords.

Salmon Fisheries

Crutchfield, James A. & Pontecorvo, Giulio. **Pacific Salmon Fisheries: A Study of Irrational; Conservation.** 1969. 8.50. Johns Hopkins.

Dodds, Gordon B. **Salmon King of Oregon: R. D. Hume & the Pacific Fisheries.** 1963. 6.00. U of NC Pr.

Donaldson, Ivan & Cramer, Frederick. **Fishwheels of the Columbia.** (Illus.). 1971. 10.00. Binfords.

Salmon Fishing

Bates, Joseph C., Jr. **Atlantic Salmon Flies & Fishing.** (Illus.). 1970. 14.95. Stackpole.

Holm, Don. **Pacific North.** Orig. Title: Sport Fishing in the North Pacific. 1969. 12.50. Caxton.

Humphrey, William. **Spawning Run.** 1970. 4.50. Knopf.

Royce, William F., et al. **Salmon Gear Limitations in Northern Washington Waters.** Bd. with Management of the High Seas Fisheries of the Northeastern Pacific. pap. 3.50. U of Wash Pr.

Salt Water Fishing

Bauer, Erwin A. **Salt-Water Fisherman's Bible.** (Illus.). pap. 2.50. Doubleday.

Becker, A. C., Jr. **Gulf Coast Fishing.** (Illus.). 1970. 8.50. A S Barnes.

Bender, Bob. **A Guide to Florida Saltwater Fishes.** (Illus.). 4.00. Reel Trophy.

Benedict, J. Nelson, et al. **Successful Ocean Game Fishing.** Moss, Frank T., ed. (Illus.). 1971. 12.50. Intl Marine.

Brooks, Joe. **Saltwater Game Fishing.** (Illus.). 1968. 9.95. Har-Row.

Cadieux, Charles E. **Introduction to Ocean Fishing.** (Illus.). 1972. 5.95. Stackpole.

Cannon, Raymond. **How to Fish the Pacific Coast.** 3rd ed. (Illus.). 1967. pap. 2.95. Lane.

Evanoff, Vlad. **How to Fish in Salt Water.** (Illus.). 1962. 6.95. A S Barnes.

— — **How to Fish in Salt Water.** (Illus.). 1973. pap. 1.95. B&N.

— — **Surf Fishing.** (Illus.). 1974. 6.95. Har-Row.

Goadby, Peter. **Big Fish & Blue Water.** 1972. 14.95. HR&W.

Holm, Don. **Pacific North.** Orig. Title: Sport Fishing in the North Pacific. 1969. 12.50. Caxton.

Lyman, Henry & Woolner, Frank. **Tackle Talk.** 1971. 8.95. A S Barnes.

March, Edgar J. **Sailing Trawlers: The Story of Deep-Sea Fishing with Longline & Trawl.** 1970. 25.00. Intl Marine.

Migdalski, Edward C. **Angler's Guide to the Salt Water Game Fishes: Atlantic & Pacific.** (Illus.). 1958. 19.95. Ronald.

Mitchell, John. **Better Fishing: Saltwater.** (Illus.). 1971. 5.00. Intl Pubns Serv.

Nix, Sam. **Salt-Water Fly-Fishing Handbook.** (Illus.). 1973. 6.95. Doubleday.

Reiger, George. **Profiles in Salt Water Angling.** (Illus.). 1973. 14.95. P-H.

Rosko, Milt. **Fishing from Boats.** (Illus.). 1968. 6.95. Macmillan.

Sand, George X. **Salt Water Fly Fishing.** (Illus.). 1970. 8.95. Knopf.

Scharff, Robert. **Standard Handbook of Salt-Water Fishing.** rev. ed. (Illus.). 1966. 8.95. T Y. Crowell.

Schwind, Phil. **Striped Bass & Other Cape Cod Fish.** (Illus.). 1972. pap. 3.95. Chatham Pr.

Turnill, Gordon. **Sea Fishing.** (Illus.). pap. 2.75. (SpS). Soccer.

Wisner, Bill. **How to Catch Saltwater Fish.** (Illus.). 1973. 8.95. Doubleday.

Woolner, Frank. **Modern Saltwater Sport Fishing.** (Illus.). 1972. 7.50. Crown.

Seafood Processing

Gillies, M. **Seafood Processing.** 1971. 36.00. Noyes.

Seafood

Castle, Molly. **Health & Beauty from the Sea.** 1971. 5.95. Mason/Charter.
Gibbons, Euell. **Stalking the Blue-Eyed Scallop.** 1964. 7.95; pap. 3.95. McKay.

Sea Turtles

Bustard, Robert. **Sea Turtles: Their Natural History & Conservation.** (Illus.). 1973. 11.95. Taplinger.
Carr, Archie. **So Excellent a Fishe: A Natural History of Sea Turtles.** (Illus.). 1973. pap. 2.95. Doubleday.
Carr, Archie F. **So Excellent a Fishe: A Natural History of Sea Turtles.** (Illus.). 1967. 5.95. Natural Hist.
Jacobs, Francine. **Sea Turtles.** (Illus.). 1972. 4.50. Morrow.
Rebel, Thomas P. **Sea Turtles & the Turtle Industry of the West Indies, Florida, & the Gulf of Mexico.** 1974. 10.00. U of Miami Pr.

Sea Water

Goodman, Joe & Thompson, Thomas G. **Characteristics of the Waters in Sections from Dutch Harbor, Alaska, to the Strait of Juan De Fuca & from the Strait of Juan De Fuca to Hawaii.** 1940. pap. 1.50. U of Wash Pr.
Harvey, Hildebrande W. **Chemistry & Fertility of Sea Waters.** 2nd ed. 1957. 14.95. Cambridge U Pr.
Levine, Sumner N, ed. **Selected Papers on Desalination & Ocean Technology.** (Illus.). 1967. pap. 4.50. Dover.
Martin, Dean F. **Marine Chemistry,** Vol. 1. 2nd rev ed. 1972. 10.50. Dekker.
— — **Marine Chemistry,** Vol. 2: Theory & Applications. 1970. 10.50. Dekker.
Tyler, J. E. & Smith, R. C. **Measurements of Spectral Irradiation Underwater.** 1970. 28.25. Gordon.

Sharks

Ashley, Laurence M. **Laboratory Anatomy of the Shark.** 2nd ed. (Illus.). 1969. pap. 2.50. Wm C Brown.
Baldridge, H. David. **Shark Attack.** 1974. 8.95. Droke-Hallux.
Budker, Paul. **Life of Sharks.** Whitehead, Peter, tr. (Illus.). 1971. 12.50; pap. 3.95. Columbia U Pr.
Burgess, Robert F. **Sharks.** (Illus.). 1971. 3.95. Doubleday.
Clark, Eugenie. **Lady & the Sharks.** (Illus.). 1969. 6.95. Har-Row.
Cook, Joseph & Wisner, William L. **Nightmare World of the Shark.** (Illus.). 1968. 4.50. Dodd.
Cousteau, Jacques-Yves & Cousteau, Philippe. **Shark: Splendid Savage of the Sea.** (Illus.). 1970. 9.95. Doubleday.
Eddy, Samuel, et al. **Guide to the Study of the Anatomy of the Shark, Necturus, & the Cat.** 3rd ed. 1960. text ed. 4.50. Wiley.
Gans, Carl & Parsons, Thomas S. **Photographic Atlas of Shark Anatomy: The Gross Morphology of Squalus Acanithias.** 1964. 4.50. Acad Pr.
Gilbert, Perry W., ed. **Sharks & Survival.** 1963. 12.95. Heath.
Gilbert, Perry W., et al, eds. **Sharks, Skates, & Rays.** (Illus.). 1967. 20.00. Johns Hopkins.
Helm, Thomas **Shark.** 1963. pap. 1.25. Macmillan.
Lineaweaver, Thomas H., III & Backus, Richard H. **The Natural History of Sharks.** (Illus.). 1973. pap. 2.50. Doubleday.
Lineaweaver, Thomas H., 3rd & Backus, Richard H. **Natural History of Sharks.** (Illus.). 1970. 6.95. Lippincott.

McCormick, Harold W., et al. **Shadows in the Sea: The Sharks, Skates & Rays.** (Illus.). 1963. 8.95. Chilton.
Pope, Patricia. **Dictionary of Sharks.** (Illus.). 1973. 5.95; pap. 1.95. Great Outdoors.
Riedman, Sarah R. & Gustafson, Elton T. **Focus on Sharks.** (Illus.). (gr. 7 up). 1969. 5.95. Abelard.
Scharp, Hal. **Shark Safari.** (Illus.). 1974. 9.95. A S Barnes.
Tinker, Spencer W. & DuLuca, Charles J. **Sharks & Rays: A Handbook of the Sharks & Rays of Hawaii & the Central Pacific Ocean.** 1973. 7.25. C E Tuttle.

Shark Fishing

Cropp, Ben. **Shark Hunters.** 1971. 7.50. Macmillan.
Helm, Thomas. **Shark.** 1963. pap. 1.25. Macmillan.
Housby, Trevor. **The Rubby-Dubby Trail: Shark Fishing in British Waters** (Illus.). 1974. 11.50. Intl Pubns Serv.
Joseph, S. **Shark Bites Back.** 1970. text ed. 2.04. McGraw.
Pope, Patricia. **Dictionary of Sharks.** (Illus.). 1973. 5.95; pap. 1.95. Great Outdoors.
Wisner, Bill & Mundus, Frank. **Sportfishing for Sharks.** (Illus.). 1971. 10.95. Macmillan.

Shellfish

Sinderman, C. J. **Principal Diseases of Marine Fish & Shellfish.** 1970. 23.00. Acad Pr.

Spin Fishing

Evanoff, Vlad. **Spin Fishing.** (Illus.). 6.95. A S Barnes.
Michalak, David. **Spinfishing for Beginners.** (Illus.). 1973. 8.95. A S Barnes.
Strung, Norman & Rosko, Milt. **Spin-Fishing: The System That Does It All.** (Illus.). 1973. 8.95. Macmillan.

Striped Bass

Karas, Nicholas. **The Complete Book of the Striped Bass.** 1974. 8.95. Winchester Pr.
Lyman, Henry & Woolner, Frank. **Complete Book of Striped Bass Fishing.** (Illus.). 1954. 5.95. A S Barnes.

Trawls and Trawling

Piper, Steven. **The North Ships: The Life of a Trawlerman.** LC 74-76187. 1974. 10.95. David & Charles.

Trout

Bergman, Ray. **Trout.** rev ed. (Illus.). 1952. 12.50. Knopf.
Brooks, Charles E. **The Trout & the Stream.** 1974. 7.95. Crown.
Heacox, Cecil E. **The Compleat Brown Trout.** 1974. 12.50. Winchester Pr.
Jordan, David S. **Trout & Salmon of the Pacific Coast.** facs. ed. 1906. pap. 1.25. Shorey.
Needham, Paul. **Trout Streams.** rev. ed. Bond, Carl E., ed. (Illus.). 1969. 8.50. Winchester Pr.
Needham, Paul R. **Trout Streams: Conditions That Determine Their Productivity & Suggestions for Stream & Lake Management.** Bond, Carl E., ed. (Illus.). 1969. 11.95. Holden-Day.
Ripper, Charles L. **Trout.** (Illus.). 1966. 4.75. Morrow.
Schwiebert, Ernest. **Trout.** 1975. 20.00. Weybright.

Van Gytenbeek, G. P. **The Way of a Trout.** (Illus.). 1972. 8.95. Lippincott.

Trout Fishing

Bashline, L. James. **Night Fishing for Trout.** (Illus.). 1973. 7.95. Freshet Pr.
Bergman, Ray. **Trout.** rev ed. (Illus.). 1952. 12.50. Knopf.
Bigelow, Ogden. **Mulberry Trout.** (Illus.). 1969. 5.00. C E Tuttle.
Blaisdell, Harold F. **Trout Fishing in New England.** new ed. (Illus.). 1973. 6.50; pap. 3.50. Stone Wall Pr.
Bradford, Charles. **The Brook Trout & the Determined Angler.** (Illus.). 1970. boxed 6.75. Freshet Pr.
Brooks, Charles E. **Larger Trout for the Western Fly Fisherman.** (Illus.). 1970. 9.50. A S Barnes.
Brooks, Joe. **Trout Fishing.** (Illus.). 1972. 10.00. Har-Row.
— — **Trout Fishing.** (Illus.). 1972. 10.00. Har-Row.
Draper, Keith. **Trout Flies in New Zealand.** (Illus.). 1971. 8.50. Reed.
Fox, Charles K. **This Wonderful World of Trout.** 1971. 9.95; leather special ed. 35.00. Freshet Pr.
Freeman, James **Practical Steelhead Fishing.** (Illus.). 1966. 7.95. A S Barnes.
Gingrich, Arnold. **The Joys of Trout** (Illus.). 1973. 7.50. Crown.
Gordon, Theodore, et al. **American Trout Fishing.** Gingrich, Arnold, ed. (Illus.). 1966. 6.95. Knopf.
Grove, Alvin R., Jr. **The Lure & Lore of Trout Fishing.** (Illus.). 1971. boxed 9.95. Freshet Pr.
Haldane, A. R. **By River, Stream & Loch: Thirty Years with a Trout Rod.** 10.50. David & Charles.
Hills, John W. **History of Fly Fishing for Trout.** 1971. boxed 8.95. Freshet Pr.
Holland, Dan. **Trout Fisherman's Bible.** (Illus.). pap. 2.50. Doubleday.
Janes, Edward C. **Salmon Fishing in the Northeast.** new ed. (Illus.). 1973. 6.50; pap. 3.50. Stone Wall Pr.
Jennings, Preston. **Book of Trout Flies.** Lyons, Nick, ed. (Illus.). 1970. 7.50. Crown.
MacDougall, Arthur R. **Trout Fisherman's Bedside Book.** 1963. 5.00. S&S.
Mansfield, Kenneth, ed. **Trout & How to Catch Them.** (Illus.). 1972. 4.95. St. Martin.
Marinaro, Vincent C. **Modern Dry-Fly Code.** (Illus.). 1970. 10.00. Crown.
Needham, Paul. **Trout Streams.** rev. ed. Bond, Carl E., ed. (Illus.). 1969. 8.50. Winchester Pr.
Nibler, C. W. **Goodbye Mr. Trout.** 1973. 3.75. Vantage.
Ovington, Ray. **How to Take Trout on Wet Flies & Nymphs.** 1974. 9.95. Freshet Pr.
— — **Tactics on Trout.** (Illus.). 1969. 8.95. Knopf.
Quick, James. **Fishing the Nymph.** (Illus.). 1960. 6.50. Ronald.
Raymond, Steve. **Kamloops: An Angler's Study of the Kamloops Trout.** (Illus.). 1971. 12.50. Winchester Pr.
Schwiebert, Ernest G., Jr. **Matching the Hatch.** (Illus.). 1962. 7.50. Macmillan.
Shingleton, John D. **Trout, the Whole Trout, & Nothing but the Trout: Solemnly Sworn Testimony on America's No. 1 Gamefish & How to Hook Him.** (Illus.). 1974. 5.95. Winchester Pr.
Talleur, Richard W. **Fly Fishing for Trout: A Guide for Adult Beginners.** 1974. 10.00. Winchester Pr.
Traver, Robert. **Trout Madness.** 1960. 6.95. St. Martin.
— — **Trout Magic.** 1974. 7.50. Crown.
Ure, James. **Bait for Trout: Being the Confessions of an Unorthodox Angler.** (Illus.). 1973. 5.95. Regnery.
Walker, C. F. **Art of Chalk Stream Fishing.** (Illus.). 1969. 6.50. Stackpole.

Magazines and Periodicals
of Interest to the Angler

All Outdoors Magazine (M)
Established 1947
Circulation: 165,250
Ralph Dice, Editor
Southwestern Associates, Inc., Publisher
P.O. Box 700
Denison, Texas 75020
(214) 463-2440

American Field (W)
Established 1874
Circulation: 14,590
W. F. Brown, Editor
American Field Publishing Co.
222 West Adams Street
Chicago, Illinois 60606
(312) 372-1383

Angler's News (W)
Established 1963
Circulation: 13,827
Fred Walczyk, Editor
Mike Zicarelli, Publisher
330 Kennedy Boulevard
Bayonne, N.J. 07002
(201) 436-8888

Argosy (M)
Established 1882
Circulation: 1,002,127
Gil Paust, Editor
Popular Publications, Inc.
420 Lexington Avenue, Suite 2540
New York, N.Y. 10017
(212) 689-4900

Bassmaster Magazine (BM)
Established 1968
Circulation: 189,000
Bob Cobb, Editor
P.O. Box 3044
Montgomery, Alabama 36109
(205) 272-9530

Field and Stream (M)
Established 1895
Circulation: 1,894,889
Jack Samson, Editor
CBS Publications
383 Madison Avenue
New York, N.Y. 10017
(212) 688-9100

The Fisherman Newspaper (M)
Established: 1971
Circulation: 43,000
Alene Brehm, Editor
John Kollman, Publisher
106 Broadway, Suite 339
San Antonio, Texas 78299
(512) 225-4044, 225-5918

Fishing and Hunting News (W)
Established 1944
Circulation: 108,670
Ken McDonald, Editor
Fishing and Hunting News, Inc., Publisher
511 Eastlake E.
Seattle, Washington 98109
(206) 624-3845

Fishing Facts (M)
Established 1963
Circulation: 169,038
George Pazik, Editor
Northwoods Publishing Co., Inc.
P.O. Box 609
Menomonee Falls, Wisconsin 53051
(414) 255-4800

Fishing Tackle Trade News (10 x yr.)
Established 1952
Circulation not shown
Clem Dippel, Editor
Fred E. Owens, Publisher
P.O. Box 70
Wilmette, Illinois 60091
(312) 256-0650

Fishing World (BM)
Established 1955
Circulation: 192,683
Keith Gardner, Editor
Allsport Publishing Co., Publisher
51 Atlantic Avenue
Floral Park, L.I., N.Y. 11001
(516) 352-9750

Florida Sportsman (BM)
Established 1969
Circulation: 55,800
Vic Dunaway, Editor
Wickstrom Publishers, Inc.
2701 South Bayshore Drive
Miami, Florida 33133
(305) 858-3546

Fly Fisherman (7 x yr.)
Established 1969
Circulation: 50,483
Donald D. Zahner, Editor
Fly Fisherman Magazine, Inc., Publisher
Manchester, Vermont 05254
(802) 867-5951

Fur-Fish-Game (Harding's Magazine) (M)
Established 1905
Circulation: 163,332
A. R. Harding, Editor
A. R. Harding Publishing Co.
2878 East Main Street
Columbus, Ohio 43209
(614) 231-9585

Great Lakes Sportsman (BM)
Established 1970
Circulation: 200,654
Harold Dobrowa, Editor
Sportsman Publications, Inc.
26555 Evergreen Road, Suite 410
Southfield, Michigan 48076
(313) 355-1270

KaHagon (M)
Established 1969
Circulation not shown
Gene Coleman, Editor
George E. Zorgo, Sr., Publisher
131 North Main Street
Pittston, Pennsylvania 18640
(717) 654-8831

Michigan Out-of-Doors (M)
Established 1947
Circulation: 126,329
James V. Stabile, Editor
Michigan United Conservation Clubs, Inc.
P.O. Box 2235
Lansing, Michigan 48911
(517) 371-1041

New England Sportsman (BM)
Established 1973
Circulation: 100,276
Sportsman Publications, Inc.
26555 Evergreen Road, Suite 410
Southfield, Michigan 48076
(313) 355-1270

Outdoor Arizona (M)
Established 1928
Circulation: 37,821
Robert L. Hirsch, Editor
Phoenix Publishing, Inc.
1230 East Camelback Road
Phoenix, Arizona 85014
(602) 248-8900

Outdoor Life (M)
Established 1898
Circulation: 1,901,085
Chat Fish, Editor
Times Mirror Magazines, Inc.
380 Madison Avenue
New York, N.Y. 10017
(212) 687-3000

Outdoor Press (W)
Established 1966
Circulation: 23,923
Fred L. Peterson, Editor
The Outdoor Press, Inc.
N. 2012 Ruby Street
Spokane, Washington 99207
(509) 328-9392

Explanation of Symbols: (M) Monthly; (BM) Bi-monthly; (SM) Semi-monthly; (W) Weekly; (Q) Quarterly

Outdoors Today (W)
Established 1970
Circulation: 93,427
Earl A. Shelsby, Editor
Outdoors Today, Inc.
P.O. Box 6852
St. Louis, Missouri 63144
(314) 727-2722

Pennsylvania Angler (M)
Established 1931
Circulation: 46,000
James F. Yoder, Editor
Pennsylvania State Chamber of Commerce,
    Publisher
222 North 3rd Street
Harrisburg, Pennsylvania
(717) 238-0441

Pennsylvania's Outdoor People (SM)
Established 1959
Circulation: 27,121
G. M. Dennis and A. Dardanell, Editors
Dardanell Publications, Inc.
610 Beatty Road
Monroeville, Pennsylvania 15146
(412) 373-7900

Popular Mechanics (M)
Established 1902
Circulation: 1,758,424
Jim Liston, Editor
The Hearst Corp., Publisher
224 West 57th Street
New York, N.Y. 10010
(212) 262-4282

Popular Science (M)
Established 1872
Circulation: 1,799,840
Hubert P. Luckett, Editor
Times Mirror Magazines, Inc.
380 Madison Avenue
New York, N.Y. 10017
(212) 687-3000

Saga (M)
Established 1950
Circulation: 142,900
Martin M. Singer, Editor
Gambi Publishing Corp.
333 Johnson Avenue
Brooklyn, N.Y. 11026
(212) 456-8600

Salt Water Sportsman (M)
Established 1939
Circulation: 84,998
Frank Woolner, Editor
Salt Water Sportsman, Inc., Publisher
10 High Street
Boston, Massachusetts 02110
(617) 426-4074

Southern Outdoors (BM)
Established 1953
Circulation: 100,442
Bob Cobb, Editor
Ray Scott, Publisher
P.O. Box 3543
Montgomery, Alabama 36109
(205) 277-3940

Sporting Goods Business (M)
Established 1968
Circulation: 21,084
Claude Rose, Editor
Giralla Publications, Inc.
1501 Broadway
New York, N.Y. 10036
(212) 868-0750

Sporting Goods Buyer (BM)
Established 1970
Circulation not shown
Harold Martin, Editor
Malcolm Wolff, Publisher
33 West 60th Street
New York, N.Y. 10023
(212) 757-3700

Sports Afield (M)
Established 1887
Circulation: 1,403,691
Lamar Underwood, Editor
Robert F. Navin, Publisher
250 West 55th Street
New York, N.Y. 10019
(212) 262-8852

Sports and Recreation (BM)
Established 1946
Circulation not shown
Robert Bushnell, Editor
Roland E. Nystrom, Publisher
207 South Manitoba Avenue
Wayzata, Minnesota 55391
(612) 545-9182, 473-8595

Trout (Q)
Established 1960
Circulation: 23,181
Alvin R. Grove, Jr., Editor
Trout Unlimited, Publisher
4260 East Evans Avenue
Denver, Colorado 80222
(814) 757-7144

True (M)
Established 1937
Circulation: 1,104,025
Clare Conley, Editor
Petersen Publishing Co., Inc.
8490 Sunset Boulevard
Los Angeles, California 90069
(213) 657-5100

Western Outdoor News (W)
Established 1953
Circulation: 79,076
Western Outdoors Publications
3939 Birch Street
Newport Beach, California 92660
(714) 546-4370

Western Outdoors (M)
Established 1960
Circulation: 110,180
Western Outdoors Publications
3939 Birch Street
Newport Beach, California 92660
(714) 546-4370

West Virginia Hills and Streams (M)
Established 1971
Circulation: 3,000
Leo Young, Editor
West Virginia Hills and Streams, Inc.,
    Publisher
Box 38
Durbin, West Virginia 26264
(304) 456-4366

Canadian Periodicals

Alberta Sportsman (6 x yr.)
Established 1966
Circulation: 6,170
Railton Publications, Ltd.
125 Talisman Avenue
Vancouver, British Columbia
(604) 876-3535

Au Grand Air (M) (French)
Established 1961
Circulation: 33,270
Harry A. Willsie, Editor
Rod and Gun Publishing Corp., Ltd.
1219 Hotel de Ville
Montreal, Quebec
(514) 861-2257

B.C. Outdoors (BM)
Established 1945
Circulation: 23,432
A. G. Downs, Editor
Northwest Digest, Ltd., Publisher
Box 900, Station A
Surrey, British Columbia V3S 4P4
(604) 574-5211

Fish and Game Sportsman (Q)
Established 1969
Circulation: 10,500
J. B. Wilkinson, Editor
Nimrod Publications, Ltd.
P.O. Box 1654
Regina, Saskatchewan
(306) 523-8384

Northwest Sportsman (6 x yr.)
Established 1946
Circulation: 9,823
Jim Railton, Editor
Railton Publications, Ltd.
125 Talisman Avenue
Vancouver, British Columbia
(604) 876-3535

Sporting Goods Trade (BM)
Established 1928
Circulation: 9,900
William Schabas, Editor
David Wells, Publisher
300 Decarie Blvd.
Montreal 379, Quebec
(514) 748-8728

Quebec Chasse et Peche (M) (French)
Established 1971
Circulation: 15,500
Henri Ponpart, Editor
Les Publications Plein Air, Inc.
3339 Desmartean Street
Montreal, Quebec
(514) 845-5141

Rod and Gun in Canada (M)
Established 1899
Circulation: 34,760
Harry A. Willsie, Editor
Rod and Gun Publishing Corp., Ltd.
1219 Hotel de Ville
Montreal, Quebec
(514) 861-2257

Western Fish and Wildlife (BM)
Established 1965
Circulation: 10,354
J. L. Grundle, Editor and Publisher
1591 Bowser Street
Vancouver, British Columbia
(604) 980-5821

Wildlife Crusader (M)
Established 1944
Circulation: 38,416
Paul F. Murphy, Editor
Manitoba Wildlife Federation, Publisher
St. James and Notre Dame
Winnipeg, Manitoba
(204) 774-2926

Directory of Organizations and Associations

**AMERICAN ASSOCIATION FOR
CONSERVATION INFORMATION**
c/o Allan S. Murray
Conservation Extension, Box 11
139 Tuxedo Blvd.
Winnpieg, Manitoba, Canada
J. W. Sizer, Pres.
Founded: 1938
Members: 68
Professional society of officials of state and provincial conservation agencies. Sponsors annual awards program whereby winners in various categories of conservation education work are selected by a panel of judges. Publications: (1) *Balance Wheel*, bimonthly; (2) *Yearbook*. Convention/Meeting: Annual — always June.

AMERICAN CASTING ASSOCIATION
P. O. Box 51   Phone: (615) 292-9427
Nashville, Tenn. 37202
Paul N. Jones, Exec. Sec.
Founded: 1906
Members: 2500
Staff: 1
Federation of 45 local clubs, five state associations, and seven regional groups of amateur tournament fly and bait casters; also includes colleges and universities teaching angling and casting. Promotes casting and angling as a recreational activity. Coordinates, regulates, and establishes rules for sanctioned tournaments; sponsors competitions; works to develop improved fishing tackle; provides instruction in workshops and clinics; compiles statistics. Committees: Youth Activities; Conservation. Publication: *Creel*, bimonthly. Formerly: (1940) National Association of Scientific Angling Clubs; (1961) National Association of Angling and Casting Clubs. Convention/Meeting: Annual.

**AMERICAN COMMITTEE FOR
INTL. WILD LIFE PROTECTION**
c/o The Wildlife Society   Phone: (202) 363-2435
3900 Wisconsin Ave., N.W., Suite S-176
Washington, D.C. 20016
Fred G. Evenden, Sec.-Treas.
Founded: 1930
Members: 55
Persons interested in conservation and preservation of wildlife of the world; stimulate, promote and finance research into status and ecology of threatened species; lend assistance to national and international organizations concerned with wildlife conservation, outside the U.S.

AMERICAN CONSERVATION ASSOCIATION
30 Rockefeller Plaza
New York, N.Y. 10020
Gene W. Setzer, Exec. V. Pres.
Founded: 1958
Trustees: 11
Not a membership group. A private foundation established "to advance knowledge and understanding of conservation and to preserve and develop natural and living resources for public use, either directly or in cooperation with federal, state, local and private conservation agencies."

AMERICAN FISHERIES SOCIETY
1319 18th St., N.W., 4th Floor   Phone: (202) 872-8282
Washington, D.C. 20036
Dr. Richard A. Wade, Exec. Sec.
Founded: 1870
Members: 5000
Regional groups: 4
Fish culturists, fish biologists, commercial fishermen, hatchery-men, fish technologists, limnologists, and oceanographers. To promote the development of all branches of fishery science and practice, and the conservation, development, and wise utilization of fisheries, both recreational and commercial. Committees: Awards; Board of Professional Certification; Editorial; Education; Endangered Species; Fish Disease; Fish Policy; International Fisheries; Metric Systems Study; Names of Fishes; Pollution — Water Quality; Student Affairs. Publications: (1) *AFS Newsletter*, bimonthly; (2) *Journal of Ichthyology* (English edition of a publication of the Academy of Sciences of the U.S.S.R.), bimonthly; (3) *Hydrobiological Journal* (English edition of a publication of the Academy of Sciences of the U.S.S.R.), bimonthly; (4) *Transactions*, quarterly; (5) *Membership Directory*, annual; also publishes career guidance booklets. Convention/meeting: Annual.

**AMERICAN FISHING TACKLE
MANUFACTURERS ASSOCIATION**
20 North Wacker Drive, Suite 2014   Phone: (312) 236-0565
Chicago, Ill. 60606
Thomas R. Schedler, Exec. V. Pres.
Founded: 1933
Members: 200
Staff: 8
Manufacturers of fishing tackle and allied products. Sponsors annual trade show. Publication: *News-Bulletin*, semimonthly. Formerly: Associated Fishing Tackle Manufacturers. Convention/Meeting: Semiannual — always May and Nov.

AMERICAN INSTITUTE OF BIOLOGICAL SCIENCES
3900 Wisconsin Ave., N.W.   Phone: (202) 244-5581
Washington, D.C. 20016
John R. Olive, Dir.
Founded: 1948
Members: 14,500
Federation of professional biological associations and individuals with an interest in the life sciences. To promote unity and effectiveness of effort among persons engaged in biological research, teaching or application of biological data; to further the relationships of biological sciences to other sciences, the arts, and industries. Conducts symposium series; arranges for prominent biologists to lecture at small liberal arts colleges and radiation biologists to visit certain medical schools; provides advisory committees and other services to the Atomic Energy Commission, Office of Naval Research, and National Aeronautics and Space Administration. Created in 1966 an Office of Biological Education which serves as a clearing-house for information and conducts programs relative to several facets of biological education. Offers annual award for outstanding vegetable research. Maintains placement service. Committees: Behavioral Biology; Bioinstrumentation; Education; Environmental Biology; Exobiology; Hydrobiology; Microbiology; Oceanic Biology; Physiology; Planetary Quarantine; Public Responsibilities; Publications; Radiation Pasteurization of Foods; Scientific Manpower Commission; Theoretical Biology. Publications: (1) *BioScience*, monthly; (2) *Directory of Bioscience Departments in the U.S. and Canada*, every 2 years; also, symposia proceedings, AEC-AIBS monographs, and select single titles. Absorbed: (1969) American Society of Professional Biologists. Convention/Meeting: Annual.

**AMERICAN INSTITUTE OF
FISHERY RESEARCH BIOLOGISTS**
404 12th Place, N.
Edmonds, Wash. 98020
F. Heward Bell, Sec.-Treas.
Founded: 1956

Members: 650
Professional society of biologists engaged in research on fish.

AMERICAN LITTORAL SOCIETY

Sandy Hook   Phone: (201) 872-0200
Highlands, N.J. 07732
Mrs. Richard Steiner, Executive Secretary
Founded: 1961
Encourages the underwater study of shore life by direct observation of the occurrence and ways of fishes and other marine animals; disseminates records of observations; assists in the solving of problems of scientific study, identification, and description; and fosters public interest in shore life and the need for conservation. Publication: *Underwater Naturalist,* quarterly. Convention/Meeting: Annual.

AMERICAN MEDICAL FLY FISHING ASSOCIATION

200 S. Main   Phone: (217) 537-3967
Hillsboro, Ill. 62049
Clinton Pace, M.D., Sec.
Founded: 1969
Members: 165
Offers physicians interested in conservation, environmental and ecological problems an opportunity to work toward achieving a better environment. Publication: *Newsletter,* irregular. Holds biennial meeting.

AMERICAN RIVERS CONSERVATION COUNCIL

324 C. Street, S.E.   Phone: (202) 547-6500
Washington, D.C. 20003
Bill Painter, Exec. Dir.
Founded: 1973
Members: 1000
Conservationists, fishermen, boaters and scientists interested in the protection of remaining wild and scenic free-flowing rivers. Promotes legislation aimed at river conservation. Works against destructive dams, channelization, and other wasteful water projects. Convention/Meeting: Annual.

AMERICAN LEAGUE OF ANGLERS

810 18th Street, N.W.   Phone: (202) 347-7475
Washington, D.C. 20006
Art Lee, Executive Director
Founded: 1973
Members: (in process of organization)
Staff: 4
Persons interested in fishing and in defending the interests of fishermen. Proposes, supports and promotes legislation vital to sport fishing conservation and the rights of anglers to enjoy their sport free of unjust charges and restrictions. Fights legislation that would destroy or damage fresh and salt water resources or infringe upon rights of sport fishermen. Monitors the performance of elected and appointed officials, backing those who act in the best interests of sport fishing and exposing and opposing those who do not. Demands vigorous enforcement of existing laws which protect sport fishing and natural resources. Works to strengthen other national, state and local anglers organizations. Promotes good fisheries conservation practices.

AMERICAN SHORE AND BEACH PRESERVATION ASSOCIATION

10812 Admirals Way   Phone: (301) 299-5603
Potomac, Md. 20854
Richard O. Eaton, Exec. Sec.-Treas.
Founded: 1926
Members: 1000
Staff: 1
Federal, state and local government agencies, private groups, and individuals interested in conservation, development and restoration of beaches and shore front of lakes and rivers. Publications: (1) *Newsletter,* monthly; (2) *Shore and Beach,* semiannual. Convention/Meeting: Annual.

ASSOCIATION OF MIDWEST FISH AND GAME COMMISSIONERS

c/o Fred Warders   Phone: (303) 825-1192x212
Kansas Fish and Game Commission
P.O. Box 1028
Pratt, Kansas 67124
Fred Warders, Sec.-Treas.
Founded: 1934
Members: 17
Fish and game commissioners and directors of 15 midwestern states and 2 Canadian provinces. Promotes conservation of wildlife and outdoor recreation. Sponsors Midwest Pheasant Council; Dove Committee. Committees: Federal-State Relations; Federal Aid; Legislation; Federal Farm Program; Wetlands. Publication: *Proceedings,* annual. Convention/Meeting: Annual.

ASSOCIATION OF SURF ANGLING CLUBS

851 Norway Ave.
Trenton, N.J. 08629
Herb Blackwell, Sec.
Founded: 1915
Members: 106
Federation of surf angling and surf casting clubs of salt water fishermen; clubs must have a minimum of 25 members to affiliate with the association. Promotes conservation of salt water fish and game; seeks enactment and enforcement of federal and state laws to prohibit pollution of fresh and salt water bodies. Sanctions casting tournaments and determines uniform rules; recognizes records, and awards trophies and medals. Sponsors competitive events for the Ocean City Cup. Convention/Meeting: Annual, always third Saturday of March.

ATLANTIC ESTUARINE RESEARCH SOCIETY

c/o William B. Cronin   Phone: (301) 268-5231
Chesapeake Bay Institute
R.D. 3, Box 32
Annapolis, Md. 21403
William B. Cronin, Exec. Sec.
Founded: 1949
Members: 334
Persons actively engaged in biological hydrographic, or related investigations of estuarine problems, particularly in the Chesapeake Bay-Carolina area. Convention/Meeting: Semiannual.

ATLANTIC SEA RUN SALMON COMMISSION

State Of Maine   Phone: (207) 947-8627
Bldg. 34, Idaho Ave.
Bangor, Maine 04401
Maynard F. Marsh, Chm.
Founded: 1948
Members: 3
Staff: 4
A cooperative agreement among the University of Maine, the U.S. Bureau of Sport Fisheries and Wildlife, and the State of Maine, united for the restoration and management of Atlantic Salmon. Represents the U.S. at international meetings concerning Atlantic salmon.

BASS ANGLERS SPORTSMAN SOCIETY

1 Bell Road   Phone: (205) 272-9530
Montgomery, Alabama 36109
Ray W. Scott, Jr., President
Founded: 1968
Members: 200,000
Regional Groups: 28 state federations; 1150 local affiliated B.A.S.S. chapters
Staff: 80 employees
For-profit organization publishing *Bassmaster Magazine* for per-

sons interested in the sport of bass fishing. Publications: *Bassmaster Magazine,* bi-monthly; *Bassmaster Fishing Annual; Bass Fishing Guide.*

BOAT MANUFACTURERS ASSOCIATION
401 North Michigan Ave.
Chicago, Ill. 60601
Matt J. Kaufman, Administrator
Founded: 1945
Members: 250
Manufacturers of boats. Staff services provided by parent body, Boating Industry Associations. Publications: (1) *Monday Morning Report,* weekly; (2) *Monthly Statistical Report;* (3) *Legislative Ledger,* monthly. Formerly: Outboard Boat Manufacturers Association. Convention/Meeting: Annual — always September, Chicago, Ill.

BROTHERHOOD OF THE JUNGLE COCK
10 East Fayette St.
Baltimore, Md. 21202
Gurney J. Godfrey, Exec. V.-Pres.
Founded: 1939
Members: 250
"Anglers dedicated to conserve game fish and teach angling technique and good sportsmanship." Convention/Meeting: Annual.

CAMP FIRE CLUB OF AMERICA
19 Rector St.   Phone:(212) WH 4-5478
New York, N.Y. 10006
William B. Osgood Field, Jr., Sec.

CITIZENS COMMITTEE ON NATURAL RESOURCES
1346 Connecticut Ave., N.W.   Phone: (202) 785-1261
Washington, D.C. 20036
Spencer M. Smith, Jr., Sec.
Founded: 1954
Directors: 50
Staff: 2
Individuals interested in lobbying in behalf of conservation program dealing with government departments.

CONSERVATION EDUCATION ASSOCIATION
c/o Robert O. Ellingson
Box 450
Madison, Wis. 53701
Robert O. Ellingson, Sec.-Treas.
Founded: 1947
Members: 950
Conservationists, educators and others interested in improving conservation education in public schools, teacher training institutions, and organization programs. Outstanding state, local and organizational conservation publications, especially those of normally limited distribution, are circulated bimonthly to members. Publications: (1) *Newsletter,* bimonthly; (2) *Proceedings,* annual. Formerly: (1953) National Committee on Policies in Conservation Education. Convention/Meeting: Annual — always August.

CONSERVATION FOUNDATION
1717 Massachusetts Ave., N.W.   Phone: (202) 265-8882
Washington, D.C. 20036
Sydney Howe, Pres.
Founded: 1948
Staff: 42
Not a membership organization. Conducts research, education and information programs to develop knowledge, improve techniques, and stimulate public and private decision-making and action to improve the quality of the environment. Carries out environmental studies, demonstration planning programs, and offers a variety of conservation services at home and abroad. Divisions: Conservation Services; Education; Energy; International Programs; Planning; Policy Studies; Public Affairs. Publication: *CF Letter,* monthly; also publishes books, pamphlets, studies.

CONSERVATION LAW SOCIETY OF AMERICA
1500 Mills Tower, 220 Bush St.   Phone: (415) 981-7800
San Francisco, Calif. 94104
Robert W. Jasperson, Gen. Coun.
Founded: 1963
Members: 105
Staff: 1
Lawyers and other individuals interested in conservation. Provides the services on a fee basis of a legal staff to research the laws, decision, and other precedents relating to conservation problems; advises conservation groups on the basis of such research, and represents these groups in court if necessary. Aids groups interested in preservation of the forest, wildlife, water, wildnerness, and natural resources of the United States, especially park, recreational, and open space areas. Active in defense of public interest lands in Western states and other areas.

CONSERVATION AND RESEARCH FOUNDATION
Department of Botany   Phone: (203) 442-5391 x306
Connecticut College
New London, Conn. 06320
Richard H. Goodwin, Pres.
Founded: 1953
Not a membership organization. To encourage biological research and promote conservation of renewable natural resources. Makes research grants; offers Jeanette Siron Pelton Award for outstanding published contributions in experimental plant morphology. Publishes *A Ten Year Report* (last one in 1963). Convention/Meeting: Annual.

CONSERVATION SERVICES, INC.
South Great Road   Phone: (617) 259-9500
Lincoln, Mass. 01773
Allen H. Morgan, Exec. Dir.
Founded: 1965
Members: 5
Staff: 5
Small Audubon and conservation groups, comprising 34,000 individual members. Purpose is to publish magazines, newsletters and environmental brochures for New England conservation organizations, and to develop television, radio and audiovisual materials that can be used in New England. Maintains extensive source files. Publications: (1) *Massachusetts Audubon Society Newsletter,* 10/year; (2) *Man and Nature* (magazine), quarterly. Formerly: Conservation Services Center.

COUNCIL OF CONSERVATIONISTS
201 East 62nd St.   Phone: (212) 838-4883
New York, N.Y. 10021
Fred Smith, Dir.
Founded: 1949
Coordinating organization for groups seeking to conserve and properly utilize water, parks, recreation facilities, forests, etc., through legislation and education. Publishes occasional bulletins and booklets on conservation.

DEFENDERS OF WILDLIFE
2000 N St., N.W.   Phone: (202) 223-1993
Washington, D.C. 20036
Mary Hazel Harris, Exec. Dir.
Founded: 1925
Members: 35,000
Persons interested in wildlife and conservation. To promote, through education and research, the protection and humane treatment of all mammals, birds, fish and other wildlife, and the elimination of painful methods of trapping, capturing and killing wildlife. Publication: *Defenders of Wildlife News,* bi-monthly.

Formerly: Anti-Steel-Trap League; Defenders of Furbearers. Convention/Meeting: Annual.

EMERGENCY COMMITTEE TO SAVE AMERICA'S MARINE RESOURCES

110 Charlotte Pl.   Phone: (201) 569-9511
Englewood Cliffs, N.J. 07632
Allan J. Ristori, Chm.
Founded: 1972
Founded to establish 200-mile fisheries limit to preserve, control and maintain natural marine resources in American waters. Efforts taking place in form of letter-writing campaign by public to have federal legislation established. Maintains funding of fellowship program at Rutgers University for research into problem of fisheries limits. Affiliated with: Seamen's Education Federation.

FEDERATION OF FLY FISHERMEN

4500 Beach Dr., S.W.
Seattle, WA 98116
Steve Raymond, Sec.
To promote fly fishing as the most enjoyable and sportsmanlike method of fishing and as the method most consistent with the preservation and conservation of fishing waters and game fish.

FEDERATION OF WESTERN OUTDOOR CLUBS

Box 548
Bozeman, Mont. 59715
Kenneth Baldwin, Pres.
Founded: 1932
Members: 1341
Outdoor clubs (41) in western United States with combined membership of 48,000, associate members 1300. Promotes conservation of forests, wildlife, and natural features. Publication: *Western Outdoor Quarterly.* Convention/Meeting: Annual — always Labor Day weekend.

FISHERMEN'S CLEAN WATER ACTION PROJECT

1832 M. St., N.W. Suite 101   Phone: (202) 833-1087
Washington, D.C. 20036
David Zwick, Dir.
Research group affiliated with Ralph Nader. To organize regional public interest firms to fight water pollution. Uses teams which employ scientists, lawyers and other professionals to work for clean water before the courts and administrative agencies and to push for stronger legislation at the state and national levels. Convention/Meetings: Annual — always held on the first Tuesday after the first Monday in June.

FRIENDS OF THE EARTH

529 Commercial St.   Phone: (212) 687-8747, 691-2130
San Francisco, Calif. 94111
David Brower, Founder
Founded: 1969
International conservation organization which concentrates on legislative and political activities in this field.

FRIENDS OF NATURE, INC.

Brooksville, Me. 04617
Martin R. Haase, Exec. Sec.
Founded: 1953
Conservationists "dedicated to maintaining the balance of nature for the mutual benefit of man and his plant and animal friends." Carries on educational work and maintains several nature sanctuaries. Holds annual meeting.

FRIENDS OF THE WILDERNESS

3515 East Fourth St.   Phone: (218) 724-7227
Duluth, Minn. 55804
William H. Magie, Exec. Sec.
Founded: 1949
Members: 17,364

Persons interested in preservation of the Boundary Water Canoe Area of Minnesota, the wilderness canoe country of the Superior National Forest. Maintains library of 400 volumes pertaining to the area. Holds annual meeting.

FRUGAL BRUGAL SOCIETY

Claybrook Rd.
Dover, Me. 02030
Frederick N. Blodgett, Pres.
Founded: 1932
Members: 100
Sportsmen from four countries, primarily those interested in fishing and shooting. (A Frugal Brugal is a drink made with unsweetened grapefruit juice and Brugal rum.) Purposes are: promotion of conviviality and camaraderie among fellow sportsmen; conservation of woodcock, partridge and ducks by strict adherence to game laws and the ability to cope therewith; improvement of game habitats in selected areas. Convention/Meeting: annual — always Oct.

GULF AND CARIBBEAN FISHERIES INSTITUTE

Rosenstiel School of Marine and   Phone: (305) 350-7533
Atmospheric Science
University of Miami
4600 Rickenbacker Causeway
Miami, Fla. 33149
James B. Higman, Exec. Dir.
Founded: 1948
Members: 500
Principally fishermen, fishery scientists and administrators. "To provide a means for exchange of information on research progress in fisheries among scientists and between scientists, industry and administrators." Publication: *Proceedings,* annual. Convention/Meeting: Annual — always November, Miami Beach, Fla.

HUDSON RIVER FISHERMEN'S ASSOCIATION, INC.

P.O. Box 303   Phone: (914) 265-3119, 271-8242
Cold Spring, New York 10516
David M. Seymour, President
Founded: 1966
Members: 400 in H.R.F.A.; another 400 in Chapters
Sport fishermen, commercial fishermen, writers, businessmen, lawyers, policemen and anyone interested in protecting the entire Hudson River and its drainage. To insure proper land use (including agriculture and all building) and to see that the river's resources are wisely managed.

INTERNATIONAL ASSOCIATION FOR GREAT LAKES RESEARCH

P.O. Box 640
Ann Arbor, Mich. 48108
John F. Carr, Treas.
Founded: 1967
Members: 450
Scientists, engineers, and others in the U.S. and Canada actively interested in research on the Great Lakes and their basins, or in research directly applicable to the understanding or management of large lakes. Presents Chandler Misener Award annually for best paper at annual conference. Publications: (1) *Lakes Letter,* quarterly; (2) *Proceedings of Annual Conference on Great Lakes Research.* Convention/Meeting (Conference on Great Lakes Research): Annual.

INTERNATIONAL ASSN. OF GAME, FISH AND CONSERVATION COMMISSIONERS

425 13th St., N.W., Suite 944   Phone: (202) 638-1016, 1017
Washington, D.C. 20004
Russ J. Neugebauer, Exec. V. Pres.
Founded: 1902
Members: 377
State and provincial game, fish and conservation departments

(61) and officials (316). To educate the public to the economic importance of conserving natural resources and managing wildlife properly as a source of recreation and a food supply; to seek better conservation legislation, administration and enforcement. Publications: (1) *Proceedings,* annual; (2) *Newsletter,* irregular. Formerly: (1917) National Association of Game Commissioners and Wardens. Convention/Meeting: Annual — always second Monday in Sept.

INTERNATIONAL ATLANTIC SALMON FOUNDATION
P.O. Box 429
St. Andrews, New Brunswick EOG 2XO (Canada)
or
425 Park Avenue
New York, N.Y. 10022
Wilfred M. Carter, Exec. Dir. & Vice Pres.
Founded: 1968
Members: 900
Conservationists, scientists, government personnel, salmon anglers. Objective is the preservation and wise management of Atlantic salmon stocks. Program includes wide-range projects in four areas — education, management, research and international cooperation. Recent projects include: International Atlantic Salmon Symposium; planning for the North American Salmon Research Center (a $2.6 million selective breeding program); grant to Iceland for fish farming studies; preparation of an audiovisual presentation on the Atlantic salmon for school and community use. Bestows grants and scholarships. Maintains library and aquarium exhibits. Publishes educational material. Bestows Conservation Award, annually. Provides secretariat for the North American Atlantic Salmon Council. Committees: International Advisory Group, International Programs; NE States Restoration; Scientific Advisory Group. Publications: (1) *Newsletter,* quarterly; (2) *Special Publication Series,* semiannual.

INTERNATIONAL COMMISSION FOR THE NORTHWEST ATLANTIC FISHERIES
P.O. Box 638   Phone: (902) 466-7587
Dartmouth, Nova Scotia, Canada
L. R. Day, Exec. Sec.
Founded: 1949
Members: 16
Staff: 7
Contracting governments united for investigation, protection and conservation of fisheries of the Northwest Atlantic Ocean in order to provide a maximum sustained catch from these fisheries. Committees: International Control; Regulatory Measures; Research and Statistics. Publications: (1) *Proceedings,* annual; (2) *Research Bulletin,* annual; (3) *Statistical Bulletin,* annual; (4) *Special Publications,* irregular; also publishes a handbook. Convention/Meeting: Annual.

INTERNATIONAL GAME FISH ASSOCIATION
3000 E. Las Olas Blvd.   Phone: (305) 523-0161
Fort Lauderdale, Fla. 33316
William K. Carpenter, Pres.
Founded: 1939
Members: 770
Federation of angling clubs (660), scientific institutions (23) and international representatives (87) interested in marine fishes. Serves as center for exchange of information between scientists and anglers on marine angling grounds, seasons, fishes and record catches. Publication: *World Record Marine Fishes* (table), annual. Affiliated with: American Museum of Natural History. Convention/Meeting: Annual.

INTERNATIONAL LIGHT TACKLE TOURNAMENT ASSOCIATION
2044 Federal Ave.   Phone: (714) 548-4273
Costa Mesa, Calif. 92627
Helen R. Smith, Exec. Sec.

Founded: 1945
Members: 59
Staff: 1
Angling clubs which are members of International Game Fish Association. Sponsors tournaments in which only light tackle is used and fish which are taken are later released. Publication: *Bulletin,* quarterly. Holds International Billfish Tournaments.

INTERNATIONAL NORTH PACIFIC FISHERIES COMMISSION, UNITED STATES SECTION
Uganik Bay
Kodiak, Alaska
Alfred Owen, Chairman
Founded: 1954
Members: 20
Intergovernmental organization of fishing industry and association representatives, state administrators, lawyers, and others interested in development of fisheries in the Pacific Northwest. INPFC, established by convention between the U.S., Canada, and Japan, works to promote and coordinate conservation programs to secure maximum sustainable production from the fisheries of the North Pacific Study Group, which recently formed a North Pacific Task Force to initiate reports on various problems. Offers guidance to U.S. commissioners to INPFC and advises federal and state government agencies and other institutions on research activities. Meets annually, prior to INPFC meetings.

INTERNATIONAL OCEANOGRAPHIC FOUNDATION
3979 Rickenbacker Causeway   Phone: (305) 361-2186
Virginia Key, Miami, Fla. 33149
F. G. Walton Smith, Pres.
Founded: 1953
Members: 65,000
Staff: 18
Scientists and laymen interested in the sea. Encourages scientific study and exploration of the oceans in all their aspects, including game and food fishes and other creatures of sea and shore; ocean currents; geology, chemistry, and physics of the sea and sea floor; submarine detection; and industrial applications of oceanography. Gives financial aid to research institutions to support scientific investigations. Awards graduate fellowships; co-sponsors international exchange of scientists with Nordic Council for Marine Biology. Gives Gold Medal Award. Plans future development of museum of marine science. Publications: (1) *Sea Secrets* (question and answer series), 6/year; (2) *Sea Frontiers* (magazine), bimonthly; also publishes young people's booklet, *Training and Careers in Marine Science.*

INTERNATIONAL PACIFIC HALIBUT COMMISSION
250 Oceanography-Teaching Bldg.   Phone: (206) ME 4-1838
Univ. of Washington
Seattle, Wash. 98105
Bernard E. Skud, Dir. of Investigations
Founded: 1923
Members: 6
Staff: 24
Intergovernmental organization of Commissioners appointed by the United States (3) and Canada (3) to be responsible for management of the halibut fishery in the North Pacific and Bering Sea. Seeks to develop stocks of Pacific halibut to levels that will permit maximum sustained yield and to maintain stocks at those levels. Applies specific types of regulation and scientific investigations. Publications: (1) *Annual Report;* (2) *Scientific Reports,* irregular; (3) *Technical Reports,* irregular. Formerly: (1954) International Fisheries Commission. Convention/Meeting: Annual.

INTERNATIONAL PACIFIC SALMON FISHERIES COMMISSION
Post Office Box 30   Phone: (604) 521-3771

New Westminister, British Columbia V3L 4X9, Canada
A. C. Cooper, Dir.
Founded: 1937
Commissioners: 6
Advisors: 12
Staff: 44
To protect, preserve, and extend the sockeye and pink salmon fisheries of the Fraser River, which flows in British Columbia passing near the United States border. Publications: (1) *Annual Report;* (2) *Bulletins,* periodically; (3) *Progress Reports,* periodically. Meets several times a year.

INTERNATIONAL SPIN FISHING ASSOCIATION
P.O. Box 81
Downey, Calif. 90241
Richard Ream, Exec. Sec.
Founded: 1953
Sportsmen's clubs and individuals interested in spin fishing. Registers fresh and salt water records made on spin tackle on line classes ranging from 2- through 12-pound test; promotes conservation.

INTERNATIONAL UNDERWATER SPEARFISHING ASSOCIATION
Los Angeles County Museum,   Phone: (213) 662-6874
Exposition Park
Los Angeles, Calif. 90007
Candida R. Davis, Sec.-Treas.
Founded: 1950
Staff: 9
To encourage underwater spearfishing as recreation and as a potential source of scientific knowledge; to maintain standardized rules for underwater spearfishing; to maintain an attested and up-to-date listing of world records for underwater spearfishing. Sponsors: Inter-America Underwater Spearfishing Championship; Junior Underwater Spearfishing Championship; U.S. National Amateur Underwater Spearfishing Athlete of the Year award. Committees: Athlete of the Year; Inter-Americas; International; National Championships; Records; Scientific; Sports. Formerly: Los Angeles Neptunes. Convention/Meeting: Biennial.

INTERNATIONAL UNION FOR CONSERVATION OF NATURE AND NATURAL RESOURCES
P.O. Box 19347   Phone: (703) 280-4086
Washington, D.C. 20036
Harold J. Coolidge, Pres.
Founded: 1948
Members: 266
International federation of national governments (29) and national and international organizations (228) in 61 countries. For the preservation of the natural environment of man and the conservation of the world's natural resources. Serves as a forum for discussion of conservation problems and studies; sponsors international youth camps; intercedes with governments on conservation matters; maintains Van Tienhoven Library. Conducts research on measures to promote and protect national parks, nature reserves, wildlife and its habitat. Provides advisory field missions. International headquarters located in Morges, Switzerland. Technical Commissions: Conservation Education; Ecology; Environmental Policy, Law, and Administration; Landscape Planning; Law and Administration; National Parks; Survival Service. Publications: (1) *IUCN Bulletin,* quarterly; (2) *Proceedings* (of conferences); also publishes *Red Data Book* (endangered species), technical reports and a UN List of National Parks and Equivalent Reserves. Formerly: (1956) International Union for the Protection of Nature. General Assembly/Technical Meeting: Triennial.

INTERNATIONAL WILDLIFE CONSERVATION SOCIETY
P.O. Box 19226
Washington, D.C. 20036

Founded: 1968
Created first working tiger sanctuary in Nepal, 50,000 acres, now staffed and run by government of Nepal and overseen by the Food and Agriculture Organization of U.N. Present projects involve wildlife research in Pacific Ocean, northwest of U.S.

INTERNATIONAL WOMEN'S FISHING ASSOCIATION
P.O. Box 2025   Phone: (305) 833-5310
Palm Beach, Fla. 33480
Mrs. Raymond J. Kunkel, Pres.
Founded: 1955
Members: 450
Staff: 1
Sportfisherwomen. Promotes angling competition among women anglers; encourages conservation; fosters fishing tournaments of all kinds. Gives monthly and yearly awards for outstanding fishing accomplishments. Has established a scholarship trust to help graduate students further their education in the field of the marine sciences. Publications: (1) *Hooks and Lines,* monthly; (2) *IWFA Yearbook.* Convention/Meeting: Annual — always Apr., Palm Beach, Fla.

IZAAK WALTON LEAGUE OF AMERICA
1800 N. Kent St., Suite 806   Phone: (703) 528-1818
Arlington, Va. 22209
Jack Lorenz, Exec. Dir.
Founded: 1922
Members: 50,000
Staff: 16
State divisions: 22
Local chapters: 600
Promotes means and opportunities for educating the public to conserve, maintain, protect and restore the soil, forest, water and other natural resources of the U.S. and promotes the enjoyment and wholesome utilization of those resources. Committees: Air Quality; Clean Water; Conservation Education; Public Lands. Publications: (1) *The Izaak Walton Magazine,* monthly; (2) *National Bulletin,* monthly; (3) *Outdoor America.* Absorbed: (1962) Friends of the Land. Convention/Meeting: Annual — always July.

J. N. "DING" DARLING FOUNDATION
c/o Central National Bank   Phone: (515) 243-8181
Des Moines, Iowa 50304
Mr. Sherry R. Fisher, Chm.
Founded: 1962
Trustees: 50
"To initiate plans and to coordinate, guide and expedite programs, research and education which will bring about conservation and sound management of water, woods and soil; to restore and preserve historical sites; to create and assist in wildlife management plans; to improve and assure outdoor recreational opportunities for present and future generations." Established 1700-acre wildlife and waterfowl sanctuary on Sanibel Island, off the west coast of Florida. Awards scholarships at Iowa State University for wildlife management students. Named for the late J. N. "Ding" Darling, a professional cartoonist long active in conservation activities. Holds annual meeting.

LEAGUE TO SAVE LAKE TAHOE
74 Los Altos Square   Phone: (414) 941-3943
Los Altos, Calif. 94022
Donald G. Ellis, Pres.
Staff: 1
Membership comprised of individuals and organizations who give financial support to the League. Purpose is to "do all things and to perform all acts necessary to keep Lake Tahoe blue and to protect and preserve the natural beauty and grandeur of the Lake Tahoe area of California and Nevada; to promote and encourage the concept that all developments, improvements and man-made changes of any kind, which may be required to ac-

commodate the proper and desirable growth of the area and provide the maximum recreational values, should place primary emphasis on preserving the natural beauty of the lake." Publication: *Newsletter,* quarterly. Convention/Meeting: Annual.

NATIONAL COALITION FOR MARINE CONSERVATION, INC.

P.O. Box 5131   Phone: (912) 234-8062
Savannah, Georgia 31403
Dr. Frank Carlton, President
Christopher M. Weld, Secretary
Founded: 1972
Members: 25,000
Recreational and commercial fishermen; fisheries scientists; federal and state administrators interested in the promotion of national policies and legislation affecting fisheries. Publication: *Right Rigger!,* monthly newsletter. Convention/Meeting: annual members' seminar.

NATIONAL FISHERIES INSTITUTE

1225 Connecticut Ave.   Phone: (202) 785-0500
Washington, D.C. 20036
Les J. Weddig, Exec. Dir.
Founded: 1945
Members: 500
Producers (boat owners), distributors, processors, wholesalers, importers and canners of fish and shellfish. Divisions: National Fish Meal and Oil Association. Publications: (1) *Flashes,* weekly; (2) *Bluebook,* annual. Convention/Meeting: Annual — always Apr.

NATIONAL WATERSHED CONGRESS

1025 Vermont Ave., N.W.   Phone: (202) 347-5995
Washington, D.C. 20005
Gordon K. Zimmerman, Chairman, Steering Committee
Founded: 1954
Members: 25
National conservation, farm, civic and business organizations interested in fostering discussion and advancement of natural resources conservation and development through upstream watershed programs. (A watershed is the drainage area usually associated with a river or lake and divided from other watersheds by ridges or other characteristics of the terrain.) Holds annual conference (Congress) planned and conducted by a steering committee chosen by the participating organizations. The Congress "does not propagandize, adopt resolutions, promote projects, or take any action" — it acts as a forum for discussion of ways and means of expediting and broadening local watershed programs. Though the first Congresses were concerned primarily with water control and soil erosion, in recent years the Congress has dealt with river basin planning, regional interstate river compacts, and national water policy in general. Publication: *Proceedings,* annual. Holds annual Congress.

NATIONAL WILDLIFE FEDERATION

1412 16th St., N.W.   Phone: (202) 483-1550
Washington, D.C. 20036
Thomas L. Kimball, Exec. V. Pres.
Founded: 1936
State affiliate members: 52
Associate members: 700,000
Staff: 20
Local chapters: 6,500
Federation of 52 state conservation organizations and 700,000 associate members, plus individual conservationist-contributors. Represents in its structure 3 million supporters. To encourage the intelligent management of the life-sustaining resources of the earth, and to promote a greater appreciation of these resources, their community relationship and wise use.

NATURAL RESOURCES COUNCIL OF AMERICA

1025 Connecticut Ave., N.W.   Phone: (202) 223-1536
Suite 911
Washington, D.C. 20036
Hamilton K. Pyles, Exec. Sec.
Founded: 1946
Members: 45
Federation of national and regional conservation organizations and scientific societies interested in conservation of natural resources. Sponsors special natural resource studies and surveys. Committee: Scientific Advisory. Publications: (1) *Legislative News Service* (actions taken by Congress on natural resources), weekly; (2) *Executive News Service* (actions taken by Executive Branch on natural resources), weekly; also publishes books on selected natural resource topics. Convention/Meeting: Semiannual — always held with North American Wildlife and Natural Resources Conference.

NEW ENGLAND ADVISORY BOARD FOR FISH AND GAME PROBLEMS

25 Franklin St.   Phone: (603) 224-1245
Concord, N.H. 03301
Robert C. Hill, Sec.
Founded: 1951
Members: 102
Sportsmen. To promote and improve conservation, hunting, fishing and recreation in New England. Convention/Meeting: 3/year.

NORTH AMERICAN WILDLIFE FOUNDATION

709 Wire Bldg.   Phone: (202) 347-1774
Washington, D.C. 20005
C. R. Gutermuth, Sec.
Founded: 1911
Contributing members: 376
Trustees: 30
"To insure, through financial support, the continuity of practical and systematic investigation into management practices and techniques throughout North America, to the end that the latest, most effective local, national, and international programs for wildlife and other natural resources will be adopted in the public interest." Foundation is not an action organization and does not attempt the actual mechanics of wildlife restoration; works through cooperating agencies, organizations, institutions. Owns Delta Waterfowl Research Station in Manitoba, Canada. Maintains library of 450 volumes on natural science subjects and wildlife restoration and management. Formerly: (1935) American Game Protective Association; (1946) American Wildlife Institute; (1951) American Wildlife Foundation.

OUTBOARD BOATING CLUB OF AMERICA

401 North Michigan Ave.   Phone: (312) 329-0590
Chicago, Ill. 60611
Matt Kaufman, Exec. Dir.
Founded: 1928. Boating Clubs. Provides members with information on current legislative problems; cruising and boating information. OBC is a consumer arm of International Expositions, Inc.

OUTDOOR RECREATION INSTITUTE

5003 Wapakoneta
Washington, D.C. 20016
Dr. Radcliffe F. Robinson, Pres.
To advance outdoor recreational interests at all levels — family, local, state, and national; to emphasize recreational objectives of natural resource conservation, through technical research and educational activities. Provides information service on recreational equipment; answers technical inquiries; gives talks to groups on recreation, nutrition, foods, camping, etc.; conducts research in biology, pollution, recreational equipment, and other topics. Divisions: Research; Educational; Consulting. Publication: *ORI Newsletter,* quarterly.

OUTDOOR WRITERS ASSOCIATION OF AMERICA

4141 W. Bradley Rd.   Phone: (414) 354-9690
Milwaukee, Wis. 53209
Edwin W. Hanson, Exec. Dir.
Founded: 1927
Members: 1400
Staff: 3
Professional organization of newspaper, magazine, radio, television, and motion picture writers and photographers (both staff and free-lance) on outdoor recreation and conservation. Gives awards for outstanding writing and films in the field; conducts surveys for educational and industrial organizations; compiles market data for writer members, and offers liaison aid in writer assignments. Committees: Awards; Educational and Scholarship; Ethics; Youth Program. Publications: (1) *Outdoors Unlimited,* monthly; (2) *Spotlight,* quarterly; (3) *National Directory of Outdoor Writers,* annual; (4) *Standard Check List of Common Names for Principal American Sport Fishes,* revised periodically; also publishes a youth education manual. Convention/Meeting: Annual.

PISCES SOCIETY OF AMERICA

61 Carthage Rd.   Phone: (914) 725-2880
Scarsdale, N.Y. 10583
J. S. Burrows, Pres.
Founded: 1965
Members: 86
Persons interested in fishing; conservationists, writers, ichthyologists, librarians, curators; clubs, lodges, publications, and business firms whose products are allied with fishing and conservation. "To educate, support, and promote angling sportsmanship, conservation, and the preservation of our wildlife and natural resources." Records outstanding catches of its fisherman-members, and offers a fishing certificate to members and others to document their catches. Presently inactive.

RED SNAPPER CLUBS

Fishing clubs in various cities in the U.S. Members charter buses and travel to Florida's Gulf Coast to fish for red snapper as well as other species. Members receive reduced rates from motels and from charter boats from which they fish.

RESOURCES FOR THE FUTURE

1755 Massachusetts Ave., N.W.   Phone: (202) 462-4400
Washington, D.C. 20036
John E. Herbert, Sec.
Founded: 1952
Staff: 40
Foundation for research and education in conservation and development of natural resources. Publication: *Resources,* 3/year.

RESTORATION OF ATLANTIC SALMON IN AMERICA, INC.

Box 164   Phone: (603) 525-3355, 3324
Hancock, N.H. 03499
Richard A. Buck, Chairman
Founded: 1973
Members: 350
Foundations, individuals, and national, regional and state conservation organizations interested in restoring Atlantic salmon to abundance in the waters of New England, and to protect these stocks wherever they may be found. Publication: *Newsletters.*

SCENIC HUDSON PRESERVATION CONFERENCE

373 Fifth Ave., 8th Floor   Phone: (212) 679-8380
New York, N.Y. 10016
Mrs. Terry Rotola, Exec. Sec.
Founded: 1963
Members: 21,000
Garden, civic, environmental, conservation and sportsmen groups

(60); various towns, villages and municipalities; and individuals who espouse "a general concern for the natural resources of the Hudson River with particular emphasis on the preservation of the Hudson River Gorge and its attendant Highlands as an irreplaceable natural area of wilderness quality." Publications: *Bulletins* and *Newsletters,* irregular.

SIERRA CLUB

1050 Mills Tower   Phone: (415) 981-8634
San Francisco, Calif. 94104
J. Michael McCloskey, Exec. Dir.
Members: 135,000
Staff: 90
Regional chapters: 42
All who feel the need to know more of nature, and know that this need is basic to man. "To protect and conserve the natural resources of the Sierra Nevada, the United States and the World; to undertake and publish scientific and educational studies concerning all aspects of man's environment and the natural ecosystems of the World; and to educate the people of the United States and the World to the need to preserve and restore the quality of that environment and the integrity of those ecosystems." Works on urgent campaigns to save threatened areas, wildlife, and resources; conducts annual environmental workshops for educators; schedules wilderness outings; presents awards; maintains library. Chapters and committees schedule talks, films, exhibits, and conferences. Committees: Economics; Energy; Environmental Education; Environmental Research; Forest Practices; International Environment; Mountaineering; National Land Use; National Water Resources; Native American Issues; Outings; Population; Wilderness; Wildlife and Endangered Species. Departments: Conservation; Publications; Outings. Publications: (1) *National News Report,* weekly; (2) *Sierra Club Bulletin,* monthly; (3) *Ascent,* Sierra Club mountaineering journal, annual; also publishes books and produces films, posters, and exhibits. Member of: United Nations (with non-government organization status). Convention/Meeting (Wilderness Conference): Biennial.

SOUTHEASTERN ASSOCIATION OF GAME AND FISH COMMISSIONERS

c/o Arnold L. Mitchell
Dept. of Fish and Wildlife Resources
State Office Bldg. Annex
Frankfort, Ky. 40601
Arnold L. Mitchell, Sec.-Treas.
Founded: 1947
Members: 16
Directors of state game and fish commissions in 16 southern states. To protect the right of jurisdiction of southeastern states over their wildlife resources on public and private lands; study state and federal wildlife legislation and regulations as they affect the area; consult with and make recommendations to federal wildlife and public land agencies on federal management programs and programs involving federal aid to southeastern states; serve as a clearing house for exchange of ideas on wildlife management and research techniques. Sponsors statistical studies at North Carolina.

SPORT FISHERY RESEARCH FOUNDATION

608 13th Street, N.W., Suite 801   Phone: (202) 737-2145
Washington, D.C. 20005
Robert G. Martin, Sec.
Founded: 1962
Members: 30
Group of organizations interested in improving sport fishing. Sole objective is to help finance the training of professional fishery workers and to support research in the sport fishery field. Seeks to create, from contributions, a series of graduate fishery fellowships of universities where cooperative fishery units have been established. Affiliated with: Sport Fishing Institute. Holds annual meeting.

SPORT FISHING INSTITUTE

Suite 801
608 13th Street, N.W.
Washington, D.C. 20005
Richard H. Stroud, Exec. V. Pres.
Founded: 1949

Phone: (202) 737-0668

Works to improve sport fishing through fish conservation research, education and service based on the philosophy that "the quality of fishing reflects the quality of living"; helps protect aquatic ecosystems by assisting first conservationists in developing new and improved fisheries research and management programs designed to protect aquatic environments and enhance vital resources. Publication: *SFI Bulletin* (10 x yr.).

TROUT UNLIMITED

4260 E. Evans
Denver, Colo. 80222
R. P. Van Gytenbeek, Exec. Dir.
Founded: 1959
Members: 15,000
Staff: 4
Chapters: 176

Phone: (303) 757-7144

To conserve and preserve the natural habitat of the trout by influencing the activities and programs of governmental agencies, and keeping the public informed on water management problems. Emphasizes the sport in fishing. Maintains offices in Washington, D.C. and Portland, Ore. Bestows annual Trout Conservation Award. Conducts many research and education programs. Committees: Field Project; Pollution; Water Quality; Water Resources; Wild Rivers. Publications: (1) *Trout Magazine,* quarterly; (2) *TU Newsletter,* quarterly; also publishes newsletters for several state councils. Convention/Meeting: Annual.

TRUSTEES FOR CONSERVATION

251 Kearny St.
San Francisco, Calif. 94108
William J. Losh, Exec. Sec.
Founded: 1954

Phone: (415) 392-2838

To secure the support of the people and the government in the preservation of national parks and monuments, wildlife.

UNITED STATES TROUT FARMERS ASSOCIATION

67 West 9000 South
Sandy, Utah 84070
Clay Robinson, Exec. Manager
Founded: 1952
Members: 1500

Phone: (801) 255-0228

Trout farmers and pay pond operators. To promote the sale of United States trout. Conducts research through state and federal agencies and colleges. Publication: *American Fishes and U.S. Trout News,* bimonthly; also publishes *Handbook of Trout Cookery, Tackle Talk and Trout* and a variety of sales and promotional aids for use by members. Holds annual meeting.

WESTERN ASSN. OF STATE GAME AND FISH COMMISSIONERS

c/o Robert L. Salter
Box 25
600 S. Walnut St.
Boise, Idaho 83707
Robert L. Salter, Sec.-Treas.
Founded: 1920
Members: 17

Phone: (208) 384-3771 ext. 50

Officials of state and provincial game and fish agencies of western states and provinces. Promotes fish and game conservation in West. Publication: *Proceedings of WASGFC,* annual. Convention/Meeting: Annual.

WILDERNESS SOCIETY

729 15th St., N.W.
Washington, D.C. 20005
Stewart M. Brandborg, Exec. Dir.
Founded: 1935
Members: 77,000
Staff: 35

Phone: (202) 347-4132

Persons interested in preserving wilderness through educational programs, scientific studies, and cooperation with local and state citizen organizations in resisting the destruction of wildland resources and wildlife. Conducts leadership training programs for citizen conservationists. Sponsors book award program for young people. Sponsors "A Way to the Wilderness" trip program. Publication: *Living Wilderness,* quarterly; also publishes *Wilderness Reports,* notices, and conservation alerts on critical conservation issues. Convention/Meeting: Annual.

WILDLIFE MANAGEMENT INSTITUTE

709 Wire Bldg.
Washington, D.C. 20005
Daniel A. Poole, Pres.
Founded: 1946
Staff: 22

Phone: (202) 347-1774

To promote better management and wise utilization of all renewable natural resources in the public interest. Sponsors annual North American Wildlife and Natural Resources Conference for government conservation administrators, technicians, scientists, educators and others interested in wildlife conservation. Publications: (1) *Outdoor News Bulletin,* biweekly; (2) *Transactions of Annual North American Wildlife and Natural Resources Conference* (and cumulative index); also publishes various books and monographs. Holds annual conference.

WILDLIFE SOCIETY

3900 Wisconsin Ave., Suite S-176
Washington, D.C. 20016
Dr. Fred G. Evenden, Exec. Dir.
Founded: 1936
Members: 7000
Sectional groups: 7

Phone: (202) 363-2435

Professional society of wildlife biologists and others interested in resource conservation and wildlife management on a sound biological basis. Publications: (1) *Journal of Wildlife Management,* quarterly; (2) *Wildlife Society News,* bimonthly; (3) *Wildlife Monographs,* irregular. Formerly: (1937) Society of Wildlife Specialists. Convention/Meeting: Annual — held with North American Wildlife and Natural Resources Conference.

WORLD WILDLIFE FUND

910 17th St., N.W., Suite 619
Washington, D.C. 20006
William C. Scheele, Exec. Dir.
Founded: 1961
Staff: 13

Phone: (202) 296-0422

Supported by contributions from individuals, funds, corporations, and foundations with a concern for conservation of wildlife and its habitat. Emphasizes preservation of endangered and vanishing species of wildlife anywhere in the world. Programs include public education, promoting law enforcement, initiating ecological and biological research, providing data on endangered species, buying land for nature reserves, and propagating threatened species in captivity. Support is given existing conservation societies, agencies, and governments to carry out projects and services. Maintains small library. Committee: Scientific Advisory. Affiliated with: World Wildlife Fund, International, and International Union for Conservation of Nature and Natural Resources, both headquartered at Morges, Switzerland. Holds semi-annual board meeting.

Directory of Federal, State and Provincial Agencies Concerned with Fish Protection and Exploitation

FEDERAL GOVERNMENT

Environmental Protection Agency
401 M Street, S.W.
Washington, D.C. 20460

Forest Service
Department of Agriculture
Building E
Rosslyn Plaza
Rosslyn, Virginia 22209

National Marine Fisheries Service
Department of Commerce
Page Building No. 2
3300 Whitehaven Parkway
Washington, D.C. 20235

Corps of Engineers
Department of Defense
Forrestal Building
Washington, D.C. 20314

Bureau of Sport Fisheries and Wildlife
Fish and Wildlife Service
Department of the Interior
18th and C Streets, N.W.
Washington, D.C. 20240

STATE GOVERNMENTS

ALABAMA
Game and Fish Division
Department of Conservation and
    Natural Resources
64 North Union Street
Montgomery, Alabama 36104

ALASKA
Department of Fish and Game
Subport Building
Juneau, Alaska 99801

ARIZONA
Game and Fish Department
2222 West Greenway Road
Phoenix, Arizona 85203

ARKANSAS
Game and Fish Commission
Game and Fish Commission Building
Little Rock, Arkansas 72201

CALIFORNIA
Department of Fish and Game
Resources Agency
1416 Ninth Street
Sacramento, California 95814

COLORADO
Division of Wildlife
Department of Natural Resources
6060 Broadway
Denver, Colorado 80216

CONNECTICUT
Division of Conservation and
    Preservation
Department of Environmental
    Protection
State Office Building
165 Capitol Avenue
Hartford, Connecticut 06115

DELAWARE
Division of Fish and Wildlife
Department of Natural Resources and
    Environmental Control
Tatnall Building
Legislative Avenue and D Street
Dover, Delaware 19901

DISTRICT OF COLUMBIA
Department of Environmental Services
1875 Connecticut Avenue, N.W.
Washington, D.C. 20009

FLORIDA
Game and Fresh Water Fish
    Commission
Farris Bryant Building
620 South Meridian Street
Tallahassee, Florida 32304

GEORGIA
Game and Fish Division
Department of Natural Resources
270 Washington Street, S.W.
Atlanta, Georgia 30334

HAWAII
Fish and Game Division
Department of Land and Natural
    Resources
1179 Punchbowl Street
Honolulu, Hawaii 96813

IDAHO
Fish and Game Department
600 South Walnut
P.O. Box 25
Boise, Idaho 83707

ILLINOIS
Division of Fisheries
Department of Conservation
605 State Office Building
400 South Spring Street
Springfield, Illinois 62706

INDIANA
Fish and Wildlife Division
Department of Natural Resources
State Office Building
Indianapolis, Indiana 46204

IOWA
Fish and Wildlife Division
Conservation Commission
300 Fourth Street
Des Moines, Iowa 50319

KANSAS
Forestry, Fish and Game Commission
P.O. Box 1028
Pratt, Kansas 67124

KENTUCKY
Department of Fish and Wildlife
    Resources
4th floor
Capital Plaza Tower
Frankfort, Kentucky 40601

LOUISIANA
Fish Division
Wildlife and Fisheries Commission
Box 44095
Capitol Station
Baton Rouge, Louisiana 70804

MAINE
Department of Inland Fisheries
    and Game
284 State Street
Augusta, Maine 04330

Department of Marine Resources
State House Annex
Augusta, Maine 04330

MARYLAND
Department of Natural Resources
Tawes State Office Building
580 Taylor Avenue
Annapolis, Maryland 21401

MASSACHUSETTS
Department of Natural Resources
Leverett Saltonstall Building
100 Cambridge Street
Boston, Massachusetts 02202

MICHIGAN
Department of Natural Resources
Stevens T. Mason Building
Lansing, Michigan 48926

MINNESOTA
Department of Natural Resources
Centennial Office Building
St. Paul, Minnesota 55155

MISSISSIPPI
Game and Fish Commission
Game and Fish Building
402 High Street
P.O. Box 451
Jackson, Mississippi 39205

MISSOURI
Department of Conservation
2901 North Ten Mile Drive
P.O. Box 180
Jefferson City, Missouri 65101

MONTANA
Department of Fish and Game
Helena, Montana 59601

NEBRASKA
Game and Parks Commission
2200 North 33rd Street
P.O. Box 30370
Lincoln, Nebraska 68503

NEVADA
Department of Fish and Game
P.O. Box 10678
Reno, Nevada 89510

NEW HAMPSHIRE
Department of Fish and Game
34 Bridge Street
Concord, New Hampshire 03301

NEW JERSEY
Fish, Game and Shellfisheries Division
Department of Environmental
 Protection
Labor and Industry Building
P.O. Box 1390
Trenton, New Jersey 08625

NEW MEXICO
Department of Game and Fish
State Capitol
Sante Fe, New Mexico 87503

NEW YORK
Division of Fish and Wildlife
Department of Environmental
 Conservation
50 Wolf Road
Albany, New York 12233

NORTH CAROLINA
Wildlife Resources Commission
Albermarle Building
325 North Salisbury Street
P.O. Box 27687
Raleigh, North Carolina 27611

NORTH DAKOTA
Department of Game and Fish
2121 Lovett Avenue
Bismarck, North Dakota 58505

OHIO
Department of Natural Resources
Fountain Square
Columbus, Ohio 43224

OKLAHOMA
Department of Wildlife Conservation
1801 North Lincoln Boulevard
P.O. Box 53465
Oklahoma City, Oklahoma 73105

OREGON
Fish Commission
307 State Office Building
Portland, Oregon 97201

Wildlife Commission
1634 Southwest Alder Street
P.O. Box 3503
Portland, Oregon 97208

PENNSYLVANIA
Fish Commission
P.O. Box 1673
Harrisburg, Pennsylvania 17120

RHODE ISLAND
Division of Fish and Wildlife
Department of Natural Resources
Veterans' Memorial Building
83 Park Street
Providence, Rhode Island 02903

SOUTH CAROLINA
Wildlife and Marine Resources
 Department
1015 Main Street
P.O. Box 167
Columbia, South Carolina 29202

SOUTH DAKOTA
Department of Game, Fish and Parks
State Office Building No. 1
Pierre, South Dakota 57501

TENNESSEE
Game and Fish Commission
Ellington Agricultural Center
P.O. Box 40747
Nashville, Tennessee 37220

TEXAS
Fish and Wildlife Division
Parks and Wildlife Department
John H. Reagan State Office Building
Austin, Texas 78701

UTAH
Division of Wildlife Resources
Department of Natural Resources
1596 West North Temple
Salt Lake City, Utah 84116

VERMONT
Department of Fish and Game
Agency of Environmental Conservation
Montpelier, Vermont 05602

VIRGINIA
Commission of Game and Inland
 Fisheries
4010 West Broad Street
P.O. Box 11104
Richmond, Virginia 23230

Marine Resources Commission
P.O. Box 756
Newport News, Virginia 23607

WASHINGTON
Department of Game
600 North Capitol Way
Olympia, Washington 98504

WEST VIRGINIA
Division of Wildlife Resources
Department of Natural Resources
1800 Washington Street, East
Charleston, West Virginia 25305

WISCONSIN
Bureau of Fish and Wildlife
 Management
Department of Natural Resources
P.O. Box 450
Madison, Wisconsin 53701

WYOMING
Game and Fish Department
P.O. Box 1589
Cheyenne, Wyoming 82001

CANADA

ALBERTA
Alberta Fish and Wildlife Division
Natural Resources Building
9833 - 109th Street
Edmonton, Alberta T5K 2E1

BRITISH COLUMBIA
Environment and Land Use
  Commission
Parliament Building
Victoria, British Columbia

Department of Land, Forest and
  Water Resources
Parliament Building
Victoria, British Columbia

MANITOBA
Department of Mines, Resources and
  Environmental Management
Fisheries Programs
9-989 Century Street
Winnipeg, Manitoba R3H OW4

Manitoba Government Travel
200 Vaughan Street
Winnipeg, Manitoba R3C OP8

NEWFOUNDLAND
Environment Canada, Fisheries and
  Marine Service
Building 308
Pleasantville
P.O. Box 5667
St. John's, Newfoundland

Department of Tourism
Wildlife Division
Confederation Building, 5th Floor
St. John's, Newfoundland

NORTHWEST TERRITORIES
Game Management Branch
Government of the Northwest
  Territories
Yellowknife, Northwest Territories

NOVA SCOTIA
Department of Environment
Box 2107
Halifax, Nova Scotia

Department of Land and Forests
Dennis Building
Granville Street
Halifax, Nova Scotia

ONTARIO
Sport Fisheries Branch
Ministry of Natural Resources
Whitnes Block
Toronto, Ontario M7A 1W3

PRINCE EDWARD ISLAND
Department of Fisheries
Box 2000
Charlottetown, Prince Edward Island

Environmental Control Commission
Box 2000
Charlottetown, Prince Edward Island

Department of Environment and
  Tourism
Box 2000
Charlottetown, Prince Edward Island

QUEBEC
Department of Tourism, Fish and
  Game
150 St. Cyrille East - 15th Floor
Quebec, Quebec G1R 4Y3

SASKATCHEWAN
Department of Natural Resources
Fisheries and Wildlife Branch
Administrative Building
Regina, Saskatchewan

YUKON TERRITORY
Game Branch
Government of the Yukon Territory
Whitehorse, Yukon Territory

Standard Check List of the Common Names and Scientific Names of the Principal American Sport Fishes

FRESH WATER FISHES

Bass, Largemouth: *Micropterus salmoides*

Bass, Rock: *Ambloplites rupestris*

Bass, Smallmouth: *Micropterus dolomieui*

Bass, Spotted: *Micropterus punctulatus*

(This is the game fish somewhat generally known as the Kentucky Bass, but as its range is far beyond that one state, the acceptable name is used in this list.)

Bass, White: *Roccus chrysops*

Bass, Yellow: *Roccus interruptus*

Bowfin: *Amia calva*

(Also known as the Mudfish and the Dogfish.)

Bluegill (See Sunfish)

Bullhead, Black: *Ictalurus melas*

Bullhead, Brown: *Ictalurus nebulosus*

Bullhead, Yellow: *Ictalurus natalis*

Carp: *Cyprinus carpio*

Catfish, Blue: *Ictalurus furcatus*

Catfish, Channel: *Ictalurus punctatus*

Catfish, Flathead: *Pylodictis olivaris*

(Also known as Shovelhead Catfish.)

Catfish, Spoonbill (See Paddlefish)

Catfish, White: *Ictalurus catus*

Char, Arctic: *Salvelinus alpinus*

(Also known as Arctic Trout and Sunapee Trout. Is found all over Europe where it is known as the Char.)

Chub, Columbia: *Mylocheilus caurinus*

Chub, Creek: *Semotilus atromaculatus*

Chub, Silver (See Fallfish)

Cisco: *Coregonus artedii*

Coaster (See Brook Trout)

Crappie, Black: *Pomoxis nigromaculatus*

Crappie, White: *Pomoxis annularis*

Dogfish (See Bowfin)

Drum, Freshwater: *Aplodinotus grunniens*

Fallfish: *Semotilus corporalis*

(Also known as Silver Chub in Northeast.)

Note: There are four species of Gars now recognized by the American Fisheries Society, but the Alligator Gar is of chief interest to the sportsman-angler.

Gar, Alligator: *Lepisosteus spatula*

Gar, Longnose: *Lepisosteus osseus*

Gar, Shortnose: *Lepisosteus platostomus*

Gar, Spotted: *Lepisosteus oculatus*

Grayling, Arctic: *Thymallus arcticus*

Grayling, Montana: *Thymallus arcticus tricolor*

Mudfish (See Bowfin)

Muskellunge: *Esox masquinongy*

Ouananiche (See Salmon)

Paddlefish: *Polyodon spathula*

(Last remnant in this country of a group of fossil fishes and confined to the Mississippi River system. Once abundant, but gradually disappearing. Taken chiefly in nets, but will take a hook. Also called Spoonbill Catfish, but is not a member of the Catfish family.)

Perch, White: *Roccus americanus*

(This is a misnomer as this fish is a bass and not a perch, but this common name is so prevalent all over its range it would be unwise to change it.)

Perch, Yellow: *Perca flavescens*

Pickerel, Barred (See Redfin Pickerel)

Pickerel, Redfin: *Esox americanus*

(Sometimes known as the Barred Pickerel.)

Pickerel, Chain: *Esox niger*

Pickerel, Grass: *Esox vermiculatus*

Pike, Northern: *Esox lucius*

(An effort was made to call it simply Pike, but some of the pickerel are called pike in many localities, so it was decided too much simplification would lead only to more instead of less confusion.)

Pumpkinseed (See Sunfish)

Salmon, Atlantic: *Salmo salar*

Salmon, Chum: *Oncorhynchus keta*

(Also referred to as Dog Salmon.)

Salmon, Coho: *Oncorhynchus kisutch*

(This species is sometimes called the Silver Salmon.)

Salmon, King: *Oncorhynchus tshawytscha*

(This species is sometimes called the Chinook Salmon.)

Salmon, Kokanee: *Oncorhynchus nerka*

(This is the small Sockeye Salmon that is landlocked and is artificially propagated and planted in large numbers in the trout waters of the Northwest, especially the state of Washington.)

Salmon, Landlocked: *Salmo salar*

(This is the game finny fighter so much sought after in Maine and parts of Canada and is being spread to other sections by artificial propagation. It is now landlocked by preference rather than by necessity. Sometimes referred to as the Sebago Salmon.)

Salmon, Ouananiche: *Salmo salar ouananiche*

(The committee does not agree with those who hold that this

fish is just a landlocked phase of the Atlantic Salmon, because in most of the area where they are taken they have easy access to the sea if they choose to take it.)

Salmon, Pink: *Oncorhynchus gorbuscha*

(Most salmon are more or less humpbacked during the spawning season, but this odd deformation is more exaggerated in this species than all the rest. In fishing circles, this species is generally known as the Humpback Salmon.)

Salmon, Sebago (See under Landlocked Salmon)

Salmon, Sockeye: *Oncorhynchus nerka*

(Commercially referred to as the Red Salmon.)

Sauger: *Stizostedion canadense*

Shee-fish: *Stenodus leucichthys*

(This is the mystery fish of the frigid waters of the Arctic Circle of Alaska. Mainly native to Northern Siberian waters, it is taken frequently enough in Alaska from the Kuskokwim River to Demarcation Point to be given a place in this listing. Sometimes called the Inconnu, which means "unknown".)

Squawfish, Coastal: *Ptychocheilus umpqua*

Squawfish, Columbia: *Ptychocheilus oregonensis*

Squawfish, Sacramento: *Ptychocheilus grandis*

Steelhead (See under Trout)

Stonecat: *Noturus flavus*

Note: While Sturgeon are taken in salty waters only by commercial fishermen, two fresh-water species furnish splendid sport in the waters of Northern Minnesota and Wisconsin and Idaho.

Sturgeon, Shovelnose: *Scaphirhynchus platyorynchus*

Sturgeon, Lake: *Acipenser fulvescens*

(Also known as the Rock Sturgeon.)

Note: While the various species of sunfish continue to be the special joy of the small boy, present-day artificial propagation and stocking of farm ponds has resulted in some crossing of species. There is also a tendency to drop some of the oldtime common names such as the Shellcracker, the Stumpknocker and the old-fashioned Pumpkinseed.

Sunfish, Bluegill: *Lepomis macrochirus*

(This species has come to be "the sunfish" of the country through its tremendous propagation and stocking. Unfortunately sometimes it has crossed with other species of the family.)

Sunfish, Green: *Lepomis cyanellus*

Sunfish, Longear: *Lepomis megalotis*

Sunfish, Pumpkinseed: *Lepomis gibbosus*

Sunfish, Redbreast: *Lepomis auritus*

Sunfish, Redear: *Lepomis microlophus*

(In the South commonly known as the Shellcracker.)

Sunfish, Spotted: *Lepomis punctatus*

Togue (See Lake Trout)

Trout, Arctic (See Arctic Char)

Trout, Blueback: *Salvelinus oquassa*

Trout, Brook: *Salvelinus fontinalis*

(This is the native Eastern Brook Trout, now found in many states thanks to artificial propagation. Known in localized areas as Squaretail and in some few areas they drop down to the mouths of tidal estuaries and are known as Coasters.)

Trout, Brown: *Salmo trutta*

(This introduced species has come to be the salvation of trout fishing in worn out Eastern streams. Like many other fresh water game fish of the West, it has in some places become sea-run. Formerly the non-migratory Brownies were known as *S. fario* and the sea-run fish as *S. trutta*, but modern listing makes no difference between the two, both being known as *S. trutta*.)

Trout, Cutthroat: *Salmo clarki*

(Some of this species have become sea-run, this tendency being manifested from Puget Sound northward through British Columbia to Southeastern Alaska.)

Trout, Dolly Varden: *Salvelinus malma*

(This species reaches its greatest concentration in Southeastern Alaska, where most of them are sea-run. Actually it is the Western form of the Eastern Brook Trout. Over much of its habitat it is known as the Salmon Trout.)

Trout, Golden: *Salmo aguabonita*

(Native only to the high Sierras at 10,000 feet or over. Several attempts have been made to reintroduce this species in California where it was once native.)

Trout, Kamloops: *Salmo gairdneri*

(This is one of the many subspecies of the Rainbow Trout, whose differences from the parent stock are either imaginary or due entirely to environment. The Kamloops reached its highest concentration in Pend d'Oreille in Northern Idaho, although it has been introduced elsewhere.)

Trout, Lake: *Salvelinus namaycush*

(This splendid game fish of northern waters is also known as the Togue in those parts of its habitat contiguous to Canada.)

Trout, Loch Leven (See under Brown Trout)

(Both the Loch Leven and the European Brown Trout were introduced into this country about the same time. In due course these two introduced species were crossbred until the present strain known as the Brown Trout resulted. It is doubtful if any true strain of Loch Leven Trout remain in this country.)

Trout, Rainbow: *Salmo gairdneri*

(Originally native to Western America, it has been introduced widely wherever suitable habitat can be found. Because of its wide geographic range, it has developed many localized subspecies, of which the more important are included in this list. Its sea-going members of the species are called Steelheads, but ichthyologists refuse to differentiate between the two scientifically. Hence, both are known as *S. gairdneri*).

Trout, Steelhead: *Salmo gairdneri*

(This is the accepted name of the sea-run branch of the Rainbow Trout, but is claimed by the experts to be the same fish in every other respect and so carries the same scientific name. In California the sea-run Cutthroat Trout is also called a Steelhead.)

Trout, Sunapee (See Arctic Char)

Walleye: *Stizostedion vitreum*

Warmouth: *Chaenobryttus gulosus*

Whitefish: *Coregonus clupeaformis*

Whitefish, Rocky Mountain: *Prosopium williamsoni*

(Sometimes erroneously referred to as a Grayling in some Western sections.)

SALTWATER FISHES

Albacore: *Thunnus alalunga*

Amberjack: *Seriola dumerili*

Amberjack, Pacific: *Seriola colburni*

Barracuda, Great: *Sphyraena barracuda*

(This is the big fellow most abundant off the Florida coast and found ranging the seas alone or in groups of two or three.)

Barracuda, Pacific: *Sphyraena argentea*

(This species is much smaller than the preceding and roams the seas in large schools. Sometimes called the California Barracuda.)

Bass, Channel: *Sciaenops ocellata*

(This is the great battler of the Atlantic surf. A list of 22 common names have been collected, of which Red Drum in the Chesapeake Bay area and Redfish in Florida are the more generally used.)

Bass, Kelp: *Paralabrax clathratus*

Bass, Sand: *Paralabrax nebulifer*

Bass, White Sea: *Cynoscion nobilis*

Bass, Black Sea, (See Sea Bass)

Bass, Giant Sea: *Stereolepis gigas*

Bass, Spotted Sand: *Paralabrax maculatofasciatus*

Bass, Sea: *Centropristes striatus*

(The young of this popular sport and food fish come into tidal estuaries in great numbers and are called Black Wills. Also known as the Black Sea Bass along the upper Atlantic coast.)

Bass, Striped: *Roccus saxatilis*

(This is the Rockfish of the Chesapeake Bay area, where it is claimed that about 90 per cent of all the Atlantic population of this species are spawned. Transplanted to the West Coast, it now flourishes all along the California and lower Oregon coast.)

Blackfish (See Tautog)

Black Bonito (See Cobia)

Bluefish: *Pomatomus saltatrix*

(This species is an erratic wanderer. However, its young under the names of Snapper Blue and Tailor run into tidal estuaries along the Atlantic coast in great numbers, providing great sport on light tackle.)

Bonefish: *Albula vulpes*

Bonito, Atlantic: *Sarda sarda*

(Although distributed all along the West Coast is generally called the California Bonito.)

Bonito, Oceanic (See Tuna, Skipjack)

Bonito, Pacific: *Sarda chiliensis*

Broadbill (See Swordfish)

Catfish, Gafftopsail: *Bagre marinus*

Catfish, Sea: *Galeichthys felis*

Cero (See King Mackerel)

Cobia: *Rachycentron canadus*

(This great battler is known by many names in many places, among them being Cabio, Sargeant Fish, Black Bonito, Ling and Lemon Fish.)

Cod: *Gadus morhua*

Cod, Pacific: *Gadus macrocephalus*

Corbina, California: *Menticirrhus undulatus*

Crevalle (See Jack Crevalle)

Croaker, Atlantic: *Micropogon undulatus*

Croaker, Black: *Chileotrema saturnum*

Croaker, Spotfin: *Roncador stearnsi*

Croaker, White: *Genyonemus lineatus*

Croaker, Yellowfin: *Umbrina roncador*

Cultus (See Lingcod)

Cunner: *Tautogolabrus adspersus*

Cutlassfish: *Trichiurus lepturus*

Devilfish (See Manta)

Dolphin: *Coryphaena hippurus*

Drum, Black: *Pogonias cromis*

Eel: *Anguilla rostrata*

(A true fish and has a right to be included in this list.)

Flounder, Starry: *Platichthys stellatus*

Flounder, Summer: *Paralichthys dentatus*

(This is the well-known Fluke of lower New England and upper Middle Atlantic waters and its newer name will be hard to make stick, but is used in this list for simplification. There is also a species *P. lethostigmus* commonly called Southern Fluke. Its range overlaps with *P. dentatus.*)

Flounder, Winter: *Pseudopleuronectes americanus*

Fluke (See under Summer Flounder)

Fluke, Summer (See under Summer Flounder)

Gag (See under Groupers)

Graysby: *Petrometopon cruentatum*

Greenling: *Hexagrammos decagrammus*

Grouper, Black: *Mycteroperca bonaci*

Grouper, Coney: *Cephalopholis fulva*

Grouper, Gag: *Mycteroperca microlepis*

Grouper, Jewfish, Black: *Epinephelus nigritus*

Grouper, Jewfish, Spotted: *Epinephelus itajara*

   (This is the largest of the Groupers.)

Grouper, Nassau: *Epinephelus striatus*

Grouper, Red: *Epinephelus morio*

Grouper, Rockhind: *Epinephelus adscenionis*

Grouper, Yellowfin: *Mycteroperca venenosa*

Note: The Grunts are a large family of tropical fishes. The following seven species are most familiar to anglers.

Grunt, Black Margate: *Anisotremus surinamensis*

Grunt, Bluestripe: *Haemulon sciurus*

Grunt, French: *Haemulon flavolineatum*

   (Also called Yellow Grunt.)

Grunt, Pigfish: *Orthopristis chrysopterus*

Grunt, Gray: *Haemulon macrostomum*

Grunt, Margate: *Haemulon album*

Grunt, White: *Haemulon plumieri*

Haddock: *Melanogrammus aeglefinus*

Hake, Silver: *Merluccius bilinearis*

Halibut, Atlantic: *Hippoglossus hippoglossus*

Halibut, California: *Paralichthys californicus*

Halibut, Pacific: *Hippoglossus stenolepis*

Herring, Common: *Clupea harengus*

   (Primarily a commercial species but used extensively for bait by anglers.)

Hind, Red: *Epinephelus guttatus*

Jack, Bigeye: *Caranx marginatus*

Jack, Crevalle, *Caranx hippos*

   (Sometimes called simply Crevalle.)

Jack, Green: *Caranx caballus*

Jack, Horse-eye: *Caranx latus*

Jewfish, Black (See Groupers)

Jewfish, Spotted (See Groupers)

Ladyfish: *Elops saurus*

   (This species is often confused with the Bonefish and is also called the Chiro and Tenpounder.)

Lemon Fish (See Cobia)

Ling (See Cobia)

Lingcod: *Ophiodon elongatus*

   (Also called Cultus.)

Lookdown: *Selene vomer*

Mackerel, Atlantic: *Scomber colias*

   (Also referred to as the Common Mackerel.)

Mackerel, Cero: *Scomberomorus regalis*

   (Sometimes called the Painted Mackerel; also the King Mackerel is often miscalled the Cero in some Atlantic waters.)

Mackerel, Chub: *Scomber colias*

Mackerel, King: *Scomberomorus cavalla*

   (Called Cero in some Atlantic waters and sometimes called the Kingfish by commercial fishermen.)

Mackerel, Pacific Chub: *Scomber japonicus*

Mackerel, Spanish: *Scomberomorus maculatus*

Manta: *Manta birostris*

   (This is not exactly a sport fish, but it furnishes fine sport with the harpoon. Also known as the Devilfish.)

Marlin, Black: *Makaira indica*

   (The real range of this species is south of the border of the United States, but enough stragglers are taken or seen above the line to call for insertion in this list.)

Marlin, Blue: *Makaira nigricans*

   (Occurs in the Atlantic and Tropical Pacific oceans.)

Marlin, Striped: *Tetrapturus audax*

Marlin, White: *Tetrapturus albidus*

Menhaden: *Brevoortia tyrannus*

   (An extensively used bait fish; also called the Fatback.)

Moonfish: *Vomer setapinnis*

Mullet, Striped: *Mugil cephalus*

   (This is chiefly a food and bait fish, but in some sectors is taken also for sport as well as for bait.)

Muttonfish (See Snapper)

Palometa: *Trachinotus falcatus*

   (This species of pompano is not too numerous anywhere, but is taken frequently in Florida waters.)

Permit: *Trachinotus goodei*

   (The young of Permit are called Round Pompano.)

Pigfish: *Orthopristis chrysopterus*

Pollock, Atlantic: *Pollachius virens*

Pollock, Pacific: *Theragra chalcogramma*

Pompano: *Trachinotus carolinus*

Pompano, African: *Alectis crinitus*

Porgy, Grass: *Calamus arctifrons*

Porgy, Jolthead: *Calamus bajonado*

Porgy, Northern: *Stenotomus chrysops*

   (Called Scup in some parts of its range.)

Porkfish: *Anisotremus virginicus*

Queenfish: *Seriphus politus*

Note: While the Rays cannot be classed as sport fishes exactly, the do furnish quite a bit of fun to the angler in some sections and so the more familiar species are presented to complete this check list.

Ray, Eagle: *Myliobatus freminvillei*

Ray, Northern Sting: *Dasyatis centroura*

Ray, Southern Sting: *Dasyatis americana*

Ray, Stingaree: *Dasyatis sabina*

Ray, Spotted Eagle: *Aetobatus narinari*

   (Also known in some waters as the Spotted Whip Ray.)

Redfish (See Channel Bass)

Robalo (See Snook)

Rockfish (See Striped Bass)

Rockhind (See Groupers)

Runner, Blue: *Caranx crysos*

Runner, Rainbow: *Elagatis bipinnulatus*

Sablefish: *Anoplopoma fimbria*

Sandfish: *Diplectrum formosum*

(Also known as the Sand Perch.)

Note: Icthyologists are at odds over several subspecies of Sailfish, but there is no need to recognize any of them for the purpose of this checklist except the two following species. Even these two are believed to be the same fish, whateevr difference there may be in size or action when hooked being environmental in origin.

Sailfish, Atlantic: *Istiophorus albicans*

Sailfish, Pacific: *Istiophorus greyi*

Sailor's Choice: *Haemulon parrai*

Sawfish: *Pristis pectinatus*

(Hardly a sport fish, but it has been taken often enough with rod and reel in the Gulf of Mexico off the Texas coast to gain a place in this check list.)

Schoolmaster (See Snapper)

Note: The controversy continues between the use of Weakfish or Seatrout as the basic name for the four species following. As far as can be determined, adherents of each are about evenly divided. For the purposes of this check list, the four species will appear under both of these names.

Seatrout: *Cynoscion regalis*

Seatrout, Sand: *Cynoscion arenarius*

Seatrout, Silver: *Cynoscion nothus*

Seatrout, Spotted: *Cynoscion nebulosus*

Shad: *Alosa sapidissima*

(Formerly a strictly commercial fish, of late it has become a fine sport fish being taken on a fly, streamer or spoon on its way to the spawning grounds in the upper reaches of tidal estuaries. Sometimes referred to as the White Shad.)

Shad, Hickory: *Alosa mediocris*

Note: Recreational angling for various species of sharks in the waters coming within the range of this check list is becoming more and more popular. Below you will find those species, and others, for which official records are kept by the International Game Fish Association.

Shark, Atlantic: *Isurus oxyrinchus*

(This shark is also sometimes called the Mackerel Shark.)

Shark, Blacktip: *Carcharhinus limbatus*

Shark, Hammerhead: *Sphyrna zygaena*

(Generally found in the open ocean and near the surface and gives a good account of itself whenever hooked on rod and line.)

Shark, Mako: *Isurus glaucus*

(This is the kingpin of all the sharks from the angler's view-point. Taken on rod and reel it gives the tops in sport. Also called Bonito Shark.)

Shark, Mackerel (See Atlantic Shark)

Shark, Porbeagle: *Lamna nasus*

Shark, Spinner: *Carcharhinus maculipinnis*

(This species is called the Spinner-Shark from its habit of shooting vertically out of the water and turning several times on its axis before falling back with a great splash.)

Shark, Thresher: *Alopias vulpinus*

Shark, Tiger: *Galeocerdo cuvieri*

Shark, White: *Carcharodon carcharias*

(This is the species sometimes called the Man Eater Shark.)

Sheepshead: *Archosargus probatocephalus*

Snapper Blue (See under Bluefish)

Note: The Snappers compose a large family, chiefly tropical. In the members of this family covered in this list there are two genera and seven species of interest to the recreational angler and four species that are important commercially.

Snapper, Dog: *Lutjanus jocu*

Snapper, Lane: *Lutjanus synagris*

Snapper, Mahogany: *Lutjanus mahogoni*

Snapper, Mangrove: *Lutjanus griseus*

Snapper, Mullet: *Lutjanus aratus*

Snapper, Muttonfish: *Lutjanus analis*

Snapper, Red: *Lutjanus blackfordi*

Snapper, Schoolmaster: *Lutjanus apodus*

Snapper, Silk: *Lutjanus vivanus*

Snapper, Yellowtail: *Ocyurus chrysurus*

Snook: *Centropomus undecimalis*

(Called by many the Robalo in parts of its habitat.)

Spot: *Leiostomus xanthurus*

Surf Perch: *Phanerodon furcatus*

(This is one of a number of similar small fish found in the Pacific surf, but of too little importance to be enumerated in full in this list.)

Swordfish: *Xiphias gladius*

(The only representative of its family hence it becomes unnecessary to use the prefix Broadbill.)

Tailor (See Bluefish)

Tarpon: *Megalops atlantica*

Tautog: *Tautoga onitis*

Tomcod: *Microgadus tomcod*

Toadfish: *Opsanus tau*

(Given a place in this list because of its great nuisance value to all fishermen.)

Tripletail: *Lobotes surinamensis*

Note: Following is the latest official listing of the Tuna family as published by the American Fisheries Society Committee. Authorities continue to differ over whether the Atlantic and the Pacific

Yellowfin Tunas are the same fish. For the present at least, this list carries both.

Tuna, Allison (See Yellowfin Tuna)

Tuna, Blackfin: *Thunnus atlanticus*

Tuna, Bluefin: *Thunnus thynnus*

(The young of this species migrate closer to the shoreline and are commonly called School Tuna. The fully developed Bluefins are often called Giant Tuna. This is the principal tuna of the sportsman-angler and the commercial fisherman.)

Tuna, Giant (See Bluefin Tuna)

Tuna, Little: *Euthynnus alletteratus*

(This is a species sometimes called False Albacore, but it is a true tuna and is now recognized as such.)

Tuna, Skipjack: *Euthynnus pelamis*

(Found off both coasts. Known as Oceanic Bonito on the Atlantic Coast.)

Tuna, School (See Bluefin Tuna)

Tuna, Yellowfin: *Thunnus albacares*

(It is now agreed by most of the authorities that the so-called Allison Tuna is simply either an age or sex phase of the Yellowfin Tuna and so it has been dropped from the official check list.)

Wahoo: *Acanthocybium solandi*

Note: See statement regarding interchanging names of Weakfish and Seatrout under the Seatrout listing.

Weakfish: *Cynoscion regalis*

(In one sector of its range, this species is known as the Squeteague.)

Weakfish, Sand: *Cynoscion arenarius*

Weakfish, Silver: *Cynoscion nothus*

Weakfish, Spotted: *Cynoscion nebulosus*

Whitefish, Ocean: *Caulolatilus princeps*

Whiting, Gulf (See Silver Whiting)

Whiting, King (See Northern Whiting)

Whiting, Northern: *Menticirrhus saxatilis*

(This frequenter of the surf along upper Atlantic shores is also known as both the Kingfish and the King Whiting.)

Whiting, Southern: *Menticirrhus americanus*

Whiting, Silver: *Menticirrhus littoralis*

(Also known as the Gulf Whiting.)

Yellowtail (See Snapper)

Yellowtail, Pacific: *Seriola dorsalis*

—Compiled by the Outdoor Writers Association of America and reprinted with their permission.

Directory of Manufacturers of Fishing Equipment

Tony Accetta & Son, Inc.
932 Avenue "E"
Riviera Beach, Florida   33404
Lures

Acme Tackle Company
69 Bucklin Street
Providence, R.I.   02907
Lures

S.S. Adams Company
P.O. Box 369
Neptune, N.J.   07753
Accessories

Aitken-Warner Corporation
427 Beech Street
Green Camp, Ohio   43322
Lures

Aladdin Laboratories, Inc.
620 South 8th Street
Minneapolis, Minn.   55404
Reels, Accessories

Alpha Equipment Sales Corp.
13942 Clifton Blvd.
Lakewood, Ohio   44107
Hooks

Al's Goldfish Lure Co.
Indian Orchard, Massachusetts 01051
Lures, Accessories

American Foreign Industries
420 Bryant Street
San Francisco, Calif.   94107
Accessories

The American Import Company
1167 Mission Street
San Francisco, Calif.   94103
Rods, Reels, Lures, Leaders, Accessories

American Vanguard Corp.
1812 Griffin Avenue
Los Angeles, Calif.   90031
Accessories

America's Cup
1109 South Fremont
Alhambra, Calif.   91803
Accessories

Ande, Inc.
1500 53rd Street
W. Palm Beach, Florida   33407
Lines

Anglers Manufacturing Corp.
7729 N. Eastlake Terrace
Chicago, Illinois   60626
Accessories

Angler Products, Inc.
210 Spring Street
Butler, Penn.   16001
Lures, Accessories

Apelco
676 Island Pond Rd.
Manchester, New Hampshire   03103
Accessories

Aqua-Troll, Inc.
P.O. Box 149
Lynnwood, Wash.   98036
Accessories

Fred Arbogast Co., Inc.
313 W. North Street
Akron, Ohio   44303
Lures

Arco Mfg. Co. of Racine
1501 Clark
Racine, Wisconsin   53403
Accessories

Arnold Tackle Corp.
Div. of I.N.C., Inc.
100 Commercial Avenue
Paw Paw, Michigan   49079
Lures, Accessories

Axelson Fishing Tackle Mfg. Co., Inc.
1559 Placentia Avenue
Newport Beach, Calif.   92660
Accessories

Bachmann Bros., Inc.
1400 E. Erie Avenue
Philadelphia, Pa.   19124
Accessories

Back Porch Industries, Inc.
P.O. Box 835
Old Orangeburg Road
Summerville, S.C.   29483
Accessories

Jim Bagley Bait Co., Inc.
P.O. Box 110
Winter Haven, Florida   33880
Lures

J.R. Baker & Sons Co.
Div. of L.D. Baker, Inc.
P.O. Box 230
Kendallville, Indiana   46755
Accessories

Baker Mfg. Co.
P.O. Box 28
Columbia, Pa.   17512
Accessories

Bane Advertising
391 Monterey Blvd.
San Francisco, Calif.   94131
Reels

Bass-Buster, Inc.
Box 118
Amsterdam, Mo.   64723
Lures

Bausch & Lomb
Rochester, N.Y.   14602
Accessories

Bead Chain Co.
Div. of Bead Chain Mfg. Co.
110 Mountain Grove St.
Bridgeport, Conn.   06605
Lures

L.L. Bean, Inc.
Freeport, Maine   04032
Accessories

Bear Paw Tackle Co.
Bellaire, Mich.   49615
Lures, Leaders, Accessories

Belvin-Wilcox Line Co.
Div. of Brownell & Co., Inc.
Moodus, Conn.   06469
Lures

Berger Co., Inc.
394 Broadway
New York, N.Y.   10013
Accessories

Berkley & Company
Spirit Lake, Iowa   51360
Rods, Reels, Lines, Leaders

Big Jon, Inc.
14393 Peninsula Dr.
Traverse City, Michigan   49684
Accessories

Biscayne Rod Mfg., Inc.
3321 N.W. 7th Avenue
Miami, Florida   33127
Rods, Accessories

Blakemore Sales Corp.
P.O. Box 505
Branson, Missouri   65616
Lures

Blue Jacket Ind.
Box 334
Napoleon, Ohio   43545
Accessories

Bomber Bait Company
326 Lindsay
P.O. Box 716
Gainesville, Texas   76240
Lures

Bornemann Prod. Co.
5613 W. Greenfield Ave.
Milwaukee, Wisconsin   53214
Accessories

Boss Sports Division
Boss Mfg. Co.
221 West First St.
Kewanee, Ill.   61443
Accessories

Bowen Knife Co.
Div. of Adventure Prods., Inc.
P.O. Box 14028
593 Westminster Drive N.E.
Atlanta, Ga.   30324
Accessories

Browning
P.O. Box 500
Morgan, Utah   84050
Rods, Reels

W.E. Brownlee Co.
215 St. Marys
Suttons Bay, Michigan   49682
Accessories

Buck Knives
1717 No. Magnolia Avenue
El Cajon, Calif.   92022
Accessories

Burke Flexo-Products
1969 So. Airport Road
Traverse City, Michigan   49684
Lures

Byrd Industries, Inc.
Sub. of St. Louis Diecasting Corp.
201 Rock Industries Park Road
Bridgeton, Missouri   63044
Accessories

Bystrom Brothers, Inc.
2200 Snelling Ave.
So. Minneapolis, Minn.   55404
Accessories

C & G Tackle Mfg. Co.
P.O. Box 1402
Tulsa, Oklahoma   74101
Accessories

Camillus Cutlery Co.
Camillus, New York   13031
Accessories

Capitol Plastics of Ohio, Inc.
333 Van Camp Road
Bowling Green, Ohio   43402
Rods

W.R. Case & Sons Cutlery Co.
Bradford, Penn.   16701
Accessories

Chace Leather Products
Div. of Textile Belting & Strapping Co.
507 Alden Street
Fall River, Mass.   02723
Accessories

Lew Childre & Sons, Inc.
P.O. Box 535
Foley, Alabama   36535
Rods, Reels, Accessories

Colorado Tent & Awning Co.
3333 E. 52nd Avenue Cook St.
Denver, Colorado   80216
Accessories

Continental Arms Corp.
697 5th Avenue
New York, N.Y.   10022
Reels

Converse Rubber Co.
55 Fordham Road
Wilmington, Massachusetts   01887
Accessories

Cortland Line Company
Cortland, New York   13045
Lines

Cosom
Division of ITT Thermotech
6030 Wayzata Blvd.
Minneapolis, Minnesota   55416
Accessories

Mel Cox Baits and Lures
    Manufacturing Co.
Box 1432
Fort Worth, Texas   76101
Lures

Creek Chub Bait Co.
Garrett, Indiana   46738
Lures

Creme Lure Company
P.O. Box 87
Tyler, Texas   75701
Lures

Crest Tool & Supply, Inc.
P.O. Box 474
San Carlos, California   94070
Accessories

Cuba Specialty Mfg. Co., Inc.
P.O. Box 38
Houghton, N.Y.   14744
Accessories

Dacor Corp.
161 Northfield Road
Northfield, Illinois   60093
Accessories

Daiwa Corporation
P.O. Box 2287
14011 So. Normandie Ave.
Gardena, Calif.   90247
Rods, Reels, Lines

The Danielson Company
755 North Central
Kent, Washington   98031
Rods, Reels, Lures, Lines, Leaders,
    Accessories

Dart Mfg. Co.
1724 Cockrell Ave.
Dallas, Texas 75215
Accessories

Data Sport, Inc.
5636 Abbott Ave. South
Edina, Minnesota   55410
Accessories

Les Davis Fishing Tackle Co.
1565 Center St.
Tacoma, Washington   98409
Lures, Lines, Accessories

Dorbo Mfg. Co.
1914 Dana Ave.
Cincinnati, Ohio   45207
Accessories

Dragon Fly Company, Inc.
P.O. Drawer 1349
823 Broad St.
Sumter, So. Carolina   29150
Lures, Lines, Leaders, Accessories

Duofold, Inc.
P.O. Drawer A
Mohawk, New York   13407
Accessories

E.I. Du Pont de Nemours & Co., Inc.
Wilmington, Delaware   19898
Lines

Durbin Durco, Inc.
1435 Woodson Road
St. Louis, Mo.   63132
Accessories

Eagle Claw Fishing Tackle
(see Wright & McGill Co.)

Eagle Mfg. Co.
Wellsburg, West Virginia   26070
Accessories

Earlybird Co.
P.O. Box 1485
Boise, Idaho   83701
Accessories

Emco Specialties, Inc.
P.O. Box 864
Des Moines, Iowa   50304
Accessories

Endicott Johnson
A McDonough Co.
Endicott, New York   13760
Accessories

Engineering Lab., Inc.
P.O. Box 286
Colfax & W. Oakland Ave.
Pompton Lakes, N.J.   07442
Lures

John C. Engstrom
Star Route 1-A
Spooner, Wisconsin   54801
Lures

Lou J. Eppinger Mfg. Co.
6340 Schaefer Hwy.
Dearborn, Michigan   48126
Lures

Eska Company
2400 Kerper Blvd.
Dubuque, Iowa   52001
Accessories

Fablok Mills, Inc.
140 Spring St.
Murray Hill, N.J.   07974
Accessories

Factory Distributors
500 No. 7th St.
Fort Smith, Arkansas   72901
Lures

Farber Bros., Inc.
821-41 Linden Ave.
Memphis, Tenn.   38101
Accessories

Fatsco
251 No. Fair Avenue
Benton Harbor, Michigan   49022
Accessories

Featherweight Prods.
Div. of Western Grinders
3454-8 Ocean View Blvd.
Glendale, California   91208
Rods, Lures, Accessories

Feldmann Engineering & Mfg. Co., Inc.
633-639 Monroe St.
Sheboygan Falls, Wisconsin   53085
Accessories

Fenwick
P.O. Box 729
Westminster, California   92683
Rods, Lures, Accessories

Feurer Bros., Inc.
77 Lafayette Ave.
No. White Plains, New York   10603
Reels

Fish It
Div. of It, Inc.
P.O. Box 1033
Torrington, Conn.   06790
Lures

Fishmaster Products, Inc.
P.O. Box 9635
Tulsa, Oklahoma   74107
Accessories

Fitzgerald Mfg. Co.
P.O. Box 238
Torrington, Connecticut   06790
Lures

Flambeau Products Corp.
801 Lynn Avenue
Baraboo, Wisconsin   53913
Accessories

Fle-Fly Manufacturers, Inc.
Drawer F
Tulsa, Oklahoma   74115
Lures

Isaac Franklin Co., Inc.
630 No. Pulaski St.
Baltimore, Md.   21217
Accessories

Arthur T. Freer
Gilbertsville, New York   13776
Lures

John Fujita Mfg. Co.
74 White St.
Watsonville, California   95076
Lures

The Gaines Company
Box 35
Gaines, Pennsylvania   16921
Lures

A. J. Gallager
319 Delsea Drive (Route 47)
Westville, N.J.   08093
Lures, Accessories

Gapen Tackle Co.
Big Lake, Minnesota   55309
Lures

The Garcia Corporation
329 Alfred Avenue
Teaneck, N.J.   07666
Rods, Reels, Lures, Lines, Accessories

Gaunt Industries
6217 Northwest Highway
Chicago, Illinois   60631
Accessories

Generic Systems, Inc.
P.O. Box 256
Rockaway, N.J.   07866
Lures, Accessories

Gentex Corp.
Carbondale, Pennsylvania   18407
Accessories

Gesco Cutlery Co., Inc.
P.O. Box 517
Orange Park, Florida   32073
Accessories

Stan Gibbs Lures, Inc.
Buzzards Bay, Massachusetts   02532
Lures, Accessories

Gladding Corporation
P.O. Box 586
Back Bay Annex
441 Stuart St.
Boston, Massachusetts   02116
Rods, Reels, Lures, Lines, Leaders,
   Accessories

Glas-Lite
Div. of Plas Steel Products, Inc.
Walkerton, Indiana   46574
Rods

Gloy's
Division of Amdis Corp.
899 Broadway
New York, N.Y.   10003
Accessories

Gold Medal Folding Furniture Co.
1700 Packard Avenue
Racine, Wisconsin   53403
Accessories

Gott Mfg. Co., Inc.
P.O. Box 652
Winfield, Kansas   67156
Accessories

Gudebrod Bros. Silk Co., Inc.
Fishing Tackle Division
12 South 12th St.
Philadelphia, Pa.   19107
Lines

Hackensack Cable Corp.
3275 Sunset Blvd.
West Columbia, South Carolina   29169
Accessories

Hamilton Skotch Division
Plattner Industries, Inc.
P.O. Box 378
Ottawa, Kansas   66067
Accessories

Herben Manufacturing Co.
2101 No. Green Bay Road
Racine, Wisconsin   53405
Accessories

Hardman, Inc.
Belleville, New Jersey   07109
Accessories

Hardy Bros.
(See Harrington & Richardson)

Harmony Enterprises, Inc.
704 Main Ave. North
Harmony, Minnesota   55939
Accessories

Harrington & Richardson
Industrial Row
Gardner, Massachusetts   01440
Rods, Reels

Hartig's Spinning Lure Co.
56640 Garfield St.
Osceola, Indiana   46561
Lures

Healthways
Subsidiary of Eldon Ind., Inc.
5340 W. 102nd St.
P.O. Box 45055
Los Angeles, California   90045
Accessories

James Heddon's Sons
Div. of Victor Comptometer Corp.
Dowagiac, Michigan   49047
Rods, Reels, Lures

Helin Tackle Co.
4099 Beaufait Ave.
Detroit, Michigan   48207
Lures

Herter's, Inc.
Waseca, Minnesota   56093
Rods, Lures, Accessories

John J. Hildebrandt Corp.
P.O. Box 50
Loganport, Indiana   46947
Lures

Hollowguide Fishing Rod Co.
1983 Camden Avenue
San Jose, California   95124
Lures, Accessories

Hopkins Fishing Lure Co., Inc.
1130 Boissevain Avenue
Norfolk, Virginia   23507
Lures

Hubs-Chubs Lures
103 South West Street
Arcadia, Indiana   46030
Lures, Accessories

Hycor, Inc.
1 Gill Street
Woburn, Massachusetts   01801
Accessories

Ideal Products, Inc.
Sykesville, Pennsylvania   15865
Rods, Reels, Lures, Lines, Accessories

Ikelheimer-Ernst, Inc.
601 West 26th Street
New York, N.Y.   10001
Accessories

International Hook & Tackle
1830 So. Acoma St.
Denver, Colorado   80223
Rods, Lures, Accessories

IPCO
331 Lake Hazeltine Dr.
Chaska, Minnesota   55318
Accessories

Jabsco Prods.
1485 Dale Way
Costa Mesa, California   92626
Accessories

Jack's Rod & Fly Shop
P.O. Box 41
Roscommon, Michigan   48653
Leaders, Accessories

Jay's Mfg. Co.
1081 Genesee St.
Buffalo, New York   14211
Lures

Ray Jefferson Division
Jetronics Industries
Main & Cotton Streets
Philadelphia, Pennsylvania   19127
Accessories

Jet-Aer Corp.
100 6th Ave.
Paterson, New Jersey   07524
Accessories

Louis Johnson Co.
1547 Old Deerfield Road
Highland Park, Illinois   60035
Lures

Johnson & Johnson
New Brunswick, New Jersey   08901
Accessories

Johnson Reels Co.
Div. of Johnson Diversified Co.
Johnson Park
Mankato, Minnesota   56001
Reels

Jorgensen Bros.
P.O. Box 69
Pleasanton, California   94566
Reels, Accessories

Kassnar Imports
P.O. Box 6097
Harrisburg, Pennsylvania   17112
Rods, Reels, Lures, Accessories

King Athletic Goods Corp.
2615 W. Hunting Park Ave.
Philadelphia, Pennsylvania   19129
Accessories

Klamerus & Co.
Div. of S.P. Steel Prod., Inc.
4557 West 59th St.
Chicago, Illinois   60629
Accessories

Knight Manufacturing Co., Inc.
P.O. Box 3162
Tyler, Texas   75701
Lures

Knotmaster, Ind.
P.O. Box 23201
San Diego, California   92123
Accessories

Kodiak Corp.
P.O. Box 467
Ironwood, Michigan   49938
Rods

Koplin Mfg., Inc.
P.O. Box 231
Berlin, Wisconsin   54923
Accessories

John C. Kremer
542 13th St.
West Palm Beach, Florida   33401
Lures

L&S Bait Co., Inc.
Beadley, Illinois   60915
Lures

Lakeland Ind.
Isle, Minnesota   56342
Lures, Lines, Accessories

Lasco Rubber Co.
Div. of Inter Seaway Trading Co.
1382 West 9th St.
Cleveland, Ohio   44113
Accessories

Law-Lure
332 S. Juniper, Suite 100
Escondido, California   92025
Lures, Accessories

Lazy Ike Corp.
P.O. Box 1177
Fort Dodge, Iowa   50501
Lures

Lee-Dee Imports Co.
1165 Broadway
New York, N.Y.   10010
Accessories

Lehigh Sales & Prods., Inc.
1929 Vultee St.
Allentown, Pennsylvania   18105
Accessories

H.L. Leonard Rod Co.
25 Cottage Street
Midland Park, N.J.   07432
Rods, Hooks

Lisk Fly Mfg. Co.
P.O. Box 5126
Greensboro, North Carolina   27403
Lures, Accessories

Loop-A-Line
1896 Coolidge Ave.
Melborne, Florida   32935
Lures

Lowrance Electronics, Inc.
12000 East Skelly Drive
Tulsa, Oklahoma   74128
Lures

Mac-Jac Manufacturing Co.
1590 Creston Street
P.O. Box 821
Muskegon, Michigan   49443
Accessories

Magic Match Patch Co.
652 Lk. Angelus Road
Pontiac, Michigan   48055
Accessories

Major Rod Mfg. Co. Ltd.
7389 17th Ave.
Montreal, Quebec   H2A 3L5
Canada
Rods

Mann's Bait Co.
P.O. Box 604
Eufaula, Alabama   36027
Lures, Accessories

Marathon Rubber Products Co.
510 Sherman St.
P.O. Box 509
Wausau, Wisconsin   54401
Accessories

Jerry Martin Co.
4411 Grand Ave.
Gurnee, Illinois   60031
Accessories

Martin Reel Company
Mohawk, New York   13407
Rods, Reels, Lures, Accessories

**Martin Tackle & Manufacturing
    Company**
512 Minor Ave. North
Seattle, Washington   98109
Lures, Lines, Leaders, Accessories

M.C. Matthews Cutlery Co.
Box 33095
Decatur, Georgia   30033
Accessories

Joseph Mennen Co., Inc.
192 Vincent Ave.
Lynbrook, New York   11563
Accessories

Mepps
(See Sheldon's, Inc.)

Mighty-Mac, Inc.
Gloucester, Massachusetts   01930
Accessories

Miller Lure Manufacturing Co.
121 Fairgrounds Road
Hamburg, New York   14075
Lures, Accessories

Minnesota Apollo Corp.
4480 Parklawn Ave.
Suite 307
Minneapolis, Minnesota   55435
Accessories

**Minn Kota Manufacturing Co.
Division of Johnson Diversified, Inc.**
201 No. 17th St.
P.O. Box 759
Moorhead, Minnesota   56560
Accessories

Bruce B. Mises, Inc.
1122 South Robertson Blvd.
Los Angeles, California   90035
Lines, Accessories

Mitchell Manufacturing Co., Inc.
913 Broadway
Monett, Missouri   65708
Accessories

Miya Epoch U.S.A., Inc.
P.O. Box 338
Lomita, California   90717
Reels, Accessories

O. Mustad & Son, Inc.
Box 838
185 Clark St.
Auburn, N.Y.   13021
Hooks

F.J. Neil Co., Inc.
345 Hillside Ave.
Williston Park, N.Y.   11596
Rods, Hooks, Lures, Lines, Accessories

Nicholl Bros., Inc.
1204 West 27th St.
Kansas City, Missouri   64108
Accessories

Norman Manufacturing Co., Inc.
P.O. Box H
Greenwood, Arkansas   72936
Lures, Accessories

Normark Corp.
1710 E. 78th St.
(Highway 494 & Cedar Ave.)
Minneapolis, Minnesota   55423
Rods, Reels, Lures, Accessories

Nova Products, Inc.
P.O. Box 116
Carrollton, Georgia   30117
Accessories

Nylon Net Co.
7 Vance Ave.
P.O. Box 592
Memphis, Tennessee   38101
Lures

Oberlin Canteen Co.
Oberlin, Ohio   44074
Lures

Old Pal
(See Woodstream Corporation)

Olsen Knife Co., Inc.
Howard City, Michigan   49329
Accessories

The Orvis Company, Inc.
Manchester, Vermont   05254
Rods, Reels, Lines, Leaders

Outers Laboratories, Inc.
Onalaska, Wisconsin   54650
Accessories

P.C. Fishing Tackle, Inc.
720 West Second St.
Owensboro, Kentucky   42301
Lures

Padre Island Co.
P.O. Box 5310
2617 N. Zarzamora
San Antonio, Texas   78201
Lures

Panef Manufacturing Co., Inc.
5700 W. Douglas Ave.
Milwaukee, Wisconsin   53218
Accessories

Paulin Products Co.
Sub. of Johnson Diversified, Inc.
30520 Lakeland Blvd.
Willowick, Ohio   44094
Accessories

Pautzke Bait Co., Inc.
P.O. Box 36
Ellensburg, Washington   98926
Accessories

Penguin Industries, Inc.
P.O. Box 97
Parkersburg, Pennsylvania   19365
Accessories

Penn Fishing Tackle Mfg. Co.
3028 W. Hunting Park Ave.
Philadelphia, Pennsylvania   19132
Reels

Pequea Fishing Tackle, Inc.
Strasburg, Pennsylvania   17579
Accessories

Peterson Manufacturing Co.
155 Packinghouse Road
Sarasota, Florida   33577
Accessories

Pflueger
P.O. Box 310
Hallandale, Florida   33009
Rods, Reels, Lures, Lines, Accessories

Phillips Fly & Tackle Co.
P.O. Box 188
Alexandria, Pennsylvania   16611
Lures

Phillipson
(See 3M Company)

Pioneer Tackle Company
6925 Reseda Blvd.
Reseda, Calif.   91335
Accessories

Plano Molding Company
Plano, Illinois   60545
Accessories

J.R. Plasters Co.
Division of Decker Manufacturing Co.
111 No. Denver
Kansas City, Missouri 64123
Accessories

Plastilite Corp.
P.O. Box 12235
Florence Station
Omaha, Nebraska 68112
Accessories

Pompanette, Inc.
Bryan Road
North of Stirling Road
Dania, Florida 33004

Powerscopic Corp.
P.O. Box 278
Westwood, New Jersey 07675
Rods

Prandis, Inc.
P.O. Box 963
575 Elm St.
Maywood, N.J. 07607
Lures

Pueblo Tent & Awning Co., Inc.
106 W. First St.
Pueblo, Colorado 81002
Accessories

Quick Corporation of America
620 Terminal Way
P.O. Box 938
Costa Mesa, California 92627
Rods, Reels, Lines

Ranger Tackle Co., Inc.
P.O. Box "H"
Highway 96 East
Greenwood, Arkansas 72936
Accessories

Ranging, Inc.
90 Lincoln Road North
East Rochester, New York 14445
Accessories

Ray-O-Vac Div.
ESB, Inc.
Box 488
Brainerd, Minnesota 56401
Lures, Accessories

Raytheon Co.
Manchester, New Hampshire 03101
Accessories

Reardon Products
103 W. Market St.
Morrison, Illinois 61270
Accessories

Rectack of America
4982 Firestone Blvd.
South Gate, California 90280
Reels

Redhead Brand Corp.
4100 Platinum Way
Dallas, Texas 75237
Accessories

Reece Enterprises
P.O. Box 496
Columbus, Nebraska 68601
Accessories

Paul Reed, Inc.
Charlevoix, Michigan 49720
Accessories

Reflector Hardware Corp.
1400 No. 25th Ave.
Melrose Park, Illinois 60160
Accessories

Reydeco, Inc.
New Kensington, Pennsylvania 15068
Accessories

Riley Company
P.O. Box 1108
Grand Rapids, Michigan 49501
Lures, Accessories

Riviera Manufacturing, Inc.
3859 Roger Chaffee Blvd. S.E.
Grand Rapids, Michigan 49508
Reels, Accessories

Hank Roberts
Box 171
Boulder, Colorado 80302
Lures, Accessories

Rod Caddy Corp.
920 W. Cullerton St.
Chicago, Illinois 60608
Accessories

Rod Klip Company
1006 Clark Ave.
St. Louis, Missouri 63102
Lures, Accessories

Rogers World Champion Lures
P.O. Box 142
Lamar, Missouri 64759
Lures, Accessories

Rogue River Fishing Creel, Inc.
P.O. Box 123
Coos Bay, Oregon 97420
Accessories

Rome Industries, Inc.
1703 W. Detweiller Dr.
Peoria, Illinois 61614
Accessories

H.S. Ross
347 Buchanan St.
Twin Falls, Idaho 83301
Accessories

Bob Rudd Manufacturing Co.
716 N.W. 68th St.
Vancouver, Washington 98665
Rods, Reels, Accessories

Ruff'N Ready Manufacturing Co.
P.O. Box 6267
Branwood Station
6 Andrews St.
Greenville, South Carolina 29601
Accessories

Saf-T-Beacon
332 S. Juniper
Suite 100
P.O. Box 1524
Escondido, California 92025
Accessories

Sampo, Inc.
Barneveld, New York 13304
Lures, Leaders, Accessories

San Angelo Die Casting &
   Manufacturing Co.
706-714 Knickerbocker
San Angelo, Texas 76901
Accessories

Sanders Manufacturing Co.
122-124-126 Fourth Ave. So.
Nashville, Tennessee 37201
Accessories

Sargent & Co.
100 Sargent Dr.
New Haven, Conn. 06509
Accessories

Saunders Archery Co.
Box 476
Industrial Site
Columbus, Nebraska 68601
Reels, Lines, Accessories

Joe Schabo
411 Southwest 31st Ave.
Fort Lauderdale, Florida 33312
Accessories

Schram Adv. Co.
170 W. Washington St.
Chicago, Illinois 60602
Accessories

Scientific Anglers, Inc.
(See 3M Company)

T.R. Seidel Co.
7645 Vance Drive
Arvada, Colorado 80002
Lures, Accessories

Seron Manufacturing Co.
254 Republic Ave.
Joliet, Illinois 60435
Accessories

Shakespeare Company
P.O. Box 246
Columbia, South Carolina 29202
Rods, Reels, Lines, Accessories

Shannon Lure Co.
3654 W. Montrose Ave.
Chicago, Illinois 60618
Lures, Accessories

Shape-A-Wate Co.
P.O. Box 3082
Arcadia, California   91006
Lures

Sheldon's, Inc.
P.O. Box 508
Antigo, Wisconsin   54409
Lures, Accessories

Shurkatch Fishing Tackle Co., Inc.
50 Elm St.
P.O. Box 850
Richfield Springs, New York   13439
Rods, Lines, Accessories

Siberian Salmon Egg Co.
4660 E. Marginal Way South
Seattle, Washington   98134
Lures

Silvertrol
Division of G & R Industries, Inc.
Purdy, Missouri   65734
Lures, Accessories

Smith & Wesson
P.O. Box 2208
Springfield, Massachusetts   01101
Accessories

Jack K. Smithwick & Son
P.O. Box 1205
Shreveport, Louisiana   71163
Lures

Snag Master
Franklin, Kentucky   42134
Accessories

Sportsmen's Lab, Inc.
Box 732
Anoka, Minnesota   55303
Accessories

St. Croix Corporation
9909 So. Shore Dr.
Minneapolis, Minnesota   55441
Rods, Reels, Lures, Accessories

Standard Portable Products, Inc.
Mayville, New York   14757
Accessories

Stan's Tackle Shop
521 So. Washington St.
Bremen, Indiana   46506
Lures

Stearns Manufacturing Co.
P.O. Box 1498
St. Cloud, Minnesota   56301
Accessories

Steffey Manufacturing Co.
No. Huntington, Pennsylvania   15642
Lures

Stembridge Products, Inc.
P.O. Box 90756
East Point, Georgia   30344
Lures, Accessories

Stratton & Terstegge Co.
P.O. Box 1859
Louisville, Kentucky   40201
Accessories

Strike Master, Inc.
411 Washington Ave.
Minneapolis, Minnesota   55401
Rods, Accessories

Subria Corp.
P.O. Box 113
Montclair, New Jersey   07042
Lures, Accessories

Suick Lure Manufacturing Co.
P.O. Box C
Highway 45 North
Antigo, Wisconsin   54409
Lures

Suncoast Industries
3179 23rd Ave. North
St. Petersburg, Florida   33713
Hooks, Lures, Accessories

Syl-Mark Enterprises
P.O. Box 806
Northridge, California   91324
Accessories

Taylor Instrument
Sybron Corp.
Arden, North Carolina   28704
Accessories

Telisons International Corp.
7075½ Vineland Ave.
No. Hollywood, California   91605
Accessories

Tempo Products Co.
6200 Cochran Road
Cleveland, Ohio   44139
Accessories

Thomas Spinning Lures, Inc.
316 Wayne Ave.
Hawley, Pennsylvania   18428
Lures

3M Company
P.O. Box 2001
Midland, Michigan   48640
Rods, Reels, Lines, Accessories

Tiki Lures, Inc.
1805 E. 11 Mile Road
Madison Heights, Michigan   48071
Lures

Todd Enterprises, Inc.
702 Eddy St.
Providence, R.I.   02903
Accessories

**Tri Fin Fishing Tackle Manufacturing
    Corp.**
P.O. Box 80
Smithtown, Long Island, New York
    11787
Lures

Trimarc Corp.
High Point Plaza
Hillside, Illinois   60162
Rods, Reels, Accessories

True Temper Corp.
1623 Euclid Ave.
Cleveland, Ohio   44115
Rods, Reels, Accessories

Tru-Nord Division
Molin Industries
204 No. Ninth St.
Brainerd, Minnesota   56401
Accessories

Tucker Duck & Rubber Co.
P.O. Box 4167 Station B
Fort Smith, Arkansas   72901
Accessories

Tycoon/Fin-Nor Corp.
7447 N.W. 12th St.
Miami, Florida   33126
Rods, Reels, Lines

Umco
P.O. Box 608
Watertown, New Mexico   55388
Accessories

Uniroyal Consumer Products
Naugatuck Footwear Plant
58 Maple St.
Naugatuck, Connecticut   06770
Accessories

United Products, Inc.
116 No. Hill St.
Griffin, Georgia   30223
Accessories

Universal Vise Company
22 Main Street
Westfield, Mass.   01085
Lures, Leaders, Accessories

Bill Upperman
P.O. Box 1428
Atlantic City, New Jersey   08404
Lures

Uslan Rod Mfg. & Sales Corp.
18679 W. Dixie Highway
North Miami Beach, Fla.   33160
Rods

Utica Duxbak Corp.
Utica, N.Y. 13502
Accessories

Varmac Mfg. Co.
4201 Redwood Ave.
Los Angeles, Calif.   90066
Rods, Accessories

Vexilar, Inc.
9345 Penn Ave. S.
Minneapolis, Minn.   55431
Accessories

Visa-Therm Products, Inc.
247 Madison Avenue
Bridgeport, Conn.   06604
Accessories

Vlchek Plastics Co.
Middlefield, Ohio   44062
Accessories

Vogels of California
P.O. Box 593
17416 Pioneer Blvd.
Artesia, Calif.   90701
Lures

Fritz Von Schlegell
1409 Santa Fe Avenue
Los Angeles, Calif.   90021
Accessories

W.S.M. Industries
106 White Gate Road
Pittsburgh, Pa.   15238
Hooks, Lures

Waller Corp.
Box 340
4220 Waller Dr. (Ridgefield)
Crystal Lake, Ill.   60014
Accessories

Weber Tackle Company
Stevens Point, Wis.   54481
Lures, Lines, Leaders, Accessories

Weinbrenner Shoe Company
Merrill, Wisconsin   54452
Accessories

Weldon Mfg. Co.
7010 St. Clair Ave.
Cleveland, Ohio   44103
Lures, Accessories

Erwin Weller Co.
P.O. Box 3204
2105 Clark St.
Sioux City, Iowa   51102
Lures

Western Cutlery Co.
5311 Western Ave.
Boulder, Colo.   80302
Accessories

Westex Products Co., Inc.
P.O. Box 951
Electra, Texas   76360
Accessories

Whopper Stopper, Inc.
P.O. Box 1111
Sherman, Texas   75090
Lures, Accessories

Wittmann Lures
P.O. Box 12701
Tucson, Arizona   85732
Lures

Wolverine World Wide, Inc.
Rockford, Michigan   49351
Accessories

Woodstream Corp.
Lititz, Penn.   17543
Rods, Accessories

Worth Fishing Tackle Company
P.O. Box 88
Stevens Point, Wisconsin   54481
Lures, Leaders, Accessories

Wright & McGill Co.
P.O. Box 16011
Denver, Colorado   80216
Rods, Reels, Hooks

Zak Tackle Mfg. Co.
235 South 59th St.
Tacoma, Washington   98408
Lures, Accessories

Zebco
Div. of Brunswick Corp.
P.O. Box 270
Tulsa, Oklahoma   74101
Rods, Reels, Lures, Accessories

Index

A selection of antique fishing tackle catalog pages has been reproduced on the inside front and back covers to capture the flavor of a past which is gone but not forgotten.